ROCK-FORMING MINERALS

ROCK-FORMING MINERALS

Vol. 4   Framework Silicates

W. A. Deer, M.Sc., Ph.D., F.R.S.
Professor of Mineralogy and Petrology, Cambridge University

R. A. Howie, M.A., Ph.D., F.G.S.
Reader in Geology, London University (King's College)

and

J. Zussman, M.A., Ph.D., F.Inst.P.
Reader in Mineralogy, Oxford University

LONGMANS

LONGMANS, GREEN AND CO LTD
48 Grosvenor Street, London W.1

Associated companies, branches and representatives
throughout the world

MADE AND PRINTED IN GREAT BRITAIN BY
WILLIAM CLOWES AND SONS, LIMITED, LONDON AND BECCLES

66/   8671

PREFACE

In writing these volumes the primary aim has been to provide a work of reference useful to advanced students and research workers in the geological sciences. It is hoped, however, that it will also prove useful to workers in other sciences who require information about minerals or their synthetic equivalents. Each mineral has been treated in some detail, and it has thus been necessary to restrict the coverage to a selection of the more important minerals. The principle in this selection is implied in the title *Rock-Forming Minerals*, as, with a few exceptions, only those minerals are dealt with which, by their presence or absence, serve to determine or modify the name of a rock. Some may quarrel with the inclusion or omission of particular minerals; once committed, however, to the discussion of a mineral or mineral series the less common varieties have also been considered.

Most of the information contained in this text is available in the various scientific journals. An attempt has been made to collect, summarize and group these contributions under mineral headings, and the source of information is given in the references at the end of each section. The bibliography is not historically or otherwise complete, but the omission of reference to work which has been encompassed by a later and broader study does not belittle the importance of earlier investigations; where many papers have been published on a given topic, only a limited number have been selected to illustrate the scope and results of the work they report.

The collection of data and references should bring a saving of time and labour to the research worker embarking on a mineralogical study, but it is hoped also that the presentation of the results of study from many different aspects, and in particular their correlation, will further the understanding of the nature and properties of the minerals. Determinative properties are described and tabulated, but the intended function of this work is the understanding of minerals as well as their identification, and to this end, wherever possible, correlation has been attempted, optics with composition, composition with paragenesis, physical properties with structure, and so on. For each mineral the body of well-established data is summarized, but unsolved and partially solved problems are also mentioned.

The rock-forming minerals are dealt with in five volumes. The silicates are allocated on a structural basis: vol. 1. *Ortho- and Ring Silicates*, vol. 2. *Chain Silicates*, vol. 3. *Sheet Silicates*, vol. 4. *Framework Silicates*. *Non-silicates* are grouped chemically in the various sections of volume 5.

With a few exceptions, the treatment of each mineral or mineral group is in five sub-sections. In the *Structure* section, in addition to a brief description of the atomic structure, descriptions of X-ray methods for determining chemical composition and any other applications of X-rays to the study of the mineral are given. The *Chemistry* section describes the principal variations in chemical composition and includes a table of analyses representative, wherever possible, of the range of chemical and paragenetic variation. From most analyses a structural formula has been calculated. The chemistry sections also consider the synthesis and breakdown of the minerals and the phase equilibria in relevant chemical systems, together with d.t.a. observations and alteration products. The third section lists *Optical and Physical Properties* and discusses them in relation to structure and chemistry. The fourth section contains *Distinguishing Features* or tests by which each mineral may be recognized and in particular distinguished from those with which it is most likely to be confused. The *Paragenesis* section gives the principal rock types in which the mineral occurs and some typical mineral assemblages: possible derivations of the minerals are discussed and are related wherever possible to the results of phase equilibria studies. The five sub-sections for each mineral are preceded by a condensed table of properties together with an orientation sketch for biaxial minerals and an introductory paragraph, and are followed by a list of references to the literature. The references are comprehensive to 1960 but later additions extend the coverage for some sections to 1962. In the present text, mineral data are frequently presented in diagrams, and those which can be used determinatively have been drawn to an exact centimetre scale, thus enabling the reader to use them by direct measurement: numbers on such diagrams refer to the number of the analysis of the particular mineral as quoted in the tables. The presentation of X-ray powder data was recognized as desirable but the additional labour and consequent delay in publication which would have been involved were thought to be prohibitive: the accessibility of the A.S.T.M. powder data file also influenced our decision to omit such data. In this volume, however, X-ray powder data for the zeolites are tabulated, the zeolite minerals being relatively more difficult to differentiate by other simple methods.

The dependence of these volumes upon the researches and reports of very many workers will be so obvious to the reader as to need no emphasis, but we wish especially to record our indebtedness to those authors whose diagrams have served as a basis for the illustrations and thus facilitated our task. In this connection we would thank also the many publishers who have given permission to use their diagrams, and Mr H. C. Waddams, the artist who has so ably executed the versions used in the present text. *Mineralogical Abstracts* have been an indispensable starting point for bringing many papers to our attention: in by far the majority of cases reference has been made directly to the original papers; where this has not been possible the *Mineralogical Abstracts* reference is also given *e.g.* (M.A. 13–351). Our warmest thanks are due also to our ex-colleagues in the Department of Geology, Manchester University, who have been helpful with discussions and information, and who have tolerated, together with the publishers, repeatedly over-optimistic reports about the work's progress and completion. In writing the section on felspars we have been particularly fortunate in having Dr W. S. MacKenzie close at hand and are most grateful for his criticism and advice. We wish to thank Miss J. I. Norcott who has executed so efficiently the preparation of the typescript and also Longmans, Green & Co. for their continued co-operation.

October 1962

CONTENTS *Vol. 4.* *Framework Silicates*

NOTES

Cell parameters, interplanar and interatomic distances are generally given in Ångstrom Units. The factor $1 \cdot 00202$ has been used to convert kX to Å units and this factor has also been applied to all data published before 1944 which were then stated as being in Å units.

ABBREVIATIONS AND SYMBOLS

The following abbreviations have been used in the text except where otherwise stated.

A	Ångstrom units (10^{-8} cm.)
a	cell edge in the x direction
a_{rh}	rhombohedral cell edge
a_{hex}	hexagonal cell edge
anal.	analysis or analyst
b	cell edge in the y direction
Bx_a	acute bisectrix
C	(in association with λ) red light (656 mμ)
c	cell edge in the z direction
calc.	calculated
D	specific gravity
D	(in association with λ) sodium (yellow) light (589 mμ)
d	interplanar spacing
d.t.a.	differential thermal analysis
2E	apparent optic axial angle measured in air
F	(in association with λ) blue light (486 mμ)
H	hardness (Mohs scale)
Li	(in association with λ) lithium (red) light (671 mμ)
mμ	millimicron
M.A.	*Mineralogical Abstracts*
max.	maximum
min.	minimum
m. eq./g.	milliequivalents per gram (cation exchange capacity)
n	refractive index (for a cubic mineral)
O.A.P.	optic axial plane
P	pressure
R	metal ions
$r < v$ (or $r > v$)	the optic axial angle in red light is less than (or greater than) that in violet light
rh	rhombohedral
T	temperature
Tl	(in association with λ) thallium (green) light (535 mμ)
2V	the optic axial angle
x, y, z	the crystal axes
Z	number of formula units per unit cell
α, β, γ	least, intermediate and greatest refractive indices

α, β, γ	angles between the positive directions of the y and z, x and z, and x and y crystal axes
α, β, γ	the vibration directions of the fast, intermediate and slow ray; also these rays
δ	birefringence
ϕ	polar coordinate: azimuth angle measured clockwise from [010]
ρ	polar coordinate: polar angle measured from z
λ	wavelength
ϵ	extraordinary ray, refractive index
ω	ordinary ray, refractive index

ACKNOWLEDGMENTS

For permission to redraw diagrams we are indebted to the following: The Editors, *Amer. Journ. Sci.*, *Bull. Geol. Soc. Amer.*, *Nature*; The Secretary-General, International Geological Congress; The Secretary, Consejo Superior de Investigaciones Cientificas, Madrid; Akademische Verlagsgesellschaft mbH, Frankfurt, for diagrams from *Zeit. Krist*; The Carnegie Institute of Washington for diagrams from *Ann. Rep. Dir. Geophys. Lab.*; The Faraday Society for a diagram from *Trans. Far. Soc.*; The Mineralogical Society of London for a diagram from *Min. Mag.*; The Mineralogical Society of America for diagrams from *Amer. Min.*; Oxford University Press for diagrams from *Journ. Petrol.*; Pergamon Press Ltd. for a diagram from *Geochim. et Cosmochim. Acta*; The Royal Society of London for diagrams from *Proc. Roy. Soc. A*; E. Schweizerbart'sche Verlagsbuchhandlung, Stuttgart, for diagrams from *Neues. Jahrbuch Mineralogie*; University of Chicago Press for diagrams from *Journ. Geol*; and from Eitel, *The Physical Chemistry of the Silicates* (Copyright 1954 by the University of Chicago) and Sir Lawrence Bragg and the Cornell University Press for diagrams from *Atomic Structure of Minerals*.

FELSPAR GROUP

Alkali Felspars   (K, Na) [AlSi$_3$O$_8$]
Plagioclase   Na [AlSi$_3$O$_8$]–Ca[Al$_2$Si$_2$O$_8$]

INTRODUCTION

The members of the felspar group of minerals are the most abundant constituents of the igneous rocks, some sixty per cent. of which consist of these minerals. Thus the felspars are the most important mineral group in the upper lithosphere. The ubiquity of the felspars together with their wide range in composition has led inevitably to their use as the primary tool in the classification of the igneous rocks. In the great majority of these rocks, whether acid, alkaline, intermediate or basic, the felspars are the major constituents, and they are absent only from some ultrabasic and rare alkaline rocks. Felspars are the most important constituents of the simple pegmatites and are common in mineral veins. They are major constituents of most gneisses and schists, and occur also in many thermally as well as regionally metamorphosed rocks. Although the felspars are susceptible to alteration and weathering they are second in abundance to quartz in the arenaceous sediments, in which they occur as detrital grains and as authigenic crystals. It is only in the argillaceous, and to a greater degree in the carbonate rocks, that the felspars are of relatively minor importance.

The complex nature of the felspar minerals has resulted in their being subdivided into many categories according to their chemical, physical and structural characteristics. Thus the literature contains numerous names for different kinds of felspar many of which are universally accepted and consistently applied; it is inevitable, however, that as new information is acquired and better understanding achieved, some changes in nomenclature should prove necessary. Some felspar names, therefore, are used in different senses by different workers. The following paragraphs briefly outline a classification and nomenclature of the felspar minerals, and more detailed discussion follows in later sections. In our selection of nomenclatures we have been guided principally by Dr. W. S. MacKenzie, whose assistance is gratefully acknowledged.

To achieve a proper understanding of felspar relationships it has proved necessary to characterize them not only according to chemical composition, but also according to structural state, which depends upon the temperature of crystallization and upon subsequent thermal history. A felspar which has been quenched so that it retains the structure appropriate to its high temperature formation is called a high-temperature felspar. Most felspars of volcanic rocks are of this type. Low-temperature felspars are those with structures appropriate either to crystallization at low temperature, or to slow cooling from elevated temperatures; these are found for example in plutonic rocks. Felspars may occur also in an intermediate-temperature structural state.

The majority of felspars may be classified chemically as members of the ternary system $NaAlSi_3O_8$–$KAlSi_3O_8$–$CaAl_2Si_2O_8$. These compositions are referred to respectively as sodium, potassium and calcium felspar (rather than soda, potash and lime felspar). Members of the series between $NaAlSi_3O_8$ and $KAlSi_3O_8$ are called alkali felspars, and those between $NaAlSi_3O_8$ and $CaAl_2Si_2O_8$ plagioclase felspars. The alkali felspars generally contain less than 5 to 10 per cent. of the calcium "molecule" in solid solution, but the sodium-rich members can contain a little more. Similarly the plagioclase felspars generally contain

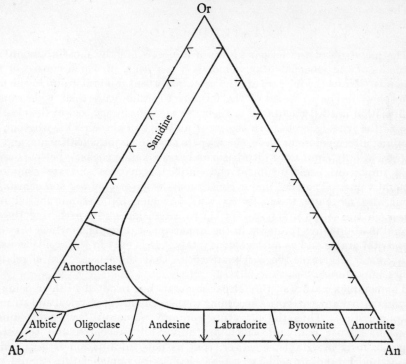

FIG. 1.   Illustrating solid solution in the felspars.   The nomenclature of the plagioclase series and the high-temperature alkali felspars is also shown.

less than 5 to 10 per cent. of the potassium "molecule". The distinction between alkali and plagioclase felspar at compositions with approximately equal calcium and potassium content is somewhat arbitrary (see Fig. 1).

The pure calcium end-member, anorthite, is triclinic, and no essentially different names are used to describe structural states at different temperatures. The potassium end-member can exist in a number of different structural states. Those with structures corresponding to the highest temperatures of crystallization are monoclinic and are called sanidines, while a lower temperature monoclinic potassium felspar is called orthoclase. The lowest temperature potassium felspars are microclines. These are triclinic, but different specimens of microcline have crystal lattices with different obliquities (p. 12). Those with maximum obliquity are called maximum microclines while others are termed intermediate microclines. A further potassium felspar, adularia, is one which is recognized principally by its habit and paragenesis, and which has no specific structural or optical characteristics. The pure sodium end-member is called low-albite or high-albite (or intermediate-albite) according to structural state. For a number of reasons the term high-albite is preferred to the term analbite which has sometimes been used in its place. The albites are normally triclinic but at high temperatures a transition to monoclinic symmetry occurs. (Such monoclinic albites are sometimes referred to as "monalbite".) Pericline is the sodium felspar counterpart of adularia, and it has a similarly restricted paragenesis and a characteristic habit.

The alkali felspars have been classified, on the basis of their optical properties, into four series. These are:

1. high-albite–high-sanidine
2. high-albite–low-sanidine
3. low-albite–orthoclase
4. low-albite–microcline

The high-albite–high-sanidine series is one of complete solid solution, but within it there is a change of symmetry from triclinic (Ab_{100} to Ab_{63}) to mono-clinic (Ab_{63} to Ab_0). The triclinic members of this series are called anorthoclase[1] and the remainder range from sodium-rich to potassium-rich sanidine. In the second high-temperature series, high-albite–low-sanidine, solid solution is limited at each end, and specimens with intermediate composition consist of two phases separated on a sub-microscopic scale. These are called cryptoperthites, and this series also is divided at Ab_{63}, so that it contains anorthoclase, anortho-clase cryptoperthites, sanidine cryptoperthites and sanidines.

In the lower temperature series, low-albite–orthoclase and low-albite–microcline, solid solution is more limited in extent and phase separation occurs on a scale which can be seen with the aid of a microscope. These intergrowths are called orthoclase or microcline microperthites. If the presence of two phases can be seen without the aid of a microscope, the term perthite is used. Some alkali felspars, called moonstones, display on particular surfaces a sheen or iridescence, attributed to lamellar micro- or cryptoperthitic intergrowth. The term "moonstone", however, is sometimes applied also to plagioclase felspars showing similar phenomena.

For the plagioclase series, as for the alkali felspars, the terms high-tempera-ture, low-temperature (and intermediate-temperature) are again relevant. A purely chemical definition of a plagioclase can be given in terms of Ab–An "molecular" percentages, but specific names are used to denote the six com-positional ranges into which the series has been divided. Thus albite, oligo-clase, andesine, labradorite, bytownite and anorthite refer to An percentages 0–10, 10–30, 30–50, 50–70, 70–90 and 90–100 respectively. These divisions were chosen merely for convenience and have no structural significance. Position within a chemical range may be further indicated by such phrases as sodium-rich (or sodic) oligoclase, calcic bytownite, etc. The high-temperature series from albite to anorthite is one of almost complete solid solution, but

---

[1] See, however, Laves (1960).

X-ray investigation has shown that the low-temperature series is structurally complex. The various structural types designated are: low-albite, peristerite, intermediate, body-centred anorthite, transitional anorthite and anorthite (Fig. 96). It should be noted that "intermediate" in this sense means intermediate between two low-temperature states, and it should be noted also that body-centred anorthite and transitional anorthite do not have the chemical composition of anorthite. Plagioclases with peristerite structure are known to consist of a fine intergrowth of two phases, and some specimens show iridescence. The exhibition of a similar sheen by some labradorites may be called "labradorescence".

Most perthites are intergrowths of sodium-rich felspar in a potassium-rich felspar host; an intergrowth of potassium-rich felspar in a plagioclase host is called antiperthite.

The derivation of the name felspar has been studied historically by Zenzén (1925) and a further discussion is given by Spencer (1937). The name as originally given by D. Tilas (1740) was *feldtspat* and it is believed that this had reference to the presence of the spar (spath) in tilled fields (Swedish: *feldt* or *fält*) overlying granite. Another Swedish form was given by Wallerius (1747) as *feltspat*. A 1750 German translation of Wallerius' work gave *feldspath* and the 1772 English translation of a text-book by Cronstedt gave field-spar. In his text-book in English, Kirwan (1784) used felt-spar, but later in his second edition (1794) altered the spelling to felspar, possibly believing that the name was of German origin and derived from *Fels*, rock. Spencer (*loc. cit.*) pointed out that if any change from felspar was really needed it should be to the original Swedish form feldtspar or feltspar, without stopping half-way at the form feldspar (of German derivation).

Orthoclase takes its name from the combination of the Greek *orthos* (upright) and *klasis* (fracture) in allusion to its two prominent cleavages at right angles to each other; similarly the name plagioclase is derived from Greek *plagios* (oblique), as its {001} and {010} cleavages are oblique to one another. Microcline has a cleavage angle only slightly greater than a right angle (approximately $90\frac{1}{2}°$) and its name is a combination of *mikros* (small) and *klinein* (to incline). In a similar fashion the name anorthoclase is compounded of the negative prefix *an* together with *orthos* (upright) and *klasis* (fracture) meaning that again the cleavages are non-rectangular. Adularia is called after the locality in the Adular Mountains, Switzerland. Sanidine is named from the Greek *sanis* (tablet) and *-idos* (appearance) in allusion to the typical tabular habit of this mineral. Perthite takes its name from Perth, Quebec, an early locality. Albite is derived from the Latin *albus* (white) in allusion to its colour, while oligoclase is of Greek derivation from *oligos* (little) and *klasis* (fracture) as it was thought to have a less perfect cleavage than albite. Andesine was named after a locality in the Andes and occurs in the rock type andesite. Labradorite is so called after a locality on the coast of Labrador (Isle of St. Paul), likewise bytownite derived its name from the locality Bytown (now Ottawa), Canada. Anorthite is compounded from the Greek negative prefix *an* together with *orthos* (upright) in reference to its oblique (triclinic) crystal form. Hyalophane is also of Greek derivation from *hualos* (glassy) and *-phanes* (appearance) in allusion to transparent crystals, while celsian is named after the Swedish naturalist A. Celsius. The variety peristerite is named from the Greek *peristera* (pigeon) in allusion to its play of colours somewhat resembling those on a pigeon's neck.

REFERENCES

Kirwan, R., 1784. *Elements of Mineralogy*. London.
Kirwan, R., 1794. *Elements of Mineralogy*, 2nd Edition. London.
Spencer, L. J., 1937. Some mineral names. *Amer. Min.*, vol. 22, p. 682.
Tilas, D., 1740. *Akad. Handl.* Stockholm, vol. 1, p. 199.
Wallerius, J. G. 1747. *Mineralogia eller mineralriket*. Stockholm.
Zenzén, N., 1925. On the first use of the term feldtspat (= feldspar, etc.) by Daniel Tilas in 1740. *Geol. För. Förh.* Stockholm, vol. 47, p. 390.

Alkali Felspars

$(K,Na)[AlSi_3O_8]$

	Microcline, Microcline microperthite,	Orthoclase, Orthoclase microperthite,	Sanidine, Anorthoclase,	High-sanidine,
	Low-albite series	Low-albite series	High-albite series	High-albite series
α	1·514–1·529	1·518–1·529	1·518–1·527	1·518–1·527
β	1·518–1·533	1·522–1·533	1·522–1·532	1·523–1·532
γ	1·521–1·539	1·522–1·539	1·522–1·534	1·524–1·534
δ	0·007–0·010	0·006–0·010	0·006–0·007	0·006–0·007
$2V_\alpha$	66°–103°	33°–103°	18°–54°	63°–54°
$\alpha : (001)$	15°–20°	5°–19°	5°–9°	— 9°

For optic orientation see Figs. 24–27, pp. 56, 57.

Dispersion:	$r>v$ $r<v$	$r>v$ $r<v$	$r>v$ $r>v$	$r<v$ $r>v$
D	2·56–2·63	2·55–2·63	2·56–2·62	2·56–2·62
H	6–6½	6–6½	6	—

Cleavage: {001},{010}perfect ; {100},{110},{Ī10},{Ž01}partings.

Twinning: Simple, multiple and repeated twinning. Principal twin laws : Carlsbad, Baveno, Manebach ; albite, pericline and "tartan" twinning shown by triclinic felspars only. For details see pp. 21–32.

Colour: Normally colourless or white, but sometimes pink, yellow, red or green; colourless in thin section.

Unit cell: K-felspar, $a \simeq 8·6$, $b \simeq 13·0$, $c \simeq 7·2$ Å, $\beta \simeq 116°$ Z=4.
Na-felspar, $a \simeq 8·2$, $b \simeq 12·8$, $c \simeq 7·1$ Å, $\beta \simeq 116°$ Z=4.
Sanidine and orthoclase are monoclinic, $C2/m$; microcline and Na-felspars are triclinic, $C\bar{1}$.[1] For details see Table 2.

The alkali felspars are common constituents of the acid and alkaline plutonic and volcanic rocks, the acid gneisses, and thermally metamorphosed argillaceous rocks. In the latter the alkali felspar is usually a potassium-rich orthoclase. The potassium, unlike the sodium, felspar rarely approximates to the end-member composition, and sanidine, orthoclase and microcline usually have a relatively large content of $NaAlSi_3O_8$. Adularia is the only alkali felspar consistently to have a composition in which the potassium component is greater than 80 per cent. Four series may be distinguished : high-sanidine–high-albite,

---

[1] A primitive cell can of course be chosen for each of the triclinic felspars, but it is convenient to show their relation to monoclinic felspars by choice of the C-face-centred cell with the parameters given above.

sanidine–high-albite, orthoclase–low-albite, microcline–low-albite. Alkali felspars with transitional optics and structure, however, are known, and the demarcation of the last three series above is somewhat arbitrary. The nomenclature of the alkali felspars of intermediate composition is not as precise as in the plagioclase series, and generally their composition cannot be determined by the measurement of a single optical property. Although $KAlSi_3O_8$ and $NaAlSi_3O_8$ form a continuous solid solution series at high temperature, except in rare examples, unmixing takes place on cooling, and the gap in the isomorphous series increases with decreasing temperature. Thus the alkali felspars generally consist of two phases, one potassium-rich, the other sodium-rich, and the resulting textures are described as cryptoperthitic, microperthitic or perthitic.

STRUCTURE

The following section on structure is divided into three parts: 1. Potassium felspars with little or no sodium; 2. Sodium felspars with little or no potassium 3. Alkali felspars in general.

1. Potassium felspars

Sanidine. The essential features of the crystal structure of the felspar minerals were first determined by Taylor (1933) in his study of a sanidine. Its unit cell was determined as monoclinic, space group $C2/m$, with a 8·4 Å, b 12·9 Å, c 7·1 Å, β 116°, and $4K(Si_3Al)O_8$ per cell. The structure is typical of a "framework" silicate in which tetrahedra of $(Si,Al)O_4$ are linked to one another (by shared oxygens) in all directions rather than in chains or in sheets. Although discrete chains of tetrahedra do not exist in the structure, its nature may be more easily understood by considering the atomic arrangement as the linking of chains in two directions perpendicular to their length. The chains themselves are formed by the linking of horizontal rings of four tetrahedra as shown in Fig. 2a. The repeat distance in the chain direction is approximately four times the height of a tetrahedron. When viewed in the direction of the chain axis a horizontal ring appears approximately as in Fig. 2b, and this can be further simplified in its representation as in Fig. 2c. In the actual structure the rings are considerably distorted; they are tilted out of the horizontal plane, and are twisted about the chain axis direction. Successive horizontal rings of a chain are, however, related by vertical glide planes (reflection in (010) and translation of $a/2$) passing through their centres, and the view down the chain axis may be idealized as in Fig. 2d. The first, third, fifth, etc., rings are represented by thick and the even number rings by thin lines. The linkage of rings in directions at right angles to their length is as follows. At the level of the first ring a network of oxygen linkages is formed as shown in black in Plate 1, producing a plane of four-membered and eight-membered rings of tetrahedra. Vertical symmetry planes and glide planes are marked MM′ and GG′. A similar network is formed by the rings of second tetrahedra below the first network and this is shown in red in Plate 1; the two arrays are linked by the oxygen atoms (such as P, Q, Fig. 2) forming vertical four-membered rings. The resultant framework of tetrahedra contains large interstices which are occupied by potassium ions, and these too are shown in Plate 1, lying on reflection planes and approximately midway between horizontal diad axes. They are rather irregularly co-ordinated by nine oxygens, the K–O distances being about 3 Å. Plate 1 shows in black a foreshortened view along x of a continuous sheet $K_1L_1K_1$, etc., sloping in the direction [102] (see Fig. 3): Plate 1 shows in red a similar sheet $L_2K_2L_2$ at a distance $a/2$ below, and when the two are superimposed an idealized projection of the complete structure results. This projection can also be regarded as a foreshortened view of (100) planes of the structure. By choosing the cell edge c instead of c' (Fig. 3) the volume of the cell is halved and the sequence of rings in the z direction is $K_1K_2K_1K_2$, etc.

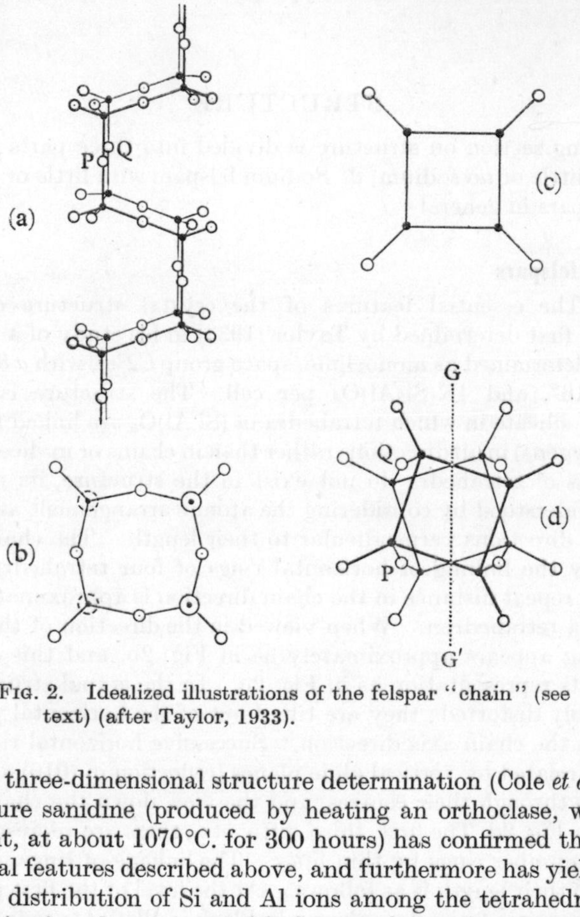

FIG. 2.   Idealized illustrations of the felspar "chain" (see text) (after Taylor, 1933).

An accurate three-dimensional structure determination (Cole *et al.*, 1949) of a high-temperature sanidine (produced by heating an orthoclase, with very low sodium content, at about 1070°C. for 300 hours) has confirmed the correctness of the structural features described above, and furthermore has yielded information about the distribution of Si and Al ions among the tetrahedral sites. Although the projection along x is suitable for visualizing the structure as a whole, other projections yield simpler views of a single formula unit, and are more favourable for structure determinations. A projection of the sanidine structure on (010) is shown in Fig. 4, in which atoms are labelled only within the unique area, and Fig. 5a shows part of the structure as viewed along the normal to (001). Consideration of y co-ordinates shows that atoms K and O_{A_2} are in special four-fold positions on symmetry planes, O_{A_1} is in a special fourfold position on a diad

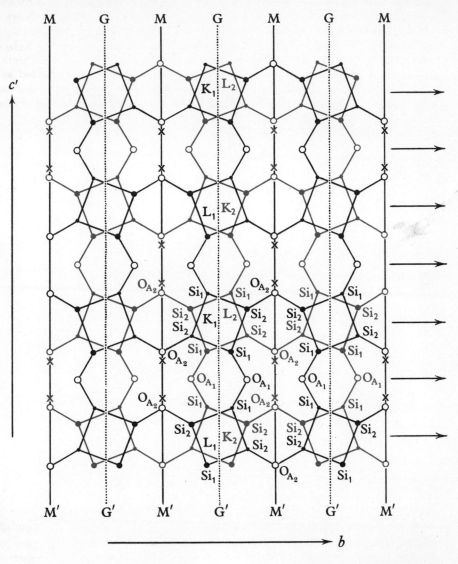

Plate 1. In black: schematic illustration of the cross linkage of the felspar "chains" to
form a "sheet" in the plane $K_1L_1K_1$ of Fig. 3.

In red: similar "sheet" to that shown in black but $a/2$ below it and related to it by
a vertical glide plane. This "sheet" lies in the plane $L_2K_2L_2$ of Fig. 3. Oxygens
linking tetrahedra within the "chains" are not shown on this diagram. (After
Taylor, 1933.)

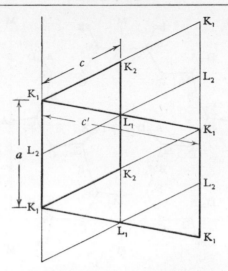

Fig. 3. (010) projection illustrating the
relation of Plate 1 to the cell by which
felspars are usually described. Plate
1 shows the plane $K_1L_1K_1$ as viewed
along a and also shows $L_2K_2L_2$.
The cell normally referred to has
edges c and a.

axis, and the remaining atoms are in general eightfold positions. Accurate cell
parameters for this sanidine are given in Table 2, p. 15.

Since all (Si,Al)–O distances were found to be equal (1·64 Å) it is inferred that
the Al atoms (one to every three silicons) are distributed randomly between the

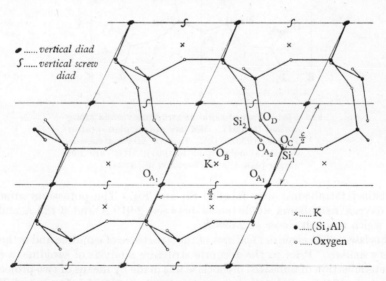

Fig. 4. (010) projection of sanidine.

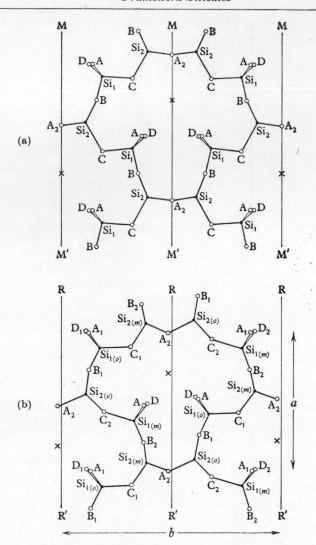

Fig. 5 (a). Part of sanidine structure viewed along normal to (001). MM′ are mirror planes (after Taylor, 1933). (b). Part of albite structure viewed along normal to (001). RR′ are not mirror planes (after Taylor *et al.*, 1934).

two distinct tetrahedral sites labelled Si_1 and Si_2. The potassium atom has eight oxygen neighbours at distances between 2·919 Å and 3·129 Å and one (O_{A_2}) which is much closer at 2·698 Å.

Orthoclase. The essential features of the structures of sanidine and orthoclase are very similar. Prior to the accurate structure analysis of sanidine, a structure determination of unheated orthoclase was made by means of two projections (Chao *et al.*, 1940). A detailed structure determination by Jones and Taylor

(1961) has shown that in orthoclase there is partial ordering of the (Si,Al) atoms, with approximately (0·30 Al + 0·70 Si) at site Si_1 and (0·19 Al + 0·81 Si) at site Si_2, rather than complete ordering (1·0 Si at Si_2) as proposed by Chao *et al.* (1940). Accurate cell parameters of the unheated orthoclase are compared with those of the heated specimen in Table 2 and it is seen that a and b are slightly larger in the latter case, while c and β are slightly smaller. It is argued that these changes are consistent with the re-arrangement of Al atoms suggested to occur in the process of sanidinization. The environment of the potassium atom is essentially the same in both structures. Jones and Taylor have found that the potassium atom electron density peak shows some anisotropy in each of the three potassium felspars. This may represent a distribution of the potassium atom's position, varying from cell to cell with the (Si,Al) ordering in its immediate neighbourhood.

If the monoclinic potassium felspars have true holohedral symmetry there must be two groups of eight equivalent tetrahedral ions. With a total of 12Si + 4Al per cell the eight sites cannot be equivalent in any one cell, but statistical equivalence may be effected by random distribution of Al atoms among all sites or among either Si_1 sites or Si_2 sites. Further segregation of Al atoms within one of these groups (Si_1 say), so that the eight equivalent positions become two fourfold, or four twofold positions, must reduce the cell symmetry to monoclinic hemihedral, or non centrosymmetric triclinic respectively. Laves (1952, 1960) considers that orthoclase contains submicroscopically twinned triclinic domains: no final decision has been reached on the true symmetry of orthoclase but any departure from monoclinic symmetry is probably small (Jones and Taylor, 1961). Statistical tests for the presence or absence of a centre of symmetry (Bailey *et al.*, 1951) show that sanidine and orthoclase possess centres of symmetry, but it is doubtful whether such tests would reveal departures from centrosymmetry involving only the Si,Al distribution and attendant minor deviations. Further discussion of order–disorder relations occurs later.

Microcline. The lowest temperature form of potassium felspar, microcline, is triclinic. The cell parameters of microcline (space group $C\bar{1}$) vary in different specimens, but those of one for which an accurate structure determination has been carried out (Bailey and Taylor, 1955) are given in Table 2. This specimen is microperthitic, but the minor sodium felspar phase was disregarded in the course of the three-dimensional structure analysis. The statistical test for centro-symmetry was applied by Bailey and Taylor and found to be satisfied, although again this does not exclude the possibility of slight non-centrosymmetry on account of Al–Si distribution. Since the microcline cell is triclinic it does not possess the symmetry planes and axes of the monoclinic felspars, and in accordance with this loss of symmetry the number of equivalent general positions is reduced from eight to four. Instead of oxygens $O_B O_C O_D$ there are pairs of fourfold oxygens $O_{B1} O_{B2}$, $O_{C1} O_{C2}$, $O_{D1} O_{D2}$; and instead of silicons Si_1, Si_2 there are Si_1(o) and Si_1(m), Si_2(o) and Si_2(m).[1] The potassium atom and oxygens O_{A1}, O_{A2} remain fourfold but are no longer in special positions. The essential features of triclinic felspars are best illustrated by a projection on (001) in which the atoms of only one formula unit are inserted. This is done for the albite structure in Fig. 5b, and although structural detail differs, the labelling and

[1] For recommended notation see Megaw (1956).

approximate location of atom sites are valid for microcline too (with replacement of Na by K).   The microcline structure may be contrasted with that of sanidine in Fig. 5a.   The atoms K and O_{A2} are no longer exactly on the plane $y = 0$, and O_{A1} is not exactly on the line $(0,y,0)$.   Other atoms also have slightly changed co-ordinates, and the potassium atom has a smaller amplitude of thermal vibration than in sanidine.

It is important to note that the $12Si + 4Al$ in the unit cell of microcline must be distributed among four non-equivalent sets of fourfold tetrahedral sites, instead of among two sets of eightfold sites as in sanidine and orthoclase (see Table 1).   The average bond lengths Si–O in the four different tetrahedra in this case are not equal, and thus it is inferred that partial ordering of the Al atoms occurs.   The fraction of each site occupied by Al was determined as 0.25, 0.56, 0.07, 0.08 for sites $Si_1(o)$, $Si_1(m)$, $Si_2(o)$, $Si_2(m)$ respectively.   The effects of these substitutions on the lengths of cell edges as compared with sanidine are those expected.

MacKenzie (1954) and Goldsmith and Laves (1954) have shown that variations in the microcline cell can occur, ranging from a specimen which is barely distinguishable from monoclinic, to one which has the angles $\alpha = 90° 41'$, $\gamma = 87° 30'$ and which is termed "maximum microcline": others are known as "intermediate microclines".   Laves (1950) reported a "triclinic adularia" with $\alpha = 90°$, $\gamma = 89\frac{1}{2}°$, but this has subsequently been recognized as an intermediate microcline.   The degree of departure from monoclinic symmetry has been called "triclinicity" but the term obliquity is preferable and can be quantitatively expressed as the angle between y and y^*.   MacKenzie (1952, 1954) described a method for estimating the variation in γ^* by measuring the separation of $1\bar{3}0$ and 130 in X-ray powder patterns from microclines.   Goldsmith and Laves (1954) use $1\bar{3}1$ and 131.

The concept of order–disorder relationships for the (Al,Si) distribution, which was suggested (Barth, 1934) to explain the grosser differences between microcline and sanidine, may be invoked again to explain the continuous series of microcline obliquities.   In support of this Goldsmith and Laves (1954) have shown that on heating a microcline at 1050°C. its obliquity diminishes with duration of heating and eventually a sanidine is produced.   Change of obliquity could not, however, be observed when microclines were heated hydrothermally to any temperature, for in these circumstances microclines were partially converted to sanidine at much lower temperatures, and the amount of sanidine produced varied with duration of heating, nature of specimen, and temperature. Sanidine could not be produced below 525°C. but the nature of the experiments make it unwise to assume that this is the critical temperature for the ordering process.   Microclines with less obliquity were more readily converted to sanidine.

MacKenzie (1954) suggests that the amount of sodium in solid solution in a microcline might also be a factor influencing obliquity, which increases as sodium content falls, and moreover that microcline occurs as the stable form of potassium felspar in rocks which have been regionally metamorphosed, because this treatment favours exsolution of sodium felspar.   Both disorder and chemistry might well be involved, the ordering of (Si,Al) atoms perhaps being controlled in the first place by the unmixing of Na and K phases.   Whether or not this hypothesis is correct, it is certain that Na content can affect the $130-1\bar{3}0$ peak separation, and therefore care must be taken in correlating this measurement with degree of order.

Microcline rarely occurs untwinned, sometimes shows either albite or pericline twinning, and most often shows both, in the well-known cross-hatched or "tartan" pattern. The peculiar relations between pericline and albite twinning in a microcline crystal are taken to be evidence that it first crystallized with monoclinic symmetry and subsequently became triclinic (Laves, 1950). Mac-Kenzie (1954) describes two cases where monoclinic and triclinic potassium felspars occur together; in one the triclinic portions are twinned and have a constant obliquity, while in the other gradations of obliquity occur.

Infra-red absorption measurements (Hafner and Laves, 1957) and nuclear magnetic resonance (Brun *et al.*, 1960) have been used to study the order–disorder relations in felspars. The method distinguishes between different degrees of order whether or not these are discernible as a change in symmetry by X-ray methods. A difference is observed between high- and low-sanidine, which may be related to the different ways in which a monoclinic felspar can be disordered. Table 1 illustrates the ways in which 4Al and 12Si atoms can be distributed in the felspar cell.

Table 1. WAYS IN WHICH Al AND Si ATOMS CAN BE DISTRIBUTED AMONG THE GROUPS OF EQUIVALENT SITES IN THE POTASSIUM FELSPAR CELL (after Laves, 1950).

Monoclinic	1st 8-fold position		2nd 8-fold position	
1.	Si + Al		Si + Al	
2.	Si		Si + Al	

Triclinic	1st 4-fold	2nd 4-fold	3rd 4-fold	4th 4-fold
3.	Si + Al	Si + Al	Si + Al	Si + Al
4.	Si	Si + Al	Si + Al	Si + Al
5.	Si	Si	Si + Al	Si + Al
6.	Si	Si	Si	Al

Table 1 indicates that many stages of ordering are theoretically possible.[1] For the monoclinic case maximum disorder would occur with (6Si + 2Al) in each column, and maximum order with 8Si and (4Si + 4Al). A higher degree of ordering could only be attained by transition to lower symmetry. In the triclinic case maximum disorder would occur with (3Si + Al) in each column (see also Laves, 1960).

Adularia. The potassium felspar adularia shows variations in optical and structural parameters in different areas of single grains. Laves (1952) suggests that under normal circumstances it would have crystallized as microcline, but the rate of crystal growth has been very rapid so that the ordering process expected for a low-temperature felspar was prevented from taking place. Adularia is a distinctive variety by virtue of its morphology and its restricted paragenesis.

[1] Si and Al which occur in the same column must be randomly distributed among the 4 or 8 sites if the crystal is truly centrosymmetric.

Iron sanidine. Synthetic iron sanidine, $KFeSi_3O_8$, is apparently structurally analogous to the aluminium felspar high-sanidine. It is monoclinic $C2/m$ with a 8·69, b 13·12, c 7·32, β 116° 06', D calc. 2·72 (Wones and Appleman, 1961). A triclinic polymorph similar to microcline has also been synthesized.

2. Sodium felspars

The structure of albite, $Na(Si_3Al)O_8$, is in general similar to that of the potassium felspars. Taylor *et al.* (1934) demonstrated this and also showed in which respects the structures are different. Sodium felspar is triclinic, with space group $C\bar{1}$, and its cell parameters are listed in Table 2. Comparison of cell edges with those of the potassium felspars shows a marked contraction in a, the direction of the "chain" axis, and little change in b and c. The positions of atoms in one formula unit, viewed in the direction normal to (001), are depicted in Fig. 5b. Compared with sanidine, shifts of atoms of up to 0·3 Å are involved and the loss of symmetry planes is apparent. The full structural detail shows also the absence of diad axes. As in the case of microcline the number of general equivalent positions is reduced with lowering of symmetry, from eight to four. The cell content $Na_4(Si_3Al)_4O_{32}$ is disposed so that eight oxygens (O_{A1}, O_{A2}, O_{B1}, O_{B2}, O_{C1}, O_{C2}, O_{D1}, O_{D2}) and the sodium atom are in fourfold positions, and there are also four distinct fourfold positions for occupation by (Si,Al), labelled $Si_1(o)$, $Si_1(m)$, $Si_2(o)$, $Si_2(m)$.

Two modifications of albite are known to occur in nature, a low-temperature form which occurs mainly in plutonic rocks and a high-temperature albite which occurs in lavas, and can be produced artificially by prolonged heating of low-temperature albite. The structures of both have been determined recently with high accuracy (Ferguson *et al.*, 1958) and, in addition to confirming the correctness of the essential features of earlier results, this work reveals important detail. The principal structural difference between low- and high-temperature albite lies in the distribution of Al atoms among the four non-equivalent tetrahedral sites. In low-albite their approximate content is given as $Al_{0·80}$, $Al_{0·0}$, $Al_{0·22}$, $Al_{0·10}$ in sites $Si_1(o)$, $Si_1(m)$, $Si_2(o)$, $Si_2(m)$ respectively. The three-dimensional structure analysis also shows that in low-albite the sodium atom appears to have anisotropic thermal vibration, with maximum amplitude parallel to the y axis. This alternatively can be taken to mean that the atom occupies at random in different cells one of two positions separated by about 0·1 Å along y.

In the case of high-temperature albite the (Si,Al)–O bond length is the same for all tetrahedral sites, corresponding to occupation of each by ($\frac{3}{4}Si + \frac{1}{4}Al$), and it is inferred that the Si,Al distribution is completely disordered. The amplitude of thermal vibration of the sodium atom is larger in all directions than that found in low-albite and its anisotropy is considerably more marked, and could be interpreted in terms of two Na sites separated by about 0·6 Å along y. In both low- and high-temperature albites the sodium atom is co-ordinated by six or seven nearest oxygen neighbours, by contrast with the ninefold co-ordination of potassium in the case of potassium felspar. It is clear that the order–disorder characteristics of low- and high-temperature albites are in some respects similar to those of the potassium felspars, microcline and high-sanidine. High-albite and high-sanidine have highly disordered (Si,Al) distributions, whereas low-albite and microcline represent arrangements with a considerable degree of order. In the latter two cases Al is concentrated principally in corresponding tetrahedral sites (Si(o) rather than Si(m)). Further similarity lies in the thermal vibration of the alkali ions which, both for potassium and sodium, is of greater average amplitude in the high-temperature forms. The anisotropy of the electron density peak representing sodium is not, however, so markedly exhibited in the case of potassium. Cell parameters of high- and low-albite are presented in Table 2, and it is seen that in both potassium and sodium felspars the increasing disorder of the higher temperature forms is accompanied by slight increase of b and decrease of c.

A comparatively rare sodium felspar, with characteristic habit, called pericline, bears a similar relation to low-albite as does adularia to microcline. It too shows variation in optical properties and evidence of variation in structural parameters in different regions of a single specimen.

Relations between high- and low-temperature forms of natural and synthetic albites have been investigated by several workers (*e.g.* Tuttle and Bowen, 1950; MacKenzie, 1957; Schneider, 1957). Since the principal differences between low- and high-temperature albite appear to be associated with ordering of the Si and Al atoms it would be expected that stable forms with intermediate degrees of ordering should exist, as indeed is the case for the potassium felspars. Although intermediate plagioclases are found, with the exception of one specimen (Baskin, 1956) no natural intermediate-albite has been reported. In the case of hydrothermally synthesized albites, however, specimens with intermediate lattice parameters (indicated by separation of 131, 1$\bar{3}$1 reflections) were prepared (MacKenzie, 1957), and attempts were made to ensure that these specimens represented equilibrium states. Goldsmith (1950) synthesized sodium and potassium felspars in which germanium substitutes for silicon, or gallium for aluminium, and showed their similarity to sanidine and albite. Because of the markedly different scattering powers but similar sizes of Ge and Al, and Si and Ga, such compounds may provide useful information on the distribution of Si and Al in natural felspars.

Table 2. CELL PARAMETERS OF ALKALI FELSPARS

	a Å	b Å	c Å	α	β	γ	Specimen and Reference
Sanidine	8·5642	13·0300	7·1749	90°	115°59·6′	90°	Cole *et al.* (1949); heat treated.
Orthoclase	8·5616	12·9962	7·1934	90°	116° 0·9′	90°	As above, unheated.
Intermediate microcline	8·5784	12·9600	7·2112	90° 18′	115° 58′	89° 7½′	Bailey & Taylor (1955).
Maximum microcline	8·57$_4$	12·98$_1$	7·22$_2$	90° 41′	115° 59′	87° 30′	MacKenzie (1954). Blue Mountain, Ontario.
High-albite	8·149	12·880	7·106	93° 22′	116° 18′	90° 17′	Ferguson *et al.* (1958); Amelia, Virginia; heat treated.
Low-albite	8·139	12·789	7·156	94° 20′	116° 34′	87° 39′	Ferguson *et al.* (1958). Ramona, California.

3. Alkali felspars

Most natural alkali felspars are not homogeneous but contain separate potassium-rich and sodium-rich phases. The highest temperature forms of alkali felspar, however, do form a complete solid solution series. It is proposed to deal in turn with the crystallography of each of the series high-albite–high-sanidine, high-albite–sanidine, low-albite–orthoclase, low-albite–microcline, and then to discuss some relationships between them.

High-albite–high-sanidine. All synthetic alkali felspars belong to this series but only the potassium-rich end ($>Or_{67}$) is represented in nature. The series is one of complete solid solution although at the composition $Or_{37}Ab_{63}$ there is a change in symmetry: specimens more potassium-rich than this are monoclinic at room temperature while those which are more sodium-rich are triclinic. The composition at which this change in symmetry occurs is temperature dependent, and above 1000°C. all compositions up to Ab_{100} are monoclinic in symmetry (MacKenzie, 1952). Prolonged heat treatment of

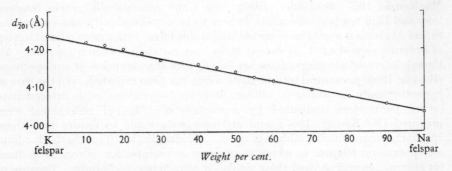

Fig. 6. Spacing of $\bar{2}01$ planes in a series of alkali felspars crystallized at 900°C. and 300 bars pressure of H_2O (after Bowen and Tuttle, 1950).

natural alkali felspars alters their properties so that they conform to the high-albite–high-sanidine series, and their compositions can then be estimated by measurement of the $\bar{2}01$ spacing (Fig. 6) in an X-ray powder pattern (Bowen and Tuttle, 1950).

High-albite–sanidine. In natural specimens belonging to this series, unmixing of sodium-rich and potassium-rich phases appears to occur within the range of composition Or_{25}–Or_{60}. The change in symmetry from triclinic at the sodium-rich end to monoclinic at the potassium-rich end divides the series into anorthoclases ($<Or_{37}$) and sanidines ($>Or_{37}$). The unmixing in the range Or_{25}–Or_{60} occurs on a very fine scale (detectable by X-rays but not with the microscope) yielding anorthoclase and sanidine cryptoperthites. Although part of the series is triclinic, nevertheless the angle of the $\bar{2}01$ reflection (which does not depend upon b, α or γ) again can be used to determine the composition of anorthoclases and sanidines and, when measured for a homogenized cryptoperthite, gives its bulk composition. Whether or not an alkali felspar is unmixed often can be determined from a powder pattern; if the phases have sufficiently different composition two $\bar{2}01$ peaks will appear instead of only one for a homogeneous specimen. It does not seem wise, however, to use the positions of either or both $\bar{2}01$ reflections to estimate composition of the separate phases (*cf.* Laves, 1952). The intensity ratios of the two $\bar{2}01$ peaks appear to vary systematically as a function of both bulk composition and thermal state (Kuellmer, 1959, 1960). Single-crystal X-ray photographs have been used to examine alkali felspars, and these show not only whether or not unmixing has occurred, but also indicate the number and nature of the constituent phases (Smith and MacKenzie, 1955). Potassium phase and sodium phase reflections occur in groups, with those from the potassium phase occurring at lower angles.

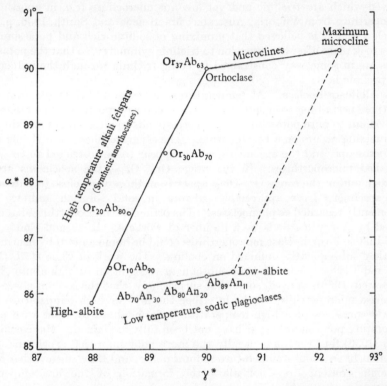

Fig. 7. Plot of α^* against γ^* for synthetic anorthoclases, microclines and low-temperature sodic plagioclases (after MacKenzie and Smith, 1956).

The potassium phase (in lower temperature perthites) may be either monoclinic or triclinic and these can generally be distinguished and recognized in the photograph. The sodium phase is, with rare exceptions, triclinic, and is generally twinned. Sometimes both albite and pericline twinning occurs resulting in a cluster of four spots accompanied by a fifth for the potassium phase. The separation of twin pairs in either or both cases yields values of α^* and γ^*. The values of α^* and γ^* for high-albite and for synthetic anorthoclases (Donnay and Donnay, 1952) are plotted against one another (Fig. 7, after MacKenzie and Smith, 1956) and are seen to lie on a straight line terminating at Or_{37} where $\alpha^* = \gamma^* = 90°$. The measured values for the sodium phase of several natural cryptoperthites lie close to this line, and it is found that the presence of some

2—R.F.M. IV.

calcium does not affect the determination. It is important to note that in the unmixed felspars which have been allocated to the high-albite–anorthoclase–sanidine series on the basis of their optical properties, the sodium-rich phase is a high-temperature one, whereas perthites of the orthoclase–low-albite series generally have a low-temperature sodium phase. For low-temperature sodium felspars α^* and γ^* are different.

Untwinned anorthoclase gives a single-crystal pattern from which its triclinic nature can be deduced by unsymmetrical intensity relationships. The potassium phase of a cryptoperthite is generally monoclinic, but some have been observed which are triclinic and yet are not microclines (*e.g.* in anorthoclase cryptoperthite from Victoria, Australia; MacKenzie and Smith, 1956, p. 422). In such a case it is believed that unmixing of sodium-rich and potassium-rich phases took place after the inversion to triclinic symmetry, so that the potassium phases are in some way constrained to being triclinic through the influence of their triclinic host.

Low-albite–orthoclase. At temperatures on the equilibrium diagram lower than those pertaining to cryptoperthites, a greater proportion of the range from pure sodium to pure potassium felspar corresponds to a region of unmixing, and the unmixing occurs on a coarser scale. The separate phases are visible under the microscope, and the specimens, which appear to be restricted to Or_{20}–Or_{85} are called microperthites. In the range Or_{85}–Or_{100} the specimens are not unmixed, and in the range Or_0–Or_{20}, apart from those very close to pure albite, most specimens have appreciable calcium in solid solution and are more conveniently regarded as plagioclases. The orthoclase microperthites have been studied by X-ray methods by a number of workers. Kôzu and Endô (1921) found that some orthoclase microperthites could be homogenized by heating and that they subsequently unmixed on cooling. The work of Chao *et al.* (1939), Chao and Taylor (1940), and the subsequent recognition of high-albite (Tuttle and Bowen, 1950), showed, somewhat surprisingly, that the sodium phase of an orthoclase microperthite can be in either the low- or high-temperature form. These occurrences of a high-temperature sodium phase together with a low-temperature potassium felspar have not been fully explained. MacKenzie and Smith (1956) find that it is usually the more potassium-rich specimens (Or_{79}–Or_{85}) that have a high-temperature sodium phase, and they suggest that a high potassium content does not allow the formation of the low-temperature structure.

The sodium phase in microperthites can show either pericline or albite twinning or both. For the limited number of specimens which have been examined, those in the range Or_{75}–Or_{85} show pericline twinning, while those more sodium-rich than Or_{60} have a sodium phase showing either albite or albite plus pericline twinning. Those with intermediate content (Or_{60}–Or_{75}) exhibit a complicated superstructure which it is believed has some relation to albite twinning. This "albite twin superstructure" may also be a consequence of a relatively high potassium content, and it may be an intermediate step in the formation of a twinned crystal. Specimens with least potassium generally yield simple twin X-ray patterns and no superstructure. As in the case of the cryptoperthites the single-crystal technique described by Smith and MacKenzie (1955) is very useful in determining from pairs of twin reflections the angles α^* and γ^*, which can be used to distinguish between low- and high-temperature forms of sodium felspar. For the orthoclase microperthites, however, these angles cannot be used for the precise determination of chemical composition. It was found that γ^* is influenced considerably by calcium content and could perhaps be used for its estimation (MacKenzie and Smith, 1955a), and although α^* is affected less by calcium substitution its quantitative dependence on the potassium content is nevertheless uncertain. Some specimens (peristerites) contain two sodic plagioclase phases of different composition together with a monoclinic potassium phase. Fig. 7 shows α^* and γ^* values for low-temperature sodium phases as well as those for anorthoclases previously discussed.

Although intermediates between low- and high-temperature forms would be expected to occur in perthites, none have been reported. A possible reason for this (MacKenzie, 1957) is that the low-albite structure can accommodate only very little potassium, whereas high-albite can accept much more. The large potassium content of a high-temperature sodium felspar may prevent its transition by means of the ordering process to low-albite.

The potassium phases of orthoclase microperthites usually have been described as monoclinic, but MacKenzie and Smith have shown that a triclinic potassium phase, which can be detected by X-ray single-crystal methods, is often also present. The presence of a triclinic phase gives rise to a higher 2V than would be expected for normal members of this series.

Low-albite–microcline. There is very little solid solution in this series and the distinction between it and the orthoclase series becomes meaningful only at the potassium-rich end. Microcline itself, although discussed previously as a single phase, is usually perthitic or microperthitic, so that in effect the low-albite–microcline series, such as it is, has been dealt with in the section on microcline.

It remains to discuss relationships between the three principal alkali felspar series. Förstner (1884), Laves (1952) and MacKenzie (1952) showed that natural anorthoclases and synthetic sodium-rich felspars which are triclinic at room temperature acquire monoclinic symmetry[1] on heating, and revert to triclinic symmetry on re-cooling. The change of symmetry can be followed in X-ray powder patterns by the positions of 111 and 1$\bar{1}$1 reflections which become coincident at the transition point and remain as a single peak on further heating. The temperature of inversion to monoclinic symmetry is affected, however, by the potassium and calcium content. The cross-hatched twinning generally exhibited by anorthoclase suggests (as in the case of microcline) that it originally crystallized with monoclinic symmetry, *i.e.* above the inversion temperature, and subsequently became triclinic on cooling. Although microclines and anorthoclases both show cross-hatched twinning they should not be confused; microclines are potassium-rich low-temperature forms, and anorthoclases are sodium-rich high-temperature forms, and the two are readily distinguishable by their optical properties and lattice geometries (see pp. 32, 58; fig. 7, p. 17).

---

[1] Monoclinic sodium felspars have been given the name monalbite (see Laves, 1960; Brown 1960). Brown also shows that the monoclinic–triclinic displacive transformation can occur in previously heat-treated $NaAlSi_3O_8$ at temperatures ranging from near melting point to below room temperature. He considers that these changes are due to changes in (Si, Al) distribution, and that this rather than composition has the greatest influence on lattice constants.

The result of heating orthoclase microperthites in the region 600°–1025 °C. is an exchange of sodium and potassium between the sodium- and potassium-rich phases (MacKenzie and Smith, 1955). The lattice angles of the sodium phase change from those of a low-temperature sodium felspar towards those of maximum microcline and the angles of the potassium phase change towards those of low-albite. However, whereas sanidine cryptoperthites homogenize completely to sanidines at about 700°–900 °C., orthoclase microperthites of intermediate composition cannot be homogenized unless they are heated to above about 1050 °C., by which temperature they have become members of the high-sanidine series. Kuellmer (1961), by measurements of $2\theta(\bar{2}01)$ at elevated temperatures, studied the re-mixing of a number of perthitic alkali felspars, and concluded that in general the closer the perthite is to its original homogeneous high-temperature state, the more readily and completely it will re-mix on heating. It was also found that the more porphyritic specimens re-mixed more easily and completely.

MORPHOLOGY AND TWINNING

Since triclinic felspars do not deviate greatly from monoclinic symmetry several characteristic habits are common to both monoclinic and triclinic members of the felspar group of minerals. Some of the habits which occur most frequently have well developed {001} and {010} forms, and the presence of {110} in addition often yields a prominent prism zone parallel to the z axis (Fig. 8a). Sometimes, as in felspar microlites, crystals are elongated parallel to the x axis and the prism zone formed by {010} and {001} predominates (Fig. 8b). While orthoclases and microclines can have either of these typical habits, sanidines generally have the flattened appearance shown in Fig. 8c. Albite crystals are also often tabular parallel to (010) but they are sometimes elongated parallel to y as in the "pericline" habit (Fig. 8d). Sodium felspars with pericline habit are of particularly restricted occurrence, as are the potassium felspars called adularia which also have a characteristic development, illustrated in Fig. 8e. Adularia crystals look almost orthorhombic because (001) and (10$\bar{1}$) make nearly equal angles with the z axis. The high-temperature sodium-rich felspar anorthoclase is often found in rhomb-shaped crystals (Fig. 8f).

Felspars have perfect {001} and good {010} cleavages which in the monoclinic varieties intersect at right angles; in the triclinic felspars these cleavages are only approximately perpendicular to one another.

Perthites. Micro- and cryptoperthitic intergrowths are thought to be responsible for the schiller effects seen in those alkali felspar specimens which are generally referred to as moonstones. Antiperthites are specimens which have small regions of potassium-rich felspar in a sodium-rich felspar host. The segregation of potassium- and sodium-rich felspar sometimes occurs in irregular blebs but more often takes place at definite planes in the crystal. These planes, which can be seen best on (010) sections of microperthites, are approximately parallel to the y axis and generally make an angle of about 73° with (001) (Bøggild, 1924; Anderson, 1928; Spencer, 1930). This plane of segregation, which is the plane from which schiller reflections could occur, appears to lie near the crystallographic plane (60$\bar{1}$) or (70$\bar{1}$); see also p. 55. It is also often an additional plane of cleavage or easy parting in orthoclase and microcline along which decomposition readily occurs, and has been referred to as the Murchisonite cleavage. Other orientations of perthite lamellae have been reported (Bøggild, 1924; Spencer, 1930; Alling, 1938). The framework of the felspar structure is probably continuous across the boundaries of the perthite lamellae, and diffusion of sodium and potassium ions must occur when perthites are homogenized by heating.

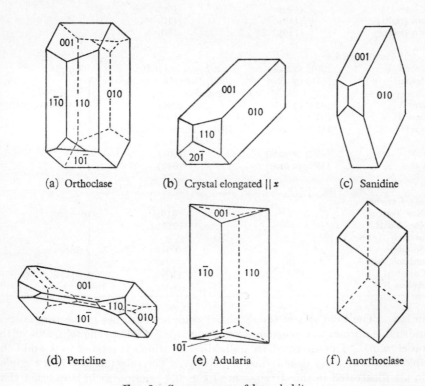

(a) Orthoclase   (b) Crystal elongated || *x*   (c) Sanidine

(d) Pericline   (e) Adularia   (f) Anorthoclase

FIG. 8. Some common felspar habits.

Twin laws. Many different kinds of pseudo-symmetry are exhibited by the felspar structures and accordingly twinning is very common and may follow a number of different laws. In Table 3 the more common twin laws which are applicable to felspars are divided into three groups; normal, parallel and complex. Normal twins have their twin axis normal to a possible crystal face and this face is parallel to the composition plane. For a centrosymmetric crystal this twinning process is equivalent to reflection in the composition plane. Parallel twins have as twin axis a possible crystal edge (*i.e.* a zone axis); the composition plane is parallel to the twin axis and need not define a possible crystal face. Sometimes an individual B is related to one A by a normal twin law, and an individual C is related to B by a parallel twin law with the same composition plane as the normal twin. C and A are then related by a "complex"

Table 3.   FELSPAR TWIN LAWS

Name	Twin axis	Composition plane	Remarks
Normal twins			
Albite	$\perp$ (010)	(010)	Repeated; triclinic only.
Manebach	$\perp$ (001)	(001)	Simple.
Baveno (right)	$\perp$ (021)	(021)	} Simple, rare in
Baveno (left)	$\perp$ (0$\bar{2}$1)	(0$\bar{2}$1)	} plagioclases.
X	$\perp$ (100)	(100)	
Prism (right)	$\perp$ (110)	(110)	
Prism (left)	$\perp$ (1$\bar{1}$0)	(1$\bar{1}$0)	
Parallel twins			
Carlsbad	[001] (z axis)	($hk0$), usually (010)	Simple.
Pericline	[010] (y axis)	($h0l$), "rhombic section" parallel to y.	} Repeated;
Acline A	[010] (y axis)	(001)	} triclinic only.
Acline B	[010] (y axis)	(100)	
Estérel	[100] (x axis)	($0kl$) "rhombic section" parallel to x.	}
Ala A	[100] (x axis)	(001)	} Repeated.
Ala B	[100] (x axis)	(010)	}
Complex twins			
Albite–Carlsbad (Roc Tourné)	$\perp$ z	(010)	}
Albite–Ala B	$\perp$ x	(010)	}
Manebach–Acline A (Scopie)	$\perp$ y	(001)	} Repeated.
Manebach–Ala A	$\perp$ x	(001)	}
X–Carlsbad	$\perp$ z	(100)	}
X–Acline B	$\perp$ y	(100)	}

twin law.   The twin axis of the resultant complex twin lies in the composition plane and is normal to a possible crystal edge (*i.e.* at 90° to the twin axis of the parallel twin).   The intermediate individual B, which is related to A and C by simple twin laws, may or may not be present.   The relationships in a complex twin are illustrated in the stereogram of Fig. 9.[1]   Simple twin laws other than those listed have been reported for felspars, and other complex twins are possible.   Combinations of twins which do not have a common composition plane, *e.g.* Carlsbad with pericline, also occur.

Illustrations of some common felspar twins are presented in Fig. 10.   Carlsbad, Baveno and Manebach twins are found in both monoclinic and triclinic felspars, mainly with only two individuals but sometimes with three, four or even six. The relationship between the twin laws and the crystal structure of felspars was described by Taylor *et al.* (1934), and is summarized and illustrated below.

Carlsbad twinning [parallel twin; axis [001]; composition plane (010)] is best understood by reference to an (010) projection, part of which is illustrated

---

[1] Some complex twins differ only very slightly from a counterpart among the parallel twins.   For example Manebach-acline A differs from Ala A only because the x axis of a triclinic felspar is not perpendicular to y ($\gamma \neq 90°$).   Such pairs of twins are indistinguishable by optical methods. Similarly distinction between X–Carlsbad and acline B depends upon deviation of α from 90°.

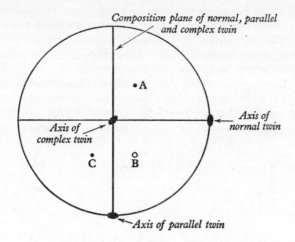

FIG. 9. Stereographic illustration of relationships in
a complex twin.

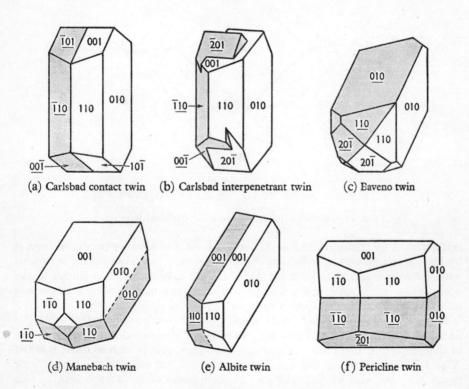

(a) Carlsbad contact twin   (b) Carlsbad interpenetrant twin   (c) Baveno twin

(d) Manebach twin   (e) Albite twin   (f) Pericline twin

FIG. 10. Some common felspar twins.

in Fig. 11 (compare with Fig. 4, p. 9). Heavy lines are drawn connecting silicon atoms in order to represent simply a single chain running parallel to the x axis. In the untwinned structure another chain running in the same direction is produced by reflection in the (010) plane which contains the bridging oxygen atoms A. The positions marked A_T are those related to A by a twin axis which is parallel to z and which lies in the horizontal reflection plane. It is seen that A_T lies close to A, and furthermore that the effect of the twin axis on the vertical diads D_1 and D_2 is to bring each into almost exact coincidence with the other (a result of the relationship $c/2 \simeq a \cos \beta$). Starting with oxygen atoms A_T a "chain" can be built up related to the first chain by the twin axis. This chain

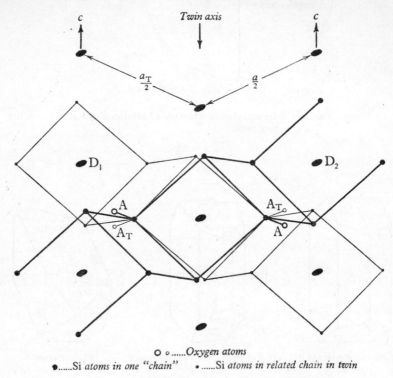

O o ......*Oxygen atoms*

●......*Si atoms in one "chain"*   • ......*Si atoms in related chain in twin*

Fig. 11. (010) projection illustrating Carlsbad twinning.

is illustrated by thin lines in Fig. 11, and if further chains are produced from it by the normal process of reflection in (010) planes, a twin component is formed with cell axes c and a_T. In order that the twin halves should be joined in the composition plane (010) the positions A and A_T are merged into a single site half-way between them which is occupied by the bridging oxygen.

Baveno twinning [normal twin; axis $\perp$ (021); composition plane (021)] is illustrated in Fig. 12 (*cf.* Plate 1). Because of the pseudotetragonal nature of this projection along the x (chain axis) direction, chains such as those marked X and X_T are related in the untwinned structure, not only by the true mirror plane MM, but also by GG, the pseudo-glide plane of symmetry (021). Differences in (y,z) positions of atoms produced by twinning across GG, and those produced by reflection across MM (as in the untwinned crystal), are so slight that they cannot be indicated clearly in this diagram. The difference between the two operations is revealed, however, by the positions of equivalent silicon atoms. In the right-hand half of the twin across (021) the positions of Si_1 and Si_2 would be interchanged in the untwinned structure. Since O_A and the oxygen atom occupying position $O_{A(T)}$ in the untwinned structure have slightly different x coordinates, but have the same x coordinates when related by the twin plane, there must be some adjustment of the positions of these atoms, and (for similar reasons) of the silicon atoms closest to the composition plane. It is seen that in the twin produced by glide reflection in (021), the mirror planes M_TM_T are approximately at right angles to MM, and diads D_T are nearly normal to diads D.

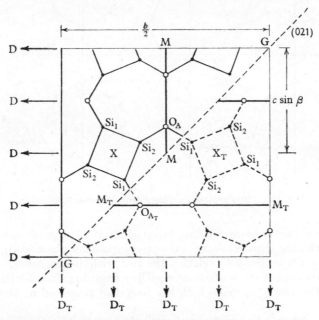

Fig. 12. (201) projection illustrating Baveno twinning.

Manebach twinning [normal twin; axis $\perp$ (001); composition plane (001)] is illustrated in Fig. 13. Above the horizontal line MM is shown one layer of linked four-membered rings as seen along the x axis (*cf.* Plate 1). In the untwinned crystal the structure below MM is related to that above by a diad axis D passing through the oxygen atoms A. The silicon atoms bonded to O_A are therefore in two planes, above and below the horizontal plane containing the diad. In the case of Manebach twinning the silicons in one individual Si_T have the same x coordinates as do the silicons in the other, and MM is a mirror plane instead of a diad axis.

Albite and pericline twins occur very frequently in triclinic alkali felspars and of the two the albite law is the most common. The structures of triclinic felspars do not deviate very much from monoclinic symmetry; (010) is a pseudo-mirror plane and y is a pseudo-diad axis. In albite twinning [normal twin; axis $\perp$ (010); composition plane (010)], at the junction of the twin individuals

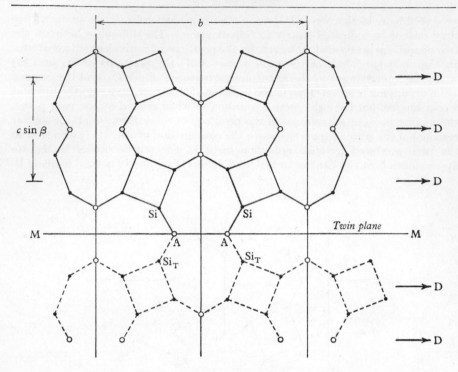

FIG. 13. (201) projection illustrating Manebach twinning.

(010) is a real mirror plane relating the triclinic structures on either side. In pericline twinning [parallel twin; axis y; composition plane $(h0l)$], at the twin junction y is a true diad axis relating the two triclinic structures. The mono-clinic felspars cannot show albite or pericline twinning since for them the twin axes ($\perp$ (010), and y) coincide with the true diad possessed by the untwinned structure.

Rhombic section. In pericline twinning the composition plane lies in the zone of faces parallel to y ($h0l$ faces); it contains the y axis, but its precise location is determined by the geometry of the triclinic cell. The composition plane is known as the "rhombic section" since its intersections with (110) and (1$\bar{1}$0) (or these faces produced) form the sides of a rhombus. The position of the rhombic section is specified by the angle σ which its trace makes with the trace of (001), measured on (010). Two examples are illustrated in Fig. 14, the first (a) with a small positive value of σ and the second (b) with a numerically larger negative value of σ.

The location of the rhombic section can be alternatively described by use of the property of the rhombus that its diagonals intersect at right angles. One diagonal is the y axis itself and the other is the intersection of the rhombic section with the plane (010). Thus the pericline twin plane can be defined as that which contains the y axis and which cuts (010) in a line 90° from y. This definition is useful in showing the relationships between the rhombic section and various crystallographic elements by means of stereographic projections.

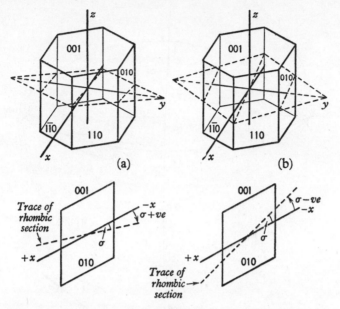

Fig. 14. Rhombic section (indicated by broken lines) in two different orientations (after Chudoba, 1933).

Examples are given in Fig. 15a, b and c of stereographic projections for triclinic cells with parameters similar to those of an anorthoclase, a microcline and a low-albite respectively. In each example the trace of the rhombic section on (010) is marked T and the pole of the rhombic section is marked R. The angle σ can be derived without constructing the rhombic section since it is also the angle between two planes which pass through the normal to (010), one through (001) and the other through the y axis. The value of σ can be calculated using the formula:

$$\cot \sigma = \frac{\cos \alpha^*}{\cot \gamma} = \frac{\cos (001)(010)}{\cot \gamma}$$

or in terms of direct lattice angles only (Storey-Maskelyne, 1895; Lewis, 1899; Tunell, 1952):

$$\cot \sigma = \cot \beta - \frac{\cos \alpha}{\cos \gamma \sin \beta}$$

It is apparent from Fig. 15, or by calculation, that very small changes in the α and γ angles of the lattice can result in a marked change in the position of the rhombic section.

An *acline A* twin [parallel twin; axis y; composition plane (001)] is similar to a pericline twin in that it has the same twin axis and its composition plane is a member of the zone of $(h0l)$ faces. In some circumstances it may be difficult to distinguish between the two laws since the rhombic section may lie near to (001), the composition plane of an acline A twin. A number of observations, however, point to the existence of acline A and B twinning in their own right,

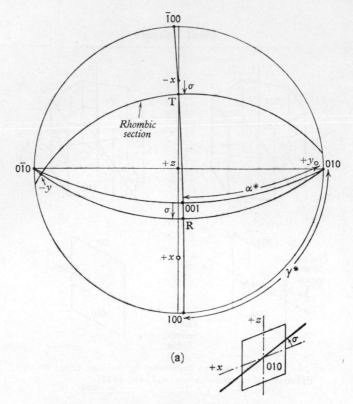

FIG. 15. Stereograms showing relation of rhombic section to other crystallographic elements.

(a) With σ small and negative as in high-albite or anorthoclase.

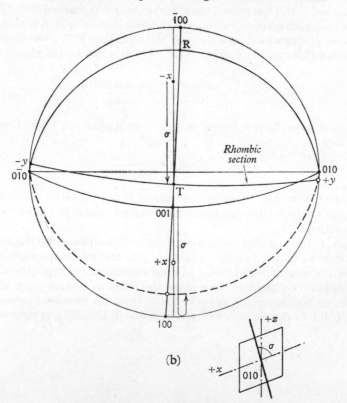

(b) With σ large and negative as in microcline.

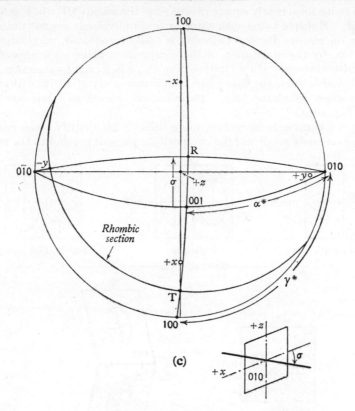

FIG. 15. (c) With σ small and positive as in low-albite.

and not merely as special cases of pericline twinning in which σ happens to be zero or $(180° - \beta)$ respectively (see also p. 106).

Estérel twins are far less common than pericline but are analogous in that their composition plane is the rhombic section in the zone of $(0kl)$'s and contains x as twin axis instead of y (Franke, 1920). *Ala* twins bear a similar relation to Esterel twins as acline to pericline in that they have x as twin axis and have fixed composition planes (010) and (001) in the zone of $(0kl)$ faces.

In the following paragraphs each of the alkali felspar species is discussed in turn with reference to the twin laws which it exhibits.

Orthoclase. For orthoclase Carlsbad twins are most common and other twins are rarely found. Carlsbad twins may be either of the interpenetrant or contact type, and in the latter the re-entrant angle between the (001) and ($\bar{1}$01) normals is very small. Under the microscope the twins are best seen in sections cut parallel to the y crystallographic axis (*i.e.* normal to the composition plane). Since orthoclase is monoclinic both individuals show straight extinction, but except in sections parallel or normal to the z axis they show different birefringence (Fig. 16a). If the crystal is rotated about y both halves remain in extinction.

Baveno twins form nearly square prisms since the angle (001) : (021) is approximately 45°. Multiple twins with three or four individuals are not uncommon. Under the microscope Baveno twinning is easily recognized, particularly on a (100) section, by the orientation of the composition plane with respect to the {001} or {010} cleavage. In a (100) section there is straight extinction in each individual, and because the twin plane is approximately at 45° to (010) the two parts extinguish simultaneously. Their optical orientations however will be opposed (Fig. 16b).

Manebach twinning is in general more difficult to identify since re-entrant angles are extremely small and the composition plane is parallel to the principal

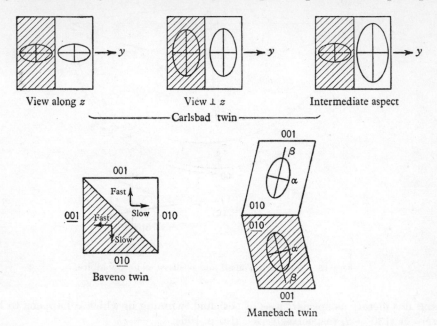

FIG. 16. Illustration of optical relationships in (a) Carlsbad, (b) Baveno and (c) Manebach twinning in orthoclase.

cleavage. Sections cut parallel to *y* show straight extinction in each individual and, except for those accurately parallel or normal to (001), the birefringences differ. In (010) sections extinction directions make an angle of about 10° on either side of the composition plane (001) (Fig. 16c). Other twin laws are sometimes exhibited by orthoclase, such as the "prism" twin with (110) as normal twin plane, and a similar twin with (130) or even an (*hkl*) face as twin plane. A number of uncommon laws however are more appropriately described as combinations of other laws. For example if A and B are related by the Carlsbad law, and B and C by Manebach twinning, then C and A are related as if twinned in an (*h0l*) plane. Acceptance of this as a new twin law is particularly likely if the intermediate B is unobservable, and the name "Emfola" has been used to describe it. Similarly the name "Neustad" had been used to describe a combination of Carlsbad and Baveno twin laws. Combinations of Manebach and Baveno twin laws have also been reported (see, for example, Nicolas, 1961).

Sanidine. For sanidine, as for orthoclase, Carlsbad twinning occurs most frequently, but Baveno and Manebach twins are also found.

Albite. Sodium felspars may show simple twinning on the Carlsbad, Baveno or Manebach laws but more often they twin on the albite, pericline, acline, Estérel or Ala laws. In all of these, twinning is usually repeated and the albite and pericline laws are by far the most common. The twinning of albite is discussed more fully in the section on plagioclases, but it is convenient to note here that albite crystals may display albite and pericline twinning simultaneously. This is shown also by microclines and by anorthoclases, but in the case of albite the relationship differs from that found in the other two cases and is illustrated

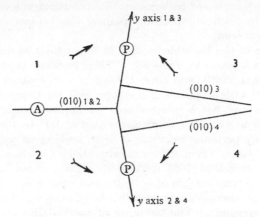

FIG. 17. Simultaneous albite and pericline twinning. (3) and (4) are related by the (010) twin plane of (1) and (2) but not by their own (010) planes.

by Fig. 17. Individuals (2) and (3) are related to (1) by albite and pericline laws respectively. Because of the deviation from monoclinic symmetry (2) and (3) are not simply related, and moreover if a twin (4) is produced from (2) by the pericline law this will not be related to (3) by the albite law or in any simple manner. Individuals (3) and (4) do not have a common (010) plane and meet in an irrational composition plane, but they are related across the (010) plane of individuals (1) and (2). If either (3) or (4) were to twin next by the albite law the new individuals would bear no simple relationship to any of the previous ones. A similar situation would arise if (1) and (2) were pericline twins and each had an albite twin. The two new individuals would be related by the y axis of the original pair and not to each other by the pericline law. Thus albite and pericline twinning cannot alternate in a cyclic manner.

Microcline. Microcline is characterized by a combination of albite and pericline twinning which is different from that found in albite. Most microclines are microperthitic and retain the morphology of the monoclinic felspar from which they have unmixed. They sometimes have in addition a monoclinic potassium-rich phase the orientation of which serves to describe the twinning relationships. Pericline individuals are twinned about their y axes which coincide with the morphological axis and with the y axis of the monoclinic potassium phase. Albite twinned individuals have their common y^* axis parallel to this direction (MacKenzie, 1954; MacKenzie and Smith, 1955). (It should be noted that y^* cannot be parallel to y in a single triclinic crystal.) The peculiar relationship between the two twin laws in microcline, and their accommodation by the crystal structure, are discussed by Laves (1950), and may be taken as evidence that microclines originally crystallized in the monoclinic system. Parts of the crystal have become triclinic with y parallel to the monoclinic y axis and these twin on the pericline law; other parts become triclinic with (010) parallel to (010) of the monoclinic lattice and these twin on the albite law. The regions in which albite and pericline twinning take place are closely interwoven, and when viewed between crossed polarizers in a direction approximately parallel to both composition planes, the typical cross-hatched, or "tartan" pattern is seen.

The orientation of the rhombic section in microclines as determined by the lattice parameters is given by $\sigma \simeq -83°$. Their pericline twinning is best seen on (001) rather than (100), and since the albite composition plane makes an angle of nearly 90° with all planes of the type ($h0l$), the twinning is well defined on (001), and the cross-hatch intersections are approximately at right angles. On (100) only albite twinning is seen, roughly at 90° to the (001) cleavage, while on (010) only pericline twinning is seen, making an angle of about 83° with the (001) cleavage. Sometimes microperthitic lamellae are also seen on (010), lying in the direction [106], making an angle of about 73° with (001).

Anorthoclase. A combination of pericline and albite twinning similar to that found in microcline also occurs in anorthoclases, showing that these too were probably once monoclinic. The twinning of anorthoclase and microcline can be distinguished, however, since their pericline twin composition planes (rhombic sections) are in very different orientations (MacKenzie, 1956). The value of σ for anorthoclase lies between $-2°$ and $-5°$ as compared with $-38°$ for micro-

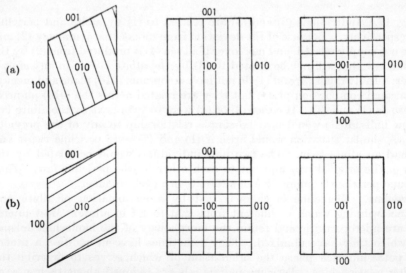

FIG. 18(a). Albite and pericline twinning in microcline. (b). Albite and pericline twinning in anorthoclase.

cline and $+35°$ for low-albite. The two cases are illustrated in Fig. 18 which shows the twinning visible on principal sections. In both microcline and anorthoclase, and indeed in any example of pericline twinning, if a section is viewed strictly along the y axis direction (*i.e.* along the twin axis) adjacent pericline lamellae will show similar birefringence and optical orientation so that the twin boundaries may not be visible.

Twinning by a number of less common laws has been reported for the triclinic alkali felspars. Most of these cases have y as twin axis, but their composition planes have been variously described. For example microclines have been reported with $(15,0,\bar{2})$ as composition plane (Dolar-Mantuani, 1952), some with composition plane (100), and some between these two positions. Composition planes $(15,0,\bar{2})$ and (001) have been observed together (the latter corresponding to the acline A twin law), and occasionally pericline, albite and acline twinning occur together (Chaisson, 1950).

CHEMISTRY

The alkali felspars are essentially a series varying from pure $KAlSi_3O_8$ to pure $NaAlSi_3O_8$ but normally also contain a certain amount of $CaAl_2Si_2O_8$ in solid solution. The amount of anorthite present is fairly small, generally less than 5 per cent. for $Or_{100}Ab_0$ to $Or_{50}Ab_{50}$, and then tends to increase slightly towards the sodic end of the series (see Fig. 46, p. 107). Other ions which may be present in limited amounts include Ba, Ti, Fe^{+3}, Fe^{+2}, Mg, Sr and rarely Mn. Analyses of alkali felspars are shown in Tables 4–8, where each analysis has been recalculated on the basis of 32 oxygen atoms in the unit cell. The barium-rich felspars (those with more than about 2 per cent. BaO) are treated in a separate section, and the iron-rich potassium felspars from Madagascar are listed separately in Table 9: for the remaining felspars the Ba is considered to substitute for K, while for all the iron-bearing alkali felspars Fe^{+3} is considered to replace Al, as also is the small amount of Ti sometimes found. Mg, the minor amounts of Fe^{+2}, Sr, and occasional Mn, are all taken to be replacing Ca and re-calculated into the anorthite molecule, though, as noted for the plagioclase felspars, it is doubtful whether appreciable Fe^{+2} does in fact occur in the structure, rather than in impurities.

Analyses. The analyses of Tables 4–9 have been selected from approximately twice their number of relatively recent analyses on the grounds of having a reasonable total, being apparently free from impurities, and recalculating to conform to the general formula $(K,Na,Ca)_4(Si,Al)_{16}O_{32}$ with in most cases the X group (K,Na,Ca) having a value of not less than 3·9: they have also been selected to illustrate the varying paragenesis of this series. Many such analyses of the members of this series are to be found in the papers of Spencer (1937), Kracek and Neuvonen (1952) and Hewlett (1959). Reference must also be made to the compilations and recalculations of Byelyankin (1915, 1925), Vogt (1926) and Belyankina (1953), the latter including 136 alkali felspar analyses, together with the analyses listed by Spence (1932) and Solodovnikova (1935), and for microcline and microcline perthite those given by Simpson (1952) and Higazy (1949) (see also the plot of microcline compositions given by Rottenbach, 1936). Belyankina investigated the variations between the determined and calculated values of the major oxides for analysed alkali felspars and found that while 70 had excess

SiO_2 and Al_2O_3, 35 were deficient in both SiO_2 and Al_2O_3, 17 had excess Al_2O_3 and a deficiency in SiO_2, and 14 had excess SiO_2 and a deficiency in Al_2O_3. From the present compilation, as for the plagioclase series, the commonest variation is seen to be an excess of both SiO_2 and Al_2O_3 and this may be more apparent than real if no account is taken of the substitution of K, Na and Ca by small amounts of other ions. In Tables 4–9 the values calculated for the Z group (Si, Al, Fe^{+3}, Ti) on the basis of 32 oxygens are fairly close to the theoretical 16·0: the general tendency is for a slight excess, with values ranging around 16·05 but the maximum excess is less than 1 per cent.

In *orthoclase* and *microcline* TiO_2 is generally low, but Fe_2O_3 may be present in appreciable amounts: it is probable, however, that for normal alkali felspars Fe_2O_3 in excess of about 0·5 per cent. represents either impurities, or material which has exsolved on cooling. The latter is present, either as discrete particles of iron-bearing mineral, or as iron staining on the grain boundaries and cleavage planes. The solubility of Fe_2O_3 in microcline in the solid state was determined by Rosenqvist (1951), using radioactive iron, and was found normally to be low. He suggested that *aventurine felspar*, with inclusions of haematite, originally crystallized from a magma poor in aluminium or rich in alkalies, allowing the felspars to become rich in iron: a subsequent aluminium metasomatism could then have replaced the iron atoms in the structure, expelling them to form haematite lamellae. MgO is low, but BaO may sometimes become important and amount to 1 per cent. or greater: indeed it is probable that most alkali felspars contain small amounts of barium, although in many cases it has not been sought by the analyst. Alkali felspars reported to contain more than 2 per cent. BaO are considered separately as barium felspars (p. 166). In some pegmatite microclines the rare alkalies may reach major element amounts, a particularly well-known example being the Varuträsk rubidium-microcline (Adamson, 1942) containing 0·53–3·30 per cent. Rb_2O (Table 5, anal. 12): this microcline is also notably rich in caesium, and contains in addition up to 0·34 per cent. Li_2O. Rubidium-microcline was earlier described from the Ilmen Mountains by Vernadsky (1913), and Tolmachev and Filippov (1935) reported over 1 per cent. Rb and 0·5 per cent. Cs in amazonites from this locality: 1·02 per cent. Rb_2O was determined in green microcline from Amelia, Virginia (Wells, 1937) (see also Erämetsä *et al.*, 1943). Thallium has also been detected, but only in trace amounts (Adamson, 1942; Ahrens, 1945).

A certain amount of the Na_2O reported in the analyses, rather than representing the substitution of Na for K is, together with some of the CaO, in the plagioclase phase in microperthite or perthite. This plagioclase phase is present almost invariably to a greater or lesser degree, and is usually so dominantly sodic as to be albite, though more calcic perthitic blebs are known. One of the few cases where the perthitic phase has been carefully separated before analysis is represented by anal. 15 (Table 5) where a pegmatitic microcline contains approximately 5 per cent. of plagioclase in solid solution: in other cases the amount of plagioclase present as a separate phase may be estimated by modal analysis of the perthite or from an X-ray diffraction pattern, and an allowance made for the amount of Na_2O (and CaO) present.

Analyses of *sanidine* and *anorthoclase*, in consequence of their higher temperature of formation, often show slightly greater amounts of alien ions in solid solution. TiO_2 may amount to around 0·1 per cent. while Fe_2O_3 varies from

0·04 to 0·40 per cent. even in glass-clear crystals and is sometimes present in still greater quantity. MgO is generally small and variable, several reliable analyses reporting it to be either absent, or present only in trace amounts. BaO may be appreciable, and although it is often unrecorded in the analysis, several sanidines and anorthoclases show amounts varying from 0·12 to 1·31 per cent.: SrO is less liable to occur and generally does so only in trace amounts. The rare alkalies are considerably less common in these felspars than in the microclines although Li_2O and Rb_2O are occasionally reported in small amounts (*e.g.* Table 7, anal. 9). The anorthite molecule is generally fairly low in sanidine, which typically has less than 1 per cent. CaO but sometimes as much as approximately 1·5 per cent.: in anorthoclase, however, the amount of CaO tends to rise as the Na/K ratio increases towards the composition of albite, with 3–4 per cent. CaO sometimes being found in anorthoclases, as in the "potash-oligoclases" from Mt. Erebus, Antarctica (Table 7, anals. 2 and 3). Further analyses of sanidine and anorthoclase are given by Carmichael (1960) and by Brousse (1961).

Adularia is confined to the Alpine vein type of paragenesis and as such its compositional range is relatively small, a typical composition being around $Or_{90}Ab_9An_1$ (Table 8). Iron and magnesium are usually fairly low while barium is noticeably rather high and may approach 1 per cent. BaO. The anorthite molecule is generally relatively low with CaO less than 0·5 per cent.

Iron-rich potassium felspar was first reported from Madagascar by Lacroix (1913), and the locality at Itrongay, near Fianarantsoa, remains the only occurrence known. The clear yellow crystals from a miarolitic pegmatite are of gem quality and as a consequence have often been studied both chemically and optically: eight analyses of this material are given in Table 9 (see also Faust, 1936, and Coombs, 1954). Their compositions have been recalculated to molecular percentage of the components Or, Ab, An and the iron-orthoclase molecule $(KFeSi_3O_8)$ Fe-Or, and show a range of up to 10 per cent. of iron-orthoclase. The Fe^{+3} ion replaces Al in the structure and in this natural material from Madagascar does so only in the potassium felspar component. Shand (1931) recorded a microcline from the Transvaal abnormally rich in K_2O (15·9 per cent.) which had 1·02 per cent. Fe_2O_3 represented as "ferric orthoclase": this sample, however, almost certainly contained fragments of ferromagnesian material. The possible existence of other ferrian felspars was discussed by Faust (1936), who established beyond doubt the replacement of Al by Fe^{+3} in potassium felspar. Faust assumed in recalculation that all the iron was in the ferric state: this has not been followed here but the amount of ferrous iron reported is either nil or so small as not to have any significant effect on the recalculated end-member values, and, as remarked by Coombs (1954), the small amounts of FeO reported are at most not much greater than the blank likely to be encountered in a normal FeO determination. CaO and MgO are both low.

In general, alkali felspars have been analysed by the classical procedures for silicate analysis, with recently the determination of the alkalies by means of flame photometry. When a full analysis is not available it has sometimes been sufficient to determine only the three oxides, K_2O, Na_2O and CaO, from which the proportion of the orthoclase, albite, and anorthite molecules in the felspar has been calculated. A first attempt at the determination of alkali felspars by radioactivation analysis was reported by Bradley and Bradley (1956) who

Table 4.　ORTHOCLASE, ORTHOCLASE MICROPERTHITE

	1.	2.	3.	4.	5.	6.	7.	8.
SiO_2	65·76	65·67	64·98	64·76	65·40	64·50	65·16	65·33
TiO_2	0·08	—	—	—	—	—	nil	—
Al_2O_3	20·23	20·84	19·64	19·96	19·89	20·25	19·44	18·82
Fe_2O_3	0·18	—	0·64	0·08	0·27	0·47	0·10	—
FeO	—	—	—	tr.	—	—	nil	—
MgO	0·10	—	tr.	tr.	tr.	tr.	nil	—
BaO	0·63	—	—	—	—	—	—	—
CaO	1·19	0·50	0·84	0·84	0·14	0·48	0·16	0·39
Na_2O	8·44	7·59	6·00	5·54	5·30	4·72	4·56	4·23
K_2O	3·29	5·49	7·33	8·12	8·92	9·60	10·10	10·20
H_2O^+	0·37	—	}0·40	}0·54	}0·30	}0·28	0·50	}0·78
H_2O^-	0·08	—					0·08	
Total	100·35	100·09	99·83	99·84	100·22	100·30	"100·20"	99·75
α	1·528	1·527	1·5255	1·5256	1·5230	1·5232	1·522	1·5219
β	1·533	1·530	1·5301	1·5296	1·5270	1·5274	1·526	1·5257
γ	1·537	1·533	1·5324	1·5326	1·5302	1·5299	1·529	1·5275
$2V_\alpha$	78°	83°	71·3°	82·8°	83·5°	73·7°	74°	70°
Ext. on (010)	14°	14°	11·7°	11·7°	11·0°	10·5°	—	—
D	—	—	2·5948	2·5950	2·5890	2·5848	—	2·582

NUMBERS OF IONS ON

	1.	2.	3.	4.	5.	6.	7.	8.
Si	11·719	11·701	11·761	11·750	11·807	11·690	11·858	11·948
Al	4·249	4·377	4·190	4·269	4·232	4·326	4·170	4·068
Fe^{+3}	0·024	—	0·087	0·011	0·036	0·064	0·014	—
Ti	0·011	—	—	—	—	—	—	—
Mg	0·027	—	—	—	—	—	—	—
Na	2·916	2·622	2·106	1·949	1·855	1·659	1·609	1·500
Ca	0·227	0·095	0·163	0·163	0·027	0·093	0·031	0·076
K	0·748	1·249	1·692	1·880	2·055	2·220	2·345	2·381
Ba	0·044	—	—	—	—	—	—	—
Z	16·00	16·08	16·04	16·03	16·07	16·08	16·04	16·02
X	3·96	3·97	3·96	3·99	3·94	3·97	3·99	3·96
Mol. % { Or	20·0	31·5	42·7	47·1	52·2	55·9	58·8	60·2
Ab	73·6	66·1	53·2	48·8	47·1	41·8	40·4	37·9
An	6·4	2·4	4·1	4·1	0·7	2·3	0·8	1·9

1. Sodium-rich orthoclase cryptoperthite, ijolite–nepheline-syenite, Sinkwa, Mogok, Burma (Tilley, 1954).
   Anal. J. H. Scoon.
2. Microperthite ("cryptoperthite"), nordmarkite, Spålen, Nordmark, Oslo district, Norway (Oftedahl, 1948).　Anal. Lars Lund.
3. Orthoclase microperthite with deep blue schiller, Fredriksvärn, Norway (Spencer, 1937).　Anal. E. Spencer.
4. Orthoclase microperthite with white schiller (Mogok ?), Burma (Spencer, 1930).　Anal. E. Spencer.
5. Orthoclase microperthite with white schiller, Oksaung Daung, 3¼ miles E.N.E. of Mogok, Burma (Spencer, 1937).　Anal. E. Spencer.
6. Orthoclase microperthite (moonstone) pegmatite, Ambalangoda, Ceylon (Spencer, 1937).　Anal. E. Spencer.
7. Orthoclase microperthite (moonstone–"anorthoclase"), Ceylon (Kracek & Neuvonen, 1952).　Anal. O. von Knorring.
8. Orthoclase (microperthite ?), Ceylon (Byelyankin, 1915).

AND ORTHOCLASE PERTHITE ANALYSES

9.	10.	11.	12.	13.	14.	15.	16.	
63·94	64·66	64·02	64·28	63·90	65·30	63·01	63·66	SiO_2
—	—	—	—	nil	—	tr.	—	TiO_2
20·02	19·72	19·58	19·40	20·46	18·84	19·73	19·54	Al_2O_3
0·40	0·08	0·32	0·34	}0·09	0·16	}0·62	0·10	Fe_2O_3
—	—	tr.	—		—			FeO
0·07	tr.	0·16	tr.	0·08	—	0·19	—	MgO
0·17	—	—	—	0·36	—	0·50	—	BaO
0·58	0·34	0·33	0·48	0·16	0·34	0·26	0·50	CaO
3·60	3·42	3·02	2·74	2·38	1·62	1·51	0·80	Na_2O
10·86	11·72	12·12	11·80	12·61	14·18	14·53	15·60	K_2O
}0·60	}0·18	}0·28	}0·58	0·12	—	—	—	H_2O^+
				—	—	0·08	—	H_2O^-
100·24	100·12	99·83	99·62	100·16	100·44	100·43	100·20	Total
1·521	1·5217	1·5220	—	1·521	1·5199	—	1·5188	α
—	1·5259	1·5262	—	1·525	1·5240	—	1·5230	β
1·528	1·5279	1·5277	—	1·527	1·5248	—	1·5236	γ
60°	69·1°	61·5°	61°	70°	46·2°	52–60°	43·6°	$2V_\alpha$
—	9·5°	7·7°	—	7°	6·2°	—	5·3°	Ext. on (010)
—	2·5778	2·5831	—	2·55	2·5673	—	2·5632	D

THE BASIS OF 32(O)

9.	10.	11.	12.	13.	14.	15.	16.	
11·696	11·794	11·755	11·825	11·694	11·935	11·647	11·759	Si
4·317	4·240	4·238	4·207	4·414	4·059	4·299	4·254	Al
0·005	0·011	0·044	0·027	0·012	0·022	0·086	0·014	Fe^{+3}
—	—	—	—	—	—	—	—	Ti
0·019	—	0·044	—	0·022	—	0·052	—	Mg
1·277	1·209	1·075	0·977	0·844	0·574	0·541	0·286	Na
0·114	0·066	0·065	0·095	0·031	0·067	0·051	0·099	Ca
2·535	2·727	2·839	2·768	2·944	3·307	3·427	3·676	K
0·012	—	—	—	0·026	—	0·040	—	Ba
16·07	16·04	16·04	16·05	16·12	16·02	16·03	16·03	Z
3·96	4·00	4·02	3·84	3·87	3·95	4·11	4·06	X
64·3	68·1	70·6	72·1	76·8	83·8	84·3	90·5	Or }
32·3	30·2	26·7	25·4	21·8	14·5	13·2	7·1	Ab } Mol. %
3·4	1·7	2·7	2·5	1·4	1·7	2·5	2·4	An }

9. Orthoclase ("anorthoclase"), syenite, Supsa river, W. Georgia, Transcaucasia (Kazakashvili & Topuria, 1939).

10. Orthoclase microperthite (moonstone), Ambalangoda, Ceylon (Spencer, 1937). Anal. E. Spencer.

11. Orthoclase microperthite (moonstone, strong white schiller), Mogok, Burma (Spencer, 1930). Anal. E. Spencer.

12. Orthoclase microperthite, phenocryst, adamellite, Shap, Westmorland (Spencer, 1938). Anal. E. Spencer.

13. Orthoclase microperthite, porphyroblasts in paragneiss, Lovewell Mts., New Hampshire (Heaid, 1950b). Anal. F. A. Gonyer.

14. Orthoclase microperthite (moonstone, faint blue schiller), Mogok, Burma (Spencer, 1930). Anal. E. Spencer.

15. Orthoclase microperthite, intermediate pyroxene granulite of the charnockite series, Salem district Madras (Howie, 1955). Anal. R. A. Howie.

16. Colourless orthoclase, Mogok, Burma (Spencer, 1930). Anal. E. Spencer.

Table 5. Microcline, microcline microperthite

	1.	2.	3.	4.	5.	6.	7.	8.
SiO₂	65·90	65·58	65·11	64·66	63·67	61·56	64·20	64·26
TiO₂	—	—	—	—	—	—	—	—
Al₂O₃	19·45	19·58	18·95	20·10	19·60	21·40	19·10	19·72
Fe₂O₃	1·03	0·21	0·62	}0·35	—	—	0·40	0·10
FeO	—	—	0·11		—	—	—	—
MnO	—	—	—	tr.	—	—	—	—
MgO	0·00	0·12	0·12	0·12	—	—	—	tr.
BaO	—	—	—	0·00	0·98	—	—	—
CaO	0·61	0·49	0·39	0·60	0·40	1·51	0·34	0·31
Na₂O	7·12	5·90	5·54	4·21	3·62	2·39	2·60	2·28
K₂O	6·20	7·88	9·06	10·19	11·16	12·76	12·76	13·42
Rb₂O	—	—	—	—	—	—	—	—
Cs₂O	—	—	—	—	—	—	—	—
Li₂O	—	—	—	—	—	—	—	—
H₂O⁺	0·19	0·23	0·20	}0·11	}0·33	}0·33	}0·72	}0·18
H₂O⁻	0·03	0·14	0·13					
Total	100·53	100·13	100·23	100·34	99·76	99·95	100·12	100·27
α	1·5261	—	—	1·5210	1·5223	—	1·5204	1·5206
β	—	—	—	1·5247	1·5260	—	1·5240	1·5243
γ	1·5314	—	—	1·5273	1·5283	—	1·5265	1·5266
2V$_α$	80, 84, 85°	—	—	80°	—	68–86°	79·9°	76·0°
Ext. on (010)	—	—	—	5½–6°	—	—	7·5°	7·5°
D	2·591	2·587	—	2·569	2·595	—	2·5771	2·5747

Numbers of ions on

	1.	2.	3.	4.	5.	6.	7.	8.
Si	11·790	11·825	11·820	11·713	11·748	11·384	11·831	11·777
Al	4·102	4·162	4·056	4·292	4·262	4·665	4·148	4·260
Fe⁺³	0·138	0·029	0·085	0·047	—	—	0·055	0·014
Ti	—	—	—	—	—	—	—	—
Mg	—	0·032	0·033	0·033	—	—	—	—
Li	—	—	—	—	—	—	—	—
Fe⁺²	—	—	0·017	—	—	—	—	—
Mn	—	—	—	—	—	—	—	—
Na	2·470	2·063	1·950	1·478	1·295	0·857	0·929	0·810
Ca	0·117	0·095	0·074	0·116	0·079	0·299	0·067	0·061
K	1·415	1·813	2·098	2·355	2·627	3·010	3·000	3·138
Ba	—	—	—	—	0·071	—	—	—
Rb	—	—	—	—	—	—	—	—
Cs	—	—	—	—	—	—	—	—
Z	16·03	16·02	15·96	16·05	16·01	16·05	16·03	16·05
X	4·00	4·00	4·17	3·98	4·07	4·16	4·00	4·01
Mol. % { Or	35·4	45·3	50·3	59·2	66·3	72·3	75·1	78·3
Ab	61·7	51·5	46·7	37·1	31·8	20·6	23·2	20·2
An	2·9	3·2	3·0	3·7	1·9	7·1	1·7	1·5

1. Microcline microperthite ("microcline–anorthoclase"), nordmarkite, Grorud, Oslo district, Norway (Soustov, 1936). Average of 2 analyses.
2. Microcline perthite, nepheline-syenite, Fukushin-zan district, Korea (Yoshizawa, 1933). Anal. H. Yoshizawa.
3. Microcline perthite, khibinite, Khibina tundra, Kola Peninsula, Russia (Makhlaev, 1946).
4. Untwinned microcline microperthite, pegmatite in gneissic charnockite, Koli-Koli rock-hole, Musgrave Ranges, Central Australia (Wilson, 1950). Anal. A. F. Wilson.
5. Glassy microcline microperthite showing very fine perthitization, Savelev ravine ,Ilmen Mts., Russia (Byelyankin, 1915).
6. Microcline perthite, syenite, Plauen, near Dresden, Germany (Byelyankin & Tomkeieff, 1915).
7. Microcline microperthite, quartz–felspar–tourmaline pegmatite, nr. Ryagada Gorge, Orissa, India (Spencer, 1937). Anal. E. Spencer.
8. Microcline microperthite, graphite-bearing pegmatite, Patna State, Orissa, India (Spencer, 1937). Anal. E. Spencer.

AND MICROCLINE PERTHITE ANALYSES

9.	10.	11.	12.	13.	14.	15.	16.	
65·10	63·68	64·38	63·58	64·40	64·29	64·46	63·92	SiO_2
0·01	0·01	—	0·00	—	—	—	—	TiO_2
18·80	19·57	19·50	17·80	19·09	19·40	18·55	18·50	Al_2O_3
}0·10	0·29	0·11	0·03	0·31	0·09	0·14	—	Fe_2O_3
	0·24	—	—	—	—	—	—	FeO
—	—	—	0·01	0·01	—	0·00	—	MnO
0·09	0·05	tr.	0·04	0·04	0·11	0·00	—	MgO
—	0·30	—	—	—	0·06	—	—	BaO
0·02	0·40	0·28	0·40	0·05	0·32	0·17	0·64	CaO
1·99	1·56	1·48	0·50	1·09	0·38	0·49	—	Na_2O
14·14	14·21	14·32	12·30	15·26	15·62	16·07	15·70	K_2O
—	—	—	3·30	—	—	—	—	Rb_2O
—	—	—	0·60	—	—	—	—	Cs_2O
—	—	—	0·34	—	—	—	—	Li_2O
0·11	0·04	}0·28	0·64	—	}0·16	—	}1·17	H_2O^+
0·01	0·07		0·20	0·00		0·06		H_2O^-
100·37	100·42	100·35	100·41	100·25	100·43	99·94	99·93	Total
1·518	—	1·5195	—	—	—	—	—	α
1·522	—	1·5232	—	—	—	—	—	β
1·525	—	1·5255	—	—	—	—	—	γ
—	83–86°	76·2°	—	—	—	—	—	$2V_\alpha$
—	—	7·5°	—	—	—	—	—	Ext. on (010)
2·544	—	2·5692	—	—	—	—	—	D

THE BASIS OF 32(O)

9.	10.	11.	12.	13.	14.	15.	16.	
11·926	11·730	11·824	12·013	11·856	11·834	11·938	11·944	Si
4·060	4·249	4·222	3·964	4·143	4·209	4·050	4·075	Al
0·014	0·040	0·015	0·004	0·043	0·012	0·019	—	Fe^{+3}
0·001	0·001	—	0·004	—	—	—	—	Ti
0·024	0·014	—	0·011	0·011	0·030	—	—	Mg
—	—	—	0·257	—	—	—	—	Li
—	0·037	—	—	—	—	—	—	Fe^{+2}
—	—	—	0·002	0·002	—	—	—	Mn
0·707	0·557	0·528	0·183	0·389	0·136	0·176	—	Na
0·004	0·078	0·055	0·080	0·010	0·063	0·033	0·128	Ca
3·305	3·340	3·355	2·965	3·585	3·668	3·797	3·743	K
—	0·024	—	—	—	0·004	—	—	Ba
—	—	—	0·401	—	—	—	—	Rb
—	—	—	0·048	—	—	—	—	Cs
16·00	16·02	16·06	15·98	16·03	16·05	16·01	16·02	Z
4·04	4·05	3·94	3·95	4·00	3·90	4·01	3·87	X
81·8	83·1	85·2	86·5	89·8	94·1	94·8	96·7	Or ⎫
17·5	13·7	13·4	11·1	9·7	3·5	4·4	—	Ab ⎬ Mol. %
0·7	3·2	1·4	2·4	0·5	2·4	0·8	3·3	An ⎭

9. Microcline, Bedford, New York (Rosenholtz & Smith, 1942). Anal. Rock Anal. Lab., Univ. Minnesota.
10. Microcline microperthite, type-specimen of charnockite, St. Thomas' Mount, Madras, India (Howie, 1955). Anal. R. A. Howie.
11. Microcline microperthite, mica-bearing pegmatite, Kodarma, Bihar, India (Spencer, 1937). Anal. E. Spencer.
12. Rubidium microcline perthite, pegmatite, Varuträsk, Sweden (Adamson, 1942). Anal. T. Berggren (Includes P_2O_5 0·64, F 0·03).
13. Maximum microcline microperthite, nepheline-syenite, Blue Mountains, Ontario (MacKenzie, 1954). Anal. J. H. Scoon (Analysed sample has 2% albite).
14. Microcline perthite, pegmatite, S. of Iron Creek, Pennington County, Black Hills, S. Dakota (Higazy, 1949). Anal. R. A. Higazy.
15. Maximum microcline, pegmatite in grennaite, Norra Kärr, Sweden (MacKenzie, 1954). Anal. J. H. Scoon.
16. Third generation microcline, natrolite vein, Khibinsky massif, Kola Peninsula, Russia (Fersman, 1923).

Table 6.   SANIDINE

	1.	2.	3.	4.	5.	6.	7.	8.
SiO_2	65·52	67·27	63·49	66·38	63·92	64·40	65·44	64·03
TiO_2	0·09	—	tr.	—	—	0·27	tr.	—
Al_2O_3	19·39	18·35	20·93	18·92	19·83	19·50	18·73	19·92
Fe_2O_3	0·62	}0·92	0·29	0·40	0·30	0·35	0·04	}0·62
FeO	—		—	tr.	—	0·05	0·07	
MgO	—	nil	0·03	—	0·10	0·07	nil	0·01
BaO	—	—	0·46	—	1·15	0·27	—	—
SrO	—	—	0·38	—	—	—	—	—
CaO	1·10	0·15	0·93	0·10	1·54	1·19	0·06	0·45
Na_2O	6·35	6·45	6·05	6·06	4·55	4·19	4·82	4·57
K_2O	6·58	7·05	7·27	7·90	7·95	9·40	10·01	10·05
H_2O^+	0·42	0·08	—	}0·50	0·50	0·03	0·68	}0·26
H_2O^-	0·40	0·08	—		0·14	0·10	0·33	
Total	100·47	100·35	99·83	100·26	99·98	99·85	100·18	99·91
α	—	1·5232	1·5264	1·5228	—	1·528–1·530	1·521	—
β	—	1·5289	1·5309	1·5284	—	1·531–1·534	1·525	—
γ	—	1·5296	1·5317	1·5292	—	1·535–1·539	1·526	—
$2V\alpha$	—	33°	47° 45′	39·1°	15½–18½°	38–57°	29°	33°
Ext. on (010)	—	—	6·3°	8·7°	—	2–6°	5°	—
D	—	—	2·606	—	2·577	—	—	—

NUMBERS OF IONS ON

	1.	2.	3.	4.	5.	6.	7.	8.
Si	11·800	12·030	11·527	11·954	11·689	11·731	11·951	11·718
Al	4·116	3·868	4·479	4·016	4·275	4·186	4·032	4·297
Fe^{+3}	0·084	0·124	0·039	0·054	0·041	0·048	0·005	0·085
Ti	0·012	—	—	—	—	0·037	—	—
Mg	—	—	0·008	—	0·027	0·019	—	0·003
Fe^{+2}	—	—	—	—	—	0·008	0·011	—
Na	2·216	2·236	2·130	2·116	1·613	1·480	1·706	1·621
Ca	0·212	0·029	0·181	0·019	0·302	0·232	0·012	0·088
Sr	—	—	0·040	—	—	—	—	—
K	1·512	1·609	1·684	1·815	1·855	2·185	2·332	2·347
Ba	—	—	0·033	—	0·082	0·019	—	—
Z	16·01	16·02	16·04	16·02	16·00	16·00	15·99	16·10
X	3·94	3·87	4·08	3·95	3·88	3·94	4·06	4·06
Mol. % ⎧ Or	38·4	41·5	42·1	45·9	49·9	55·9	57·4	57·8
⎨ Ab	56·2	57·7	52·3	53·6	41·6	37·5	42·0	40·0
⎩ An	5·4	0·8	5·6	0·5	8·5	6·6	0·6	2·2

1. Authigenic sanidine ("anorthoclase"), fuller's earth, Combe Hay, Somerset (Newton, 1937).
2. Sanidine, Mitchell Mesa Rhyolite, Texas (Tuttle, 1952b). Anal. J. H. Scoon.
3. Sanidine ("anorthoclase"), theralite, Bo Plei, western Siam (Weigel & Krüger, 1934).
4. Glass-clear idiomorphic sanidine crystals (moonstone), Kanchin-do, Meisen-gun, north-east Korea (Spencer, 1937). Anal. E. Spencer.
5. Phenocrysts of sanidine showing zonal structure, dacite, Zvečan, Yugoslavia (Tućan, 1939).
6. Ellipsoidal masses of sanidine, trachybasalt, Black Point, near Huntingdon Lake, central Sierra Nevada, California (Hamilton & Neuerburg, 1956). Anal. F. H. Neuerburg (Includes P_2O_5 0·03).
7. Single clear crystal of sanidine, moonstone pegmatite, Grant County, New Mexico (Kracek & Neuvonen, 1952). Anal. O. von Knorring.
8. Sanidine ("anorthoclase"), riebeckite trachyte, N. coast of Madara Island, W.-Matura County, Saga Prefecture, Japan (Aoyama, 1941). Anal. Imp. Geol. Surv. (Quoted from Harada, 1948).

ANALYSES

9.	10.	11.	12.	13.	14.	15.	16.	
63·90	65·72	64·65	63·58	63·62	66·11	64·70	64·24	SiO_2
—	—	0·00	0·00	0·08	nil	—	—	TiO_2
20·09	18·89	19·43	19·07	19·12	18·63	18·56	20·24	Al_2O_3
0·79	0·27	}0·04	0·18	}0·47	—	0·20	0·22	Fe_2O_3
—	0·02		0·07		—	tr.	—	FeO
—	0·09	0·03	0·65	0·05	0·12	tr.	—	MgO
—	0·40	—	—	1·56	—	1·31	—	BaO
—	tr.	—	—	—	—	—	—	SrO
0·62	0·17	0·38	0·69	0·05	0·25	tr.	0·56	CaO
4·02	4·10	3·71	2·77	2·66	2·52	2·46	1·80	Na_2O
10·10	10·99	10·97	11·96	12·09	12·71	12·72	12·87	K_2O
}0·62	—	0·50	0·57	0·11	—	}0·42	}0·50	H_2O+
	—	0·30	0·22	0·00	—			H_2O-
100·14	100·65	100·04	99·76	99·81	100·34	100·37	100·43	
—	—	1·5229	1·522	—	—	1·5202	—	α
—	—	1·5294	1·527	—	—	1·5247	—	β
—	—	1·5296	1·527	—	—	1·5249	—	γ
—	(2E 38° 33')	17° 40'–18° 15'	27°	—	—	24·0°	13°	$2V_\alpha$
—	7·5°	4–6°	6°	—	—	5°8°	—	Ext. on (010)
—	2·564	2·56–2·57	—	—	—	—	—	D

THE BASIS OF 32(O)

11·670	11·907	11·838	11·749	11·770	12·009	11·936	11·748	Si
4·325	4·024	4·194	4·154	4·169	3·989	4·036	4·363	Al
0·109	0·037	0·005	0·025	0·096	—	0·028	—	Fe^{+3}
—	—	—	—	0·011	—	—	—	Ti
—	0·024	0·008	0·179	0·013	0·033	—	—	Mg
—	0·003	—	0·011	—	—	—	—	Fe^{+2}
1·423	1·439	1·317	0·993	0·954	0·888	0·880	0·638	Na
0·121	0·033	0·075	0·137	0·010	0·049	—	0·110	Ca
—	—	—	—	—	—	—	—	Sr
2·353	2·540	2·563	2·820	2·855	2·946	2·994	3·002	K
—	0·028	—	—	0·113	—	0·095	—	Ba
16·10	15·97	16·04	15·93	16·05	16·00	16·00	16·11	Z
3·90	4·07	3·96	4·14	3·95	3·92	3·97	3·75	X
60·4	63·1	64·7	68·1	75·5	75·2	77·8	80·1	Or ⎱
36·5	35·4	33·2	24·0	23·9	22·7	22·2	17·0	Ab ⎰ Mol. %
3·1	1·5	2·1	7·9	0·6	2·1	—	2·9	An ⎰

9. Sanidine ("anorthoclase"), Drachenfels, Siebengebirge, Rhine, Germany (Spencer, 1937). Anal. E. Spencer.
0. Twinned crystals of sanidine, decomposed quartz rhyolite, Mt. Somlyód, near Végardó, Slovakia (Zsivny, 1923). Anal. V. Zsivny (Optics quoted from Vendl, 1922).
11. Colourless, transparent sanidine ("potash–anorthoclase"), tuffaceous liparite, Taiji Kii province, Japan (Kimizuka, 1932) (Includes P_2O_5 0·03).
12. Sanidine, phenocrysts in lava, Kokomo, Colorado (Kracek & Neuvonen, 1952). Anal. O. von Knorring.
13. Sanidine, leucite–nepheline dolerite, Meiches, Vogelsberg, Hesse, Germany (Tilley, 1958). Anal. J. H. Scoon.
14. Sanidine, Eifel district, Germany (Kôzu & Seto, 1921). Anal. K. Seto.
15. Sanidine, probably from basaltic tuff, Eifel, Rhineland, Germany (Spencer, 1937). Anal. E. Spencer.
16. Sanidine, Mt. Cimino, Viterbo, Italy (Spencer, 1937, p. 476 footnote). Anal. E. Spencer.

Table 7.   ANORTHOCLASE

	1.	2.	3.	4.	5.	6.	7.
SiO_2	66·58	62·79	62·49	65·83	66·29	63·70	65·86
TiO_2	—	—	—	—	—	—	—
Al_2O_3	19·82	22·12	21·86	19·97	19·65	21·83	20·66
Fe_2O_3	0·61	0·36	0·30	0·75	0·78	0·18	0·29
FeO	—	0·41	1·31	—	—	—	0·10
MgO	0·43	—	0·16	0·05	0·38	0·14	0·12
BaO	—	—	—	0·53	—	—	0·12
SrO	—	—	—	0·29	—	—	—
CaO	1·64	3·76	3·74	0·22	0·75	2·75	1·50
Na_2O	8·28	7·35	7·20	8·70	8·43	7·55	8·17
K_2O	2·01	2·98	3·26	3·10	3·66	3·75	3·88
H_2O^+	}0·20	0·19	0·04	0·18	}0·24	}0·19	}0·17
H_2O^-		0·07	—	0·07			
Total	99·57	100·03	100·36	99·69	100·18	100·09	100·87
α	—	1·536	1·536	—	1·5190	1·5290	1·5275
β	—	1·539	1·539	—	1·5222	1·5350	1·5334
γ	—	1·541	1·541	—	1·5243	1·5365	1·5349
$2V_\alpha$	46–66°	62°	62°	—	51° 04′	51–52°	52½°
Ext. on (010)	—	4·7°	2·6°	—	8°	6–8°	—
D	2·646	2·620	2·620	2·608	2·582–2·590	2·589	2·587

NUMBERS OF IONS ON

	1.	2.	3.	4.	5.	6.	7.
Si	11·797	11·257	11·211	11·774	11·780	11·383	11·651
Al	4·140	4·675	4·623	4·210	4·116	4·598	4·308
Fe^{+3}	0·081	0·048	0·041	0·101	0·104	0·024	0·038
Ti	—	—	—	—	—	—	—
Mg	0·113	—	0·043	0·013	0·100	0·038	0·032
Fe^{+2}	—	0·061	0·196	—	—	—	0·015
Na	2·844	2·554	2·504	3·017	2·904	2·616	2·802
Ca	0·312	0·722	0·719	0·042	0·143	0·526	0·284
Sr	—	—	—	0·030	—	—	—
K	0·454	0·681	0·746	0·707	0·830	0·855	0·876
Ba	—	—	—	0·037	—	—	0·009
Z	16·02	15·98	16·07	16·08	16·00	16·00	16·00
X	3·72	4·02	4·01	3·85	3·98	4·03	4·02
Mol. % { Or	12·2	17·0	18·6	19·4	20·9	21·2	22·0
Ab	76·4	63·5	62·4	78·4	73·0	64·8	69·8
An	11·4	19·5	19·0	2·2	6·1	14·0	8·2

1. Anorthoclase ("calcium–anorthoclase") trachyliparite, Beshtau, northern Caucasus (Gerasimov, 1936).
2. Loose crystals of anorthoclase ("potash–oligoclase"), Crater of Mt. Erebus, Ross Island, Antarctica (Mountain, 1925). Anal. E. D. Mountain.
3. Loose crystals of anorthoclase ("potash–oligoclase"), Crater of Mt. Erebus, Ross Island, Antarctica (Mountain, 1925). Anal. E. D. Mountain. (In this analysis Fe^{+2} is placed with Fe^{+3}).
4. Anorthoclase, monchiquite dyke, W. side of Camas an Fhâis, ½ mile N.E. of Rudha Fionn-aird, Ardmucknish, Argyllshire (Quoted from Guppy, 1931). Anal. W. Pollard.
5. Crystals of anorthoclase, tuff, Monte Guardia di Mezzo, Ustica, Sicily (Montalto, 1937).
6. Clear, colourless anorthoclase, inclusions in augite, Monte Gemolo, Euganean Hills, Italy (Schiavinato, 1951). (Cell size and dispersion also given).
7. Rhomb-shaped phenocrysts of anorthoclase, trachyte, Ropp, Nigeria (Joyce & Game, 1952).

ANALYSES

8.	9.	10.	11.	12.	13.	14.	
66·24	65·26	64·33	64·30	66·46	66·97	64·80	SiO_2
—	—	—	0·08	—	0·04	—	TiO_2
19·89	21·36	20·94	20·85	18·89	18·75	21·14	Al_2O_3
0·08	—	0·20	0·38	0·75	}0·88	0·68	Fe_2O_3
0·07	—	0·58	—	—		—	FeO
0·00	—	—	0·07	—	0·00	0·10	MgO
—	0·19	—	—	—	—	—	BaO
—	0·25	—	—	—	—	—	SrO
0·25	1·01	2·01	2·00	0·61	0·36	1·18	CaO
8·93	7·68	7·22	7·26	7·68	7·88	6·94	Na_2O
3·95	4·50	4·71	4·77	5·17	5·39	5·26	K_2O
0·44	}0·12	0·27	0·06	}0·69	0·01	}0·20	H_2O^+
0·09		0·10	0·15		0·03		H_2O^-
99·94	100·38	100·36	99·92	100·25	100·31	100·30	Total
1·5253	1·524	1·526	1·527	1·5255	1·5239	—	α
1·5311	—	1·530	1·532	1·531	1·5299	—	β
1·5321	1·530	1·532	1·536	1·532	1·5308	—	γ
47°	42°	51°	78°	49–55°	46°	57½°	$2V_\alpha$
—	—	7·8°	7–9°	—	—	—	Ext. on (010)
—	2·59	2·602	—	2·606	—	—	D

THE BASIS OF 32(O)

8.	9.	10.	11.	12.	13.	14.	
11·826	11·607	11·529	11·537	11·910	11·932	11·568	Si
4·186	4·479	4·424	4·410	3·990	3·938	4·449	Al
0·010	—	0·027	0·051	0·101	0·118	0·091	Fe^{+3}
—	—	—	0·011	—	0·005	—	Ti
—	—	—	0·019	—	—	0·027	Mg
0·011	—	0·087	—	—	—	—	Fe^{+2}
3·091	2·648	2·509	2·525	2·669	2·722	2·402	Na
0·048	0·192	0·386	0·384	0·117	0·069	0·226	Ca
—	0·026	—	—	—	—	—	Sr
0·900	1·021	1·077	1·092	1·182	1·226	1·198	K
—	0·013	—	—	—	—	—	Ba
16·02	16·06	15·98	16·00	15·91	15·99	16·11	Z
4·05	3·90	4·06	4·02	3·97	4·02	3·85	X
22·2	26·5	26·5	27·2	29·8	30·5	31·1	Or⎫
76·3	67·9	61·8	62·8	67·3	67·8	62·3	Ab⎬ Mol. %
1·5	5·6	11·7	10·0	2·9	1·7	6·6	An⎭

8. Colourless anorthoclase crystals, evidently from lava, Victoria, Australia (Kracek & Neuvonen, 1952). Anal. O. von Knorring. (Optics quoted from Tuttle, 1952).

9. Water-clear crystal of anorthoclase, basaltic lava, Darigan region, S.E. Mongolia (Vlodavetz & Shavrova, 1953). (Includes Li_2O 0·0005, Rb_2O 0·005).

10. Anorthoclase, crater slopes, Mt. Kenya, Kenya, East Africa (Mountain, 1925). Anal. E. D. Mountain.

11. Lime-rich anorthoclase (now partly unmixed to oligoclase and orthoclase), larvikite, quarry near Larvik, near Oslo, Norway (Muir & Smith, 1956). Anal. J. H. Scoon.

12. Anorthoclase, with undulose extinction and cross-hatching, riebeckite trachyte, Berkum, Rhine, Germany (Byelyankin, 1915).

13. Anorthoclase, Grande Caldeira, Azores (Tuttle, 1952). Anal. J. H. Scoon.

4. Homogeneous non-schillerized anorthoclase, phenocrysts in kenyte, Mt. Kenya, East Africa (Spencer, 1937). Anal. E. Spencer.

Table 8. ADULARIA ANALYSES

	1.	2.	3.	4.	5.	6.	7.	8.
SiO_2	64·87	64·00	64·84	64·80	64·45	64·28	64·35	64·69
TiO_2	—	—	—	—	—	—	—	0·00
Al_2O_3	18·51	19·25	19·50	18·40	18·97	19·19	19·41	18·69
Fe_2O_3	0·23	—	0·00	0·32	0·07	0·09	—	}0·04
FeO	—	—	—	—	0·25	—	—	
MgO	—	—	—	—	0·03	0·10	0·24	0·07
CaO	0·23	0·15	0·43	0·26	0·53	0·11	0·07	0·03
BaO	0·92	0·41	—	0·68	—	0·11	0·23	—
Na_2O	1·99	1·86	1·61	1·46	0·95	0·92	0·82	0·74
K_2O	13·08	14·01	13·98	13·70	14·98	15·30	15·22	15·78
H_2O^+	—	}0·50	—	—	0·11	}0·36	}0·08	0·07
H_2O^-	0·07		—	0·09	0·06			0·03
Total	99·90	100·18	100·36	99·71	100·40	100·46	100·42	100·14
α	—	1·5191	1·5200	—	1·5178	1·5192	1·5189	1·519
β	—	1·5228	1·5238	—	1·5205	1·5228	1·5235	1·523
γ	—	1·5249	1·5249	—	1·5240	1·5245	1·5253	1·525
$2V_\alpha$	—	—	—	—	56° 50′	68·4°	64° 30′	—
$\alpha:x$	—	—	—	—	—	5·25°	6° 20′	—
D	2·572	2·570	—	2·568	—	2·5661	2·577	2·559

NUMBERS OF IONS ON THE BASIS OF 32(O)

	1.	2.	3.	4.	5.	6.	7.	8.
Si	11·957	11·831	11·850	11·972	11·865	11·852	11·831	11·939
Al	4·022	4·195	4·201	4·007	4·116	4·170	4·207	4·066
Fe^{+3}	0·032	—	—	0·044	0·010	0·012	—	0·006
Mg	—	—	—	—	0·008	0·028	0·066	0·019
Fe^{+2}	—	—	—	—	0·039	—	—	—
Na	0·711	0·666	0·571	0·523	0·339	0·329	0·292	0·264
Ca	0·045	0·030	0·084	0·051	0·104	0·022	0·014	0·006
K	3·076	3·305	3·260	3·230	3·518	3·599	3·570	3·715
Ba	0·066	0·030	—	0·049	—	0·008	0·017	
Z	16·01	16·03	16·05	16·02	15·99	16·03	16·04	16·01
X	3·90	4·03	3·92	3·85	4·01	3·99	3·96	4·00
Mol. % ⎰ Or	80·6	82·7	83·3	85·1	87·8	90·5	90·6	92·8
⎱ Ab	18·2	16·5	14·6	13·6	8·5	8·3	7·4	6·6
An	1·2	0·8	2·1	1·3	3·7	1·2	2·0	0·6

1. Adularia, Bourg d'Oisans, Dauphiné, France (Zaniewska-Chlipalska, 1937).
2. Adularia, St. Gotthard, Switzerland (Byelyankin, 1915).
3. Adularia, Ridertobel, Bristenstock, Switzerland (Seto, 1920). Anal. K. Seto. (Optics quoted from Kôzu, 1916).
4. Adularia, Krimml, Salzburg, Austria (Zaniewska-Chlipalska, 1937).
5. Alpine-type adularia crystals, with quartz, in drusy cavities in quartz veins traversing schists, Kukutzu, Taiwan (Formosa). (Huang, 1953). Anal. H. Tai.
6. Clear inner portion of large crystal (about 3 in. diam.) of adularia, St. Gotthard, Switzerland (Spencer, 1937). Anal. E. Spencer.
7. Adularia, with quartz, chlorite and sphene, in crevices in gneiss, Mt. Forno, Val Devero, Ossola, Piedmont, Italy (Azzini, 1933).
8. Adularia, Val Cristallina, Grisons, Switzerland (Rosenholtz & Smith, 1941). Anal. Rock Anal. Lab., Univ. Minnesota.

Table 9. IRON-RICH POTASSIUM FELSPAR ANALYSES

	1.	2.	3.	4.	5.	6.	7.	8.
SiO_2	65·10	64·40	64·21	64·05	64·76	64·94	64·19	64·25
TiO_2	0·02	—	—	0·00	0·00	0·00	—	—
Al_2O_3	17·82	18·70	17·78	17·17	17·22	16·74	16·62	16·06
Fe_2O_3	0·57	0·62	1·15	1·31	1·50	2·56	2·88	2·93
FeO	0·06	0·09	0·09	0·00	0·00	0·00	0·18	0·25
BaO	—	—	—	0·03	—	—	—	—
MgO	tr.	tr.	0·00	0·07	0·04	0·04	—	0·00
CaO	0·04	tr.	0·07	0·00	0·06	0·03	—	tr.
Na_2O	0·67	0·46	0·42	1·62	0·47	0·79	0·34	0·44
K_2O	15·91	16·14	15·21	15·36	16·00	15·33	15·81	16·15
H_2O^+	0·08	—	—	0·52	—	—	—	—
H_2O^-	0·06	—	—	0·18	0·00	0·00	—	—
Total	100·33	100·41	"99·63"	100·31	100·05	100·43	100·02	100·08
α	1·521	1·5194	1·5185	—	1·522	1·5265	1·5197	1·5216
β	1·524	1·5237	1·5225	—	1·5265	1·531	1·5248	1·5259
γ	1·525	1·5241	1·5239	—	1·5265	1·5315	1·5253	1·5261
$2V_\alpha$	23°	34·8°	—	28°	11½–17°	32–33½°	34° 6′	—
$\alpha:x$	6°	5·2°	—	7°	5½°	5°	—	—
D	—	2·5625	—	—	—	—	—	—

NUMBERS OF IONS ON THE BASIS OF 32(O)

Si	12·023	11·886	—	—	12·017	12·011	11·971	12·013
Al	3·879	4·068	—	—	3·767	3·650	3·654	3·540
Fe^{+3}	0·079	0·086	—	—	0·209	0·356	0·404	0·412
Ti	0·003	—	—	—	—	—	—	—
Mg	—	—	—	—	0·011	0·011	—	—
Fe^{+2}	0·009	0·014	—	—	—	—	0·028	0·039
Na	0·240	0·164	—	—	0·170	0·283	0·123	0·160
Ca	0·008	—	—	—	0·012	0·006	—	—
K	3·749	3·801	—	—	3·788	3·618	3·762	3·852
Z	15·98	16·04	15·52	15·92	15·99	16·02	16·03	15·97
X	4·01	3·98	3·68	4·27	3·98	3·92	3·91	4·05
Mol. % Or	91·6	93·4	91·3	81·2	89·9	83·4	86·2	84·7
Fe-Or	2·0	2·1	4·0	4·6	5·3	9·0	10·0	10·4
Ab	6·0	4·1	4·0	13·7	4·2	7·2	3·1	4·9
An	0·4	0·4	0·7	0·5	0·6	0·4	0·7	—

1. Clear crystals of "ferriferous orthoclase", Fianarantsoa, Madagascar (Kracek & Neuvonen 1952). Anal. O. von Knorring.
2. Yellow ferrian orthoclase, Madagascar (Spencer, 1930). Anal. E. Spencer (SiO_2 and Al_2O_3 quoted from Spencer, 1937).
3. Pale yellow ferrian potassium felspar, Madagascar (Seto, 1923). Anal. K. Seto.
4. Clear crystals of "ferriferous orthoclase", Itrongay, Madagascar (Kracek & Neuvonen, 1952). Anal. F. A. Gonyer.
5. Pale yellow "ferriferous orthoclase", Itrongay, Madagascar (Coombs, 1954). Anal. J. H. Scoon.
6. Amber-yellow "ferriferous orthoclase", Itrongay, Madagascar (Coombs, 1954). Anal. J. H. Scoon.
7. Yellow ferriferous potassium felspar, Madagascar (Lacroix, 1922). Anal. Boiteau.
8. Yellow ferriferous potassium felspar, Madagascar (Seto, 1923). Anal. K. Seto (optics quoted from Kôzu, 1916).

irradiated small amounts of adularia and amazonite in an atomic pile for four weeks and subsequently analysed the resultant radiation.

Experimental work. Experimental work on the alkali felspars can be said to have been begun by Day and Allen (1905) who investigated their isomorphism and thermal properties: Morey and Bowen (1922), using pure synthetic orthoclase prepared by heating $KAlSi_3O_8$ with water vapour under pressure, were able to show that orthoclase has an incongruent melting point between 1170° and 1530°C. due to the breaking down of the material into liquid of more siliceous composition together with leucite. Although Morey and Bowen were able to give only the general form for the equilibrium diagram, Schairer and

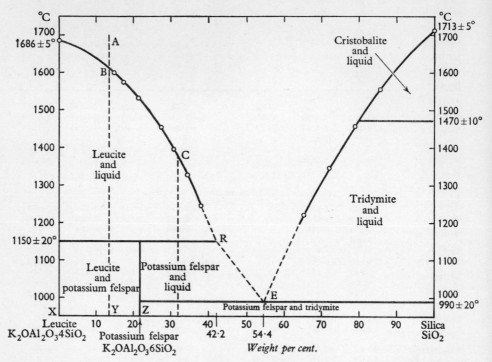

Fig. 19. Equilibrium diagram of the binary system $KAlSi_2O_6$ (leucite)–SiO_2 (after Schairer and Bowen, 1955).

Bowen (1938) presented a preliminary diagram for the system $KAlSi_2O_6$ (leucite) –SiO_2, and on the basis of some further data in the system K_2O–Al_2O_3–SiO_2 the final diagram was given by Schairer and Bowen (1947b), and both the diagram and data by Schairer and Bowen (1955). The incongruent melting point of potassium felspar is thus now placed at 1150°C. ± 20°C. (Fig. 19) and the composition of the liquid formed is leucite 57·8, silica 42·2 per cent.: the eutectic temperature between potassium felspar and tridymite is placed at 990°C. ± 20°C. at a composition leucite 45·6, silica 54·4 per cent. (or potassium felspar 58·2, silica 41·8 per cent.). Thus a melt of composition A, undersaturated with respect to silica, would cool to B, when leucite would begin to crystallize. With continued falling temperature and crystallization of leucite the composition of the melt would move along the liquidus curve from B to R : at this reaction point R the liquid reacts with the leucite transforming it into orthoclase; the orthoclase forms roughly twice as rapidly as leucite goes into solution, the reaction being approximately represented by :

$$5KAlSi_2O_6 + \underbrace{3KAlSi_3O_8 + 5SiO_2}_{melt} \rightarrow 8KAlSi_3O_8$$

leucite · orthoclase

With the original composition of the melt at A, crystallization is completed while some leucite remains, the final product being leucite and orthoclase in the ratio YZ : XY. For a melt with a slight excess of silica, *e.g.* of composition C, some liquid will remain after the conversion at the reaction point R of all the leucite to orthoclase. The temperature would then continue to fall and the composition of the melt would move along the curve RE with orthoclase continuing to crystallize : at the eutectic E crystallization would be completed and the whole mass would solidify as a mixture of orthoclase and tridymite. If, however, perfect equilibrium is not obtained, the leucite being mantled by an armour of orthoclase so that it fails to react completely with the liquid at R, even melts of composition A may give a final product including both orthoclase and free silica.

Schairer and Bowen (1955) remark on the considerable difficulty experienced in obtaining crystals of potassium felspar within its stability field in the system $K_2O-Al_2O_3-SiO_2$. Even after several months of crystallization at temperatures about 50° to 75° below liquidus temperatures only a few per cent. of very small felspar laths were present in the glasses : they could be distinguished from the other phases and the glass by their shape and mean refractive index, but were unsuitable for precise optical or X-ray determinations and were therefore referred to as potassium felspar rather than orthoclase, microcline or sanidine. It is almost certain, however, that these synthetic crystals are of the highest temperature form, *i.e.* high-sanidine. Wyart (1947) obtained orthoclase (and kalsilite) by the interaction of muscovite, silica, and KOH in aqueous solution under pressure at moderate temperatures, and Barrer and Hinds (1950) reported the hydrothermal synthesis of a potassium felspar, with the X-ray pattern of orthoclase, at 200°C. by first crystallizing analcite, digesting it at 150°C. in a saturated solution of KCl to produce leucite, and digesting this artificial leucite for 16 hours at 195°–200°C. : see also Barrer *et al.* (1953). Laves (1951) prepared microcline artificially by coating a cleavage flake of albite with a glass powder of composition $KAlSi_3O_8$ and heating it for 6 hours at 1060°C. : the outer zone then showed a gradual change of extinction angle on the (001) cleavage from the 3° of albite, through 0°, to the 15° of microcline. Barrer and Baynham (1956) reported the formation of a potassium felspar (? sanidine) as a minor species occurring in the preparation of a hydrated potassium analcite at 400°–500°C. : it crystallized in an analcitic habit when the pH of the mother liquor was raised by the addition of KOH solution. Gard *et al.* (1955) reported the production of very thin (down to 70 Å) lamellar crystals of potassium felspar in some hydrothermal preparations with leucite.

Goranson (1938) demonstrated that orthoclase no longer melts incongruently at a water pressure of about 2500 bars. Tuttle (1948) later developed a new relatively simple hydrothermal quenching apparatus allowing material to be subjected to pressures up to 30,000 lb./in.[2] and temperatures to 900°C. followed by rapid cooling. He was able to show that with 6–21 per cent. water in the melt the melting point of orthoclase was 100°–400°C. below that for the dry melt. Potassium felspar crystals with adularia habit have been grown hydrothermally at 500°C. and 1000 bars H_2O pressure in bombs with a temperature gradient (Euler and Hellner, 1961): some of the crystals are monoclinic while others are triclinic but with only a slight departure from monoclinic symmetry.

Day and Allen (1905) and Bowen (1913) were unable to crystallize albite and used natural material to determine its melting point. Greig and Barth (1938), however, and later Schairer and Bowen (1947b, 1956) obtained a melting point of 1118°C. on synthetic material. Greig and Barth, because of the viscosity of an albite liquid, had to determine the melting point of the pure material by finding a temperature at which crystals of albite melted to an albite liquid, and then finding a second (lower) temperature at which they grew in an albite liquid; then by making longer runs the difference between the two temperatures was narrowed. Such difficulties were also reported by Schairer and Bowen (1956): one preparation of glass of albite composition was, for example, held for five years at 1025°C., almost 100°C. beneath the melting point; it was cooled, crushed and examined for crystals once a month but none appeared. They were, however, able to develop a technique of "acclimating" the albite glass, by annealing it at successively lower temperatures for long periods of time, when it developed crystals of albite within a few hours at 1050°C. Using this albite, quenching runs of two weeks duration showed that the crystals were growing at 1115°C. and dissolving at 1120°C., and the melting point was taken as 1118° ±3°C.

Bowen and Tuttle (1950) were able to crystallize albite from a glass in the presence of water vapour and found that under a pressure of water vapour of 1000 bars albite crystals melt at about 900°C. to a hydrous albitic liquid. Tuttle and Bowen (1950) showed that such material synthesized in the laboratory had X-ray and optical properties different from those of natural albites from pegmatites, but that the natural albites could in some cases be converted, by prolonged heating at a temperature near the melting point, to a form essentially the same as the synthetic material. The synthetic material is referred to as high-temperature albite whereas most naturally occurring albite is low-temperature albite. The synthetic crystals of Tuttle and Bowen (*loc. cit.*) were all of the high-temperature form even when crystallized at temperatures as low as 250°C. MacKenzie (1952) first discovered slight differences in the various synthetic albites from their X-ray diffraction patterns. It was also noted that the temperature of their inversion to monoclinic symmetry on heating was inversely related to their crystallization temperature. Later a glass of composition $NaAlSi_3O_8$ was crystallized in the presence of water vapour under pressure, at temperatures between 450°C. and 1000°C. for varying periods of time (MacKenzie, 1957), and it was suggested that at any temperature in this range there is a stable crystalline form of $NaAlSi_3O_8$ which is intermediate between high-temperature albite and low-temperature albite, high-temperature albite being stable only above about 1000°C. and low-temperature albite below about 450°C. These studies also show that the form of albite which crystallizes at all temperatures in experiments of short duration is the high-temperature form. At temperatures below 1000°C. this high-temperature form is metastable and it will tend to change gradually to the form stable at the prevailing temperature. Some natural albites from typical low-temperature environments are believed to have crystallized as the high-temperature form, but at low temperatures these metastably crystallized minerals have partially inverted to the low-temperature form. The variations in the properties of albites from low-temperature veins of Alpine type are consistent with this interpretation (MacKenzie, 1957).

Extending consideration of synthetic work from the end-members to mixtures of the alkali felspars, preliminary work was reported by Schairer and Bowen (1935), and later Schairer (1950) investigated the alkali felspar join, KAlSi$_3$O$_8$–NaAlSi$_3$O$_8$, in the system NaAlSiO$_4$–KAlSiO$_4$–SiO$_2$. He demonstrated that there is an unbroken series of solid solutions between the alkali felspars, with a minimum on the melting and freezing curves at 1063° ± 3°C. at 35 wt. per cent. potassium felspar, and that all alkali felspar compositions with more than 49 wt. per cent. potassium felspar melt incongruently and give rise to leucite which only disappears at higher temperatures. Bowen and Tuttle (1950), using the hydrothermal quenching apparatus previously described (Tuttle, 1948), extended the work of Goranson (1938) on the individual melting relations of albite and orthoclase in the presence of water at high pressures to the whole alkali felspar series. When glasses of the system KAlSi$_3$O$_8$–NaAlSi$_3$O$_8$ were crystallized at 900°C. under a water vapour pressure of 300 bars, complete crystallization of all compositions was readily attained. The X-ray powder diffraction patterns for the products showed a linear relationship between the spacing for the $\bar{2}$01 reflection and the substitution of K for Na expressed in terms of weight per cent. KAlSi$_3$O$_8$ and NaAlSi$_3$O$_8$ (Fig. 6); this is taken to be satisfactory evidence for complete solid solution. The composition–temperature projections of the equilibrium diagrams for the system at 2000 bars, 1000 bars and, effectively, zero water vapour pressure are shown in Fig. 20 from which it will be seen that the first 1000 bars of water pressure lowers the minimum of the liquidus by about 220°C., but an additional 1000 bars gives a further lowering of only 73°C., indicating that the lowering effect rapidly decreases with increasing pressure. The leucite field is seen to be almost eliminated at 2000 bars pressure of water, and according to Goranson's (1938) determination it is suppressed entirely at 2500 bars pressure of water: it is certainly eliminated at approximately twice this pressure (Yoder *et al.*, 1956). When alkali felspar glasses were crystallized at low temperatures with water vapour under pressure to facilitate crystallization, instead of a single homogeneous felspar, two felspars were obtained (Bowen and Tuttle, 1950). The position of the solvus, or unmixing curve, is indicated in each of the three diagrams of Fig. 20 and it will be seen that unlike the solidus and liquidus curves, the position of the solvus is only slightly altered by the change of water pressure (as water does not take part in the equilibria involved at the solvus). Bowen and Tuttle (1950) showed that for 1000 bars water pressure the solvus is at 660° ± 10°C. at a composition close to 55 per cent. NaAlSi$_3$O$_8$: the asymmetry of this solvus indicates that at temperatures below about 500°C. albite can have only small amounts of potassium felspar in solid solution. The solvus at 5000 bars water pressure was later determined by Yoder *et al.* (1957) who were able to show that pressure raises the maximum on the solvus

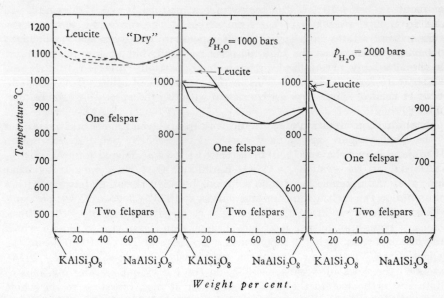

FIG. 20. Isobaric equilibrium diagrams for the alkali felspars in dry melts and at 1000 bars and 2000 bars pressure of H_2O (after Bowen and Tuttle, 1950).

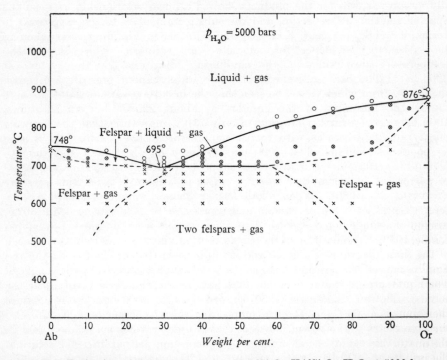

FIG. 21. Projection of the ternary system $NaAlSi_3O_8$–$KAlSi_3O_8$–H_2O at 5000 bars pressure of H_2O (after Yoder *et al.*, 1957).

by about 14°/1000 bars. The projection for the ternary system $KAlSi_3O_8$–
$NaAlSi_3O_8$–H_2O at 5000 bars water pressure is given in Fig. 21. On the basis
of their experimental data these authors placed the maximum for the solvus, at
5000 bars total pressure, at $715° \pm 5°C$. and $Or_{45}Ab_{55} \pm 3$ wt. per cent. Sections
for the system $KAlSi_3O_8$–$NaAlSi_3O_8$–H_2O at 5000 bars and 710° and 720°C.
(Yoder *et al.*, 1957, Figs. 39 and 40) show that the relatively large amount of
about 11 per cent. H_2O is present in the liquids in this system. MacKenzie and
Smith (1955b) pointed out that the solvus determined for synthetic felspars is
applicable only to natural felspars if they are high-temperature forms and have a

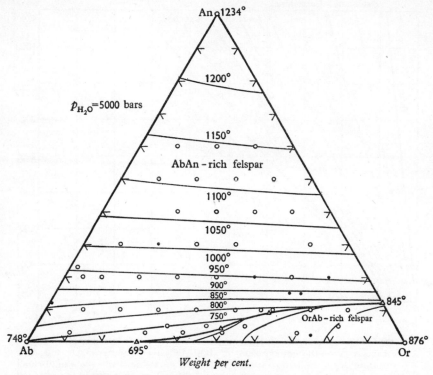

FIG. 22. Projection of the quaternary system $NaAlSi_3O_8$–$KAlSi_3O_8$–$CaAl_2Si_2O_8$–
H_2O at 5000 bars pressure of H_2O (after Yoder *et al.*, 1957).

calcium content low enough for it to have no significant effect in raising the
temperature of the solvus.

The ternary system $KAlSi_3O_8$–$NaAlSi_3O_8$–$CaAl_2Si_2O_8$ was investigated by
Franco and Schairer (1951) using glasses at 10 per cent. composition intervals.
The liquidus was plotted from microscopical examination of the products which
could distinguish glass, leucite and felspar: the felspar crystals were too small for
their composition to be determined. Having studied the three bounding ternary
systems at 5000 bars water pressure, Yoder *et al.* (1957) were able to consider
the quaternary system $KAlSi_3O_8$–$NaAlSi_3O_8$–$CaAl_2Si_2O_8$–H_2O at that pressure:
the projection of the determined liquidus diagram when gas is present is given
in Fig. 22. Compared with the anhydrous system investigated by Franco and

Schairer (*loc. cit.*) it is notable for the generally low temperatures involved, temperatures readily attainable within the range of magmatic activity. It is also important to note the alkali-rich nature of the liquids along the four-phase boundary curve. Yoder *et al.* (1957), in advance of further experimental data, produced a schematic representation of the field boundary surfaces separating the two felspar region, the one felspar, and the two felspar + liquid + gas regions of the Ab–Or–An–H_2O system at 5000 bars water pressure: this diagram differs from that deduced for the system at about 2000 bars (Bowen and Tuttle, 1950). It is believed therefore that, assuming equilibrium was maintained and an

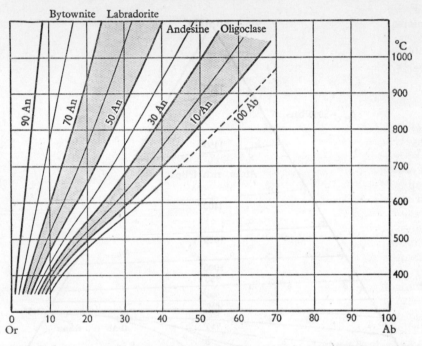

FIG. 23. The co-existence of alkali felspar and plagioclase (after Barth, 1956b). Abscissa gives the composition of alkali felspars in terms of Or and Ab; ordinate gives the temperature (°C.). The curves indicate the equilibrium relation between the composition of the plagioclases and the composition of the alkali felspars at various temperatures.

estimate of pressure based on the depth of crystallization is available, the compositions of the coexisting felspars can yield a measure of the temperature of formation. This problem has also been approached from a theoretical viewpoint by Barth (1956a) who showed, by plotting the compositions of felspar phases from rocks whose crystallization temperatures were considered to be known relatively accurately, that the distribution of Na_2O between the two phases is a function of temperature (*cf.* Barth, 1951). The available analytical data were used later to construct a diagram relating the compositions of the plagioclase and the coexisting alkali felspar phases to the temperature (Barth, 1956b), see Fig. 23.

Other experimental work involving end-members of the alkali felspar series includes that of Schairer and Bowen (1947a) on the $KAlSi_3O_8$–$CaAl_2Si_2O_8$ join in the system $KAlSi_2O_6$(leucite)–$CaAl_2Si_2O_8$(anorthite)–SiO_2, and that of Yoder *et al.* (1956, 1957) on the ternary system $KAlSi_3O_8$–$CaAl_2Si_2O_8$–H_2O at 5000 bars water pressure: in the latter system the maximum amount of $CaAl_2Si_2O_8$ in solid solution with $KAlSi_3O_8$, at 850°C., is less than 3 wt. per cent. Systems involving $NaAlSi_3O_8$ and non-felspar phases are discussed in the section on plagioclase chemistry.

Further experimental work on the alkali felspars includes various attempts to substitute other ions in $KAlSi_3O_8$. Faust (1936) has synthesized iron-orthoclase, $KFeSi_3O_8$, with Fe^{+3} substituting for Al: it melts incongruently to iron-leucite and a liquid, the iron-leucite subsequently melting incongruently to haematite and a liquid. In a study of synthetic biotite in the system K_2O–SiO_2–Fe–O–H_2O, Wones and Appleman (1961) have shown that the mica reacts to form iron felspar:

$$2KFe_3FeSi_3O_{10}(OH) + 5/4O_2 \rightarrow 2KFeSi_3O_8 + Fe_3O_4 + 3/2Fe_2O_3 + 2H_2O$$
$$\text{mica} \qquad\qquad\qquad \text{felspar} \quad \text{magnetite} \quad \text{haematite}$$

The monoclinic polymorph iron sanidine typically results, but under different experimental conditions a triclinic polymorph can be synthesized. Goldsmith (1950) was able to replace Al by Ga in both potassium and sodium felspars, or alternatively to replace Si by Ge: the X-ray powder patterns show a great similarity to that of synthetic orthoclase. The fully substituted type $KGaGe_3O_8$ also was synthesized. Ge-orthoclase and Ga-Ge-orthoclase melted incongruently to the Ga(Ge)-containing equivalent of leucite and a siliceous liquid. The rarer alkalies were substituted for potassium by Barrer and McCallum (1953) who synthesized the rubidium felspar $RbAlSi_3O_8$ hydrothermally from gels, and also obtained mixed crystals with Tl partly replacing K. On heating albite with LiCl at 450°C. and 450 bars a crystalline material with composition close to $LiAlSi_3O_8$ was obtained by Šćavničar and Sabatier (1957), and named Li-felspar. This Li-felspar is tetragonal ($D = 2·405$), and on heating with a solution of NaCl at 500°C. it is converted to albite.

Thermochemistry. The thermochemistry of the alkali felspars has been investigated by White (1909, 1919), who determined the high-temperature specific heats of orthoclase and microcline, by Mulert (1913) who measured the heats of solution in HF of adularia and microcline, and more recently by Kracek and Neuvonen (1952) who performed heats of solution (decomposition) measurements in 20 per cent. HF at 74·7°C. for a number of alkali felspars, the chemical analyses of several of which are given in Tables 4–9. The latter authors considered that the alkali felspars have thermal properties highly dependent on their origin and thermal history: the heats of formation of high-temperature alkali felspars from the two end-members, albite and orthoclase, were shown to be positive, but the actual relationships in the series need further investigation. Rosenqvist (1954) heated samples of sanidine, anorthoclase, orthoclase and microcline microperthite at various temperatures with radioactive CaO and measured the radioactivity of the silicate after leaching with 10 per cent. HCl: the relative reactivity rates of the felspars were thus determined.

The d.t.a. curves for alkali felspars have generally been reported to show neither endo- nor exothermic peaks, though Rosenqvist (1954) noted in some cases a small endothermic peak at about 900°C. which he tentatively interpreted as representing a phase-change. Köhler and Wieden (1954) recorded a sharp endothermic peak at 820°C. for an albite from Rischuna, Switzerland. The infra-red absorption spectra of adularia were studied by Matossi and Bronder (1938).

Alteration. The alkali felspars are very apt to undergo alteration from the action of hydrothermal solutions and from the normal processes of weathering. Decomposition products commonly include kaolinite, halloysite, sericite, quartz or gibbsite. A pale yellowish green unctuous and compact mineral identified as pinite was recorded as an alteration product of felspar in granite by Smyth (1922). Although the turbid, brownish appearance of many felspars, particularly orthoclase, has often been ascribed to the presence of a kaolin-like mineral or incipient sericite, Folk (1955) has shown that in many cases when the "turbid" objects are examined under a high-power microscope they are seen to consist of liquid-filled vacuoles with a fairly strong negative relief. These were thought to be primary or deuteric, trapped during crystallization of a magma, or by related hydrothermal activity: some of the vacuoles, however, appear to form on weathering.

Considerable experimental work has been done on the alteration and weathering of the alkali felspars, beginning with the classic work of Daubrée (1897) who agitated fragments of orthoclase with water for 192 hours, and from 5 kg. of felspar obtained 12·6 g. K$_2$O in the filtered solution. Later Smirnov (1915) investigated the action on orthoclase of humic acid at room temperature, and of pure water in an autoclave at 151°–158°: the alkalies and silicon were the most abundant ions in the resulting solution; in both experiments aluminium was relatively less soluble. Further experimental decomposition of potassium felspars under various conditions of acidity and alkalinity were carried out by Stevens (1934), Norton (1937, 1939, 1941), Correns and Engelhardt (1938) and Gruner (1944). The results obtained by these authors have been correlated by Folk (1947) who presented the data on diagrams in relation to temperature, acidity or basicity, and the Al/K ratio. Folk concluded that kaolin forms in acid solutions up to about 350°C. if Al is rather high and K is low; muscovite forms from as low a temperature as 200°C. and as high as 525°C. in solutions which are only slightly acid or slightly alkaline if both K and Al are high; pyrophyllite forms from about 300°C. to 550°C. if K and Al are both low. In most conditions of hydrothermal alteration of felspars associated with ore deposits sericite is formed because most metalliferous solutions are alkaline: kaolin, however, is formed near the surface by acid waters and may replace sericite because of leaching by carbonate and sulphate waters (Folk, *loc. cit.*). The action of hot water under pressure on felspars has been investigated by Morey and Chen (1955) who subjected microcline to a temperature of 350°C., at 5000 lb./in.^{2}, for 103 days: the dissolved material contained a molecular proportion of K$_2$O:Al$_2$O$_3$:SiO$_2$ of 1·11:1:6·76, while the potassium felspar remaining had a white coating of muscovite and boehmite, and further boehmite was found in the bomb (see also Morey and Fourier, 1961). The pH of the solution obtained from orthoclase ground for two minutes in CO$_2$-free water was measured by Stevens (1934) as 8·8–9·2. The hydration of alkali felspars and their surface chemistry has been discussed from a theoretical standpoint by DeVore (1956).

The feasibility of using the radioactive decay of ^{40}K to ^{40}Ar in potassium

felspars as an accurate method of geological dating was investigated by Wasserburg and Hayden (1955), following the discovery by Aldrich and Nier (1948) of
appreciable quantities of radiogenic ^{40}Ar in some potassium minerals, and the
work on sylvine (Smits and Gentner, 1950) and on stony meteorites (Gerling and
Pavlova, 1951). The $^{40}K/^{40}Ar$ ratio is now accepted as a useful additional
method of age determination, particularly in the absence of uranium or thorium
minerals, and the ages of many potassium felspars or potassium felspar-rich
rocks have been determined (*e.g.* Holmes *et al.*, 1955): for a general review of the
method see Carr and Kulp (1957).

OPTICAL AND PHYSICAL PROPERTIES

Although the potassium and sodium felspars form a complete solid solution
series at the crystallization temperatures of silicate melts, most naturally
occurring alkali felspars, except for the potassium- and sodium-rich members,
unmix on cooling, and consist of two phases. The potassium-rich phase may
be monoclinic or triclinic, the sodium-rich phase is triclinic. Unmixing may
occur on an ultramicroscopic (cryptoperthitic), microscopic (microperthitic), or
megascopic (perthitic) scale. The range of composition within which unmixing
occurs increases with decreasing temperature of formation. In the alkali
felspars belonging to the (high-albite)–sanidine series unmixing occurs in the
composition range Or_{25}–Or_{60}, and in the sanidines and anorthoclases the unmixing is usually on a cryptoperthitic scale. Alkali felspars formed at lower
temperatures unmix from a wider range of composition, approximately Or_{20}–
Or_{80}. The unmixing leads to the formation of orthoclase microperthite,
consisting of a potassium-rich phase, in general having monoclinic symmetry,
and a sodium-rich phase with triclinic symmetry. These felspars, nevertheless,
show monoclinic morphology, and frequently also optical monoclinic symmetry.
Microcline, the lowest temperature form of the potassium-rich alkali felspars, is
triclinic, and except in crystals containing a very high percentage (> 92) of the
potassium phase is either perthitic or microperthitic.

The optical properties of alkali felspars are affected both by the degree of
order in the distribution of Si and Al in the tetrahedral sites of the felspar
structure, and by the presence, on a submicroscopic scale, of intergrowths of
materials possessing different refractivities, *e.g.* the unmixing of plagioclase
from a potassium-rich host, or the partial conversion of orthoclase to microcline.
In addition the optical properties are affected by the degree of substitution of Al
by Fe^{+3}, and of (K,Na) by Ca, Ba, and Sr, as well as by the sympathetic substitution of Si by Al necessary to maintain electrostatic neutrality consequent
on the replacement of monovalent by divalent cations.

Some alkali felspars, and in particular those called moonstones, exhibit
marked blue schiller effects. These have been explained as due to interference
effects in reflections from planes of segregation in the perthitic textures (see for
example Bøggild, 1924). An alternative explanation (Raman *et al.*, 1950)
suggests that the schiller colours are due to diffusion of light by neighbouring
small domains with different optical properties.

Optic orientation and optic axial angle. In the alkali felspars usually described
as adularia and orthoclase (Fig. 24), occurring in rocks considered to have formed
at low temperatures, or slowly cooled from higher temperatures, the optic axial

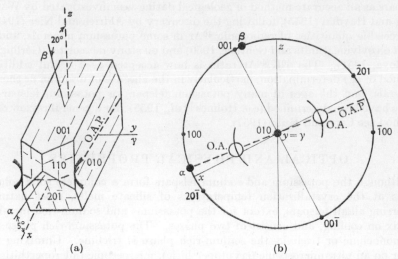

FIG. 24(a). Optical orientation of orthoclase. (b) Stereogram of the optical
orientation of orthoclase.

plane is normal to (010). The same orientation is shown by many of the alkali
felspars in volcanic rocks, but in a small number of sanidines occurring in rocks
formed at high temperatures and cooled rapidly the optic axial plane is parallel
to (010) (Fig. 25). On heating potassium-rich alkali felspars which have
formed at low temperatures or slowly cooled from higher temperatures, the
optic axial angle decreases with rising temperature, and on prolonged heating at
1075°C. opens out in the plane parallel to (010). Thus the optic axial angles,

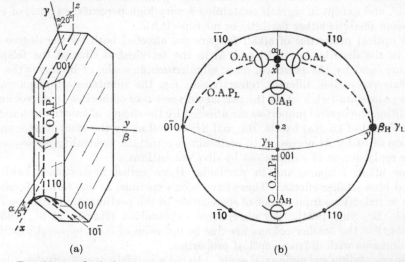

FIG. 25(a). Optical orientation of high-sanidine. (b) Stereogram showing the
optical orientation of high- and low-sanidine. Optic axial plane of high-
sanidine, O.A.P$_H$, optic axial plane of low-sanidine O.A.P$_L$.

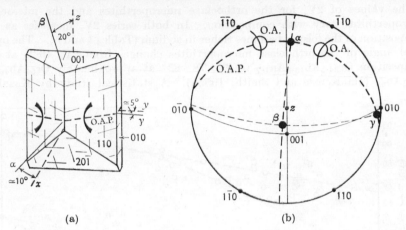

FIG. 26(a). Optical orientation of anorthoclase. (b) Stereogram showing the optical orientation of anorthoclase.

and the orientation of the optic axial plane, may be used to distinguish alkali felspars formed at low temperatures, or slowly cooled from higher temperatures, from those formed at high temperatures and rapidly chilled. The optic axial angles and the orientation of the optic plane are the most important and easily measured diagnostic optical properties by which the alkali felspars can be divided into four series. This division of the alkali felspars depends on the sympathetic variation of the increasing value of the optic axial angle and of the degree of unmixing, the latter itself being a function of increasing Al/Si ordering. It is emphasized, however, that the optical properties of all alkali felspars do not correspond precisely with those given for each of these series. Felspars with transitional optical properties occur, and are discussed later.

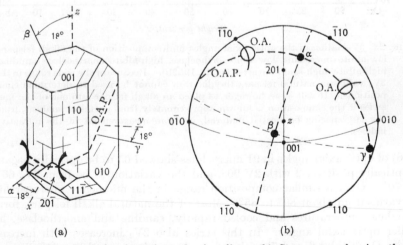

FIG. 27(a). Optical orientation of microcline. (b) Stereogram showing the optical orientation of microcline.

The values of $2V_\alpha$ for the orthoclase microperthites and the microcline microperthites vary with composition. In both series $2V_\alpha$ increases as the composition of the felspar becomes richer in sodium (Tables 4 and 5). The optic axial angle of the orthoclase microperthites changes from $2V_\alpha$ 46·2° at the composition $Or_{84·5}Ab_{13·8}An_{1·7}$ to $2V_\alpha$ 78°–83° at approximately $Or_{54}Ab_{46}$ to $Or_{32}Ab_{68}$ (MacKenzie and Smith, 1955a). A statistical study by Kazakov

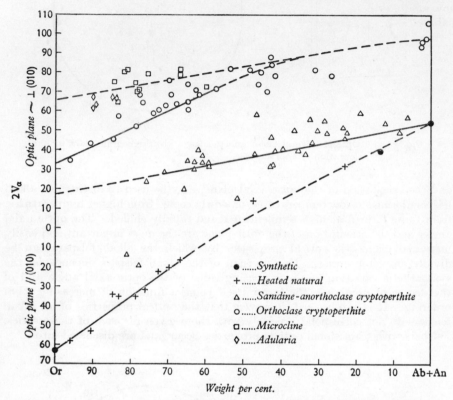

Fig. 28. Variation of the optic axial angles and composition of the alkali felspars, low-albite–microcline, low-albite–orthoclase, high-albite–anorthoclase–sanidine, high-albite–high-sanidine (after Tuttle, 1952b). Because of the wide range in the $2V_\alpha$ values of natural felspars the diagram cannot be used to determine compositions. It will serve, however, to place an alkali felspar into one of the four series if the composition is known approximately from chemical analysis, from the $\bar{2}01$ spacing on heated material, or from measurement of the refractive indices.

(1956) of optic axial angles in 91 microclines showed 65 to be optically negative, 24 optically positive, 2 with 2V 90°, and the variation to be from $2V_\alpha$ 66° to $2V_\gamma$ 70°. Over a similar composition range in the microcline microperthites, $2V_\alpha$ varies from about 80° to 85°. Most of the natural alkali felspars, formed at higher temperatures and cooled rapidly, sandine and anorthoclase, have smaller optic axial angles. In this series also $2V_\alpha$ increases with increasing $NaAlSi_3O_8$ (Tables 6 and 7), rising from approximately 21° to 24° at a composition $Or_{66}Ab_{31}$ to 54° at $Or_{22}Ab_{78}$. The fourth series of alkali felspars, the high-sanidine–high-albite series, is known mainly from heating natural minerals in the laboratory at 1075°C., but also from synthetic felspars and a small number of natural high-sanidines. In this series $2V_\alpha$ changes from approximately 62° in the plane parallel to (010), for pure $KAlSi_3O_8$, to approximately 55° in the plane perpendicular to (010) for high-temperature albite. The variation in the optic axial angles with chemical composition in the four series, microcline–low-albite, orthoclase–low-albite, sanidine–anorthoclase–high-albite, and high-sanidine–high-albite is shown in Fig. 28.

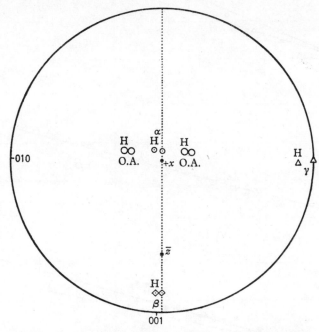

FIG. 29. Stereographic projection of the optical orientation of anorthoclase $Or_{23}Ab_{76}An_1$ before and after homogenization by heating at 900°C. for 20 hours (after Tuttle, 1952). α, β, γ and optic axes of heated specimen are shown by H.

The presence of calcium in alkali felspars in quantities greater than the equivalent of 3–4 per cent. of the anorthite molecule increases the optic axial angle (see, for example, Carmichael, 1960). This effect is most pronounced in the sanidine–anorthoclase–high-albite series, and estimates of composition based on the measurement of 2V in this series may not be more precise than ± 10 per cent. $KAlSi_3O_8$. The optic axial angles of the ferriferous orthoclases from Madagascar in which the content of $KFeSi_3O_8$ varies from 2·8 to 12·5 weight per cent. (Coombs, 1954) show an almost continuous range from 51° parallel to (010) to 36° perpendicular to (010). In these ferriferous felspars there is, however, no direct relationship between the chemical composition and the variation in 2V and optical orientation.

The classification of the alkali felspars outlined above does not differ fundamentally from that based on their general optical properties, proposed earlier

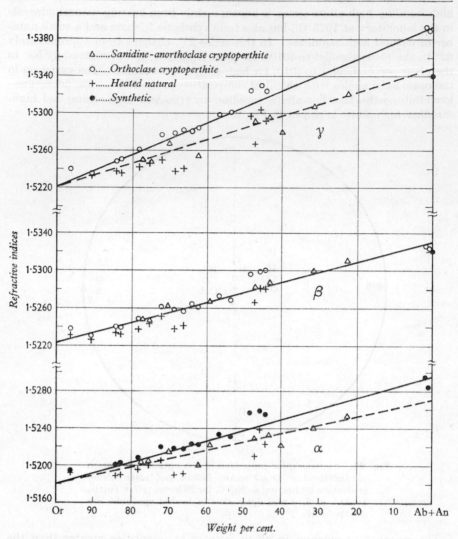

FIG. 30. Variation of refractive indices with composition of the alkali felspars (after
Tuttle, 1952b). α and γ for the sanidine–anorthoclase–high-albite series are shown as
dashed lines, α and γ for the orthoclase–low-albite as full lines. The β index is
essentially the same in both series.

by Oftedahl (1948), which is useful in their preliminary classification into a high-,
intermediate- or low-temperature series.

The orientation of the optical indicatrix of sodium-rich alkali felspars shows
considerable variation. Felspars in the composition range Ab_{35} to Ab_{100},
although triclinic (Donnay and Donnay, 1952), often have monoclinic optics.
Tuttle (1952) has suggested that the monoclinic properties of such cryptoperthites may result from the fact that the felspars are intergrowths of a monoclinic
potassium and a triclinic sodium felspar, the latter twinned so as to give mono-

clinic optical properties. In the more potassium-rich alkali felspars the exsolution lamellae of sodium felspar have triclinic symmetry, yet the majority
of these felspars have monoclinic optics. The monoclinic symmetry of these
microperthites is considered by Oftedahl to be due to the development of
pseudomonoclinic symmetry in the albite resulting from submicroscopic twinning. Many anorthoclases are cryptoperthitic, and show variable orientation
even in different grains from the same sample. Tuttle has shown that consistent
results can be obtained by the homogenization of these felspars on heating at
900°C. for 20 hours, and an example of an anorthoclase ($Or_{23}Ab_{76}An_1$) with
monoclinic optics before and triclinic optical orientation after heating is given
in Fig. 29.

Refractive indices. The refractive indices of the alkali felspars increase
progressively with increasing amounts of the albite molecule. The correlation
of refractive indices with chemical composition has been investigated by Spencer
(1930, 1937), Larsen (1938), Oftedahl (1948), Tuttle (1952b) and Hewlett
(1959). Compared with the sanidine–anorthoclase–high-albite series, the rate of
increase for the α and γ values is greater in the orthoclase–orthoclase microperthite–low-albite series (Fig. 30). Although in the orthoclase–low-albite
series the γ-index varies between 1·522 and 1·539, estimates of composition
from refractive index measurements, because of the relatively large effects of
small quantities of anorthite in solid solution (see Table 4, anals. 4, 5), and
because of the uncertainty of the thermal state of the felspar, can be used only
as approximations. The value of refractive indices as a means of estimating
chemical composition of the alkali felspars is further reduced by the relatively
large effect on this property of small contents of Ba, Sr, Rb and Fe^{+3}. Oftedahl
constructed an Or–Ab–An diagram (Fig. 31) correlating the chemical composition of the felspars of his intermediate series with the average, $(\alpha+\gamma)/2$,
index of refraction and with the extinction angle, $\alpha:x$ on (010). The values
obtained from this diagram for nine of the alkali felspars in Table 4, except for
the potassium-rich orthoclase microperthite (anal. 16), show a fair comparison
with the chemical composition. Oftedahl's figure applies to completely unmixed alkali felspars and should not be used to estimate the compositions of
partially unmixed cryptoperthites. The influence of varying tenor of iron on
refractive indices of some ferriferous potassium felspars has been investigated
by Coombs (1954); the α and γ indices increase approximately 0·003 per unit
weight per cent. Fe_2O_3.

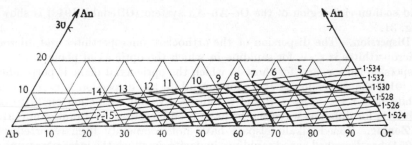

FIG. 31. Variation of the average index of refraction, $\frac{1}{2}(\alpha+\gamma)$, and the extinction
angle on (010) with the composition of the orthoclase–low-albite series (after
Oftedahl, 1948).

Extinction angles. The extinction angles on (010), $\alpha' : (001)$ cleavage, in the orthoclase–low-albite series (Spencer, 1937) vary proportionally with the content of potassium and sodium, increasing from 5° for pure potassium felspar, to 19° for low-albite. A comparable increase in the extinction angle does not occur in the sanidines (Larsen, 1938), and it has been shown by Tuttle (1950) that the extinction on (010) in the sanidine–anorthoclase–high-albite series varies systematically, but is lower for equivalent compositions. The differences in the extinction angle in the two series are greatest in the sodium-rich members (Fig. 32). The variation of the extinction angle $\alpha' : x$ on (010) in the potassium-

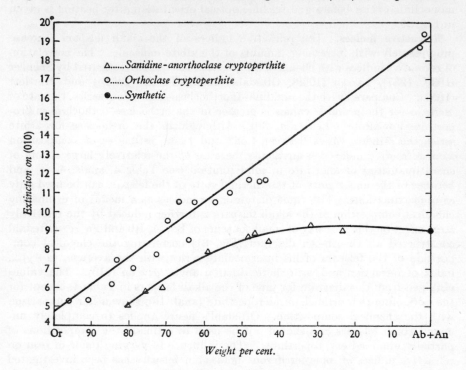

FIG. 32. Variation of the extinction angle on (010) and composition in the sanidine–anorthoclase–high-albite, and orthoclase–low-albite series (after Tuttle, 1952b).

and sodium-rich region of the Or–Ab–An system (Oftedahl, 1948) is shown in Fig. 31.

Dispersion. The dispersion of the orthoclase microperthites and microcline microperthites is $r > v$, for sanidine in which the optic axial plane is (010) the dispersion is $r < v$, and for those in which the optic axial plane is perpendicular to (010) the dispersion is $r > v$; for low-albite the dispersion is $r < v$, for high-albite it is $r > v$. The α, β and γ indices, 2V and extinction on (010) of an adularia for different wavelengths have been measured by Brautigam (1922).

Zoning. Zoned alkali felspars have not commonly been reported. Hsu (1954) has described zoned sanidines in dacite, in which the more potassium-rich cores have $2V_\alpha$ 15°, γ 1·527, $\alpha : x$ 4°, and the more sodium-rich margins, $2V_\alpha$ 30°, γ 1·529, $\alpha : x$ 8°, corresponding respectively to the compositions Or_{77} and Or_{60}.

Continuous zoning from high-sanidine, $2V_\alpha$ 7·8° and optic axial plane parallel to (010), to low-sanidine $2V_\alpha$ 17·5° and optic axial plane perpendicular to (010), with an intermediate uniaxial zone, has been described by MacKenzie (1956).

Cleavage. In addition to the perfect cleavages parallel to {001} and {010}, planes which involve only the breaking of the silicon–oxygen bonds linking one chain of four rings (Plate 1) to adjacent chains, a number of independent partings may be present. These partings are usually parallel to (100), (110), ($\bar{1}$10) and ($\bar{2}$01). In some felspars there is a tendency for the partings to develop along planes parallel to possible vicinal faces between (100) and (110) or ($\bar{1}$10), and between (100) and ($\bar{2}$01). Transitional partings have been described, and the previous literature reviewed, by Yuan (1953).

Transitional optics. The optic axial angles and the refractive indices of some members of the orthoclase–low-albite, the microcline–low-albite (Tuttle, 1952), and the sanidine–high-albite series (Tuttle and Keith, 1954) appear to be gradational, and the distinction, solely on optical properties, of the various members of the potassium-rich alkali felspars is not always possible. In the variety of potassium felspar usually described as adularia, distinguishable only by crystal habit and mode of occurrence, individual crystals may be optically monoclinic or triclinic, and in some cases show a gradual variation between monoclinic and triclinic optics (Chaisson, 1950). Adularia showing indications of albite and pericline twinning with some cross-hatching and extinction angles of 2°–3° in the lamellae have been described by Köhler (1948a), who reported that the triclinic optics develop most frequently around inclusions and fractures, and at the crystal margins. The uncertainty of the precise chemical composition obtained from the measurement of the optic axial angle is also illustrated by the orthoclase microperthites, in which the potassium phase may either be solely monoclinic or consist of both a monoclinic and a triclinic potassium phase (MacKenzie and Smith, 1955a). Thus a microperthite ($Or_{84\cdot5}Ab_{13\cdot8}An_{1\cdot7}$) with a single, monoclinic, potassium phase has $2V_\alpha$ 46·2°, yet in another, closely comparable in composition ($Or_{83\cdot3}Ab_{14\cdot9}An_{1\cdot8}$) but having a triclinic potassium phase in addition to the monoclinic potassium phase, $2V_\alpha$ is 57·6°. Crystals of adularia from Val Casatscha, Switzerland, consisting of domains possessing sanidine optics, others possessing microcline optics, as well as others showing a continuous series of intermediate optical orientation, have been described by Bambauer and Laves (1960).

Effects of heating on optical and physical properties. Many observations on the changes in the optical properties of heated alkali felspars have been made since Des Cloizeaux in 1861 first reported a decrease in the optic axial angle of sanidine with rising temperature. Kôzu and Suzuki (1923) reported that the optic axial angle returns to its original value provided the mineral is not heated above 850°C., but that at approximately 900°C. an abrupt change occurs, the magnitude of which depends on the heating temperature. Schmidt and Baier (1928) noted that whereas, on heating to 1100°C. and cooling to room temperature, the partial birefringence β–α shows an hysteresis effect but no permanent change, the value γ–α does not return completely to the original value on cooling. Spencer (1930) showed that in addition to the destruction of the schiller colour and perthitic structure of Ceylon moonstone, by heating between 750° and 1050°C., the extinction angle on (010), the optic axial angle, and the density are also reduced. The results of heating sixteen alkali felspars, varying in

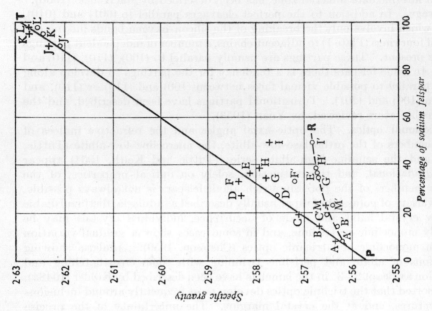

FIG. 33(b). Effect of heat treatment on specific gravity in the alkali felspars (after Spencer, 1930). Curve PR shows specific gravities after heating, PT before heating, letters A to M refer to felspars used by Spencer.

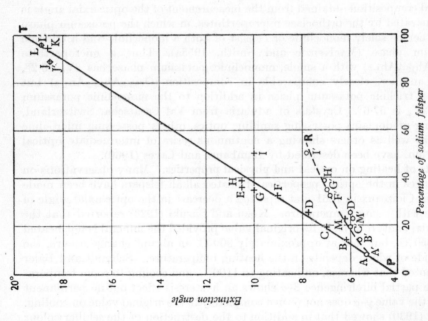

FIG. 33(a). Effect of heat treatment on extinction angle in the alkali felspars (after Spencer, 1930). Curve PR shows extinction angles after heating, PT before heating, letters A to M refer to felspars used by Spencer.

composition from $Or_{90.9}$ to $Or_{2.6}$, showed that in felspars with up to 40 per cent. $NaAlSi_3O_8$ the reduction in the extinction angle and density is approximately proportional in amount to the percentage of the sodium component in the felspar (Fig. 33). The non-perthitic felspars, approaching pure potassium and sodium felspar in composition, show no appreciable change in extinction on (010), or in density. The response of the density to heating is more rapid than that of the extinction angle, the change occurring in a few minutes at approximately 800°C., and preceding the homogenization of the microperthites.

A further extensive study (Spencer, 1937) on the effects of heating alkali felspars for short periods (1–2 hours at 50° and 100°C. intervals) showed that whereas the refractive indices of microperthites decrease, those of the potassium-rich non-perthitic felspars remain unchanged. The reduction on heating to 850°C. of the α, β and γ indices of the felspars increases approximately linearly in the composition range 8 to 30 per cent. $NaAlSi_3O_8$; between 30 and 50 per cent. $NaAlSi_3O_8$ the reduction is less. The refractive indices are restored almost completely by slow cooling. For felpars of the orthoclase microperthite series, containing as much as 33 per cent. $NaAlSi_3O_8$, after prolonged heating at 1075°C., the optic axial angle develops in the symmetry plane (010). With increasing content of sodium the optic axial angle is more resistant to change, and the size of the angle decreases with increasing $NaAlSi_3O_8$ (Fig. 28). The dispersion of the heated felspars in which the optic axial angle is in the symmetry plane is $v > r$.

MacKenzie and Smith (1956) measured the optic axial angle in a number of crystals from twenty unheated and heated (900°C. for 24 hours) members of the sanidine–anorthoclase–high-albite series, ranging in composition from 82 to 19·5 per cent. $KAlSi_3O_8$. The majority showed less variation in the heated compared with the unheated samples, and it is possible that the variation in the heated crystals might reduce to zero if the minerals were held for a sufficient time at a fixed temperature. In those felspars with more than 60 per cent. potassium felspar in their bulk composition the mean value of $2V_\alpha$ decreases slightly, in the compositional range Or_{60}–Or_{40} it increases, and in the felspars with less than 40 per cent. bulk potassium felspar it either increases slightly or shows no change. The reason for the different response of the three compositional groups to this heat treatment is not known.

The green variety of microcline *amazonite* is decolorized by heating at temperatures above 270°C. The rate of decolorization has been determined by Oftedal (1957). Approximately 80 per cent. loss of colour occurs after heating for 16 hours at 300°C., and is almost instantaneous at 500°C. The decolorization data indicate that the colour probably developed at approximately 250°C. in an already crystallized and cooled felspar. Oftedal suggested that the "colour centra" are due to the replacement of a small number of the oxygens in the felspar structure by fluorine ions.

DISTINGUISHING FEATURES

The alkali felspars are distinguished from the members of the plagioclase series by the absence (except in microcline and anorthoclase) of lamellar twinning, lower refractive indices, lower specific gravity and the presence of cryptoperthitic or perthitic textures: from quartz by twinning, lower refractive indices and biaxial character.

Orthoclase may be distinguished from sanidine and anorthoclase by higher optic axial angle, and the presence of microperthitic textures, and from high-sanidine by the orientation of the optic axial plane. Orthoclase is distinguished from microcline by the straight extinction in the zone [010] and the absence of multiple twinning. The cleavage angle (001):(010) in orthoclase is 90° and serves to distinguish it from plagioclase, in which the angle is $\simeq 94°$. It is not possible to distinguish orthoclase and sanidine from either of the triclinic alkali felspars, anorthoclase or microcline, by cleavage angle.

Microcline is distinguished from other felspars, except in rare examples, by the "tartan" twinning in which the two sets of twin lamellae are approximately at right angles to each other, and in which the twinning corresponding to the pericline twins of plagioclase is approximately perpendicular to (001). For most plagioclase compositions the albite and pericline twin lamellae are not at right angles, the trace of the pericline twins makes a small angle with the (001) plane and is not seen in sections parallel to the basal plane. In the tartan twinning of microcline, the spindle-shaped albite and pericline lamellae wedge out in proximity to each other.

Anorthoclase may be distinguished from sanidine and orthoclase by its tartan twinning, and from orthoclase by lower optic axial angle. The twinning is on a much finer scale than that in microcline and its pericline twin lamellae are almost parallel to (001). It is also distinguished from microcline by a smaller optic axial angle and extinction angle on (001).

Techniques for staining potassium felspar in thin sections so that it may easily be distinguished from quartz or untwinned plagioclase felspar were described by Gabriel and Cox (1929) and Keith (1939). More recent modifications to this staining technique have been given by Chayes (1952) (see also Shand, 1949), while further modifications allowing the test to be performed at room temperature were described by Rosenblum (1956). The latter method involves uncovering the thin section and etching it with HF by placing it face downwards over an HF bath for 15–30 seconds, to prepare the minerals for staining. The stain is applied by immersing the section in a solution of sodium cobaltinitrite (60 g. per 100 ml. water) for 15–20 seconds, after which the section is rinsed immediately in cold water. Potassium felspar takes a pale yellow stain and although white mica and the clay minerals may also sometimes absorb the stain they may be distinguished, where potassium felspar is also present for comparison, by their different relief and intensity of stain. Quartz and plagioclase felspar are unaffected, though in antiperthite the alkali felspar blebs may take the stain.

PARAGENESIS

The potassium-sodium felspars are essential constituents of alkali and acid gneous rocks, and are particularly abundant in syenites, granites, granodiorites and their volcanic equivalents; the alkali felspars are also major constituents in pegmatites and in many acid and intermediate gneisses. In the plutonic rocks the alkali felspar is usually described as orthoclase, orthoclase microperthite, microcline, microcline microperthite, or microcline perthite, and in the volcanic rocks as sanidine, sanidine cryptoperthite, anorthoclase cryptoperthite, or anorthoclase. The pure potassium felspar has not been reported from natural occurrences, and in plutonic rocks the range of the potassium component of the alkali felspars is Or_{20} to Or_{97} (Tables 4, 5). In the acid plutonic rocks in particular, the variation in composition is more restricted and many of the alkali felspars of these rocks have a composition of about Or_{70} (Table 4, anal. 12). In many syenites and their pegmatites the alkali felspar is an orthoclase microperthite (Table 4, anals. 1, 2), microcline microperthite (Table 5, anal. 1) or microcline perthite (Table 5, anal. 2), containing between 20 and 50 per cent. of the potassium end-member. Less sodium-rich alkali felspars, however, are not uncommon in syenites; thus Solodovnikova (1937) has described orthoclase microperthites, containing between 60 and 80 per cent. of the orthoclase molecule, in the khibinite and foyaite of the Khibina area, and the alkali felspar in the mica nephelite-syenite of the same area is stated to have an even higher potassium content. The composition of a microcline perthite (from a khibinite) containing 50 per cent. of the orthoclase molecule is shown in Table 5, anal. 3. In the alkali felspar adularia, of "alpine" vein paragenesis, the content of the potassium component is consistently high (see Table 8, in which the potassium felspar molecule of eight adularias varies between 80 and 93 per cent.).

There is a considerable overlap in the compositions of the alkali felspars of plutonic and volcanic rocks, but in the latter the potassium component rarely exceeds 75 per cent. The compositions of sanidines detailed in Table 6 range from 38 to 80 per cent. $KAlSi_3O_8$, and the compositions of anorthoclases from 12 to 31 per cent. $KAlSi_3O_8$ (Table 7).

The alkali felspars of the more acid volcanic rocks are generally richer in potassium than the felspars of alkaline rocks. Thus in many rhyolites the composition of the alkali felspar varies between Or_{40} and Or_{65} (Table 6, anals. 2, 5, 10) whereas in the trachytes the alkali felspar composition is commonly in the range Or_{20}–Or_{30} (Table 7, anals. 7, 12). Exceptions, however, are not unusual, and some trachytic alkali felspars (Table 6, anals. 8, 9) are as rich in potassium as those occurring in rhyolites. The alkali felspars are uncommon in basic rocks, but occur in association with olivine in some lamprophyres, and in small amounts, in teschenite, theralite (Table 6, anal. 3), shonkinite and monchiquite (Table 7, anal. 4). An association of approximately equal amounts of sanidine (Table 6, anal. 6), magnesium olivine, augite and calcic plagioclase has been reported in trachybasalt (Hamilton and Neuerburg, 1956). The unusual mineralogy of these rocks is considered to have resulted from the assimilation by the basalt of granitic and smaller amounts of ultrabasic material. Large inclusions of anorthoclase (Table 7, anal. 9) in basalt lava are reported by Vlodavetz and Shavrova (1953).

Except for those felspars close to albite in composition, and a few sanidines, the alkali felspars consist of two phases, one potassium- and the other sodium-rich. The texture and appearance of the alkali felspars show considerable variations and depend partly on their composition, and partly on their post-crystallization history. A nomenclature to describe the habit and appearance of the microperthites and perthites was proposed by Alling (1938), and some of the common types of perthitic blebs are illustrated in Fig. 34. A classification according to the modes of formation, unit shapes and other morphological features has been proposed by Rudenko (1954).

The genetic classification of perthites, based on the size of the exsolved phase, proposed by Tuttle (1952a), in which the various types of perthite are correlated with decreasing temperature of formation and increasing time subsequent to the crystallization of a homogeneous felspar, is shown below:

1. Sanidine or anorthoclase   Homogeneous crystals
2. Sub X-ray perthite <15 Å $\perp$ ($\bar{2}01$) direction
3. X-ray perthite $<1\ \mu$
4. Cryptoperthite 1–$5\ \mu$
5. Microperthite 5–$100\ \mu$
6. Perthite 100–$1000\ \mu$ (1 mm.)
7. Orthoclase (or microcline) and albite

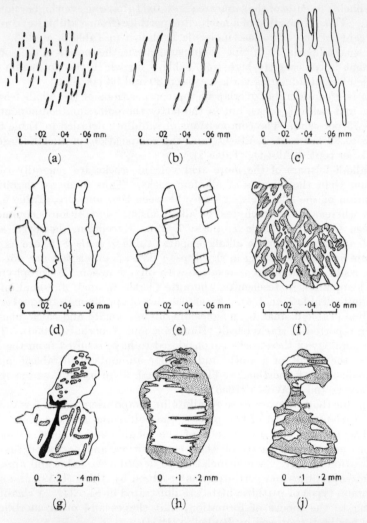

Fig. 34.   Perthite types (a) stringlets, (b) strings, (c) rods, (d) beads, (e) fractured beads, (f) interlocking, (g) interpenetrating, (h) and (j) replacement (after Alling, 1938).   Scales in millimetres.

In terms of their geological environment, Tuttle considered that sanidine or anorthoclase, sub X-ray, and X-ray perthite may be expected in volcanic rocks, cryptoperthite in small hypabyssal intrusions, microperthite and perthite in small plutons, and the individual phases orthoclase or microcline and albite in large plutons. In addition to this correlation of alkali felspar type with the

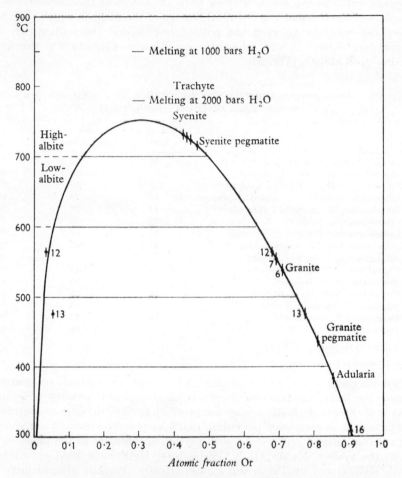

FIG. 35. The region of exsolution in the albite–orthoclase system showing the amount of the sodium component of co-existing alkali and plagioclase felspars in relation to the temperature of crystallization inferred from their paragenesis (after Barth, 1951). Numbers 6, 7, 12, 13, 16 correspond to those in Table 10.

geological environment of their formation, Barth (1951, 1956a) has shown that the amount of the sodium component in co-existing alkali and plagioclase felspars can be correlated with the temperature of crystallization of the felspars inferred from their paragenesis (Fig. 35 and Table 10; the latter includes the distribution coefficient k, *i.e.* the ratio of the mol. fraction of Ab in Or to the mol. fraction of Ab in An). The maximum on Barth's curve is approximately 100°C.

above that of the curve determined by Bowen and Tuttle (1950), and is at a composition 15 mol. per cent. richer in $NaAlSi_3O_8$ (see Fig. 20). An equilibrium phase stability diagram in which the coexisting alkali and plagioclase felspars are used as coordinates, and on which the temperature curves are projected, has been constructed by Rao (1960a). Tuttle and Bowen (1958) have stressed the potential value of the alkali felspars both as geological thermometers and as recorders of the thermal and chemical history of the rocks in which they occur. The phase relations between the potassium-rich and the sodium-rich alkali felspars are shown in the schematic equilibrium diagram for the system $NaAlSi_3O_8$–$KAlSi_3O_8$ (Fig. 20).

Table 10. DISTRIBUTION COEFFICIENTS OF SODIUM IN COEXISTING ALKALI AND PLAGIOCLASE FELSPARS (Barth, 1951).

	% Ab in alkali felspar	% Ab in plagioclase	k
1. Sanidinite ejactamenta, Laacher See	35	52	0·68
2. Labradorite trachyte, Mt. Amiata	23	38	0·61
3. Oligoclase trachyte, Ölberg, Siebengebirge	39	65	0·60
4. Oligoclase trachyte, Perlenhardt, Siebengebirge	41	70	0·60
5. Rhyodacite, Mt. Konati, California	41	72	0·57
6. Coarse granite, Baneheia, Kristiansand	29	72	0·40
7. Coarse granite, Birkeland, Norway	31	89	0·35
8. Migmatite, Cape Town, S. Africa	31	85	0·36
9. Augengneiss, Feda, Flekkefjord	27	77	0·35
10. Pegmatite, Fröyså, Iveland	27	78	0·36
11. Pegmatite, Berö, Kragerö	20	59	0·34
12. Pegmatite, Risö, Kragerö	32	97	0·33
13. Pegmatite, Stjernöy, Manda	23	83	0·28
14. Pegmatite, Fröyna, Risör	14	57	0·25
15. Pegmatite, Lyngrot, Froland	18	80	0·23
16. Alpine-type veins	$\begin{cases} 21 \\ 9 \end{cases}$	$\simeq 96$	$\begin{cases} 0·22 \\ 0·10 \end{cases}$

Plutonic rocks. The genesis of alkali felspars in acid plutonic rocks and acid gneisses has been considered by many investigators, but their mode of formation in some of these rocks is still contentious and is a facet of the granite controversy. The formation in granites of potassium-rich felspar and its relation to the sodium and calcium felspar components, with particular reference to the phase equilibria in the system $NaAlSi_3O_8$–$KAlSi_3O_8$–SiO_2–H_2O, have been examined by Tuttle (1952a) and by Tuttle and Bowen (1958). Perthite granites may have the same chemical composition as orthoclase–plagioclase granites, and Tuttle suggested that an originally homogeneous alkali felspar may have either unmixed to give a perthite in the perthite granites, or unmixed to individual crystals in the orthoclase–plagioclase granites giving rise to a nearly sodium-free microcline or orthoclase, and a sodium-rich plagioclase. A genetic classification of syenites and nepheline-syenites as well as granites has been proposed by Tuttle and Bowen. This classification is based on the distribution of the sodium felspar component between the potassium felspar and plagioclase components of the rocks. Thus the existence of granites, syenites and nepheline-syenites in which all the sodium felspar is present in perthite formed during cooling from an originally homogeneous alkali felspar, is regarded as evidence that the rocks crystallized at temperatures above that of the solvus in the binary system $NaAlSi_3O_8$–$KAlSi_3O_8$. These rocks are classified as hypersolvus granites, syenites and nepheline-syenites. The acid and alkaline rocks which contain a sodium-rich plagioclase in addition to the potassium felspar are classified as subsolvus granites, syenites and nepheline-syenites. The K_2O, Na_2O and CaO contents of fifty-seven granitic and granodioritic rocks are shown in Fig. 36. Those rocks having an oxide ratio which lies to the CaO side of the curve AB contain both plagioclase and potassium felspar; in those plotting below the curve, the amount of plagioclase varies from zero to 35 per cent.

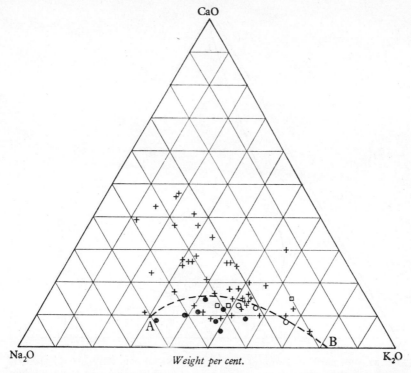

Fig. 36. Relation between CaO–Na_2O–K_2O content and modal plagioclase of 57 granites and granodiorites (after Tuttle, 1952a). Solid circles (●) no plagioclase; open circle (○) < 10 per cent. plagioclase; open square (□) < 20 per cent. plagioclase; cross (+) 20–60 per cent. plagioclase.

For the latter rocks Tuttle suggested that the plagioclase may have been derived from the unmixing of an originally homogeneous sodium-rich, and in some cases, calcium-rich alkali felspar. It is emphasized, however, that the plagioclase is not derived in all such granites from the unmixing of alkali felspars, for although plagioclase is not an important constituent in the majority of rhyolites, phonolites and trachytes, in rhyolites, especially those with an appreciable lime content, plagioclase phenocrysts are not uncommon.

In some typical larvikites (Muir and Smith, 1956; Smith and Muir, 1958) the felspars are mainly cryptoperthite, potassium-rich felspar, and oligoclase: they show textural and crystallographic relations which are consistent with unmixing

and inversion from a single calcium-bearing sodium-rich sanidine which originally crystallized in the high-temperature disordered state. The felspars in some
of the larvikites have more calcium-rich cores, unmixed to coarse microperthite,
and more potassium-rich margins, unmixed to cryptoperthite.

Volcanic rocks. In the acid volcanic rocks there is a close relationship between
the CaO content and the composition of the potassium felspar phenocrysts. In
the volcanics poor in calcium the sanidine usually contains a greater amount of
the albite than the orthoclase molecule; thus the potassium component of the

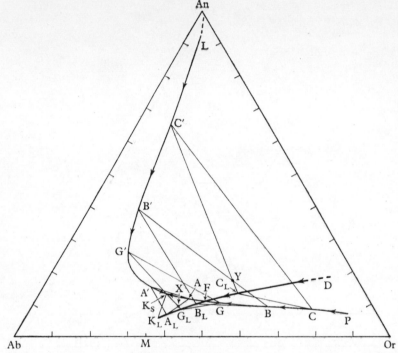

Fig. 37. Ternary diagram of the system $NaAlSi_3O_8$–$KAlSi_3O_8$–$CaAl_2Si_2O_8$
showing the approximate composition of liquids co-existing in equilibrium
with two felspars (after Tuttle and Bowen, 1958).

sanidine phenocrysts in the rhyolites and quartz latites of the San Juan region
(Larsen and Larsen, 1938) decreases from Or_{70} to Or_{40} in rocks containing 3·5
and 0·5 per cent. total lime respectively. In those rocks in which the normative
anorthite is greater than ten per cent. two felspars are present, a potassium
phase containing between 30 and 40 per cent. $NaAlSi_3O_8$, and a plagioclase
(An_{25} to An_{40}).

The crystallization of felspars in rhyolites, trachytes and phonolites has been
discussed by Tuttle and Bowen (1958) who have indicated the general trend of
crystallization and the position of the solidus (LK_SP in Fig. 37) in the ternary
system $NaAlSi_3O_8$–$KAlSi_3O_8$–$CaAl_2Si_2O_8$. The figure shows a single field
boundary K_LD which divides the fields of potassium felspar and plagioclase
felspar, and corresponds to liquid compositions which are in equilibrium with

two felspars, alkali felspars from P to K_S, and plagioclase felspar from K_S to L. The trend of crystallization in this system is illustrated in Fig. 37. For compositions to the right of the solidus curve LK_SP, equilibrium crystallization occurs with the formation of a single felspar until the composition of the liquid reaches the field boundary, when the second felspar begins to crystallize. The plagioclase felspar changes from an anorthite-rich to a more albite-rich composition along the solidus LB′, and the alkali-felspar from potassium-rich to more sodium-rich felspars, the compositions of which are represented along the solidus from P to B, until no liquid remains. Crystallization in the compositional field K_SK_LF may be illustrated by considering a liquid of composition X. A plagioclase having a calcium content initially greater than G′ crystallizes first, and the composition of the liquid changes to G_L. At this temperature the composition of the plagioclase is G′, and a potassium-rich felspar of composition G begins to crystallize. The composition of the liquid changes along the field boundary curve to A_L, the plagioclase reacts with the liquid, changing in composition from G′ to A′, and the alkali felspar changes in composition from G to A. At the temperature of A_L the mixture consists of an alkali-felspar A, liquid A_L and a small amount of plagioclase of composition A′. Just below the temperature of A_L all the plagioclase has reacted with the liquid and the mixture consists of roughly equal amounts of liquid close to A_L in composition, and an alkali felspar approximately A in composition. With further crystallization the composition of the liquid leaves the field boundary curve and moves towards the albite–orthoclase join, and the alkali felspar changes in composition towards X. Crystallization is completed when the crystals attain the composition X and no liquid remains. Thus for compositions within the field K_SK_LF crystallization is characterized by the initial formation of a plagioclase, followed later by an alkali felspar. With equilibrium crystallization the plagioclase reacts with the liquid and is resorbed completely leaving an alkali felspar and liquid, crystallization being completed when the composition of the alkali felspar reaches the composition of the original mixture. The probability that the late crystallization of rhyolite, trachyte and phonolite liquids will give rise to the formation of a single alkali felspar is increased by fractionation during crystallization. In the quickly chilled volcanic rocks such fractionation is effected by the zoning of plagioclase, and the later crystallization of a single felspar phase is indicated by the formation of sodium-rich sanidine rims around plagioclase.

Fractionation may also affect the mineral composition of rocks derived from liquids which lie to the right of the solidus curve LK_SP. Thus equilibrium crystallization of a liquid of composition Y (Fig. 37) is completed at B_L with the formation of a plagioclase and a potassium-rich felspar. Fractionation by zoning of the plagioclase would cause the liquid composition to change beyond B_L towards K_L, to leave the field boundary at a point between G_L and A_L, and change in composition along a curved path to M, the $NaAlSi_3O_8$–$KAlSi_3O_8$ binary system minimum. Thus from compositions above the solidus curve G′K_SP a single alkali felspar may form during the later stages of crystallization. Such a crystallization course has been considered by Tuttle and Bowen (1958) as a possible explanation of the felspar relationships in those granites, syenites and shonkinites in which plagioclase occurs as cores in alkali felspars. The relationships of felspar crystallization deduced by Tuttle and Bowen have been applied to some British and Icelandic Tertiary porphyritic pitchstones

(Carmichael, 1960). The felspar solidus, as represented by the composition of the phenocrysts, for these rocks is displaced towards the albite apex of the ortho-clase–albite–anorthite ternary diagram, compared with that deduced by Tuttle and Bowen for trachytic rocks. This location of the solidus closer to the albite corner indicates that the pitchstones crystallized at a lower temperature than the trachytes.

The potassium-rich components of the alkali felspar phenocrysts in some phonolite and trachyte lavas from Kenya and northern Tanganyika (Häkli, 1960) both range in composition from Or_{15} to Or_{40}. The phenocrysts from the two rock types, however, show a marked difference in anorthite content, those from the phonolites having an An content of less than 1·0 mol. per cent., in contrast to the trachyte felspars, the anorthite contents of which vary between 6·1 and 15·3 mol. per cent. Differences are also present in the groundmass felspars; thus in the phonolites the felspar consists solely of a potassium-rich monoclinic phase (Or_{82} to Or_{90}), while in the trachytes the felspar consists of two or three components, the compositions of which are Or_{88} and Or_{11}, or Or_{96}, Or_{78} and Or_6. Unmixing of the alkali felspar into a potassium-rich and a sodium-rich phase is believed to have taken place in both rocks, and the absence of a sodium-rich phase in the phonolites is considered to be due to its subsequent conversion to analcite which is an abundant constituent of the phonolites, but which is almost completely absent in the trachytes.

Different felspar phase assemblages in the porphyritic felsite and the porphyritic granophyres of the Slieve Gullion composite ring dyke have been recorded by Emeleus and Smith (1959). Many of the alkali felspar phenocrysts in these rocks are intermediate between the low-sanidine–anorthoclase and the orthoclase–low-albite series, and consist of a potassium phase, anorthoclase and a plagioclase of albite–oligoclase composition. The felspars in which the low-temperature plagioclase phase is absent are thought to have cooled in a drier environment, whereas those which cooled in the presence of higher volatile concentrations passed into the stage where the sodium-rich sanidine partially inverted to a low-temperature albite–oligoclase. Emeleus and Smith interpret the microcline-bearing specimens as xenocrysts, the preservation of the microcline phase being dependent on its resistance to conversion during the short period of heating.

Hydrothermal crystallization. During the hydrothermal stage of crystallization of granitic rocks, potassium felspar may be formed as a by-product of the transformation of biotite to chlorite (Chayes, 1955). This transformation may be represented by the following reactions:

(1) $K_2Mg_5Al_4Si_5O_{20}(OH)_4 + 4SiO_2 + 2H_2O \rightarrow Mg_5Al_2Si_3O_{10}(OH)_8 + 2KAlSi_3O_8$
$\quad$ eastonite $\qquad\qquad\qquad\qquad\qquad\qquad\qquad\qquad$ clinochlore $\qquad\qquad$ orthoclase

(2) $2KFe_3^{+2}AlSi_3O_{10}(OH)_2 + 2H_2O \rightarrow Fe_5^{+2}Fe^{+3}AlSi_3O_{10}(OH)_8 + KAlSi_3O_8 + K^+$
$\quad$ annite $\qquad\qquad\qquad\qquad\qquad\qquad\qquad$ iron chlorite $\qquad\qquad$ orthoclase

The small amount of potassium felspar fixed in the felspar granules in the chloritized biotite accounts for only a small proportion of the stoichiometric equivalent of the potassium released in the transformation. A considerable proportion of the potassium must, therefore, leave the reaction site to be added to the pre-existing potassium felspar, take part in the formation of sericite replacing plagioclase, or be removed completely from the granite.

Origin of perthite. The petrogenetic significance of perthite is still a controversial problem. Three processes, unmixing of an originally homogeneous alkali felspar, simultaneous crystallization of a potassium-rich and a sodium-rich felspar, and replacement of potassium by sodium felspar, have been considered either as the sole process in the formation of perthite, or individually for one or other specific occurrence. Perthites homogenized in the laboratory, on slow cooling may redevelop the perthitic texture, and there is no doubt that unmixing operates in some instances; an exsolution origin in the case of the fine regular perthitic intergrowths is generally accepted. Simultaneous crystallization of a potassium-rich and a sodium-rich felspar was proposed originally by Anderson (1928) to account for those perthites with a high sodium content, and more recently has been considered a possible explanation of the felspar relationships in some alkali granites (Wallace, 1956).

The replacement origin of perthite is based on the investigation of the pegmatite perthites, and regional studies particularly of metamorphic rocks, as well as on the formation of myrmekite and graphic intergrowths. The relationships of the alkali felspars in many pegmatites are difficult to explain except by a replacement hypothesis, particularly in those pegmatites in which vein perthite, patch perthite, chessboard albite and albite occur together in close association (Higazy, 1949). In the Pre-Cambrian pegmatites of southern Norway the common felspar is a microcline perthite, ranging in composition from $Or_{85}Ab_{15}$ to $Or_{68}Ab_{32}$. Anderson (1928) considered that part of the albite component was of replacement origin, but the relative constancy in composition of these microcline perthites has been interpreted by Barth (1956b) as indicative primarily of a temperature and not a metasomatic control. In the quartz felspathic gneisses of the Ørsdalen district, S. Norway (Heier, 1956) a perthite of composition $Or_{35}Ab_{57}An_8$ is associated with a more potassium-rich perthite and plagioclase. In some of these gneisses plagioclase is the dominant felspar, in others plagioclase is restricted essentially to perthitic lamellae, and the development of the more sodium-rich perthite is interpreted as an arrested stage in the replacement of plagioclase by potassium felspar. The development of perthite from plagioclase felspar by late deuteric potassium metasomatism has been described by Robertson (1959). In the quartz monzonite and alaskite of the Boulder batholith, Montana, the transformation of the plagioclase began with its marginal alteration to albite, which itself was subsequently replaced by orthoclase. Some of the albite was taken into solid solution with orthoclase while the excess sodium felspar remained as discrete relics which were later reorganized into blebs and stringers. The structural control of the formation of perthite, particularly by differential pressures, has been emphasized by Gates (1953) who observed an increased development of perthite in zones of intense fracturing. The formation of some alkaline and peralkaline pegmatites has been ascribed by Emmons (1953) to the recrystallization of aplite along shear zones, the perthite unmixing during the shearing to give rise to concentrations of sodium felspar, which in some dykes, replaced the potassium felspar.

Myrmekite. Wart-like associations of plagioclase and vermicular quartz, usually described as myrmekite, occur in granites, syenites, granite gneisses, charnockites and many other plutonic and metamorphic rocks containing large amounts of alkali felspars. Such intergrowths, which are especially common in granites, are located usually between adjacent crystals of potassium felspar and plagioclase, and commonly project from the plagioclase into the orthoclase or microcline. The intergrowths are accepted by most investigators to be of replacement origin in which the potassium felspar is replaced by a sodium-rich plagioclase, a replacement which may be expressed by the following reactions:

$$2KAlSi_3O_8 + Na_2O \rightarrow 2NaAlSi_3O_8 + K_2O$$

$$2KAlSi_3O_8 + CaO \rightarrow CaAl_2Si_2O_8 + K_2O + 4SiO_2$$

The release of silica during the transformation of potassium felspar to plagioclase is in accord with the observation that the amount of quartz in the intergrowth increases with the increasing anorthite content of the plagioclase. It appears unlikely, however, that all myrmekitic intergrowths have formed subsequently to the crystallization of the potassium felspar. Some myrmekite intergrowths are enclosed within potassium felspar, and show evidence of corrosion; the quartz, being more resistant to replacement, either remains projecting into the potassium felspar, or occurs as individual grains in the felspar isolated from the rest of the intergrowth (Bugge, 1943). Other occurrences in which the formation of myrmekite preceded the crystallization of the potassium felspar have been described by Drescher-Kaden (1939). Myrmekite intergrowths resulting from the replacement of albitic plagioclase by potassium felspar have been reported by Osterwald (1955), the silica required by this reaction being introduced during regional metamorphism. It is obvious that the reaction

$$2KAlSi_3O_8 + Na_2O \rightleftharpoons 2NaAlSi_3O_8 + K_2O$$

can give rise to either the replacement of potassium- by sodium- or sodium- by potassium felspar, and its direction depends on the relative concentration of potassium and sodium, and the solubility of the potassium and sodium felspars. The replacement origin of myrmekite was not accepted by Spencer (1945) who considered that the intergrowth is due to the segregation of microperthitic albite originally present in solid solution in the potassium felspar. Exsolution does not account, however, for the quartz fraction of the intergrowth. Sharma and Raja (1959) have attributed the formation of myrmekite to the breakdown of plagioclase during metamorphism.

Alkali felspar–quartz intergrowths. Many pegmatites contain intergrowths of alkali felspar and quartz, so-called graphic granite. The felspar is generally a microcline microperthite, but often some albite or sodic-oligoclase is included in the intergrowth. The intergrowth shows a resemblance to the products of artificial eutectic crystallization, and the relatively constant ratio of felspar to quartz led to the belief that the intergrowth was due to simultaneous crystallization of the two minerals. Where plagioclase occurs in the intergrowth it is generally of later formation than the potassium felspar and replaces it. From a study of megascopic intergrowths of quartz and felspar from many localities Wahlstrom (1939) has shown that in general the quartz in graphic granite does not display any constant orientation with respect to the felspar (Fig. 38); see also Miyakawa (1958). The quartz is often present in groups of separate parallel rods, but adjacent rods may or may not have the same optical orientation, and the z-crystal axis is not always parallel to the rod direction. Groups of parallel rods are usually confined to single crystals of felspar, but in some examples the rods cut the boundaries between adjacent grains. Wahlstrom considered that although the formation of graphic granite may result from the partial replacement of felspar by quartz or by the simultaneous growth of two minerals, most of the intergrowths appear to have formed by partial replacement of microcline by quartz along fractures or complex zones of weakness in the felspar. A reaction fabric diagram showing the orientation of quartz with respect to microcline in micrographic intergrowths in hornblende granophyres from Pepin

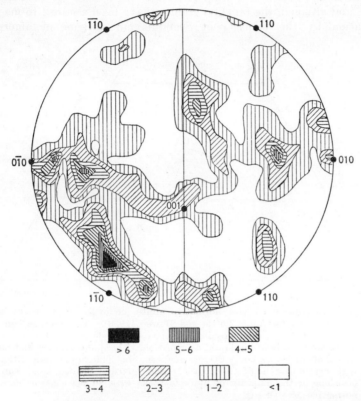

FIG. 38. Stereographic projection perpendicular to the prism zone of felspar showing the distribution of one hundred points of emergence of the *z* crystal axes of quartz in graphic granite intergrowths of quartz and felspar (after Wahlstrom, 1939).

Island, Nelson, New Zealand, has been presented by Lauder (1961). Although in these intergrowths there is no single direction in the microcline along which the quartz z axes are oriented, there is a significant concentration of the axes in the (001) plane of the felspar. Uspensky (1943) has described granite pegmatites which are considered to be derived from the hydrothermal recrystallization of aplite dykes.

Rapakivi texture. Phenocrysts or porphyroblastic potassium felspars mantled by plagioclase are the characteristic feature of the rapakivi granites. The potassium-rich felspar cores may be microcline perthite, microcline, or orthoclase, and the mantles are of albite or oligoclase composition. Unmantled alkali felspars may occur together with mantled alkali felspars in the same rock. In the Head Harbor Island granite (Terzaghi, 1940) the alkali content of the potassium felspar cores is K_2O 10·74, Na_2O 3·64 per cent., and of the plagioclase mantles K_2O 0·56, Na_2O 8·80 per cent. The problem of the rapakivi texture has been discussed by many workers and a summary of the earlier views concerning the origin of mantling of alkali felspar by plagioclase is given by Tuttle and Bowen (1958). A unique solution has not as yet been accepted generally, and although the rapakivi granites have been ascribed to magmatic differentiation by the majority of Scandinavian workers, metamorphism,

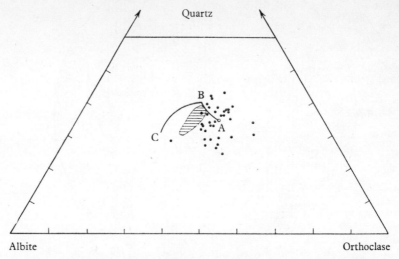

FIG. 39. The distribution of normative albite, orthoclase and quartz in rapakivi granites (after Tuttle and Bowen, 1958). The average composition of 37 rapakivi granites is shown by circle at A. Curve AB represents the change in liquid composition with equilibrium crystallization of alkali felspar, curve BC represents the change in liquid composition with crystallization of alkali felspar and quartz. Shaded area, compositions of the majority of plutonic rocks with 80 per cent. or more normative Ab + Or + Q.

metasomatism and assimilation also have been considered in various proposals put forward to explain the rapakivi texture. Thus Backlund (1938) concluded that the rapakivi granites of Fennoscandia were derived from the metasomatic transformation of a sandstone series by an influx of alkalies and aluminium. The mantling of potassium-rich felspar by sodium-rich plagioclase has been explained by Gates (1953) as the result of the local migration of sodium derived from the unmixing of perthite, and the rapakivi texture regarded as a variety of perthite formed under metasomatic conditions unfavourable to the penetration of plagioclase material. Migration of unmixed sodium plagioclase also has been used to explain the rapakivi relationship between the alkali and plagioclase felspars in the intermediate central zone rocks of the Enchanted Rock batholith, Texas (Hutchinson, 1956).

Sahama (1945) showed that compared with average granite the rapakivi

granites are richer in potassium. The mantling of potassium felspar by plagioclase has been discussed by Tuttle and Bowen (1958) with reference to the
normative content of albite–orthoclase–quartz in rapakivi granites, and the
phase relationships at 500 bars in the system $NaAlSi_3O_8$–$KAlSi_3O_8$–H_2O. In
Fig. 39 the average composition of 37 rapakivi granites is shown by the circle A.
From a liquid of this composition with 2 per cent. water, a potassium-rich felspar
crystallizes first at a temperature a little above 800°C. With equilibrium
crystallization the composition of the liquid changes along the curve AB, and
the alkali felspar becomes richer in sodium. At B, at a temperature some 30°C.
lower, approximately 15 per cent. felspar (about $Or_{72}Ab_{28}$) has crystallized.
Beyond B further crystallization occurs with the formation of quartz as well as
felspar, and the liquid composition changes towards C. At C the water content
is 10 per cent., the vapour pressure 4000 bars, the temperature 660°C., and some
78 per cent. of the original liquid has crystallized to alkali felspar and quartz.
At 660°C. the solvus of the $NaAlSi_3O_8$–$KAlSi_3O_8$ system is intersected, and
at this and lower temperatures quartz and two felspars crystallize together.
Initially the compositions of the two felspars differ only to a small degree but
with falling temperatures one becomes richer in potassium, the other richer in
sodium. The occurrence of mantled and unmantled potassium-rich felspar may
thus be explained by the later crystallization of either potassium-rich or sodium-
rich felspar, *i.e.* some alkali felspar phenocrysts are mantled by potassium
felspar, some by oligoclase.

Metasomatism. Terzaghi (1948) has described some potassium-rich acid
volcanic rocks in which potassium felspar, in amounts greater than the orthoclase equivalent of the potassium originally present in the glassy lava, has
developed during devitrification. The vitreous obsidian of the Esterel has an
approximately equal amount of potassium and sodium, but the devitrified
obsidian, and some of the rhyolites, are abnormally rich in potassium. The
potassium felspar in these devitrified rocks is considered to have formed in
part by crystallization from potassium-rich solutions, derived from the local
leaching of rhyolite, penetrating the obsidian along perlitic cracks. In some of
these alkali-rich glasses the devitrification may have occurred in two stages.
Thus in an alkali trachyte, containing phenocrysts $Or_{37}Ab_{54}An_9$ in composition,
the devitrification of the groundmass began with the crystallization of sodium-
rich plagioclase and was followed by potassium felspar, the latter forming
partly independently of the albite, but the greater proportion combining with
the albite to form a microperthite. A similar two-stage devitrification of a
liparite glass, in which lath-shaped crystals of plagioclase crystallized before
the development of potassium felspar spherulites, has been described by
Bondam (1955). Potassium enrichment during devitrification, however, is not
universal, and in many rocks the change is effected without significant alteration
in the alkali content or the ratio of potassium to sodium.

In some keratophyres the ratio of potassium-rich to sodium-rich felspar
varies widely, and in many of the earlier studies of these rocks the intergrowths
of sodium and potassium felspar were ascribed to exsolution from a homogeneous alkali felspar. Alkali metasomatism, however, may be the cause of the
variable phase mineralogy in some keratophyres; recrystallization and internal
migration, at relatively low temperatures, of alkalies and silica may modify the
original approximately equal ratio of K_2O to Na_2O, enriching some rocks in

potassium, others in sodium.   Contrasts in the alkali ratios of some keratophyres, in which extreme examples have K_2O 10·31, Na_2O 0·53, and K_2O 0·87, Na_2O 5·74 per cent. respectively, have been described by Battey (1955).   The contrasting alkali contents of these rocks are associated with highly irregular and variable proportions of sodium-rich and potassium-rich felspars, in some examples the sodium felspar being replaced completely by the potassium mineral.   The hypothesis that such potassium-rich keratophyres are formed through the metasomatic introduction of potassium is supported by the large proportion of potassium felspar in the groundmass, and its development also from the original glass.   The potassium felspar formed by the replacement of the plagioclase is a cryptoperthite, the optical properties of which are variable and dependent on the amount of unreplaced albite.   The potassium felspar replacing the original glass is stated to contain less sodium and to approach more closely in composition a pure potassium felspar.

Alkali felspar porphyroblasts.   The growth of potassium felspar in the country rocks around granites, and within xenoliths in granites, has been reported from many localities.   Potassium felspar porphyroblasts also frequently occur as augen in schists and gneisses especially in proximity to acid and intermediate plutonic rocks.   In many localities the formation process, usually described as felspathization, is considered to be one of metasomatic or solid diffusion (Perrin and Roubault, 1949).   Alkali felspar porphyroblasts are particularly characteristic of semipelitic and pelitic xenoliths, the composition of which makes it unlikely that the felspar crystallized as a result of a simple molecular reconstitution of the shale.   Their formation appears to be due to the local concentration of potassium and sodium derived either from migrating solutions or by solid diffusion.   A number of workers (*e.g.* Read, 1948; Perrin, 1956) have regarded such porphyroblasts as being identical with the potassium felspar in adjacent granites, and on this basis have proposed a metasomatic origin for the alkali felspar in the granite as well as in the surrounding gneisses and schists. The almost identical composition of orthoclase porphyroblasts from a semipelitic xenolith in Shap granite and of orthoclase phenocrysts in the granite has been demonstrated by Spencer (1938).   Large porphyroblasts of alkali felspar occur in the Kloof granite, Cape Town, and also in the shale xenoliths in the granite, the pegmatites and the adjacent migmatite zone.   Walker and Mathias (1946) suggested that the felspar in each of these different environments crystallized during a period of late potassium metasomatism.   Shand (1949) also examined the large alkali felspars in this granite and described the alkali felspar, which is surrounded by a rim of plagioclase, as a microcline microperthite.   The potassium-rich core contains a few idiomorphic crystals of plagioclase, and the sodium-rich margin has many grains of quartz and biotite.   The matrix of the granite consists of microcline, plagioclase, quartz and biotite, and the potassium felspar of the matrix is not rimmed by plagioclase.   Shand concluded that both the potassium-rich core and the mantle of plagioclase crystallized in a magma, the composition of which was modified by assimilation during the crystallization of the felspars.

Engel and Engel (1960) have shown that there are differences in both major and trace element contents, as well as in formation temperatures (determined by the distribution ratio of sodium in co-existing potassium and plagioclase felspars), of the alkali felspars in granite and surrounding gneisses of the northwest

Adirondack Mountains, New York.   In these gneisses the microcline developed during granitization occurs as fine- to medium-grained replacements of plagioclase and biotite, as well as in large porphyroblasts.   From the presence of both strained and unstrained crystals Engel and Engel suggest that the microcline porphyroblasts grew both during and somewhat later than the deformation.

The variations in the alkali felspar plagioclase ratios of a granodiorite engulfed in a younger coarsely porphyritic granite have been interpreted by Schermerhorn (1956) as the result of a potassium metasomatism which led to the microclinization of the plagioclase felspar.   The content of microcline perthite in the granodiorite increases from some 12·5 per cent. in the centre of the mass to approximately 30 per cent. in the peripheral areas, the increased content of alkali felspar being associated with a decrease from 44 to 20 per cent. in the amount of plagioclase.   The average composition of the plagioclase in the granodiorite is An_{11}, it is rimmed by a narrow zone, An_{2-5} in composition, and the width of the sodium-rich rim increases with increasing microclinization. In the younger granite the felspar phenocrysts are microcline perthite which crystallized in a fluid environment.   Schermerhorn based this conclusion on the presence of inclusions in the felspar oriented along structural directions into well-marked zonal and hour-glass patterns.   The microclinization of the granodiorite is considered to have taken place also in a partly fluid environment, the microclinized granodiorite being regarded as a regional reaction rim between the younger porphyritic granite and the older granodiorite.

Acid and intermediate hybrid rocks.   In many acid and intermediate rocks of calc-alkaline affinities the margins between the potassium felspar and plagioclase are irregular.   Veinlets of the potassium felspar penetrate the plagioclase, and small inclusions of the plagioclase occur in the potassium felspar.   Similar textural relationships are observed also between the felspars of many rocks of hybrid origin.   In such rocks the hybridization is accompanied by the gradual replacement of the plagioclase by potassium felspar, a replacement that may be arrested, either by the development of myrmekite in contact with the potassium felspar, or by the formation of a narrow rim of albite (Deer, 1935).   In some granites the plagioclase enclosed in potassium felspar shows reversed zoning, *e.g.* An_{21} core, An_{29} rim, and Osterwald (1955) has suggested that this concentration of calcium at the margins of the plagioclase may be related to the difficulty with which calcium ions can be accommodated in the potassium felspar structure.

Metamorphic rocks.   Potassium felspar is a stable product of both high grade thermal and regional metamorphism.   It occurs in a variety of thermally metamorphosed sediments, including shales, impure sandstones, and impure limestones and dolomites.   It is a typical mineral of the sillimanite zone of regional metamorphism, and in argillaceous rocks does not occur in rocks of lower metamorphic grade.   The formation of potassium felspar in high grade metamorphic rocks is due, in the main, to the instability of the micas in this temperature–pressure environment, and the following reactions may operate:

(1) $K(Mg,Fe)_3AlSi_3O_{10}(OH)_2 + 3SiO_2 \rightarrow KAlSi_3O_8 + 3(Mg,Fe)SiO_3 + H_2O$
    biotite   orthoclase   orthopyroxene

(2) $2K(Mg,Fe)_{1·5}Al_2Si_3O_{10}(OH)_2 + 3SiO_2 \rightarrow 2KAlSi_3O_8 + (Mg,Fe)_3Al_2Si_3O_{12}$
    siderophyllite   orthoclase   pyrope-almandine
$$+ 2H_2O$$

(3) $$KAl_3Si_3O_{10}(OH)_2 + SiO_2 \rightarrow KAlSi_3O_8 + Al_2SiO_5 + H_2O$$
muscovite orthoclase sillimanite

(4) $$KAl_3Si_3O_{10}(OH)_2 + CaCO_3 + 2SiO_2 \rightarrow KAlSi_3O_8 + CaAl_2Si_2O_8 + H_2O + CO_2$$
muscovite orthoclase anorthite

The alkali felspar of the granulite facies is often dark greenish to brown, or greenish black in hand specimen with a distinctive fine microperthitic structure, and hair-perthite, *e.g.* of the Lapland granulites, is one of the most specific characteristics of these rocks (Eskola, 1952). The potassium felspars of the rocks of the charnockite series are dominantly microcline perthites and microcline microperthites (Table 5, anal. 10) and the perthite blebs in their felspars are often fairly coarse (Howie, 1955). In the metamorphic terrain of the Ørsdalen district, Norway (Heier, 1957), the metamorphic grade varies from the granulite-high amphibolite facies to the greenschist facies. In the rocks of high metamorphic grade the potassium felspar is a perthite with optical and X-ray monoclinic symmetry (there are indications of small deviations from monoclinic symmetry). In the rocks of the low amphibolite to greenschist facies the potassium felspar is always a microcline. This correlation between the phase relations of the potassium felspar, and the facies of the rocks in which it occurs, can be applied strictly only where the metamorphism is isochemical. Where late potassium metasomatism has occurred the symmetry state of the potassium felspar may not be related to the grade of regional metamorphism.

With few exceptions the potassium felspar of the Pre-Cambrian granites is a microcline; thus the Pre-Cambrian granites of Finland, of late kinematic origin, are microcline granites, whereas the postkinematic granites of alpine regions are mainly orthoclase granites. These granites cannot be distinguished by their chemical composition, and the formation of the microcline in microcline granites has been correlated with their formation in a paratectonic environment (Marmo, 1958a). This contrast in the tectonic environment of orthoclase and microcline granites has led Marmo (1958b, 1961) to put forward the view that the microcline of many Pre-Cambrian microcline granites formed initially as the triclinic phase and did not arise from an originally disordered potassium felspar; this hypothesis has been criticized by Schermerhorn (1961). Orthoclase is the characteristic potassium felspar in the catazone rocks of the regionally metamorphosed gneisses of the eastern French Pyrenees, but both microcline and orthoclase occur in the gneisses of the mesozone. In the granitized areas the granites of the catazone contain orthoclase and intermediate microcline, those of the mesozone have maximum microcline, and those of the epizone contain microcline and orthoclase. Guitard *et al.* (1960) considered that the potassium felspar always crystallized initially as the monoclinic phase, a phase stable in the catazone, but which is unstable and tends to change to the triclinic phase in both the meso- and epizones. A contrasted felspar mineralogy between the anatexes and diapire granites of southern Norway has been demonstrated by Barth (1956). In the former the microcline perthite varies in composition between $Or_{85.8}$ and Or_{90} and is associated with plagioclase Ab_{76} to Ab_{70}; in the diapire granites the potassium felspar is a microcline perthite containing 27 per cent. perthite lamellae and is $Or_{71}Ab_{22}An_7$ in composition. A study by Rao (1960b) of the potassium felspars in the Pre-Cambrian gneisses of the Gjelleråsen area, Oslo, Norway, has shown that the microcline becomes increasingly disordered as the contact with a nordmarkite of Permian age is approached; close to the contact the potassium felspar was converted to a sanidine-like form. During the declining stages of metamorphism the felspars underwent varying degrees of "reversion", and now exhibit intermediate and gradational order–disorder patterns.

Sedimentary rocks. Potassium felspars crystallize during the formation of sedimentary rocks at the temperatures prevailing at the earth's surface, and at moderate depths within the crust. They are common in sandstones, siltstones, shales and calcareous sediments. Crystallization occurs either contemporaneously with sedimentation, or by later replacement. The authigenic potassium felspars almost invariably have a small, well rounded, and often altered, detrital core. The authigenic felspar can be distinguished from the detrital nucleus by its water-clear appearance and idiomorphic form. The latter features may be observed particularly where the mineral has crystallized in the original voids and cavities of the sediment (Gilbert, 1949). In many siltstones and shales the potassium felspar is restricted to the finer-grained fractions of these rocks, a fact that cannot be explained satisfactorily except on the basis of its formation *in situ.*

Heald (1950a) reports that whereas on detrital orthoclase authigenic orthoclase always crystallizes, both orthoclase and microcline may occur as authigenic growths on detrital microcline. An optical and X-ray study of authigenic potassium felspar (Baskin, 1956) has shown that the authigenic monoclinic potassium felspars crystallize as tiny rhombohedron-like crystals commonly referred to as the adularia habit. Authigenic microcline crystals have triclinic morphology. Their fourling twinning relationship is unique and contrasts with the tartan twinning of those potassium felspars which have undergone transformation from monoclinic to triclinic symmetry. The distinctive morphology of authigenic microcline is a consequence of the primary crystallization of the triclinic modification. Authigenic potassium felspars are never perthitic even when crystallization has occurred around detrital perthite. The chemical composition of the authigenic potassium felspars is in keeping with crystallization at low temperatures, and their Na_2O content rarely exceeds 0·3 per cent. (Baskin, 1956). In some rocks there is evidence that the authigenic alkali felspar is of replacement origin, its growth having taken place during the dolomitization or recrystallization of calcareous sediments. Such a replacement origin is indicated by the development of idiomorphic authigenic felspar replacing fossils and ooliths (Straaten, 1948).

Potassium felspar is a common constituent of arkosic sediments. In a sample of 277 sandstones Tallman (1949) reported 10 per cent. arkoses (felspar content greater than 28 per cent. of the detrital constituents) and 7 per cent. felspathic sandstones (felspar content 10–28 per cent. of the detrital constituents). Sanidine ($Or_{75·2}Ab_{24·8}$) has been identified in Ordovician bentonite at Kinneküile, Sweden (Byström, 1954); it also occurs in fuller's earth, in Somerset (Table 6, anal. 1).

REFERENCES

Adamson, O. J., 1942. Minerals of the Varuträsk pegmatite, XXXI. The feldspar group. *Geol. För. Förh.*, Stockholm, vol. 64, p. 19.

Ahrens, L. H., 1945. Geochemical studies on some of the rarer elements in South African minerals and rocks. No. 2. The geochemical relationship between thallium and rubidium in minerals of igneous origin. *Trans. Geol. Soc. S. Africa*, vol. 48, p. 207.

Aldrich, L. T. and **Nier, A. O.**, 1948. Argon[40] in potassium minerals. *Phys. Rev.*, vol. 74, p. 876.

Alling, H. L., 1938. Plutonic perthites. *Journ. Geol.*, vol. 46, p. 142.

Anderson, O., 1928. The genesis of some types of feldspar from granite pegmatites. *Norsk. Geol. Tids.*, vol. 10, p. 116.

Aoyama, N., 1941. *Journ. Geol. Soc., Japan*, vol. 48, p. 280.

Azzini, F., 1933. Adularia e albite di Val Devero (Ossola). *Atti. Accad. Sci. Veneto-Trentino-Istriana*, vol. 23, p. 45 (M.A. 5–366).

Backlund, H. G., 1938. The problem of the rapakivis. *Journ. Geol.*, vol. 46, p. 339.

Bailey, S. W., **Ferguson, R. B.** and **Taylor, W. H.**, 1951. X-ray determination of centrosymmetry in three felspars. *Min. Mag.*, vol. 29, p. 759.

—— and **Taylor, W. H.**, 1955. The structure of a triclinic potassium felspar. *Acta Cryst.*, vol. 8, p. 621.

Bambauer, H. U. and **Laves, F.**, 1960. Zum Adularproblem. I. Adular vom Val Casatscha: Mimetischer Lamellenbau, Variation von Optik und Gitterkonstanten und ihre genetische Deutung. *Schweiz. Min. Petr. Mitt.*, vol. 40, p. 177.

Barrer, R. M. and **Baynham, J. W.**, 1956. The hydrothermal chemistry of the silicates. Part VII. Synthetic potassium aluminosilicates. *Journ. Chem. Soc.*, p. 2882.

—— and **Hinds, L.**, 1950. Hydrothermal synthesis of potash feldspar in the range 195–200°C. *Nature*, vol. 166, p. 562.

—— **Hinds, L.** and **White, E. A.**, 1953. The hydrothermal chemistry of silicates. Part III. Reactions of analcite and leucite. *Journ. Chem. Soc.*, p. 1466.

—— and **McCallum, N.**, 1953. Hydrothermal chemistry of silicates. Part IV. Rubidium and caesium. *Journ. Chem. Soc.*, p. 4029.

Barth, T. F. W., 1934. Polymorphic phenomena and crystal structure. *Amer. Journ. Sci.*, vol. 27, p. 273.

—— 1951. The feldspar geologic thermometers. *Neues Jahrb. Min., Abhandl.*, vol. 82, p. 143.

—— 1956a. Studies in gneiss and granite. *Skrift. Norske Vidensk.-Akad., Oslo*, 1. Mat.-Nat. Kl., no. 1.

—— 1956b. Zonal structure in feldspars of crystalline schists. *3rd Réunion International de la Réactivité à l'état solide, Madrid*, sect. 3, p. 363.

Baskin, Y., 1956. A study of authigenic feldspars. *Journ. Geol.*, vol. 64, p. 132.

Battey, M. H., 1955. Alkali metasomatism and the petrology of some keratophyres. *Geol. Mag.*, vol. 92, p. 104.

Belyankina, E. D., 1953. Chemico-mineralogical study of potash–soda felspars of Caucasus and Transcaucasia. *Trans. Inst. Geol. Sci. Acad. Sci. USSR*, no. 147, Petrogr. ser., p. 185 (M.A. 12–417).

Bøggild, O. B., 1924. On the labradorization of the feldspars. *K. Danske Vidensk. Selskab. Math. fys. Meddel.*, vol. 6, no. 3 (M.A. 2–492).

Bondam, J., 1955. Petrography of a group of alkali-trachyte dyke rocks from the Julianehaab District, South Greenland. A contribution to the alkali feldspar problem. *Meddel. om Grønland*, Bd. 135, no. 2.

Bowen, N. L., 1913. The melting phenomena of the plagioclase feldspars. *Amer. Journ. Sci.*, 4th. ser., vol. 35, p. 577.

—— and **Tuttle, O. F.**, 1950. The system $NaAlSi_3O_8$–$KAlSi_3O_8$–H_2O. *Journ. Geol.*, vol. 58, p. 489.

Bradley, J. E. S. and **Bradley, O.**, 1956. A first attempt at a determination of felspars by activation analysis. *Min. Mag.*, vol. 31, p. 164.

Brautigam, F., 1922. Die Dispersion der Achsen des Orthoklases. *Min. Petr. Mitt. (Tschermak)*, vol. 35, p. 231.

Brousse, R., 1961. Minéralogie et Pétrographie des roches volcaniques du massif du Mont-Dore (Auvergne). I. Les minéraux. II. Pétrographie systematique. *Bull. Soc. franç. Min. Crist.*, vol. 84, p. 183.

Brown, P. E., 1956. The Mourne Mountains granites—a further study. *Geol. Mag.*, vol. 93, p. 72.

Brown, W. L., 1960. Lattice changes in heat-treated plagioclases. The existence of monalbite at room temperature. *Zeit. Krist.*, vol. 113, p. 297.

Brun, E., St. Hafner, P., Hartmann, F., Laves, F. and **Staub, H. H.**, 1960. Magnetische Kernresonanz zur Beobachtung des Al/Si–Ordnung/Unordnungsgrades in einigen Feldspäten. *Zeit. Krist.*, vol. 113, p. 65.

Bugge, J. A. W., 1943. Geological and petrological investigations in the Kongsberg-Bamble formation. *Norges. Geol. Undersök.*, no. 160.

Byelyankin, D. S. and **Tomkeieff, S. I.**, 1915. Sur la composition minéralogique de la syénite de Plauen (Plauenscher Grund) près Dresden. *Ann. Inst. Polytech. Pierre le Grand, Petrograd.* vol. 23 (M.A. 3–80).

Byelyankin, D., 1915. On the specific gravity and refraction of the potash–soda-felspars. *Izvyestiya Petrograd. Polytech. Inst.*, vol. 24, p. 437 (M.A. 1–89).

—— 1925. Seconde édition de la diagramme de réfraction des feldspats potasso-sodiques. *Mém. Soc. Russe Min.*, ser. 2, vol. 52.

Byström, A. M., 1954. A sanidine from Ordovician bentonite beds. *Acta Cryst.* vol. 7, p. 772.

Carmichael, I. S. E., 1960. The feldspar phenocrysts of some Tertiary acid glasses. *Min. Mag.*, vol. 32, p. 587.

Carr, D. R. and **Kulp, J. L.**, 1957. Potassium–argon method of geochronometry. *Bull. Geol. Soc. Amer.*, vol. 68, p. 763.

Chaisson, V., 1950. The optics of triclinic adularia. *Journ. Geol.*, vol. 58, p. 537.

Chao, S. H., Smare, D. L. and **Taylor, W. H.**, 1939. An X-ray examination of some potash–soda felspars. *Min. Mag.*, vol. 25, p. 338.

—— and **Taylor, W. H.**, 1940. The lamellar structure of potash–soda felspars. *Proc. Roy. Soc.*, ser. A., vol. 174, p. 57.

Chayes, F., 1952. Notes on the staining of potash feldspar with sodium cobalt-initrite in thin section. *Amer. Min.*, vol. 37, p. 337.

—— 1955. Potash feldspar as a by-product of the biotite–chlorite transformation. *Journ. Geol.*, vol. 53, p. 75.

Chudoba, K., 1933. *The determination of the feldspars in thin section* (Translated by W. Q. Kennedy). London (Murby).

Cole, W. F., Sörum, H. and **Kennard, O.**, 1949. The crystal structures of orthoclase and sanidinised orthoclase. *Acta Cryst.*, vol. 2, p. 280.

Coombs, D. S., 1954. Ferriferous orthoclases from Madagascar. *Min. Mag.*, vol. 30, p. 409.

Correns, C. W. and **Engelhardt, W. von**, 1938. Neue Untersuchungen über die Verwitterung des Kalifeldspates. *Naturwiss*, vol. 26, p. 137; *Chemie der Erde*, vol. 12, p. 1.

Daubrée, A., 1879. *Études synthétiques de géologie expérimentale.*

Day, A. L. and **Allen, E. T.**, 1905. *The isomorphism and thermal properties of the feldspars.* Carnegie Inst. of Washington, Publ. no. 31.

Deer, W. A., 1935. The Cairnsmore of Carsphairn igneous complex. *Quart. Journ. Geol. Soc.*, vol. 91, p. 47.

DeVore, G., 1956. Surface chemistry as a chemical control on mineral association. *Journ. Geol.*, vol. 64, p. 31.

Dolar-Mantuani, L., 1952. The feldspar in the intrusive rocks near Beaverdell, B.C. *Amer. Min.,* vol. 37, p. 492.

Donnay, G. and **Donnay, J. D. H.,** 1952. The symmetry change in the high-temperature alkali-feldspar series. *Amer. Journ. Sci.,* Bowen volume, p. 115.

Drescher-Kaden, F. K., 1939. Beiträge zur Kenntniss der Migmatit- und Assimilationbildungen sowie der synantetischen Reaktionsformen. *Chemie der Erde,* vol. 12.

Emeleus, C. H. and **Smith, J. V.,** 1959. The alkali feldspars. VI. Sanidine and orthoclase perthites from the Slieve Gullion area, Northern Ireland. *Amer. Min.,* vol. 44, p. 1187.

Emmons, R. C., 1953. Petrogeny of the syenites and nepheline syenites of Central Wisconsin. *Mem. Geol. Soc. Amer.,* no. 52, p. 71.

Engel, A. E. J. and **Engel, C. G.,** 1960. Progressive metamorphism and granitization of the major paragneiss, northwest Adirondack Mountains, New York. *Bull. Geol. Soc. Amer.,* vol. 71, p. 1.

Erämetsä, O., Sahama, Th.G. and **Kanula, V.,** 1943. Spektrographische Bestimmungen an Rubidium und Caesium in einigen finnischen Mineralen und Gesteinen. *Compt. Rend. Soc. géol. Finlande,* no. 15, p. 80.

Eskola, P., 1952. On the granulites of Lapland. *Amer. Journ. Sci.,* Bowen vol., p. 133.

—— 1956. Postmagmatic potash metasomatism of granite. *Bull. Comm. géol. Finlande,* vol. 172, p. 85.

Euler, R. and **Hellner, E.,** 1961. Hydrothermale und röntgenographische Untersuchungen an gesteinsbildenden Mineralen, VI. Über hydrothermal hergestellten triklinen K-Feldspat. *Zeit. Krist.,* vol. 115, p. 433.

Exner, C., 1949. Tektonik, Feldspatausbildungen und deren gegenseitige Beziehungen in den östlichen Hohen Tauein. Beiträge zur Kenntnis der Zentralgneis fazies. I. Teil. *Min. Petr. Mitt. (Tschermak),* ser. 3, vol. 1, p. 197.

Faust, G. T., 1936. The fusion relations of iron-orthoclase. With a discussion of the evidence for the existence of an iron-orthoclase molecule in feldspars. *Amer. Min.,* vol. 21, p. 735.

Ferguson, R. B., Traill, R. J. and **Taylor, W. H.,** 1958. The crystal structure of low-temperature and high-temperature albites. *Acta Cryst.,* vol. 11, p. 331.

Fersman, A. E., 1923. The Khibinsky massif. (Outline of the scientific results of the expeditions to the Khibinsky and Lovozersky tundras in the years 1920–22.) *Trans. N. Sci. and Econ. Expedition,* no. 16 (M.A. 2–263).

Folk, R. L., 1947. The alteration of feldspar and its products as studied in the laboratory. *Amer. Journ. Sci.,* vol. 245, p. 388.

—— 1955. Note on the significance of "turbid" feldspars. *Amer. Min.,* vol. 40, p. 356.

Förstner, H., 1884. Ueber künstliche physikalische Veranderungen der Feldspäthe von Pantelleria. *Zeit. Krist. Min.,* vol. 9, p. 333.

Franco, R. R. and **Schairer, J. F.,** 1951. Liquidus temperatures in mixtures of the feldspars of soda, potash and lime. *Journ. Geol.,* vol. 59, p. 259.

Franke, —— —— 1920. Über die Zwilling der Plagioklas noch dem l'Esterelschen Gesetze. *Centralblatt. Min.,* p. 254.

Gabriel, A. and **Cox, E. P.,** 1929. A staining method for the quantitative determination of certain rock minerals. *Amer. Min.,* vol. 14, p. 290.

Gard, J. A., Barrer, R. M. and **Baynham, J.,** 1955. The hydrothermal chemistry of silicates. Part VI. A lamellar habit in synthetic felspar. *Journ. Chem. Soc.,* p. 2480.

Gates, R. M., 1953. Petrogenic significance of perthite. *Mem. Geol. Soc. Amer.,* no. 52, p. 55.

Gerasimov, A. P., 1936. Sur les feldspaths de la montagne Bechtaou (Caucase du Nord). *Vernadsky jubilee vol., Acad. Sci. USSR,* vol. 2, p. 795 (M.A. 7–179).

Gerling, E. K. and **Pavlova, T. G.,** 1951. Determination of the geological age of two stony meteorites by the argon method. *Doklady Acad. Sci. USSR,* vol. 77, p. 85 (M.A. 12–527).

Gilbert, C. M., 1949. Cementation of some California Tertiary reservoir sands. *Journ. Geol.,* vol. 57, p. 1.

Goldsmith, J. R., 1950. Gallium and germanium substitutions in synthetic feldspars. *Journ. Geol.,* vol. 58, p. 518.

—— and **Laves, F.,** 1954. The microcline–sanidine stability relations. *Geochim. et Cosmochim. Acta.* vol. 5, p. 1.

Goranson, R. W., 1938. Silicate–water systems. Phase equilibria in the NaAlSi₃O₈–H₂O and KAlSi₃O₈–H₂O systems at high temperatures and pressures. *Amer. Journ. Sci.,* 5th. ser., vol. 35, p. 71.

Greig, J. W. and **Barth, T. F. W.,** 1938. The system, Na₂O.Al₂O₃.2SiO₂ (nephelite, carnegieite)–Na₂O.Al₂O₃.6SiO₂ (albite). *Amer. Journ. Sci.,* 5th. ser., vol. 35, p. 93.

Gruner, J. W., 1944. The hydrothermal alteration of feldspars in acid solutions between 300° and 400°C. *Econ. Geol.,* vol. 39, p. 578.

Guitard, G., Raguin, E. and **Sabatier, G.,** 1960. La symétrie des feldspaths potassiques dans les gneiss et les granites des Pyrénées orientales. *Bull. Soc. franç. Min. Crist.,* vol. 83, p. 48.

Guppy, E. M., 1931. Chemical analyses of igneous rocks, metamorphic rocks and minerals. *Mem. Geol. Surv. Gt. Britain.*

Hafner, St. and **Laves, F.,** 1957. Ordnung/Unordnung und Ultrarotabsorption. II. Variation der Lage und Intensität einiger Absorptionen von Feldspäten. Zur Struktur von Orthoklas und Adular. *Zeit. Krist.,* vol. 109, p. 204.

Häkli, A., 1960. On high temperature alkali felspars of some volcanic rocks of Kenya and northern Tanganyika. *Bull. Comm. géol. Finlande,* No. 188, p. 99.

Hamilton, W. B. and **Neuerburg, G. J.,** 1956. Olivine-sanidine trachybasalt from the Sierra Nevada, California. *Amer. Min.,* vol. 41, p. 851.

Harada, Z., 1948. Chemical analyses of Japanese minerals (II). *Journ. Fac. Sci. Hokkaido Univ.,* ser. IV (Geol. and Miner.), vol. 7, p. 143.

—— 1954. Chemical analyses of Japanese minerals (III). *Ibid.,* vol. 8, p. 289.

Heald, M. T., 1950a. Authigenesis in West Virginia sandstones. *Journ. Geol.,* vol. 58, p. 624.

—— 1950b. Structure and petrology of the Lovewell Mountain quadrangle, New Hampshire. *Bull. Geol. Soc. Amer.,* vol. 61, p. 43.

Heier, K., 1955. The formation of felspar perthites in highly metamorphic gneisses. *Norsk. Geol. Tidsskr.,* vol. 35, p. 87.

—— 1956. The geology of the Ørsdalen district, Rogaland S. Norway. *Norsk. Geol. Tidsskr.,* vol. 36, p. 167.

—— 1957. Phase relations of potash feldspar in metamorphism. *Journ. Geol.,* vol. 65, p. 468.

Hewlett, C. G., 1959. Optical properties of potassic feldspars. *Bull. Geol. Soc. Amer.,* vol. 70, p. 511.

Higazy, R. A., 1949. Petrogenesis of perthite pegmatites in the Black Hills, South Dakota. *Journ. Geol.,* vol. 57, p. 555.

Holmes, A., Shillibeer, H. A. and **Wilson, J. T.,** 1955. Potassium–argon ages of some Lewisian and Fennoscandian pegmatites. *Nature,* vol. 176, p. 390.

Howie, R. A., 1955. The geochemistry of the charnockite series of Madras, India. *Trans. Roy. Soc. Edin.,* vol. 62, p. 725.

Hsu, K. J., 1954. A study of the optic properties and petrologic significance of zoned sanidines. *Amer. Journ. Sci.,* vol. 252, p. 441.

Huang, C. K., 1953. Adularia from Kukutzu, Taiwan. *Acta Geologica Taiwanica*, no. 5, p. 27 (M.A. 12–532).

Hutchinson, R. M., 1956. Structure and petrology of Enchanted Rock batholith, Llano and Gillespie Counties, Texas. *Bull. Geol. Soc. Amer.*, vol. 67, p. 763.

Ito, T. and Sadanaga, R., 1952. The lamellar structure of certain microcline and anorthoclase. *Acta Cryst.*, vol. 5, p. 441.

Jahns, R. A., 1955. The study of pegmatites. *Econ. Geol.*, 50th anniv. vol., p. 1025.

Jones, J. B. and Taylor, W. H., 1961. The structure of orthoclase. *Acta Cryst.*, vol. 14, p. 443.

Joyce, J. R. F. and Game, P. M., 1952. Note on anorthoclase from Nigeria. *Bull. Brit. Mus. (Nat. Hist.), Min.*, vol. 1, p. 85.

Kazakashvili, G. G. and Topuria, P. A., 1939. On some syenite rocks of the Supsa river (west Georgia). *Doklady Acad. Sci. USSR*, vol. 23, p. 553.

Kazakov, A. N., 1956. On the occurrence of positive microclines. *Mém. Soc. Russe Min.*, vol. 85, p. 433 (M.A. 13–663).

Keith, M. L., 1939. Selective staining to facilitate Rosiwal analysis. *Amer. Min.*, vol. 24, p. 561.

Kimizuka, K., 1932. A study of potash-anorthoclase from Taiji, Kii province, Japan. *Japanese Journ. Geol. Geogr.*, vol. 9, p. 213.

Köhler, A., 1948a. Zur Optik des Adulars. *Neues Jahrb.*, sect. A, no. 5–8, p. 49.

—— 1948b. Erscheinungen an Feldspaten in ihrer Bedeutung für die Klärung der Gesteinsgenesis (Ein Versuch und eine Anregung). *Min. Petr. Mitt. (Tschermak)* ser. 3, vol. 1, p. 51.

—— and **Wieden, P.**, 1954. Vorläufige Versuche in der Feldspatgruppe mittels der DTA. *Neues Jahrb. Min., Monat.*, p. 249.

Kôzu, S., 1916a. The dispersion phenomena and the influence of temperature on the optic axial angle of sanidine from the Eifel. *Min. Mag.*, vol. 17, p. 237.

—— 1916b. The dispersion phenomena of some natural monoclinic felpars. *Min. Mag.*, vol. 17, p. 253.

—— and **Endô, Y.**, 1921. X-ray analysis of adularia and moonstone, and the influence of temperature on the atomic arrangement of these minerals. *Sci. Rep. Tôhoku Imp. Univ.*, ser. 3, vol. 1, no. 1.

—— and **Seto, K.**, 1921. Sanidine from the Eifel. *Sci. Rep. Tôhoku Imp. Univ.*, ser. 3, vol. 1, p. 25.

—— and **Suzuki, M.**, 1923. Further studies on the influence of temperature on the optic axial angle of sanidine. *Sci. Rep. Tohoku Imp. Univ.*, ser. 3, vol. 1, p. 233.

Kracek, F. C. and Neuvonen, K. J., 1952. Thermochemistry of the plagioclase and alkali feldspars. *Amer. Journ. Sci.*, Bowen vol., p. 293.

Kuellmer, F. J., 1959. X-ray intensity measurements on perthitic materials. I. Theoretical considerations. *Journ. Geol.*, vol. 67, p. 648.

—— 1960. X-ray intensity measurements on perthitic materials. II. Data from natural alkali feldspars. *Journ. Geol.*, vol. 68, p. 307.

—— 1961. Alkali feldspars from some intrusive porphyries of southwestern United States. *Instituto Lucas Mallada C.S.I.C. Cursillos y Conferencias*. Madrid, Fasc. VIII, p. 111.

Kupletsky, B. M., 1949. On the formation of certain porphyritic granities of Middle Urals. *D. S. Belyankin jubilee vol.*, Acad. Sci. USSR, p. 211.

Lacroix, A., 1913. *Minéralogie de la France.* Vol. 5, p. 28.

—— 1922. *Minéralogie de Madagascar.* Vol. 1, Paris.

Larsen, E. S. and Larsen, E. S. 3rd., 1938. Petrologic results of a study of the minerals from the tertiary volcanic rocks of the San Juan Region, Colorado. No. 8, Orthoclase. *Amer. Min.*, vol. 23, p. 417.

Lauder, W. R., 1961. Reaction of crystal structures and reaction fabric. *Amer. Min.*, vol. 46, p. 1317.

Laves, F., 1950. The lattice and twinning of microcline and other potash feldspars. *Journ. Geol.*, vol. 58, p. 548.

—— 1951. Artificial preparation of microcline. *Journ. Geol.*, vol. 59, p. 511.

—— 1952. Phase relations of the alkali felspars. *Journ. Geol.*, vol. 60, p. 436.

—— 1960. Al/Si–Verteilungen, Phasen-Transformationen und Namen der Alkali-feldspäte. *Zeit. Krist.*, vol. 113, p. 265.

Lewis, W. J., 1899. *A treatise on crystallography.* Cambridge, p. 550.

MacKenzie, W. S., 1952. The effect of temperature on the symmetry of high-temperature soda-rich feldspars. *Amer. Journ. Sci.*, Bowen vol., p. 319.

—— 1954. The orthoclase–microcline inversion. *Min. Mag.*, vol. 30, p. 354.

—— 1956. The orientation of the pericline twin lamellae in triclinic alkali felspars. *Min. Mag.*, vol. 31, p. 41.

—— 1957. The crystalline modifications of $NaAlSi_3O_8$. *Amer. Journ. Sci.*, vol. 255, p. 481.

—— and Smith, J. V., 1955a. The alkali feldspars: I. Orthoclase microperthites. *Amer. Min.*, vol. 40, p. 707.

—— —— 1955b. The alkali feldspar solvus (Annual Rep. Director Geophys. Lab.). *Carnegie Inst. Washington, Yr. Book*, no. 54, p. 122.

—— —— 1956. The alkali feldspars. III. An optical and X-ray study of high temperature feldspars. *Amer. Min.*, vol. 41, p. 405.

Makhlaev, V. G., 1946. A contribution to the problem as to chemical composition of potash–soda feldspars in the alkaline rocks of the Khibiny Tundras. *Doklady Acad. Sci. USSR*, vol. 53, p. 455.

Marmo, V. 1958a. Orthoclase and microcline granites. *Amer. Journ. Sci.*, vol. 256, p. 360.

—— 1958b. The problem of late-kinematic granites. *Schweiz. Min. Petr. Mitt.*, vol. 38, p. 19.

—— 1961. On the paper "Orthoclase, microcline and albite in granites" by L. J. G. Schermerhorn. *Schweiz. Min. Petr. Mitt.*, vol. 41, p. 37.

—— and Permingeat, F., 1957. A propos des feldspaths potassiques du granite d'Azegour (Maroc). *Bull. Soc. franç. Min. Crist.*, vol. 80, p. 509.

Matossi, F. and Bronder, O., 1938. Das ultrarote Adsorptionsspektrum einiger Silikate. *Zeit. Physik.*, vol. 111, p. 1.

Megaw, H. D., 1956. Notation for felspar structures. *Acta Cryst.*, vol. 9, p. 56.

Miyakawa, K., 1958. Graphic intergrowth of quartz and orthoclase found in a veined phyllite near a hornblende–quartz diorite mass, Wakasa-machi area. *Journ. Earth Sci. Nagoya Univ.*, vol. 6, p. 143.

Montalto, M., 1937. Anorthoclasio di Ustica. *Atti Accad. Gioenia Sci. Nat. Catania*, ser. 6, vol. 2, no. 8 (M.A. 7–294).

Morey, G. W. and Bowen, N. L., 1922. The melting of potash feldspar. *Amer. Journ. Sci.*, ser. 5, vol. 4, p. 1.

—— and Chen, W. T., 1955. The action of hot water on some feldspars. *Amer. Min.*, vol. 40, p. 997.

—— and Fournier, R. O., 1961. Decomposition of mirocline, albite and nepheline in hot water. *Amer. Min.*, vol. 46, p. 688.

Mountain, E. D., 1925. Potash-oligoclase from Mt. Erebus, Antarctic, and anorthoclase from Mt. Kenya, East Africa. *Min. Mag.*, vol. 20, p. 331.

Muir, I. D. and Smith, J. V., 1956. Crystallization of feldspars in larvikite. *Zeit. Krist.*, vol. 107, p. 182.

Mulert, O., 1913. Über die Thermochemie die Kieselsäure und der Silikate. *Zeit. anorg. Chemie*, vol. 75, p. 198.

Newton, E. F., 1937. The petrography of some English fuller's earths and the rocks associated with them. *Proc. Geol. Assoc.* vol. 48, p. 175.

Nicolas, A., 1961. Combinasions des macles Manebach-Baveno dans l'orthose du granite de Raon-l'Etape (Vosges). *Bull. Soc. franç. Min. Crist.*, vol. 84, p. 287.

Norton, F. H., 1937. Accelerated weathering of feldspars. *Amer. Min.*, vol. 22, p. 1.

—— 1939. Hydrothermal formation of clay minerals in the laboratory. *Amer. Min.*, vol. 24, p. 1.

—— 1941. Hydrothermal alteration of clay minerals in the laboratory, Part II. *Amer. Min.*, vol. 26, p. 1.

Oftedahl, C., 1948. Studies on the igneous rock complex of the Oslo region. *Skrift. Norske Vidensk.-Akad. Oslo*, 1, Mat.-Nat. Kl. no. 3.

Oftedal, I., 1957. Heating experiments on amazonite. *Min. Mag.*, vol. 31, p. 417.

Orville, P. M., 1957. Granite pegmatites. Carnegie Institution of Washington. *Annual Report of the Director of the Geophysical Laboratory*, p. 222.

Osterwald, F. W., 1955. Petrology of Pre-Cambrian granites in the northern Bighorn Mountains, Wyoming. *Journ. Geol.*, vol. 63, p. 310.

Perrin, R., 1956. Granite again. *Amer. Journ. Sci.*, vol. 254, p. 1.

—— and **Roubault, M.**, 1949. On the granite problem. *Journ. Geol.*, vol. 57, p. 357.

Phillips, F. C., 1930. Pericline and acline-A twins in the acid plagioclases. *Min. Mag.*, vol. 22, p. 225.

Raman, C. V., Jayaraman, A. and **Srinivasan, T.**, 1950. The structure and optical behaviour of the Ceylon moonstones. *Proc. Ind. Acad. Sci.*, vol. 32A, p. 123.

Rao, S. V. L. N., 1960a. Co-existence relations in feldspars and their implications. *Indian Mineral.*, vol. 1, p. 48.

—— 1960b. X-ray study of potash feldspars of the contact metamorphic zones at Gjelleråsen, Oslo. *Norsk. Geol. Tidsskr.*, vol. 40, p. 1.

Read, H. H., 1948. Granites and granites. *Geol. Soc. Amer. Mem.*, No. 28, p. 1.

Reitan, P., 1956. Pegmatite veins and the surrounding rocks. I. Petrography and structure. *Norsk Geol. Tidsskr.*, Bd. 36, p. 213.

Robertson, F., 1959. Perthite formed by reorganization of albite from plagioclase during potash feldspar metasomatism. *Amer. Min.*, vol. 44, p. 603.

Rosenblum, S., 1956. Improved techniques for staining potash feldspars. *Amer. Min.*, vol. 41, p. 662.

Rosenholtz, J. L. and **Smith, D. T.**, 1941. Linear thermal expansion of adularia. *Amer. Min.*, vol. 26, p. 391.

—— —— 1942. Thermal studies of orthoclase and microcline. *Amer. Min.*, vol. 27, p. 344.

Rosenqvist, I. Th., 1951. Investigations in the crystal chemistry of silicates. III. The relation haematite–microcline. *Norsk Geol. Tidsskr.*, vol. 29, p. 65.

—— 1954. Investigations into the crystal chemistry of the feldspars. *Proc. Internat. Symposium on reactivity of solids, Gothenburg.* Pt. I, p. 453.

Rottenbach, E., 1936. Die Dichte des reinen Kalifeldspatanteils im Mikroklin und dessen allgemeine chemische Zusammensetzung. *Zentr. Min.*, Abt. A, p. 23.

Rudenko, S. A., 1954. A morphological-genetic classification of perthite intergrowths. *Mém. Soc. Russe Min.*, vol. 83, p. 23 (M.A. 13–120).

Schairer, J. F., 1950. The alkali-feldspar join in the system $NaAlSiO_4$–$KAlSiO_4$–SiO_2. *Journ. Geol.*, vol. 58, p. 512.

—— and **Bowen, N. L.**, 1935. Preliminary report on equilibrium-relations between feldspathoids, alkali-feldspars and silica. *Amer. Geophys. Union Trans.*, 16th. Ann. Meeting, p. 325.

—— —— 1938. The system leucite–diopside–silica. *Amer. Journ. Sci.*, vol. 35A, p. 289.

—— —— 1947a. The system anorthite–leucite–silica. *Bull. Soc. géol. Finlande*, vol. 20, p. 67.

Schairer, J. F. and **Bowen, N. L.**, 1947b. Melting relations in the systems Na₂O–Al₂O₃–SiO₂ and K₂O–Al₂O₃–SiO₂. *Amer. Journ. Sci.*, vol. 245, p. 193.

—— —— 1955. The system K₂O–Al₂O₃–SiO₂. *Amer. Journ. Sci.*, vol. 253, p. 681.

—— —— 1956. The system Na₂O–Al₂O₃–SiO₂. *Amer. Journ. Sci.*, vol. 254, p. 129.

Schermerhorn, L. J. G., 1956. The granites of Transcoso (Portugal): a study of microclinization. *Amer. Journ. Sci.*, vol. 254, p. 329.

—— 1961. Orthoclase, microcline and albite in granites. *Schweiz. Min. Petr. Mitt.*, vol. 41, p. 13.

Schiavinato, G., 1951. Sull' anorthoclasio incluso in una roccia effusiva femica del Monte Gemola (Euganei). *Periodico Min. Roma*, vol. 20, p. 193 (M.A. 11–489).

Schmidt, W. and **Baier, E.**, 1928. Versuche über die Kinetik der Anderung optischen Eigenschaften mit der Temperatur. *Zeit. Krist.*, vol. 68, p. 477.

Schneider, T. R., 1957. Röntgenographische und optische Untersuchung der Umwandlung Albit–Analbit–Monalbit. *Zeit. Krist.*, vol. 109, p. 245.

Ščavinčar, S. and **Sabatier, G.**, 1957. Action du chlorure de lithium sur les feldspaths alcalins. Données nouvelles sur le feldspath–Li, le spodumène–Fe et l'α-eucryptite. *Bull. Soc. franç. Minér. Crist.*, vol. 8, p. 308.

Sederholm, J. J., 1928. On orbicular granites and on the rapakivi texture. *Bull. Comm. géol. Finlande*, no. 83.

Seto, K., 1920. Chemical study of alkali felspars. *Journ. Geol. Soc. Tokyo*, vol. 27, p. 403 (M.A. 1–141).

—— 1923. Chemical study of some felspars. *Sci. Rep. Tôhoku Univ., Japan*, ser. 3, vol. 1, p. 219.

Shand, S. J., 1931. The granite–syenite–limestone complex of Palabora, eastern Transvaal, and the associated apatite deposits. *Trans. Geol. Soc. S. Africa*, vol. 34, p. 81 (M.A. 5–223).

—— 1949. History of a feldspar crystal. A contribution to the granite problem. *Bull. Geol. Soc. Amer.*, vol. 60, p. 1213.

Sharma, S. R. and **Raja, N.**, 1959. On myrmekite. *Quart. Journ. Geol. Min. Mett. Soc. India*, vol. 31, p. 127.

Simpson, E. S., 1952. *Minerals of Western Australia*, vol. 3. Perth (Govt. Printer).

Smirnov, V. P., 1915. *On the question of the influence of humus compounds on the character of the weathering of aluminosilicates.* Kharkov (M.A. 2–377).

Smith, J. V. and **MacKenzie, W. S.**, 1955. The alkali feldspars: II. A simple X-ray technique for the study of alkali feldspars. *Amer. Min.*, vol. 40, p. 733.

—— and **Muir, I. D.**, 1958. The reaction sequence in larvikite feldspars. *Zeit. Krist.*, vol. 110, p. 11.

Smits, F. and **Gentner, W.**, 1950. Argonbestimmungen an Kalium-Mineralien. I. Bestimmungen an tertiären Kalisalzen. *Geochim. et Cosmochim. Acta*, vol. 1, p. 22.

Smyth, L. B., 1922. On a variety of pinite occurring at Ballycorus, Co. Dublin. *Sci. Proc. Roy. Soc.*, new ser., vol. 16, p. 492 (M.A. 1–421).

Solodovnikova, L. L., 1935. Beiträge zum Studium von Feldspäten, aus Pegmatitgängen Nord-Kareliens. *Trav. Inst. Lomonossoff Géochem. Crist. Min., Acad. Sci. USSR* (M.A. 7–179).

—— 1937. The feldspars of the Khibine tundras. *Trav. Soc. Nat. Leningrad sect. Geol. Min.*, 66, no. 1, p. 34 (M.A. 9–148).

Soustov, N. I., 1936. On the alkaline feldspar from the vicinity of Oslo in south Norway. *Trav. Inst. Petrogr. Acad. Sci. U.R.S.S.*, no. 7–8, p. 25 (M.A. 7–22).

Spence, H. S., 1932. *Feldspar.* Dept. Mines, Mines Branch, Ottawa, no. 731.

Spencer, E., 1930. A contribution to the study of moonstone from Ceylon and other areas and of the stability relations of the alkali-felspars. *Min. Mag.*, vol. 22, p. 291.

Spencer, E., 1937. The potash-soda felspars. I. Thermal stability. *Min. Mag.*, vol. 24, p. 453.

—— 1938. The potash-soda felspars. II. Some applications to petrogenesis. *Min. Mag.*, vol. 25, p. 87.

—— 1945. Myrmekite in graphic granite and in vein perthite. *Min. Mag.*, vol. 27, p. 79.

Spencer, L. J., 1942. Barium-felspars (celsian & paracelsian) from Wales. *Min. Mag.*, vol. 26, p. 231.

Stevens, R. E., 1934. Studies on the alkalinity of some silicate minerals. *U.S. Geol. Surv., Prof. Paper* 185–A, p. 1.

Storey-Maskelyne, N., 1895. *Crystallography*, Oxford, p. 382.

Straaten, L. M. J. U. van., 1948. Note on the occurrence of authigenic feldspar in non-metamorphic sediments. *Amer. Journ. Sci.*, vol. 246, p. 569.

Tallman, S. L., 1949. Sandstone types: their abundance and cementing agents. *Journ. Geol.*, vol. 57, p. 582.

Taylor, W. H., 1933. The structure of sanidine and other felspars. *Zeit. Krist.*, vol. 85, p. 425.

—— **Darbyshire, J. A.** and **Strunz, H.**, 1934. An X-ray investigation of the felspars. *Zeit. Krist.*, vol. 87, p. 464.

Terzaghi, R. D., 1940. The rapakivi of Head Harbor Island, Maine. *Amer. Min.*, vol. 25, p. 111.

—— 1948. Potash-rich rocks of the Esterel, France. *Amer. Min.*, vol. 33, p. 18.

Tilley, C. E., 1954. Nepheline–alkali feldspar parageneses. *Amer. Journ. Sci.*, vol. 252, p. 65.

—— 1958. The leucite nepheline dolerite of Meiches, Vogelsberg, Hessen. *Amer. Min.*, vol. 43, p. 758.

Tolmachev, Y. M. and **Filippov, A. N.**, 1935. On the presence of rare alkaline metals in amazonites. *Doklady Acad. Sci. USSR*, vol. 1, p. 322.

Tućan, F., 1939. Sanidindazit con Zvečan und Sokolica und Alunitgestein von Boljetin bei Kosovska Mitrovica. *Bull. Internat. Acad. Yougoslave, Cl. Sci. Math. Nat.*, vol. 32, p. 50 (M.A. 10–68).

Tunell, G., 1952. The angle between the a-axis and the trace of the rhombic section on the {010} pinacoid in the plagioclases. *Amer. Journ. Sci.*, Bowen vol., p. 547.

Tuttle, O. F., 1948. A new hydrothermal quenching apparatus. *Amer. Journ. Sci.*, vol. 246, p. 628.

—— 1952a. Origin of the contrasting mineralogy of extrusive and plutonic salic rocks. *Journ. Geol.*, vol. 60, p. 107.

—— 1952b. Optical studies on alkali feldspars. *Amer. Journ. Sci.*, Bowen vol., p. 553.

—— and **Bowen, N. L.**, 1950. High-temperature albite and contiguous feldspars. *Journ. Geol.*, vol. 58, p. 572.

—— —— 1958. Origin of granite in the light of experimental studies in the system $NaAlSi_3O_8$–$KAlSi_3O_8$–SiO_2–H_2O. *Mem. Geol. Soc. Amer.*, no. 74.

—— and **Keith, M. L.**, 1954. The granite problem: evidence from the quartz and feldspar of a Tertiary granite. *Geol. Mag.*, vol. 91, p. 61.

Uspensky, M., 1943. On the genesis of granite pegmatites. *Amer. Min.*, vol. 28, p. 437.

Vendl, M., 1922. Felspar of the rhyolite of Mt. Somlyód near Végardó. *Math. Természett. Értesttö, Budapest*, vol. 39, p. 174 (M.A. 2–169).

Vernadsky, W., 1913. Sur le microcline à rubidium. *Bull. Soc. franç. Min.*, vol. 36, p. 258.

Vlodavetz, V. I. and **Shavrova, N. N.**, 1953. On anorthoclase from a lava in Darigan volcanic region. Problems of petrography and mineralogy. *Acad. Sci. USSR*, vol. 2, p. 71 (M.A. 13–480).

Vogt, J. H. L., 1926. The physical chemistry of magmatic differentiation of igneous rocks. II. On the feldspar diagram Or : Ab : An. *Skrift. Norske Vidensk.-Akad.*, I. Mat.-Nat. Kl., Oslo, no. 4.

Wahlstrom, E. E., 1939. Graphic granite. *Amer. Min.*, vol. 24, p. 681.

Walker, F. and **Mathias, M.**, 1946. The petrology of two granite–slate contacts at Cape Town, South Africa. *Quart. Journ. Geol. Soc.*, vol. 102, p. 499.

Wasserburg, G. J. and **Hayden, R. J.**, 1955. A^{40}–K^{40} dating. *Geochim. et Cosmochim. Acta*, vol. 7, p. 51.

Wallace, S. R., 1956. Petrogenetic significance of some feldspars from the Judith Mountains, Montana. *Journ. Geol.*, vol. 64, p. 369.

Weigel, O. and **Krüger, E.**, 1934. Die Saphirlagerstätte von Bo Ploi in Siam. I. Teil. In *Wissenschaftliche Ergebnisse meiner Forschungsreisen in Ostasien*. Marburg (M.A. 7–331.)

Wells, R. C., 1937. Analyses of rocks and minerals from the laboratory of the U.S. Geological Survey, 1914–1936. *U.S. Geol. Surv., Bull. 878*, p. 106.

White, W. P., 1909. Specific heats of silicates and platinum. *Amer. Journ. Sci.*, 4th ser., vol. 28, p. 334.

—— 1919. Silicate specific heats. Second series. *Amer. Journ. Sci.*, 4th ser., vol. 47, p. 1.

Wilson, A. F., 1950. Some unusual alkali-felspars in the Central Australian charnockitic rocks. *Min. Mag.*, vol. 29, p. 215.

Wones, D. R. and **Appleman, D. E.**, 1961. X-ray crystallography and optical properties of synthetic monoclinic $KFeSi_3O_8$ iron-sanidine. *U.S. Geol. Surv., Prof. Paper 424-C*, p. 309.

Wyart, J., 1947. Synthèse de la kalsilite et de l'orthose. *Compt. Rend. Acad. Sci. Paris*, vol. 225, p. 944.

Yoder, H. S., Stewart, D. B. and **Smith, J. R.**, 1956, (1957). Ternary feldspars (Annual Rep. Director Geophys. Lab.). *Carnegie Inst. Washington, Yr. Book*, no. 55 (56), p. 190 (206).

Yoshizawa, H., 1933. Chikyu, vol. 19, p. 432 (Quoted from Miyashiro and Miyashiro, 1956, *Journ. Fac. Sci., Univ. Tokyo*, vol. 10, p. 43).

Yuan, C. K., 1953. Studies in sodium-poor potash feldspars. *Bull. Geol. Instit. Upsala*, vol. 34, p. 298.

Zaniewska-Chilipalska, E., 1937. Sur la composition chimique de quelques adulaires. *Archiv. Min. Soc. Sci., Warsaw*, vol. 13, p. 20 (M.A. 7–21).

Zsivny, V., 1923. The chemical composition of sanidine from Végardó. *Math. Természett. Értesítő, Budapest*, vol. 40, p. 114 (M.A. 2–223).

Plagioclase

TRICLINIC (+) OR (−)

	High-temperature Albite NaAlSi$_3$O$_8$	Albite NaAlSi$_3$O$_8$	Anorthite CaAl$_2$Si$_2$O$_8$
α	1·527	1·527	1·577
β	1·532	1·531	1·585
γ	1·534	1·538	1·590
δ	0·007	0·010$_5$	0·013$_5$
2V	45° (−)	77° (+)	78° (−)

For optic orientation see Fig. 53

Dispersion:	$r < v$	$r < v$	$r < v$
D	2·62	2·63	2·76
H		6–6$\frac{1}{2}$	6–6$\frac{1}{2}$

Cleavage: {001}Perfect,{010}good. {110}Poor.

Twinning:
(a) Multiple lamellar albite twins [Composition plane (010), twin axis ⊥ (010)].
(b) Simple Carlsbad twins [Composition plane (010), twin axis z].
(c) Many other normal, parallel and complex twins (see Table 3, p. 22).

Colour: Normally colourless or white, but sometimes yellow, pink, green or black; colourless in thin section.

Unit cell:				
	a (Å)	8·15	8·14	8·18
	b (Å)	12·88	12·79	12·88
	c (Å)	7·11	7·16	7·08$_5$ × 2
	α	93° 22′	94° 20′	93° 10′
	β	116° 18′	116° 34′	115° 51′
	γ	90° 17′	87° 39′	91° 13′

Space group[1]:	$C\bar{1}$	$C\bar{1}$	$P\bar{1}$
Z	4	4	4 × 2

Insoluble in HCl, except anorthite. Soluble in HF or molten Na$_2$CO$_3$.

The plagioclase felspars are ubiquitous and represent the commonest rock-forming mineral series. High-temperature plagioclases occur in some volcanic

[1] See footnote p. 6.

rocks while the low-temperature albite–anorthite series are found in most igneous rocks, are common in metamorphic rocks, and occur in sediments both as primary and as authigenic minerals.

It should be noted that although the variation in refractive indices of the low-temperature series is essentially continuous from albite to anorthite, many of the other optical and physical properties vary in a more complex manner between the end-member values quoted above, and for more detailed information reference must be made to the appropriate section below.

The plagioclase felspar series includes the six minerals albite, oligoclase, andesine, labradorite, bytownite and anorthite: following Calkins (1917) the divisions are taken at anorthite mol. percentages 0–10, 10–30, 30–50, 50–70, 70–90 and 90–100 respectively. The intergrowth of potassium and plagioclase felspars with plagioclase as the dominant phase or host is termed antiperthite.

STRUCTURE

The plagioclase felspars form a chemical series ranging from albite, $NaSi_3AlO_8$, to anorthite, $CaSi_2Al_2O_8$. Their structures have triclinic symmetry and are similar to those already described for albite (p. 14), involving a framework of linked (Si,Al)–O tetrahedra, the large interstices of this framework being filled by (Ca,Na) ions. In matters of detail the structures of plagioclases are complex, and vary according to chemical composition, conditions of crystallization and thermal history. The nature of these variations has been studied by many workers using X-ray methods (Chao and Taylor, 1940; Sorum, 1951; Cole *et al.*, 1951; Sorum, 1953; Gay, 1953, 1954, 1956; Gay and Taylor, 1953; Gay and Smith, 1955; Gay and Bown, 1956; Laves, 1954; Goldsmith and Laves, 1955; Laves and Goldsmith, 1951, 1954a,b, 1955; Bown and Gay, 1958; Megaw, 1960a,b,c), and their results are summarized in the following pages. [Much information has been obtained also by optical methods (*e.g.* Köhler, 1941) which are described in a later section (p. 129).]

The existence of two distinct forms of albite, stable at high and low temperature respectively, suggested that at least two plagioclase series might be found. Tuttle and Bowen (1950) conclusively demonstrated that there are two structural series of sodium-rich plagioclases from An_0 to An_{50}, and phase equilibrium studies have since shown that for the high-temperature series there is complete solid solution over the entire range. It has also been shown that plagioclases exist which have structural states intermediate between those associated with the extremes of the high- and low-temperature series. Structural evidence has been obtained of solid solution in the high-temperature series for the range $An_0–An_{90}$ characterized by the "high-albite" structure which has a C face-centred cell with $a\simeq8\cdot17$, $b\simeq12\cdot87$ and $c\simeq7\cdot11$ Å. (The structures of both low- and high-temperature albite are discussed under alkali felspars.) Specimens with composition $An_{90}–An_{100}$, when quenched from high temperatures, do not show the high-albite structure (see p. 14) perhaps because inversion from it towards the low-temperature form is extremely rapid.

The low-temperature series is not continuous but contains at least six structural divisions, the compositional ranges of which are approximately as shown overleaf:

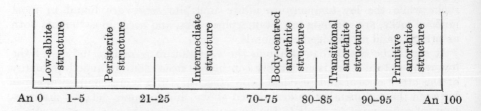

The low-albite structure can take only very little calcium into solid solution (to about An_3).

Peristerites. In the range An_{1-5} to An_{21-25}, plagioclases are generally sub-microscopic intergrowths of sodium-rich and calcium-rich regions. The two phases probably have the structures and compositions of the end-members of the range, *i.e.* low-albite and intermediate structure respectively, and they are related in orientation by having their (010) planes nearly parallel (Bøggild, 1924, gave (08$\bar{1}$) as the plane of separation; see also Brown, 1960; Ribbe, 1960). Some of these unmixed specimens show a characteristic schiller effect and consequently they have been named peristerites, but this name is sometimes applied to the whole range whether or not schiller can be seen.

Body-centred anorthite structure. Plagioclases of composition An_{70-75} to An_{80-85} have a body-centred structure which is related to that of low-albite by the absence of half of the latter's centres of symmetry, and has a doubled c axis ($a \simeq 8\cdot2$, $b \simeq 12\cdot9$, $c \simeq 14\cdot2$ Å). The loss of symmetry and doubled c axis is ascribed to segregation of Si–Al ions with a larger repeat of the ordered sequence than in the case of the alkali felspars. If X-ray reflections are indexed on the basis of the cell with $c \simeq 14$ Å, those with l odd are associated with the differences between successive small cells (*i.e.* Si, Al segregation and consequent differences in atomic parameters). Thus in c axis oscillation or rotation photographs there are the strong main layer lines of type (a) reflections [$(h+k)$ even, l even] corresponding to a 7 Å cell, and on layer lines half-way between these occur the weaker type (b) spots [$(h+k)$ odd, l odd] which result from the doubled c dimension.

It has been suggested that in the body-centred anorthite structure Ca and Na are randomly distributed among the available large cation sites. Understanding of the (Ca,Na) and (Si,Al) distribution must however await completion of the detailed structure analysis (Chandrasekhar, 1957).

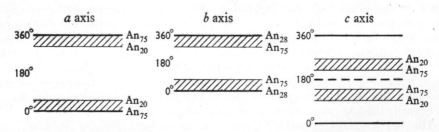

Fig. 40. Diagram showing regions in which type (e) reflections occur in X-ray diffraction photographs from intermediate plagioclases (see text).

The intermediate plagioclase structure is characteristic of plagioclases in the range An_{23}–An_{73}. Its precise nature is not known, but its effect on single crystal X-ray patterns is readily seen and is best described in relation to the pattern of body-centred anorthite. In *c* axis photographs the (b) spots described above are replaced by pairs of spots, type (e) (equidistant from them and sometimes of unequal intensity), defining a pair of weak subsidiary layer lines, the positions of which vary linearly with composition. Similar pairs of layer lines occur in *a* and *b* axis photographs. Fig. 40 illustrates the regions in which these layer lines occur on *a*, *b* and *c* axis photographs.

Displacements of subsidiaries from the main layer lines are called δa, δb, δc, and are expressed in angular measure, taking the main reciprocal lattice layer spacing as 360°. These are plotted against composition in Fig. 41 (after Gay, 1956a). Details of the location, diffuseness and intensity of these subsidiary

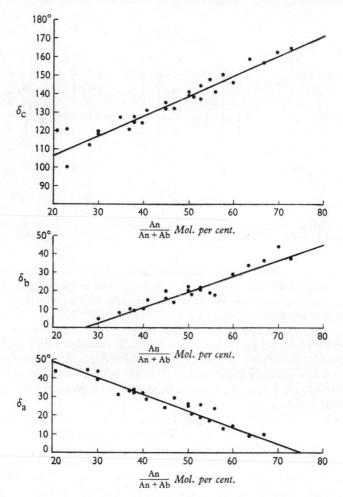

FIG. 41. Variation of δa, δb and δc with chemical composition (after Gay, 1956a).

reflections and their relation to chemical composition have been investigated further by Bown and Gay (1958). Additional pairs of subsidiary spots, type (f), which occur as satellites to the main (a) type reflections, have been reported for the more calcium-rich intermediate plagioclases.

It has been suggested that the intermediate structure embodies alternate sodium- and calcium-rich regions intermixed in a regular manner. Megaw (1960a,b,c), however, explains the diffraction effects by postulating that the structure is subject to regularly distributed stacking faults, the occurrences and nature of which are dependent upon the (Si:Al) ratio.

The boundary between intermediate structures and peristerites is not clearly defined since subsidiary spots are very weak and diffuse at these compositions. Still less is there a clear boundary between the body-centred and intermediate structures, since (c) type reflections (see below) have been observed in addition to other subsidiaries for plagioclases with as much sodium as Ab_{50}.

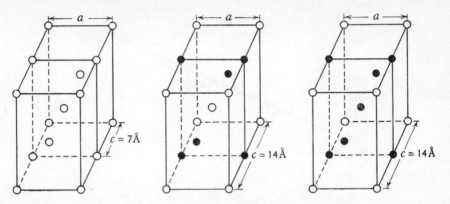

FIG. 42. Relationship between lattices of plagioclases (after Cole *et al.*, 1951). Left to right: Albite, body-centred anorthite, primitive anorthite.

With increase of calcium content beyond An_{80-85} the body-centred anorthite structure is replaced by a transitional structure, and at An_{90-95} up to An_{100} the stable structure at room temperature is that of primitive anorthite.

The primitive anorthite lattice can be derived from that of body-centred anorthite by removal of half of its centres of symmetry, and the resulting cell has $a \simeq 8.18$, $b \simeq 12.88$, $c \simeq 14.17$ Å, *i.e.* it retains the doubled c dimension. The relation between the three lattice types, primitive anorthite, body-centred anorthite, and low-albite is illustrated in Fig. 42, and it follows that some new additional reflections (type (c), $h+k$ even, l odd) are given by the primitive anorthite structure.[1]

The unit cell is built up from four albite-like sub-cells (see Megaw, 1959), each of which contains two formula units. Throughout the structure of primitive anorthite (as also in the structure of celsian, see p. 167), silicon and aluminium tetrahedra alternate; thus every Si tetrahedron is surrounded by four Al tetrahedra and vice versa. The (Si,Al) ordering is complete, and necessitates the doubling of the c parameter as compared with that of the albite cell. The

[1] A few weak reflections, type (d), with $h+k$ odd, l even, also occur.

reduction of symmetry from body-centred to primitive anorthite is associated not with (Si,Al) ordering, but with differences in coordinates for all atoms (most markedly for Ca) between the four sub-cells (Kempster, 1957; Kempster *et al.*, 1960). In all structures of the low-temperature plagioclases series it is believed that there is a high degree of Si,Al ordering.

Substitution of sodium in the primitive anorthite structure is accompanied by a gradual change, via a transitional structure, towards body-centred anorthite. The (c) type reflections become increasingly diffuse and when they have disappeared into the background the structure may be regarded as body-centred. This change was thought to occur at about Ab_{15-20} but very weak (c) type reflections have appeared for compositions well into the intermediate structure range, so that the status of body-centred anorthite as a distinct structural modification is not clearly defined.

Thermal relationships. The relationship between the high-temperature and low-temperature plagioclase series is revealed by studies of natural specimens which have formed in different geological environments, by heating experiments which induce changes in structural state, and by investigation of synthetic plagioclases. It must be emphasized that in the experiments reported, X-ray studies were made after specimens had been quenched from various temperatures and not at elevated temperatures. Thus the possibility of a partial inversion to a lower temperature state cannot be discounted. Prolonged heating changes all low-temperature plagioclases, with the exception of primitive anorthite (An_{90-95} to An_{100}), to the high-temperature high-albite structure. Heating promotes disordering of Si,Al atoms, and is accompanied by other changes which vary according to the nature of the initial structure.

For pure anorthite the doubled c dimension (and (b) type reflections) remain after quenching from all temperatures up to the melting point, indicating that Si,Al ordering is not destroyed. The effect of temperature of crystallization upon the (c) type reflections, however, is similar to the effect of sodium substitution, in that they are weaker and more diffuse for specimens crystallized above 1100 °C.; diffuseness increases for higher temperatures but (c) reflections are still visible for synthetic specimens crystallized near the melting point (about 1550 °C.). This change from the primitive, through the transitional, towards the body-centred structure, is a reversible function of temperature. In heating experiments on anorthites the diffuseness of (c) type spots is seen to be characteristic of the temperature to which a specimen had been heated prior to quenching. Annealing experiments on primitive anorthite show that the diffuse spots become sharp again at temperatures depending upon the sodium content (see Fig. 43, after Laves and Goldsmith, 1954c). Sharpening occurs at a lower temperature as the sodium content is increased, and extrapolation of these curves suggests that with more than Ab_{10} sharpening would not have occurred at room temperature, so that such specimens are normally transitional rather than primitive. With still higher Ab content, sharpening has not begun even at room temperature, *i.e.* the (c) spots are too diffuse to be visible, and the structure is effectively body-centred.

As would be expected, the effect of heat on transitional anorthites (An_{80-85} to An_{90-95}) is first to convert them to body-centred anorthites with gradual weakening and eventual disappearance of (c) type reflections. Above about 1350 °C., however, the further change to the high-albite structure takes place,

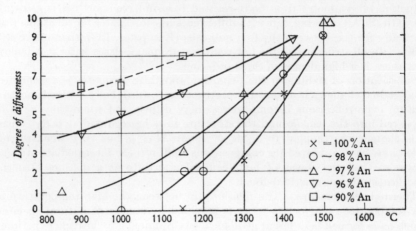

Fig. 43. Plot of degree of diffuseness of (c) type reflections against temperature for anorthites with different compositions (after Laves and Goldsmith, 1954c).

presumably involving disordering (of Si,Al), and is accompanied by continuous weakening and broadening of (b) type reflections. In natural anorthites various degrees of diffuseness of (c) type spots are observed, and provided that something is known of the chemical composition these may provide some indication of thermal history. The structural state of plagioclases may be affected by such factors as the small potassium content and by thermal conditions following crystallization.

The heating of plagioclases which have the body-centred anorthite structure at room temperature, promotes change to the high-albite structure with loss of (b) type reflections. When plagioclases in the intermediate structure range are heated, reflections on subsidiary layer lines become diffuse without change in position, and eventually are unobservable, the pattern remaining being that of a high-albite structure.

The degree of diffuseness of subsidiary [(b) and (c)] reflections, indicating transition towards the high-albite structure, is a function not only of temperature but also of composition, being greater at a given temperature for the more sodium-rich specimens. Thus for intermediate-temperature plagioclase, and for more calcium-rich specimens, the diffuseness of reflections which characterize transitional structures cannot be used to estimate composition or thermal state independently, but can give qualitative information about either if the other is known. (This difficulty does not arise in the case of subsidiaries of the intermediate structure since their positions generally serve to indicate chemical composition.)

Peristerites can be homogenized by heating for about a week at 1000°–1100°C., to yield a member of the high-temperature plagioclase series with high-albite structure (Laves, 1954; Schneider, 1957; Ribbe, 1960). According to Ribbe homogenization proceeds by stages, first by disordering of Na and Ca between domains, then by disordering of Si and Al within domains, and finally by disordering of Si and Al between domains. Schiller effects (see p. 105) are still exhibited in all but the final stage of homogenization. Homogenization cannot

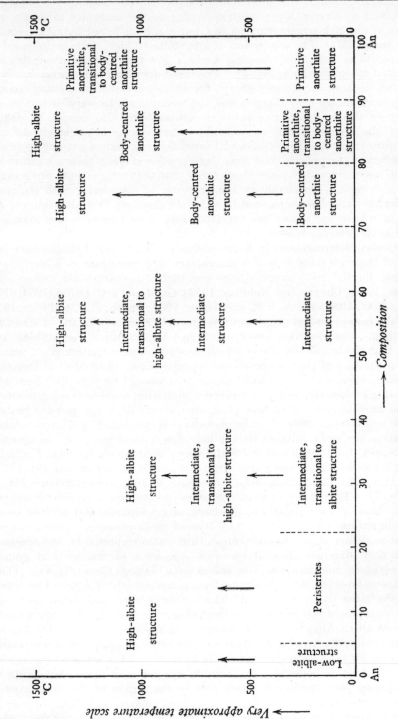

FIG. 44. Sequence of structural changes with temperature for plagioclases of various compositions.

be followed by simple X-ray methods owing to the similarity in lattice geo-metrics of the high-temperature phases, but can be followed by measurements of 2V (see p. 133).   The conversion of low-albite to high-albite is discussed on page 48.   The effect of heating various low-temperature plagioclases is illustrated schematically in Fig. 44.   Precise temperature boundaries cannot be indicated because in all cases except for those very rich in calcium, cooling transformations are very sluggish and the transition is irreversible in terms of laboratory time.   Boundaries between compositions also cannot be defined strictly; the diagram merely serves to show the sequence of changes in different composition ranges.   The studies of heated felspars and of natural specimens with different parageneses show that there is not a single high-temperature and a single low-temperature plagioclases series, but that intermediate-temperature series also exist.   For simplicity the processes of disordering with increasing temperature have been separated into those concerning Si,Al distribution, and those in which Na,Ca ions are involved, but these two processes may have considerable interdependence.

Plagioclase determination by X-ray methods.   A number of studies have been made of the variations in lattice parameters, and variations in X-ray powder patterns, for the low-, intermediate- and high-temperature plagioclase series (Claisse, 1950; Chayes and Robbins, 1953; Goodyear and Duffin, 1954, 1955; Smith, J. V., 1956; Smith, J. R. and Yoder, 1956; Smith, J. V. and Gay, 1958). As in the case of optical properties the effects of composition and of structural state (high-, intermediate-, low-temperature) are not always separable.   It is found that the lattice parameter which shows greatest variation is γ^*, particu-larly in the case of the low-temperature plagioclases.   The effect of increasing calcium content on γ^* for alkali felspars is discussed on page 19.   Instead of measuring γ^* directly, a simpler method of following changes in cell geometry is by the measurement of certain peak separations in X-ray powder patterns (Tuttle and Bowen, 1950).   Various peaks have been selected by different workers, and some are more suitable than others for specific ranges of composition. Thus Smith, J. V. (1956) and Smith and Gay (1958) use the function $\Gamma = 2\theta(131)$ $+ 2\theta(220) - 4\theta(1\bar{3}1)$ for the range An_{20}–An_{70} and the separation 131–$1\bar{3}1$, or 111–$1\bar{1}1$, or $\bar{1}32$–131, for An_0–An_{20}.   Smith, J. R. and Yoder (1956) use 131–$1\bar{3}1$ or 220–$1\bar{3}1$.   They find that a smooth curve of variation of these with composi-tion is obtained for synthetic plagioclases, and a separate and distinct smooth curve for natural specimens from thick layered mafic intrusions.   The two curves appear to define high- and low-temperature states respectively, and specimens which have different thermal histories, *e.g.* from pegmatites and granites, metamorphics, volcanics, etc., give values lying between them (Fig. 45).   (There is evidence, however, that all felspars from a layered intrusion do not necessarily have the same structural state.)   The higher temperature curve shows only slight variation of cell geometry with composition, and the two curves tend to merge at about An_{90}.   Thus for calcium-rich specimens, even in the low-tem-perature state, the X-ray method cannot give accurate estimates of composition. The curve for the low-temperature state appears to have a sharp kink at about An_{35} for which no conclusive explanation has yet been found, but Smith and Gay suggest that specimens which plot in the region of the kink have not attained equilibrium.

It is apparent that plagioclases do not fall into two unique series and that the composition of a plagioclase cannot be determined easily by X-ray methods since there is uncertainty as to how closely a particular specimen is represented by any of the available curves. For the range An_0-An_{75}, if composition has been determined by some other method, the X-ray measurements can give some indication of the structural state. Similarly, an X-ray determinative curve may in some cases be useful over a limited range of compositions of plagioclases

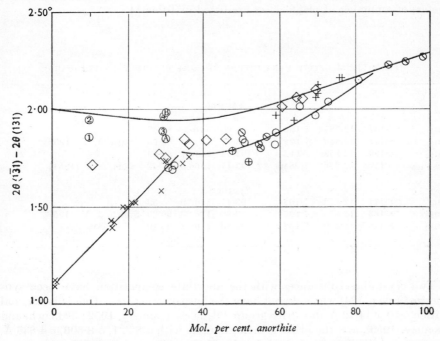

FIG. 45. Variation of $2\theta(1\bar{3}1)-2\theta(131)$ with composition for plagioclases of the following origins:

× from pegmatites and granites; ⊘ from metamorphic rocks; ◊ from volcanic rocks; + from anorthositic masses near the tops of gabbroic sills, northern Minnesota; ⊕ from Adirondack-type anorthosite massifs; ○ from miscellaneous rocks, details of occurrence not known; ① and ③ synthesized from glass at 640°C. and 10,000 bars water pressure; ② and ④ synthesized from crystalline material at 640°C. and 10,000 bars water pressure; Ⓐ natural plagioclase from pegmatite heated for 9 hours at 1122°C.; Ⓑ natural plagioclase from pegmatite heated for 24 hours at 1140°C. (after Smith and Yoder, 1956).

from a restricted environment (see, for example, Jackson, 1961). Perhaps the most reliable X-ray estimates of both composition and state are those obtainable for plagioclases in the range $An_{40}-An_{70}$, from single-crystal photographs, making use of the δ values and the diffuseness of their characteristic reflections.

In the case of anorthite, where cell geometry is only slightly affected by the low- or high-temperature structural state, some information can yet be obtained from a good X-ray powder pattern. Goldsmith and Laves (1956) show that one of the (c) type reflections, $11\bar{1}$, is visible in the powder photograph and its intensity provides a measure of the transition from the primitive to the body-centred structure. It must be remembered, however, that this transition can indicate either a higher temperature structural state or a higher sodium content.

The more recent studies (Smith, J. R. and Yoder, 1956; Smith, J. V. and Gay, 1958) have shown the limitations of earlier X-ray methods of plagioclase determination (*e.g.* Claisse, 1950; Goodyear and Duffin, 1954). Optical methods for determining plagioclases are described in a later section. The cell parameters of a number of plagioclases are listed in Table 11.

Table 11. LATTICE PARAMETERS OF SOME PLAGIOCLASE FELSPARS

	a Å	b Å	c Å	$\alpha°$	$\beta°$	$\gamma°$	
			Natural				
An_0	8·144	12·787	7·160	94·26	116·58	87·67	
An_{31}	8·171	12·846	7·129	93·75	116·44	89·25	Smith, J. V. (1956)
An_{51}	8·180	12·859	7·112	93·52	116·27	89·89	
$An_{\simeq 100}$	8·1768	12·8768	7·0845($\times 2$)	93·17	115·85	91·22	Cole, *et al.* (1951)
			Synthetic				
An_0	8·171	12·872	7·108	93·47	116·39	90·33	
An_{30}	8·163	12·875	7·107	93·39	116·27	90·29	Smith, J. V. (1956)
An_{50}	8·178	12·870	7·102	93·36	116·18	90·40	

Two crystalline substances with the anorthite composition have been synthesized (see p. 124) which do not have the felspar structure. One is hexagonal with a 5·10, c 14·72 Å and space group $P6_3/m\ cm$ (Donnay, 1952; Takéuchi and Donnay, 1959), and the other is orthorhombic with a 8·224, b 8·606, c 4·836 Å, space group $P2_12_12$ (Davis and Tuttle, 1952). These two modifications, produced by crystallization from viscous glasses, are probably unstable phases. Hexagonal $CaAl_2Si_2O_8$ is structurally similar to the high- and low-temperature forms of hexagonal $BaAl_2Si_2O_8$. There appears to be no structural relationship between orthorhombic $CaAl_2Si_2O_8$ and paracelsian. Both hexagonal and orthorhombic forms of $CaAl_2Si_2O_8$ can be changed to anorthite by sufficient heating.

MORPHOLOGY AND TWINNING

The principal forms exhibited by plagioclase crystals are similar to those of the alkali felspars, and because of the slight obliquity of the triclinic cell plagioclase habits differ but little from those of some monoclinic felspars. Crystals are often tabular with {010} prominent but are sometimes elongated parallel to the x axis, and more rarely parallel to z. The unusual pericline habit of albite which is elongated parallel to y is illustrated in Fig. 8, p. 21. The cleavelandite habit of albite is platy parallel to (010). Perfect cleavage on {001} and good {010} cleavage intersect at an angle of about 94°, and poor {110} and {1̄10} cleavages are sometimes observable. Plagioclases in the range of composition An_{1-5} to An_{21-25} are sometimes divided on a very fine scale into sodium-rich and calcium-rich regions; crystals are often iridescent, particularly when viewed on the (010) face, and are called peristerites. The way in which they reflect or diffract light is sometimes referred to as "chatoyance" and is similar to that exhibited by the perthitic intergrowths of alkali felspars; the term "moonstone" has been applied to both but is perhaps better restricted to alkali felspars. These effects are said to result from reflection (or diffraction) occurring at the boundaries between perthite or peristerite lamellae, but an alternative explanation in terms of the diffusion of light by neighbouring small domains of differing optical properties (see Raman *et al.*, 1950) has been suggested by Ribbe (1960). Bøggild (1924) gave the plane of peristerite growth as lying between (08$\bar{1}$) and ($\bar{1}$,21,$\bar{2}$), see also Brown (1960). Felspars with composition in the labradorite range often show a somewhat different type of iridescence (seen best on (010)) for which the name labradorescence has been employed. Bøggild suggests that specific planes are involved in this phenomenon, near ($\bar{1}$,12,1) and ($\bar{9}$,33,4) or (04$\bar{1}$) and (1,22,$\bar{7}$). These planes might separate regions of different composition but X-ray studies have not revealed the presence of more than one phase at labradorite compositions. Aventurine felspar has plate-like inclusions of an iron mineral which give the specimen a spangled appearance.

Plagioclase felspars usually show repeated twinning on a microscopic scale, but occasionally simple Manebach, and very rarely, simple Baveno twins occur. Carlsbad twinning is quite common and may be either repeated or simple. Repeated twins on the albite and/or pericline laws are most frequent of all, albite twinning rarely being absent, and twins on other laws (*e.g.* acline, Ala, albite–Carlsbad, albite–Ala B) are not uncommon. Manebach-acline A, and Manebach-Ala A are indistinguishable optically from Ala A and acline A respectively (see footnote, p. 22). Pericline and albite twinning often occur in the one crystal, and other combinations of two or more laws have been observed. Some features of twinning which are common to both alkali and plagioclase series have been discussed in the section on alkali felspars.

The position of the rhombic section (see p. 26) depends upon the angles of the crystal lattice and these are influenced in the plagioclase series both by chemical composition and by structural state. The measured cell parameters of natural low-temperature specimens yield values of σ ranging from about $+35°$ for An_0 to about $-20°$ for An_{100}. The values of σ for synthetic specimens representing the high-temperature structural state do not change much with composition from that of high-albite (approx. $4°-6°$). Tunell (1952) gives a table of σ values for various compositions, which differ from those which may be obtained from cell constants published elsewhere; discrepancies of this kind may well occur through differences in structural state. A further limitation of the diagnostic usefulness of pericline twinning, noted by several workers, is that the composition plane does not always coincide with the rhombic section. This situation may arise when the structural state of a felspar has changed after twinning has occurred, since although lattice angles and the rhombic section may change, the original composition plane may remain unchanged. Indeed comparison of observed and calculated pericline composition planes may be used to infer that structural changes have occurred subsequent to twinning (Laves and Schneider, 1956; Smith, 1958). Yet another difficulty in the interpretation of pericline twinning arises through the occurrence of acline A twinning which can be confused with pericline twinning in which σ happens to be zero (Gysin, 1925; Phillips, 1930).

Pericline twinning is best seen on faces near to (010) or on others approximately parallel to z, whereas albite twinning is best seen on (001) and other faces nearly parallel to y. The composition planes of the various types of twin which occur in plagioclases can be useful in many ways for their optical determination. The relation of twins to cleavages, or to each other, can be used to identify the orientation of a grain, and the extinction angles can be measured on to the trace of a composition plane. The most useful in this respect is albite twinning, and some examples of its application are given on pp. 135–140.

The frequency of twinning, and the relative frequency of twinning on different laws, in relation to chemical, structural and environmental factors, have been investigated by many workers. The "French" theory of twinning (developed by Bravais, Mallard and Friedel) involves the concept that ease of twinning is inversely related to the obliquity of the twin. Obliquity is measured by the angle between the normal to the twin plane and the lattice row quasi-normal to it.[1] In the case of albite twinning, Donnay (1943) calculated the obliquity for plagioclases of various compositions, and Gay (1956b) extended the study to include low- and high-temperature structural states. The theory predicts that ease of twinning should be greatest for plagioclases of intermediate composition and less for those towards either end of the series. Ease of twinning should be similar for high- and low-temperature plagioclases except at the sodium-rich end of the series. If numerous fine lamellae (as opposed to few broad lamellae) are taken to indicate ease of twinning, observations on natural and synthetic felspars are generally in accord with these theoretical predictions. The cases of pericline and other twin laws are more complicated.

With regard to external factors which might be correlated with twinning, Turner (1951) concludes that in metamorphic rocks twinned plagioclase is comparatively rare, and that when it does occur simple rather than multiple, and albite or pericline rather than Carlsbad or other twins, predominate. Complex twins are rarely found in metamorphic plagioclases. A statistical study by Gorai (1951) supports these findings and shows that in igneous rocks most plagioclases are twinned and all twin laws are well represented. In schists and hornfels, however, twins other than albite and pericline are rare. Gorai states further that twins other than albite, pericline and acline are more plentiful in the calcic than in the sodic plagioclases of volcanic rocks. Many of the results of other studies on the frequencies of twin laws are not in accord with the above statements nor with each other, and it is probably fair to say that general rules of correlation are not yet fully established.

CHEMISTRY

Although essentially aluminosilicates of Na and Ca varying from pure $NaAlSi_3O_8$ to pure $CaAl_2Si_2O_8$, the plagioclase series normally contains a certain amount of the orthoclase molecule, $KAlSi_3O_8$, varying up to 5 mol. per cent. Or from anorthite to labradorite and then tending to increase gradually

---

[1] Obliquity angle ϕ is given by $\cos \phi = \sin \alpha^* \sin \gamma = \sin \alpha \sin \gamma^*$

towards the sodic end of the series (Fig. 46). Other ions which may be present in very limited amounts include Ti, Fe^{+3}, Fe^{+2}, Mn, Mg, Ba and Sr. Analyses of plagioclases are shown in Tables 12–18, where each analysis has been recalculated on the basis of the 32(O) contained in the unit cell. In such re-calculations it has been considered that Fe^{+3} and such small amounts of Ti as occur are replacing Al in the structure. Most of the iron reported in felspar analyses is shown to be Fe^{+3}; the small amounts of Fe^{+2} sometimes recorded must be considered either as an impurity or, from its charge and radius, as being

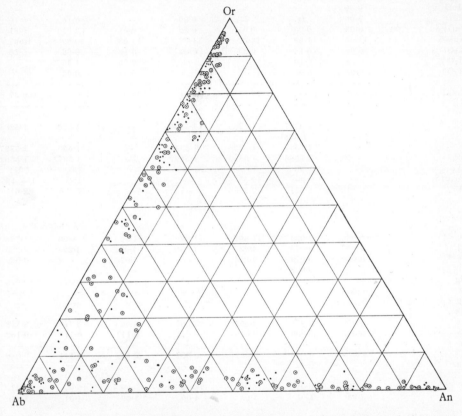

Fig. 46. Variations in composition in the felspar group. Some 300 relatively recent analyses are plotted, those used in Tables 4–8 and 12–19 being indicated ($\odot$).

together with Mn and Mg replacing Ca. In the absence of any evidence as to possible impurity in the sample, these ions, Fe^{+2}, Mn and Mg, have all therefore been considered to be replacing Ca, and contributing to the anorthite molecule. Sr also has been placed with Ca to form anorthite, while Ba is considered to substitute for K and is taken to form orthoclase.

Analyses. The analyses of Tables 12–18 have been selected, from approximately twice their number of relatively recent analyses, on the grounds of being free from impurities, having a reasonable total, and on recalculation approximating to the general formula $(Na,Ca,K)_4(Si,Al)_{16}O_{32}$ with, in most cases,

Table 12. ALBITE

(For analyses of albite from Amelia

	1.	2.	3.	4.	5.	6.	7.
SiO_2	68·30	68·05	67·10	68·71	66·84	66·26	67·41
TiO_2	0·00	0·01	—	—	—	—	—
Al_2O_3	19·64	19·73	20·44	19·63	19·62	20·16	20·50
Fe_2O_3	0·08	0·10	0·10	0·00	0·57	—	0·07
MnO	0·00	—	—	—	—	—	—
MgO	0·00	tr.	—	0·00	—	0·10	0·10
CaO	0·03	0·05	0·08	0·22	0·58	0·62	0·81
Na_2O	11·65	11·69	11·62	11·72	11·53	10·80	10·97
K_2O	0·08	0·18	0·24	0·03	0·10	0·62	0·36
H_2O^+	0·08	0·10	}0·40	—	0·73	1·30	}0·15
H_2O^-	0·03	0·03		—	0·04	0·22	
Total	100·07	99·94	99·98	100·31	100·01	100·08	100·37
α	—	1·5277–1·5281	1·5285	1·5289	—	1·526	1·5283
β	—	1·5317	1·5326	1·5330	—	1·530	1·5327
γ	—	1·5386	1·5389	1·5392	—	1·537	1·5392
$2V_\gamma$	77°	75–80·5°	79°	78° 39′	—	78°	79½°
$\alpha':(010)$	20°	—	19·5°	—	—	18°	18½–19°
D	2·612	2·621	2·6280	—	—	2·56–2·61	2·619

NUMBERS OF IONS ON

Si	11·956	11·924	11·801	11·966	11·825	11·790	11·785
Al	4·053	4·075	4·237	4·030	4·092	4·228	4·225
Fe^{+3}	0·010	0·013	0·013	—	0·076	—	0·009
Ti	—	0·003	—	—	—	—	—
Mg	—	—	—	—	—	0·027	0·026
Li	0·003	—	—	—	—	—	—
Fe^{+2}	—	—	—	—	—	—	—
Mn	—	—	—	—	—	—	—
Na	3·952	3·971	3·962	3·957	3·955	3·725	3·718
Ca	0·005	0·009	0·015	0·041	0·111	0·118	0·152
Sr	—	—	—	—	—	—	—
K	0·018	0·040	0·054	0·006	0·022	0·141	0·080
Ba	—	—	—	—	—	—	—
Z	16·02	16·01	16·05	16·00	15·99	16·02	16·02
X	3·98	4·01	4·03	4·00	4·09	4·01	3·98
Mol. % { Ab	99·4	98·8	99·2	98·8	96·7	92·9	93·5
An	0·1	0·2	0·3	1·0	2·7	3·6	4·5
Or	0·5	1·0	0·5	0·2	0·6	3·5	2·0

1. Saccharoidal albite, pegmatite, Varuträsk, Sweden (Adamson, 1942) (Includes P_2O_5 0·18, Li_2O 0·004).
2. Albite (pegmatite ?), Little Three Mine, Ramona, California.   (Emmons, 1953).   Anal. R. E. Stevens.
3. Glass-clear albite, mica-pegmatite, Kodarma, Bihar, India (Spencer 1937).   Anal. E. Spencer.
4. Albite, Alp Rischuna, Switzerland (Seto, 1923).   Anal. K. Seto (Optics by S. Kôzu).
5. Albite, chlorite schist, Bessi Mine, Ehime Prefecture, Japan (Takubo, 1941).   Anal. J. Takubo (Quoted from Harada, 1948).
6. Albite, encrusting orthoclase in drusy cavities of granite, Baveno, Piedmont, Italy (Pagliani, 1937).
7. Albite, with quartz and sphene in crevices in amphibolite, Forno glacier, Val Devero, Ossola, Piedmont, Italy (Azzini, 1933).

ANALYSES

Co., Virginia, see Table 13)

	8.	9.	10.	11.	12.	13.	14	
	67·39	66·42	66·12	66·16	67·10	65·62	65·94	SiO$_2$
	tr.	—	—	—	—	—	—	TiO$_2$
	18·97	20·41	21·00	21·38	19·95	21·72	20·47	Al$_2$O$_3$
	1·30	0·28	0·26	0·33	0·55	—	0·58	Fe$_2$O$_3$
	0·14	—	—	—	—	—	—	MnO
	0·38	tr.	—	—	0·70	—	—	MgO
	0·40	1·03	1·09	1·14	0·50	1·48	1·54	CaO
	10·67	10·20	9·53	10·43	10·30	10·54	9·91	Na$_2$O
	0·11	1·04	2·14	0·64	0·60	0·34	1·09	K$_2$O
	0·66	}0·23	}0·02	}0·13	}0·85	}0·19	}0·25	H$_2$O+
	0·13							H$_2$O−
	100·15	"99·85"	100·16	100·30	100·55	99·89	99·78	Total
	—	—	1·532	1·531	—	1·532	—	α
	—	—	1·540	1·535	—	1·536	—	β
	—	—	1·548	1·541	—	1·543	—	γ
	—	—	85°	—	—	—	—	2V$_\gamma$
	—	—	—	16°	18·5–22°	15°	—	α′ : (010)
	—	—	2·624	2·637	—	2·635	2·629	D

THE BASIS OF 32(O)

11·894	11·742	11·662	11·612	11·795	11·559	11·678	Si
3·946	4·253	4·366	4·424	4·134	4·510	4·273	Al
0·172	0·037	0·034	0·044	0·072	—	0·077	Fe^{+3}
—	—	—	—	—	—	—	Ti
0·100	—	—	—	0·184	—	—	Mg
—	—	—	—	—	—	—	Li
—	—	—	0·013	—	—	—	Fe^{+2}
0·021	—	—	—	—	—	—	Mn
3·651	3·497	3·258	3·549	3·510	3·599	3·402	Na
0·076	0·195	0·206	0·214	0·094	0·279	0·292	Ca
—	0·012	—	—	—	—	—	Sr
0·025	0·235	0·481	0·143	0·135	0·076	0·246	K
—	0·007	—	—	—	—	—	Ba
16·01	16·03	16·06	16·08	16·00	16·07	16·03	Z
3·87	3·95	3·95	3·92	3·92	3·95	3·94	X
94·3	88·6	82·6	90·6	89·5	91·0	86·3	Ab ⎫
5·1	5·4	5·2	5·8	7·1	7·1	7·4	An ⎬ Mol. %
0·6	6·0	12·2	3·6	3·4	1·9	6·3	Or ⎭

8. Albite, diabase sill, Kit Hill, St. Minver, Cornwall (Guppy, 1931).   Anal. E. G. Radley.
9. Albite antiperthite, calcite-bearing pegmatite dyke, Seiland, Finmarken, Arctic Norway (Hoel & Schetelig, 1916).   Anal. O. Røer (Includes SrO 0·11, BaO 0·11).
10. Plagioclase (albite), corundum-bearing plumasite, Val Sabiola, Piedmont, Italy (Perrier, 1930).
11. Peristerite, Monteagle, Ontario (Meen, 1933).   Anal. V. B. Meen (Includes FeO 0·09).
12. Grey, idiomorphic, authigenic albite, in limestone, Raipura, Gangpur State, Bengal, India (Spencer, 1925).   Anal. E. Spencer.
13. Peristerite, Villeneuve, Quebec (Meen, 1933).   Anal. V. B. Meen.
14. Albite ("albite-oligoclase"), Monteagle, Ontario (Chudoba & Engels, 1937).   Anal. A. Engels.

Table 13. ANALYSES OF ALBITE FROM PEGMATITE, NEAR COURT HOUSE, AMELIA COUNTY, VIRGINIA

	1.	2.	3.	4.	5.	6.	7.	8.	9.
SiO_2	68·44	68·22	67·86	68·57	67·66	67·24	67·84	68·17	68·06
TiO_2	—	—	—	—	—	—	0·00	0·01	—
Al_2O_3	19·35	19·06	19·85	19·85	20·58	20·48	19·65	19·62	20·00
Fe_2O_3	—	0·15	0·26	0·16	—	0·12	0·03	0·08	0·04
FeO	—	—	—	—	—	—	0·02	—	—
MgO	—	—	0·28	0·06	—	—	0·04	tr.	—
CaO	—	0·40	0·41	0·21	0·50	0·25	0·00	0·08	0·15
Na_2O	11·67	11·47	10·54	11·27	11·34	11·43	11·07	11·59	11·49
K_2O	0·43	0·20	0·69	0·28	0·11	0·44	0·29	0·28	0·15
H_2O^+	—	}0·69	}0·23	}0·12	}0·21	}0·30	0·56	0·11	0·01
H_2O^-	—						0·30	0·01	0·01
Total	99·89	100·19	100·12	"100·42"	100·40	100·26	99·80	99·95	99·91
α	—	—	1·5286	—	1·530	1·5292	1·529	1·5279– 1·5283	—
β	—	—	1·5325	—	1·534	1·5328	1·533	—	—
γ	—	—	1·5385	—	1·540	1·5392	1·539	1·5378– 1·5390	—
$2V_\gamma$	—	—	78° 8′	—	—	81·8°	79°	—	—
$\alpha':(010)$	—	—	19° 25′	—	19°	18·8°	—	—	—
D	2·605	—	2·625	—	2·626	2·6266	—	2·622	—

NUMBERS OF IONS ON THE BASIS OF 32(O)

	1.	2.	3.	4.	5.	6.	7.	8.	9.
Si	11·989	11·996	11·890	11·935	11·811	11·793	11·964	11·944	11·905
Al	3·996	3·951	4·100	4·073	4·235	4·234	4·085	4·052	4·125
Fe^{+3}	—	0·020	0·034	0·021	—	0·016	0·004	0·010	0·005
Ti	—	—	—	—	—	—	—	0·001	—
Mg	—	—	0·073	0·016	—	—	0·011	—	—
Fe^{+2}	—	—	—	—	—	—	0·003	—	—
Na	3·963	3·910	3·580	3·803	3·838	3·886	3·785	3·937	3·897
Ca	—	0·075	0·077	0·039	0·094	0·047	—	0·015	0·028
K	0·096	0·045	0·154	0·063	0·025	0·098	0·066	0·063	0·034
Z	15·99	15·97	16·02	16·03	16·05	16·04	16·05	16·00	16·03
X	4·06	4·03	3·88	3·92	3·96	4·03	3·87	4·01	3·96
Mol. % ⎰ Ab	97·6	97·0	92·2	97·0	97·0	96·4	98·0	98·0	98·5
An	—	1·9	3·8	1·4	2·4	1·2	0·3	0·4	0·7
⎱ Or	2·4	1·1	4·0	1·6	0·6	2·4	1·7	1·6	0·8

1. Albite, Amelia Co. (Musgrave, 1882).
2. Amelia albite (Day & Allen, 1905).
3. Albite, Amelia Co. (Fischer, 1925).   Anal. N. Sahlbom (1916).
4. Albite, Amelia Co. (Fischer, 1925).   Anal. G. A. Stephen (1921).
5. Albite, Amelia (Meen, 1933).   Anal. V. B. Meen.
6. Translucent, white to glass-clear tabular fragments of albite, Amelia (Spencer, 1930).   Anal. E. Spencer (Optics quoted from Spencer, 1937).
7. Hand picked albite crystals, pegmatite, Amelia (Kracek & Neuvonen, 1952).   Anal. E. Chadbourn.
8. Very clean albite, Rutherford Mine, Amelia (Emmons, 1953).   Anal. R. E. Stevens (1938).
9. Albite crystals, Amelia Co. (Morey and Fournier, 1961).   Anal. P.M. Montalto.

the X group (Na,Ca,K) having a value of 3·9 or greater. Many such analyses are available in recent work dealing specifically with felspars—Kracek and Neuvonen (1952) and Emmons (1953). Reference should also be made to the compilations by Spence (1932), Meen (1933) and Solodovnikova (1935).

In Tables 12–18 the analyses are re-stated in terms of the molecular percentage of the albite, anorthite and orthoclase end-members. These values vary slightly from the weight percentage figures sometimes quoted, being coincident at the albite and anorthite end-members, but having a divergence of approximately 1–1$\frac{1}{2}$ per cent. near An_{50}, where the molecular percentage gives a lower value for the anorthite component than does the weight percentage. The analysed plagioclases are classified according to their Ab/An ratio only, *i.e.* the orthoclase component has been omitted, thus leading to occasional differences in nomenclature : *e.g.* a plagioclase of composition $Ab_{48}An_{49}Or_3$, which may have been referred to as an andesine, here appears as a labradorite.

The analyses here presented do not entirely confirm the contention of Emmons (1953) that the normal amount of the orthoclase molecule in solution in plagioclase felspar is close to 1 per cent. and reaches a possible maximum of 2 or 3 per cent. in common rocks. Emmons, however, was reporting on plagioclase felspars which had been specially purified and inspected for freedom from intergrowths of potassium felspar, while in Tables 12–18 although only three plagioclases were originally described as being antiperthitic it is probable that several more may show intergrowth of a potassium-rich phase to a greater or lesser degree.

In the plagioclase analyses of Tables 12–18 there is no observable systematic variation of silica from the ideal or theoretical value, though if anything a slight deficiency is apparent. In recent discussions (Kracek and Neuvonen, 1952; Emmons, 1953, 1955) a slight excess of silica has been reported in the analyses of some plagioclases, while for pegmatitic plagioclases there is a slight silica deficiency. This has been correlated tentatively by Emmons (1953) with the conversion of such potassium felspar as has exsolved from the plagioclase to sericite with the release of silica, which in common rocks may be trapped in the remaining sericite as silica films, whereas in pegmatitic environments conditions are more favourable for the elimination of released silica. Excess SiO_2 may sometimes be more apparent than real, depending on the method of recalculation, *i.e.* if the ideal figure is taken as that appropriate to the reported Na_2O, K_2O and CaO content it may ignore the small, but by no means negligible, amounts of Ba, Sr and Mg substituting in the structure, giving too low a figure for the theoretical SiO_2 content and indicating that the analysis records excess SiO_2. Analyses which show a slight deficiency of silica are those for plagioclases from pegmatites, as noted by Emmons (1953), *e.g.* Table 12, anal. 1, 2 and 3. See also the analyses of Amelia albite, Table 13, in which the Si value is consistently below the theoretical 12·0 for pure albite although the Z group summation remains close to the theoretical 16·0, with Al replacing Si to a small extent. On the basis of experimental observations a small deficiency of silica is possible : Greig and Barth (1938) considering the system $NaAlSiO_4$(nepheline, carnegieite)–$NaAlSi_3O_8$(albite) were of the opinion that some solid solution occurs in synthetic preparations, and tentatively placed the limit (at 1075°C.) at about 96 per cent. albite (in the nepheline–albite range). It must be remembered also that the classical method of silicate analysis employed for most felspar analyses shows

Table 14.   OLIGOCLASE

	1.	2.	3.	4.	5.	6.	7.
SiO_2	64·92	64·92	64·60	64·70	63·49	64·10	63·08
TiO_2	tr.	—	—	0·00	0·00	0·00	0·00
Al_2O_3	21·34	22·20	22·04	20·72	22·76	22·66	22·90
Fe_2O_3	}1·16	—	—	0·91	0·14	0·14	0·46
FeO		—	—	—	0·04	0·17	—
MnO	0·006	—	—	—	—	0·00	0·00
MgO	0·07	—	—	0·32	0·00	0·25	tr.
CaO	2·18	2·64	2·94	2·60	3·51	3·26	3·80
Na_2O	10·15	9·72	9·28	9·32	9·46	9·89	8·80
K_2O	0·44	0·68	1·27	1·40	0·22	0·05	0·56
BaO	0·008	—	—	—	—	—	—
H_2O^+	0·09	}0·09	}0·12	—	0·52	0·17	}0·32
H_2O^-	0·02			0·06	0·19	0·06	
Total	100·38	100·25	100·25	100·03	100·33	100·75	99·92
α	1·5314	1·534	—	—	1·538	1·5351	—
β	1·5355	1·538	—	—	1·543	1·5393	1·540
γ	1·5408	1·544	—	—	1·545	1·5437	—
2V	82½°(+)	—	—	—	87°(+)	89°(+)	—
α':(010)	—	12½°	—	—	—	11½°	3°
D	2·631	2·637	2·64	—	—	2·646	—

NUMBERS OF IONS ON

	1.	2.	3.	4.	5.	6.	7.
Si	11·449	11·428	11·413	11·486	11·257	11·267	11·206
Al	4·436	4·607	4·590	4·336	4·757	4·695	4·795
Fe^{+3}	0·154	—	—	0·122	0·018	0·018	0·061
Ti	—	—	—	—	—	—	—
Mg	0·018	—	—	0·084	—	0·065	—
Fe^{+2}	—	—	—	—	0·006	0·025	—
Mn	0·001	—	—	—	—	—	—
Na	3·470	3·317	3·179	3·208	3·252	3·370	3·031
Ca	0·412	0·498	0·556	0·495	0·667	0·614	0·723
K	0·099	0·152	0·287	0·317	0·050	0·011	0·127
Ba	—	—	—	—	—	—	—
Z	16·04	16·03	16·00	15·94	16·03	15·98	16·06
X	4·00	3·97	4·02	4·10	3·98	4·08	3·88
Mol. % { Ab	86·8	83·6	79·1	78·2	81·8	82·5	78·1
An	10·7	12·6	13·8	14·1	16·9	17·2	18·6
Or	2·5	3·8	7·1	7·7	1·3	0·3	3·3

1. Pale green, glassy oligoclase ("albite-oligoclase") pegmatite, Kioo hill, 14 miles N. of Sultan Hamud station, Machakos district, Kenya (Game, 1949).   Anal. H. Tanssky.
2. Oligoclase, Monteagle, Ontario (Meen, 1933).   Anal. V. B. Meen.
3. Oligoclase, graphic granite, Monteagle township, Ontario (Walker, 1932).   Anal. E. M. Quinlan.
4. High-temperature oligoclase, rhyolite porphyry, Rabb Canyon, Grant Co., New Mexico (unpublished).   Anal. J. H. Scoon.
5. Greenish, clear crystals of oligoclase, pegmatite, South Carolina (Kracek & Neuvonen, 1952).   Anal. O. von Knorring.
6. Pale green, glassy oligoclase, pegmatite, Kioo hill, 14 miles N. of Sultan Hamud station, Machakos district, Kenya (Game, 1949).   Anal. M. H. Hey.
7. Oligoclase, border to rounded phenocrysts of perthitic orthoclase, rapakivi granite, Head Harbor Island, Maine (Terzaghi, 1940).   Anal. F. A. Gonyer.

ANALYSES

8.	9.	10.	11.	12.	13.	14.	
63·35	61·60	62·96	62·54	61·70	60·87	60·85	SiO$_2$
0·01	0·00	—	0·00	—	0·05	0·01	TiO$_2$
22·89	23·76	23·06	23·31	23·99	23·55	24·44	Al$_2$O$_3$
0·09	0·52	0·22	0·03	0·43	0·24	0·06	Fe$_2$O$_3$
—	0·00	0·00	0·04	—	0·32	0·04	FeO
—	—	0·00	0·01	—	0·01	—	MnO
tr.	0·05	0·04	0·03	0·40	0·23	0·03	MgO
4·09	4·32	4·52	4·38	5·09	4·68	5·81	CaO
8·90	8·55	8·78	8·33	8·81	7·38	7·59	Na$_2$O
0·65	0·58	0·40	0·66	0·17	1·49	0·59	K$_2$O
—	0·03	—	—	—	0·06	—	BaO
0·03	0·58	0·49	0·40	—	0·56	0·43	H$_2$O+
0·03	0·18	0·00	0·20	—	0·38	0·25	H$_2$O−
100·04	100·17	100·47	99·93	100·59	99·82	100·10	Total
1·5386	1·539	—	1·539	1·5403	1·5411	1·543	α
1·5431– 1·5435	1·543	—	1·544	1·5447	1·5452	1·548	β
1·5474	1·546	—	1·547	1·5481	1·5487	1·550	γ
84°(+)– 87·5°(+)	85°(−)	—	84°(−)	82° 25′	87°(−)	87°(−)	2V
—	—	—	—	—	—	—	α′:(010)
2·655	—	2·66	—	—	—	—	D

THE BASIS OF 32(O)

11·218	11·001	11·155	11·143	10·908	10·974	10·876	Si
4·778	5·002	4·816	4·895	5·000	5·005	5·149	Al
0·012	0·070	0·029	0·004	0·057	0·032	0·008	Fe^{+3}
0·001	—	—	—	—	0·007	0·001	Ti
—	0·013	0·011	0·008	0·105	0·062	0·008	Mg
—	—	—	0·006	—	0·048	0·006	Fe^{+2}
—	—	—	0·002	—	0·002	—	Mn
3·055	2·960	3·016	2·887	3·019	2·580	2·630	Na
0·776	0·826	0·858	0·836	0·964	0·904	1·113	Ca
0·147	0·132	0·091	0·150	0·038	0·342	0·134	K
—	0·002	—	—	—	0·004	—	Ba
16·01	16·07	16·00	16·04	15·97	16·02	16·03	Z
3·98	3·93	3·98	3·88	4·12	3·94	3·89	X
76·8	75·3	75·9	74·2	73·2	65·5	67·6	Ab ⎤
19·5	21·3	21·8	21·9	25·9	25·8	29·0	An ⎬ Mol. %
3·7	3·4	2·3	3·9	0·9	8·7	3·4	Or ⎦

8. Oligoclase, Hawk Mine, Bakersville, North Carolina (Emmons, 1953). Anal. R. E. Stevens.

9. Oligoclase, Hawk Mine, North Carolina (Kracek & Neuvonen, 1952). Anal. F. A. Gonyer.

10. Coarse, transparent, lamellar oligoclase, pegmatite vein, Edna Mays Deeps G.M., Westonia, Western Australia (Simpson, 1948). Anal. D. G. M.

11. Oligoclase, Hawk Mine, Bakersville, North Carolina (Kracek & Neuvonen, 1952). Anal. E. Chadbourn.

12. Large cleavage mass of oligoclase, Hawk Mine, Bakersville, North Carolina (Tsuboi, 1923a). Anal. S. Tsuboi (full dispersion data also listed).

13. Reddish oligoclase ("andesine") antiperthite, pegmatite dyke cutting hypersthene–quartz diorite, Volchia Tundra, Kola Peninsula (Vorobieva, 1934). Anal. V. A. Egorov.

14. Coarse crystals of oligoclase, pegmatite, Head of Little Rock Creek, Mitchel Co., North Carolina (Kracek & Neuvonen, 1952). Anal. E. Chadbourn.

8—R.F.M. IV.

Table 15. ANDESINE

	1.	2.	3.	4.	5.	6.	7.
SiO_2	60·38	60·07	62·94	59·78	59·13	58·12	59·03
TiO_2	0·01	0·16	—	0·03	0·02	—	—
Al_2O_3	24·88	24·84	22·04	25·43	25·86	26·05	25·02
Fe_2O_3	0·07	0·35	0·47	0·06	0·05	0·40	0·75
FeO	—	0·21	—	0·07	0·05	0·20	0·45
MnO	0·03	tr.	—	tr.	—	—	—
MgO	tr.	0·02	0·29	0·05	0·05	—	0·02
CaO	6·31	6·65	6·69	7·01	7·44	7·83	7·14
Na_2O	8·12	7·54	7·03	7·17	6·89	6·56	6·73
K_2O	0·12	0·34	1·02	0·25	0·32	0·76	0·46
Sr	—	—	—	0·15	0·08	—	(SrO) 0·28
Ba	(BaO) 0·01	—	—	0·03	0·02₅	—	—
H_2O^+	—	0·04	—	0·07	0·06	0·15	0·29
H_2O^-	0·09	0·05	—	0·01	0·04	0·01	0·00
Total	100·08	100·27	100·48	100·11	100·02	100·08	100·17
α	1·5432	—	—	1·5441–1·5460	1·5459–1·5473	—	1·546
β	1·5476–1·5480	—	—	1·5478	1·5492–1·5500	—	slightly zoned
γ	1·5513	—	—	1·5522–1·5537	1·5526–1·5543	—	1·555
2V	76°(+)–86°(+)	83°(−)	—	84°(−)–82°(+)	85°(−)–84°(+)	—	—
α': (010)	—	—	—	14½°–23°	14°–17°	—	—
D	2·663	—	—	2·663–2·668	2·662–2·666	2·675	—

NUMBERS OF IONS ON

	1.	2.	3.	4.	5.	6.	7.
Si	10·756	10·706	11·161	10·657	10·564	10·439	10·601
Al	5·225	5·218	4·608	5·343	5·446	5·516	5·296
Fe^{+3}	0·009	0·047	0·063	0·008	0·006	0·054	0·102
Ti	0·001	0·021	—	0·004	0·003	—	—
Mg	—	0·005	0·077	0·013	0·013	—	0·005
Fe^{+2}	(Li) 0·014	0·031	—	0·011	0·007	0·030	0·068
Mn	0·004	—	—	—	—	—	—
Na	2·805	2·605	2·417	2·478	2·387	2·284	2·343
Ca	1·204	1·270	1·271	1·339	1·425	1·507	1·374
Sr	—	—	—	0·018	0·010	—	0·029
K	0·028	0·077	0·231	0·057	0·073	0·174	0·105
Ba	0·001	—	—	0·002	0·002	—	—
Z	15·99	15·99	15·83	16·01	16·02	16·01	16·00
X	4·06	3·99	4·00	3·92	3·92	3·99	3·93

		1.	2.	3.	4.	5.	6.	7.
Mol. %	Ab	69·5	65·8	60·5	63·3	60·9	57·2	56·3
	An	29·8	32·2	33·7	35·3	37·2	38·5	41·0
	Or	0·7	2·0	5·8	1·4	1·9	4·3	2·7

1. Andesine, vein of talc–anthophyllite–vermiculite–plagioclase cutting dunite, Corundum Hill, North Carolina (Emmons 1953).   Anal. R. E. Stevens (Includes ZrO_2 0·02, Li_2O 0·02, S. 0·02).
2. Andesine, charnockite, Meanambakam, Madras (Howie, 1955).   Anal. R. A. Howie.
3. Glassy translucent andesine ("oligoclase"), Arendal, Norway (Seto, 1923).   Anal. K. Seto.
4. Andesine, gneissoid granodiorite, Spanish Peak, California (Emmons, 1953).   Anal. L. C. Peck (Anal. also includes Li 0·0005).
5. Andesine, granodiorite, Crestmore, California (Emmons, 1953).   Anal. L. C. Peck (Includes Li 0·003, Rb 0·0004).
6. Andesine ("anemousite"), Linosa, Mediterranean (Ernst & Nieland, 1934).   Anal. H. Nieland.
7. Andesine, ferrohortonolite ferrogabbro (4145), at 2175 m. in the layered series, Skaergaard Peninsula, E. Greenland (Wager & Mitchell, 1951).   Anal. W. A. Deer (Optics quoted from Carr, 1954).

ANALYSES

8.	9.	10.	11.	12.	13.	14.	
58·10	58·95	58·03	57·59	57·31	57·05	56·10	SiO_2
tr.	—	0·00	—	—	—	0·04	TiO_2
26·44	24·79	25·81	25·84	26·32	26·42	27·66	Al_2O_3
0·04	0·77	0·38	0·92	0·53	0·71	0·08	Fe_2O_3
0·15	—	0·30	n.d.	—	n.d.	0·15	FeO
—	—	0·00	—	—	—	tr.	MnO
0·03	0·74	0·04	tr.	—	0·02	0·06	MgO
7·84	7·06	8·01	8·45	8·52	9·55	9·70	CaO
6·48	6·49	6·47	6·39	6·06	5·60	5·48	Na_2O
1·10	0·99	0·46	0·55	1·06	0·64	0·62	K_2O
—	—	(SrO) 0·41	—	—	—	0·15	Sr
—	—	—	—	—	—	$0·02_2$	Ba
0·03	—	0·14	0·32	0·29	0·16	0·10	H_2O^+
0·06	—	0·00	0·05	—	0·10	0·01	H_2O^-
100·27	99·79	100·05	100·11	100·09	100·25	100·17	Total
—	—	1·549	1·551	—	1·553	1·5510–1·5529	α
—	—	slightly zoned	1·555	—	1·558	1·5557	β
—	—	1·557	1·559	—	1·564	1·5576–1·5592	γ
88°(+)	—	—	—	(74°–87°)	—	72°(+)–86°(+)	2V
—	—	—	—	(9·8°)	—	21°–28°	α': (010)
—	2·660	—	2·681	(2·666)	—	2·679–2·684	D

THE BASIS OF 32(O)

8.	9.	10.	11.	12.	13.	14.	
10·413	10·586	10·443	10·382	10·336	10·273	10·103	Si
5·586	5·248	5·475	5·491	5·595	5·608	5·872	Al
0·005	0·104	0·051	0·125	0·072	0·096	0·010	Fe^{+3}
—	—	—	—	—	—	0·005	Ti
0·008	0·198	0·011	—	—	0·005	0·016	Mg
0·023	—	0·045	—	—	—	0·023	Fe^{+2}
—	—	—	—	—	—	—	Mn
2·252	2·260	2·257	2·233	2·119	1·955	1·914	Na
1·505	1·359	1·545	1·633	1·647	1·843	1·872	Ca
—	—	0·043	—	—	—	0·018	Sr
0·252	0·227	0·106	0·126	0·244	0·147	0·143	K
—	—	—	—	—	—	0·002	Ba
16·00	15·94	15·97	16·00	16·00	15·98	15·98	Z
4·04	4·04	4·01	3·99	4·01	3·95	3·99	X
56·0	55·9	56·3	55·9	52·8	49·5	48·3	Ab ⎫
37·7	38·5	41·0	40·9	41·1	46·8	48·1	An ⎬ Mol. %
6·3	5·6	2·7	3·2	6·1	3·7	3·6	Or ⎭

8. Andesine antiperthite, "hypersthene diorite" of the charnockite series, Pallavaram, Madras, India (Howie, 1955). Anal. R. A. Howie.
9. Andesine, Nishishiadamura, Shinana, Japan (Chudoba & Engels, 1937). Anal. A. Engels.
10. Andesine, hortonolite ferrogabbro (2580), at 1700 m. in the layered series, 300 yds. W. of Main House, Skaergaard Peninsula. E. Greenland (Wager & Mitchell, 1951). Anal. W. A. Deer.
11. Andesine in iron-rich diabase, Beaver Bay, Minnesota (Muir, 1955). Anal. I. D. Muir.
12. Andesine, andesine aplite/marble contact, Alta Gracia, Cordoba Province, Argentina (Beder, 1932). Anal. J. Jakob (Optics quoted from Beder, 1927).
13. Andesine ("labradorite"), quartz dolerite, New Amalfi, Cape Province, South Africa (Muir, 1955). Anal. I. D. Muir.
14. Andesine, anorthosite, Essex County, New York (Emmons, 1953). Anal. L. C. Peck (Includes Li 0·002, Rb 0·0005).

Table 16. LABRADORITE

	1.	2.	3.	4.	5.	6.	7.
SiO_2	54·44	55·24	56·18	54·80	54·28	54·01	53·44
TiO_2	—	0·07	—	—	—	0·05	0·02
Al_2O_3	28·97	27·61	27·14	28·36	28·28	29·28	29·58
Fe_2O_3	0·51	1·22	0·54	0·89	0·97	0·05	0·13
FeO	—	—	—	—	—	0·10	0·14
MgO	0·13	—	0·04	0·40	—	0·02	0·06
CaO	10·47	10·70	10·55	10·35	11·27	11·09	11·83
Na_2O	5·57	5·40	5·10	4·90	4·85	4·77	4·51
K_2O	0·35	0·14	0·55	1·02	0·41	0·42	0·26
Ba	—	—	—	—	—	0·02₈	0·05₄
Sr	—	—	—	—	—	0·08₅	0·19
H_2O^+	—	}0·01	0·16	—	—	0·25	0·07
H_2O^-	—		0·08	—	—	0·00	0·00
Total	100·44	100·39	100·34	100·72	100·06	100·15	100·28
α	—	1·555	1·556	1·555	1·5543	1·5557–1·5564	1·5559–1·5560
β	—	1·560	1·561	1·560	1·5573	1·5580–1·5590	1·5579–1·5605
γ	—	1·564	1·566	1·564	1·5621	1·5630	1·5640
2V	—	—	—	—	75½°	70°(+)–78°(+)	68°(+)–84°(+)
α': (010)	—	18°	—	—	20°	26°–30°	25°–29°
D	—	2·712	—	2·690	2·686	2·691–2·697	2·698–2·703

NUMBERS OF IONS ON

	1.	2.	3.	4.	5.	6.	7.
Si	9·803	9·955	10·121	9·861	9·830	9·771	9·665
Al	6·149	5·865	5·764	6·016	6·037	6·244	6·306
Fe^{+3}	0·069	0·165	0·073	0·120	0·132	0·007	0·015
Ti	—	0·010	—	—	—	0·007	0·003
Mg	0·035	—	0·011	0·107	—	0·005	0·016
Fe^{+2}	—	—	—	—	—	0·015	0·021
Na	1·944	1·886	1·781	1·709	1·702	1·673	1·581
Ca	2·020	2·066	2·037	1·995	2·187	2·150	2·293
Sr	—	—	—	—	—	0·010	0·024
K	0·080	0·032	0·126	0·234	0·094	0·097	0·060
Ba	—	—	—	—	—	0·002	0·005
Z	16·02	15·99	15·96	16·00	16·00	16·03	15·99
X	4·08	3·98	3·96	4·04	3·98	3·95	4·00
Mol. % ⎧Ab	45·0	47·3	45·0	42·2	42·7	42·3	39·5
⎨An	51·8	51·9	51·8	52·0	54·9	55·2	58·9
⎩Or	3·2	0·8	3·2	5·8	2·4	2·5	1·6

1. Labradorite ("andesine"), loose crystal lapilli, Monte Rosso, Linosa, Mediterranean (Muir, 1955). Anal. J. H. Scoon.
2. Labradorite, Hawk's Bay, Labrador (Meen, 1933). Anal. V. B. Meen.
3. Labradorite, quartz dolerite, New Amalfi, Matatiele, South Africa (Muir, 1955). Anal. I. D. Muir.
4. Labradorite, portion of original bytownite of Thomson (1836), boulder at Bytown (now Ottawa), Canada (Walker & Parsons, 1927). Anal. H. C. Rickaby.
5. Black labradorite, Province of Quebec (Duparc & Gysin, 1926).
6. Labradorite, anorthosite, Tigerton, Wisconsin (Emmons, 1953). Anal. L. C. Peck (Includes Li 0·002, Rb 0·0008).
7. Labradorite, gabbro, Merrill, Wisconsin (Emmons, 1953). Anal. L. C. Peck (Includes Li 0·001, Rb 0·0003).

ANALYSES

8.	9.	10.	11.	12.	13.	14.	
53·38	52·96	52·97	51·94	52·33	52·38	52·06	SiO_2
0·06	tr.	—	0·05	—	0·11	0·07	TiO_2
29·71	29·72	29·41	30·19	30·22	30·07	30·09	Al_2O_3
0·05	0·84	0·76	0·35	0·40	0·18	0·41	Fe_2O_3
0·14	—	—	0·04	—	0·34	0·25	FeO
0·11	—	—	tr.	—	0·15	0·18	MgO
11·86	12·28	12·59	12·80	12·52	12·69	13·00	CaO
4·44	4·21	3·97	3·88	3·62	3·77	3·64	Na_2O
0·18	0·13	0·26	0·20	0·85	0·47	0·35	K_2O
0·01$_3$	—	—	—	—	0·02	0·03$_9$	Ba
0·15	—	—	—	—	0·10	0·10	Sr
0·06	}0·08	}0·22	0·40	}0·36	0·07	0·05	H_2O^+
0·01			0·12		0·01	0·03	H_2O^-
100·17	100·22	100·18	99·97	100·30	100·36	100·27	Total
—	1·560	—	1·562	1·5630	1·5590–1·5607	—	α
—	1·565	—	1·566	1·5665	1·5640–1·5655	—	β
—	1·570	—	1·571	1·5712	1·5686–1·5700	—	γ
—	—	—	83°(+)	81° 48 (+)	66°(+)–86°(+)	82°(+)–84°(+)	2V
—	23½°	—	—	—	32°–40°	36°–45°	α′: (010)
2·688–2·694	2·705	—	—	—	2·703–2·708	2·701–2·706	D

THE BASIS OF 32(O)

8.	9.	10.	11.	12.	13.	14.	
9·653	9·589	9·614	9·477	9·514	9·500	9·458	Si
6·334	6·343	6·292	6·494	6·476	6·428	6·444	Al
0·007	0·114	0·104	0·048	0·054	0·024	0·066	Fe^{+3}
0·008	—	—	0·007	—	0·016	0·010	Ti
0·029	—	—	—	—	0·040	0·049	Mg
0·021	—	—	0·006	—	0·051	0·038	Fe^{+2}
1·556	1·477	1·397	1·373	1·276	1·325	1·282	Na
2·298	2·383	2·449	2·503	2·439	2·466	2·531	Ca
0·019	—	—	—	—	0·013	0·013	Sr
0·041	0·030	0·060	0·046	0·197	0·109	0·081	K
0·001	—	—	—	—	0·001	0·003	Ba
16·00	16·05	16·01	16·03	16·04	15·97	15·98	Z
3·97	3·89	3·91	3·93	3·91	4·00	4·00	X
39·2	38·0	35·8	34·9	32·6	33·1	32·1	Ab ⎤
59·7	61·2	62·7	63·9	62·4	64·2	65·8	An ⎬ Mol. %
1·1	0·8	1·5	1·2	5·0	2·7	2·1	Or ⎦

8. Labradorite, hornblende gabbro, Shelby, North Carolina (Emmons, 1953). Anal. L. C. Peck (Includes Li 0·004).

9. Labradorite, Millard County, Utah (Meen, 1933). Anal. V. B. Meen.

10. Labradorite, norite of San Marcos gabbro, summit of San Marcos Mountains, California (Larsen & Draisin, 1948). Anal. F. A. Gonyer.

11. Labradorite phenocrysts, Clear Lake, Utah (Kracek & Neuvonen, 1952). Anal. O. von Knorring.

12. Labradorite phenocrysts, basaltic dyke, St. John's Point, Ardglass, Co. Down, Northern Ireland (Hutchinson & Campbell Smith, 1912).

13. Labradorite, anorthosite, Grand Marais, Minnesota (Emmons, 1953). Anal. L. C. Peck (Includes Li 0·003, Rb 0·0006).

14. Labradorite, diabase, Chester County, Pennsylvania (Emmons, 1953). Anal. L. C. Peck (Includes Li 0·002, Rb 0·0007).

Table 17.   Bytownite

	1.	2.	3.	4.	5.	6.	7.	8.
SiO_2	49·46	51·00	51·09	49·55	49·14	49·34	49·06	49·04
TiO_2	0·06	0·06	0·05	0·02	—	0·04	—	0·05
Al_2O_3	31·24	30·99	31·02	32·28	32·72	32·19	32·14	32·17
Fe_2O_3	0·88	0·30	0·28	0·14	—	0·32	0·27	0·33
FeO	0·07	0·21	0·12	0·09	—	0·07	—	0·10
MgO	0·10	0·13	0·27	0·06	—	0·23	0·20	0·08
MnO	—	tr.	0·01	tr.	—	0·01	—	—
CaO	14·00	13·83	13·95	14·80	15·34	15·21	15·38	15·44
Na_2O	3·36	3·29	3·30	2·96	2·82	2·60	2·57	2·49
K_2O	tr.	0·20	0·13	0·17	0·03	0·14	0·17	0·19
Ba	—	0·011	0·006	0·032	—	0·004	—	—
Sr	—	0·14	0·09	0·18	—	0·10	—	—
H_2O^+	0·68	0·14	0·07	0·10	}0·21	0·14	0·13	0·12
H_2O^-	0·34	0·00	0·05	0·03		0·01	0·03	0·00
Total	100·19	"100·31"	100·44	100·41	100·26	100·41	99·95	100·01
α	1·565	1·5632	1·5632–1·5639	1·5634–1·5654	1·568	1·5634–1·5654	1·5657	1·5660–1·5669
β	1·568	1·5657–1·5668	1·5677–1·5682	1·5693	1·573	1·5693	1·5701	1·5717–1·5726
	1·574	1·5713–1·5715	1·5722	1·5718–1·5740	1·578	1·5718–1·5740	1·5754	1·5770–1·5776
2V	89°(+)	85°(+)	82°(+)–90°	84°(−)–88°(+)	—	—	89°(−)	80°(−)–88°(+)
α': (010)	—	35°–46°	41½°–49°	43°–48°	30°	46°–50°	—	44°–50°
D	—	2·710–2·714	2·708–2·714	2·719–2·724	2·719	2·719–2·724	—	2·719–2·727

Numbers of ions on

	1.	2.	3.	4.	5.	6.	7.	8.
Si	9·111	9·282	9·277	9·034	8·969	9·001	8·990	8·983
Al	6·784	6·648	6·640	6·938	7·040	6·922	6·942	6·946
Fe^{+3}	0·122	0·041	0·038	0·019	—	0·044	0·037	0·046
Ti	0·008	0·008	0·007	0·003	—	0·006	—	0·007
Mg	0·028	0·035	0·073	0·016	—	0·062	0·055	0·022
Fe^{+2}	0·011	0·031	0·018	0·014	—	0·011	—	0·015
Mn	—	—	0·001	—	—	0·001	—	—
Na	1·200	1·161	1·161	1·046	0·998	0·920	0·913	0·884
Ca	2·764	2·697	2·714	2·892	3·000	2·973	3·020	3·031
Sr	—	0·017	0·012	0·023	—	0·013	—	—
K	—	0·046	0·031	0·039	0·003	0·033	0·040	0·044
Ba	—	0·001	—	0·002	—	—	—	—
Z	16·02	15·98	15·96	15·99	16·01	15·97	15·97	15·98
X	4·00	3·99	4·01	4·03	4·00	4·02	4·03	4·00
Mol. % { Ab	30·0	29·1	29·0	25·9	24·9	22·9	22·7	22·1
An	70·0	69·7	70·2	73·1	75·0	76·3	76·3	76·8
Or	—	1·2	0·8	1·0	0·1	0·8	1·0	1·1

1. Bytownite, anorthosite, Crystal Bay, Minnesota (Kracek & Neuvonen, 1952).   Anal. O. von Knorring.
2. Bytownite, orthoclase–quartz gabbro, Wichita Mountains, Oklahoma (Emmons, 1953).   Anal. L. C. Peck (Anal. includes Li 0·0008).
3. Bytownite, anorthosite, Grand Marais, Minnesota (Emmons, 1953).   Anal. L. C. Peck (Includes Li 0·0004).
4. Bytownite, gabbro, Lincoln County, Wisconsin (Emmons, 1953).   Anal. L. C. Peck (Includes Li 0·0006).
5. Bytownite (anorthosite?), Crystal Bay, Minnesota (Meen, 1933).
6. Bytownite, part of large phenocryst in anorthosite (all taken from one twin lamella), Split Rock Point, Minnesota (Emmons, 1953).   Anal. L. C. Peck (Includes Li 0·002).
7. Bytownite, norite, Rustenburg platinum mines, Transvaal (Kracek & Neuvonen, 1952).   Anal. A. H. Phillips.
8. Bytownite, norite, Rustenburg, Transvaal (Emmons, 1953).   Anal. Rock Anal. Lab., Univ. Minnesota.

ANALYSES

9.	10.	11.	12.	13.	14.	15.	
47·67	46·59	46·66	47·17	46·34	45·16	46·04	SiO_2
—	—	—	—	—	—	0·06	TiO_2
33·46	33·42	33·40	33·03	33·36	34·32	34·36	Al_2O_3
tr.	—	0·62	}0·82	0·54	0·20	0·88	Fe_2O_3
—	0·80	—		—	—	0·00	FeO
0·35	—	—	0·03	0·38	—	0·05	MgO
—	—	—	—	—	0·009	0·00	MnO
16·23	16·40	16·50	17·05	17·31	17·34	17·92	CaO
2·19	2·04	1·98	1·78	1·55	1·40	1·18	Na_2O
0·07	0·20	0·16	0·05	0·05	0·29	0·09	K_2O
—	—	—	—	—	—	—	Ba
—	—	—	—	—	—	—	Sr
0·00	0·43	0·49	0·39	0·23	0·71	—	H_2O^+
0·00	—	—	0·12	0·03	0·32	0·20	H_2O^-
99·97	99·88	99·81	"100·48"	99·79	99·75	100·78	Total
—	—	—	1·5702	1·5713	1·5695	—	α
zoned	1·5790	1·5760	—	1·5814	1·574	—	β
—	—	—	1·5820	1·5859	1·581	—	γ
—	78°(−)	81·1°(−)	80°(−)	84°(−)	78·4°(−)	—	2V
—	—	—	52°	—	—	—	α': (010)
—	2·756	2·742	2·73	—	2·725	—	D

THE BASIS OF 32(O)

9.	10.	11.	12.	13.	14.	15.	
8·737	8·637	8·642	8·688	8·575	8·433	8·448	Si
7·230	7·303	7·292	7·172	7·277	7·554	7·432	Al
—	—	0·86	0·113	0·075	0·028	0·121	Fe^{+3}
—	—	—	—	—	—	0·008	Ti
0·096	—	—	0·008	0·104	—	0·014	Mg
—	0·124	—	—	—	—	—	Fe^{+2}
—	—	—	—	—	0·001	—	Mn
0·778	0·733	0·711	0·635	0·556	0·507	0·420	Na
3·188	3·258	3·274	3·365	3·433	3·470	3·524	Ca
—	—	—	—	—	—	—	Sr
0·016	0·047	0·038	0·011	0·012	0·070	0·021	K
—	—	—	—	—	—	—	Ba
15·97	16·06	16·02	15·97	15·92	16·01	16·01	Z
4·08	4·04	4·02	4·02	4·10	4·05	3·98	X
19·1	18·1	17·7	15·8	13·5	12·5	10·6	Ab
80·5	80·7	81·4	83·9	86·2	85·8	88·9	An Mol. %
0·4	1·2	0·9	0·3	0·3	1·7	0·5	Or

9. Bytownite, anorthosite, Stillwater, Montana (Kracek & Neuvonen, 1952. Anal. A. H. Phillips.
10. Plagioclase, meteorite (eucrite), Juvinas, France (Game, 1957). Anal. P. M. Game.
11. Bytownite, allivalite, Barkeval Pass, Rhum, Scotland (Game, 1957). Anal. P. M. Game.
12. Bytownite, allivalite (unit 10), N.E. shoulder of Hallival, Rhum, Scotland (Brown, 1956). Anal. G. M. Brown.
13. Bytownite, anorthosite, Stillwater, Montana (Kracek & Neuvonen, 1952). Anal. A. H. Phillips.
14. Bytownite, anorthosite, Bonskar, Stockholm, Sweden (Lundegårdh, 1941).
15. Bytownite, Syowa-Sinzan, Usu volcano, Aubta, Abuta Co., Iburi Prov., Hokkaidô, Japan (Yagi, 1949) Anal. K. Yagi.

Table 18. ANORTHITE ANALYSES

	1.	2.	3.	4.	5.	6.	7.
SiO_2	44·87	45·88	44·17	43·77	43·79	43·54	43·88
TiO_2	0·01	0·04	tr.	—	—	tr.	—
Al_2O_3	34·93	34·31	34·95	36·11	35·79	35·66	36·18
Fe_2O_3	}0·09	0·83	0·56	0·09	0·43	0·58	0·08
FeO		—	0·08	—	—	0·00	0·00
MgO	—	—	0·00	0·07	0·33	0·06	—
CaO	17·41	18·28	18·63	18·73	18·69	19·53	19·37
Na_2O	0·98	0·82	0·79	0·67	0·42	0·26	0·22
K_2O	0·42	0·11	0·05	0·11	0·03	tr.	0·00
H_2O^+	0·59	}0·14	0·84	}0·40	0·59	0·20	0·28
H_2O^-	0·04		0·17		0·06	0·10	0·08
Total	100·04	100·41	100·24	99·95	100·13	99·93	100·10
α	—	—	1·574	1·574	—	1·576	1·5754
β	—	—	1·582	1·582	—	1·584	1·5833
γ	—	—	1·586	1·586	—	1·588	1·5885
$2V_\alpha$	—	—	78°	79°	—	78°	76·8–77·7°
D	—	—	—	2·759	—	—	2·749

NUMBERS OF IONS ON THE BASIS OF 32(O)

	1.	2.	3.	4.	5.	6.	7.
Si	8·353	8·444	8·237	8·125	8·133	8·098	8·126
Al	7·665	7·443	7·683	7·902	7·835	7·818	7·898
Fe^{+3}	0·012	0·115	0·078	0·012	0·060	0·081	0·011
Ti	0·001	0·005	—	—	—	—	—
Mg	—	—	—	0·019	0·091	0·017	—
Fe^{+2}	—	—	0·012	—	—	—	—
Na	0·353	0·293	0·285	0·241	0·152	0·094	0·079
Ca	3·473	3·605	3·723	3·726	3·720	3·892	3·844
K	0·100	0·026	0·012	0·026	0·006	—	—
Z	16·03	16·01	16·00	16·04	16·03	16·00	16·03
X	4·00†	3·92	4·03	4·01	3·97	4·00	3·92
Mol. % {Ab	8·8	7·4	7·1	6·0	3·8	2·4	2·0
An	88·7	91·9	92·6	93·4	96·0	97·6	98·0
Or	2·5	0·7	0·3	0·6	0·2	—	—

1. Large single crystal of anorthite ("bytownite") in vein-like mass in hornblende–actinolite schist, Olricksfjord area, N.W. Greenland (Smith & Yoder, 1956). Anal. E. H. Oslund (Includes SrO 0·70).
2. Anorthite phenocrysts in dolerite dyke, Crookdene, upper Wansbeck, Northumberland, England (Smythe, 1924). Anal. J. A. Smythe.
3. Anorthite, olivine norite, Grass Valley, California (Kracek & Neuvonen, 1952). Anal. O. von Knorring.
4. Anorthite, olivine norite, Pala Mountain, San Diego Co., California (Miller, 1935). Anal. F. A. Gonyer.
5. Anorthite, volcanic tuff, Otaru City, Sirebesi Prov., Hokkaidô, Japan (Takubo, 1941). Anal. J. Takubo.
6. Clear anorthite crystals, olivine eucrite block in tuff, Wadaki, Idu, Japan (Tsuboi, 1935).
7. Anorthite, anorthosite, Sittampundi complex, Salem district, India (Subramaniam, 1956b). Anal. S. S. Goldich & E. K. Oslund (Includes SrO 0·01).
   † Includes Sr 0·076.

an inherent tendency to yield low values for SiO_2 compensated by too high values for the Al_2O_3.

Analyses of *bytownite* and *anorthite* frequently show small amounts of MgO and the problem arises as to whether this all may be considered to substitute for Ca in the structure; from crystallochemical considerations such a substitution appears feasible. In a few cases the MgO reported may, however, represent inclusions of ferromagnesian silicates such as pyroxene or olivine, but as 0·2 per cent. MgO would be equivalent to $\simeq 1$ per cent. of augite it seems unlikely that such a percentage of ferromagnesian impurity would not have been detected and reported (*e.g.* a bytownite, anal. 13, of Table 17, with 0·38 per cent. MgO, is stated to have less than 0·2 per cent. discrete impurities). Some anorthite analyses also show a considerable amount of H_2O^+, and this trend also continues in bytownite, *e.g.* anal. 7 (Table 18) gives 0·28 per cent. H_2O^+ for snow-white transparent crystals of anorthite, and anal. 1 (Table 17) gives 0·68 per cent. for bytownite from anorthosite. On structural grounds, however, there is probably not room for a water molecule within the "cage" framework, and it must be considered unlikely that the water recorded as H_2O^+ is structural water. It is considered therefore that many of the relatively high values for H_2O^+ reported for plagioclase felspars in fact represent adsorbed water or other volatile material, some of it possibly having infiltrated along the relatively well developed cleavage planes.

In *labradorite* and *andesine* analyses MgO is generally fairly low, while Sr and Ba are both found, the former substituting for Ca. Fe^{+3} is relatively abundant with Fe_2O_3 sometimes approaching 1 per cent. The original "bytownite" material has been shown to be labradorite in composition (Table 16, anal. 4).

Washington and Wright (1910) described a plagioclase felspar from the island of Linosa the analysis of which showed it to be seriously deficient in silica: it was considered to be a solid solution between anorthite, albite and carnegieite and was named *anemousite*. Later work by Ernst and Nieland (1934) and by Muir (1955) has, however, shown that material from this locality conforms chemically with the normal plagioclase structural formula (Table 15, anal. 6; Table 16, anal. 1). A number of partial analyses of labradorites and andesines are given by Brousse (1961).

Oligoclase analyses (Table 14) show a tendency for the potassium felspar molecule to increase, and it is in the oligoclase and andesine range that the development of *antiperthite* is usually found: antiperthite is considerably less common in albite and almost unknown in labradorite and the more calcic plagioclases. The potassium content of 76 plagioclases was determined by Sen (1959) who reported that it depended less on anorthite content than on formation temperature and availability of K: the antiperthites are believed to have resulted from exsolution during cooling under appropriate conditions, the K otherwise going to form sericite. It is notable that a high-temperature oligoclase (Table 14, anal. 4) contains an appreciable amount of potassium felspar, apparently in solid solution. Several oligoclases, described as pale green or greenish in colour, show appreciable amounts of both ferrous and ferric iron in their analyses, while the reddish oligoclase antiperthite (Table 14, anal. 13) has 0·24 per cent. Fe_2O_3 and 0·32 per cent. FeO. Aventurine oligoclases from Norway have 0·1 to 0·2 per cent. Fe_2O_3 (Divljan, 1960), but in these the haematite is considered to be derived not by exsolution from the felspar structure but by regional metasomatism.

Albite entirely lacking in the anorthite molecule has been reported from the Varuträsk pegmatite, Sweden (Adamson, 1942), where it occurs with the cleave-landite habit.   Another exceptionally pure albite is the material which has been found in clear glassy crystals of cleavelandite habit in pegmatite in Amelia County, Virginia.   This material is known in many museum collections and probably has been analysed chemically more often than any other mineral from one locality.   It is now known that plagioclase of more than one composition occurs in this pegmatite, the pure albite often being associated with a massive peristeritic oligoclase.   As the analyses of Amelia albite date over seventy years, all the analyses known to the present authors have been assembled in Table 13, from which it will be seen that the results are, on the whole, remarkably consistent.

In general plagioclase felspars have been analysed by the classical procedures for silicate analysis, but recently the determination of the alkalies has been by means of flame photometry.   When a full analysis is not required it has sometimes been sufficient to determine only the three oxides Na_2O, CaO and K_2O, the proportions of the albite, anorthite and orthoclase molecules in the plagioclase then being calculated.   A first attempt at the determination of plagioclase felspars by activation analysis was reported by Bradley and Bradley (1956), who irradiated small amounts of material in an atomic pile for four weeks, and subsequently analysed the resultant radiation.   This method was found unsuitable for the determination of Ca, but was reported to show possibilities for the determination of Na and K.

Experimental work.   Experimental work on the plagioclase felspars can be said to have been begun by Day and Allen (1905) who investigated their isomorphism and thermal properties.   They determined the melting point of natural anorthite, but on progressing to the more sodic plagioclases found that these could persist in the crystalline state for considerable periods of time at temperatures above their melting temperatures, and this has since been recognized as a general property of silicates.   They found traces of melting in natural albite as low as 1100°C.   The equilibrium diagram for the plagioclase felspars (Fig. 47) was determined by Bowen (1913), and shows a solid solution without maximum or minimum, the melting point of anorthite being at 1550°C., and that of albite at 1100°C.   Bowen (1913), like Day and Allen, was unable to crystallize albite and used natural material: Greig and Barth (1938), however, and still later Schairer and Bowen (1956), obtained a melting point of 1118°C. on synthetic material.   From this equilibrium diagram it can be seen that a liquid of composition $An_{50}Ab_{50}$ (A) begins to crystallize at about 1450°C., the first crystals having the composition of approximately $An_{82}Ab_{18}$ (B).   With further cooling and attainment of perfect equilibrium both liquid and crystals change their composition along the liquidus and solidus respectively until at 1285°C. the crystals have reached a composition of $An_{50}Ab_{50}$ (D) just as the last drop of liquid of composition (C) is used up.   This continuous change in composition of the plagioclase crystals with falling temperature is only possible given sufficient time for the earlier crystals to react with the liquid: if there is insufficient time for this interchange of material the crystals will be zoned. The resultant product will then have an average composition of $An_{50}Ab_{50}$ but the inner core will be more calcic and the outer zones more sodic. Thus as a result of fractionation by zoning a continuous offsetting of the composition of the liquid towards albite is brought about, together with a great increase in the range of consolidation temperatures. Such zoning, from more calcic cores to sodic rims, is common in plagioclases, but examples are also fairly common with oscillatory zoning where the composition is alternately less and more calcic: simple

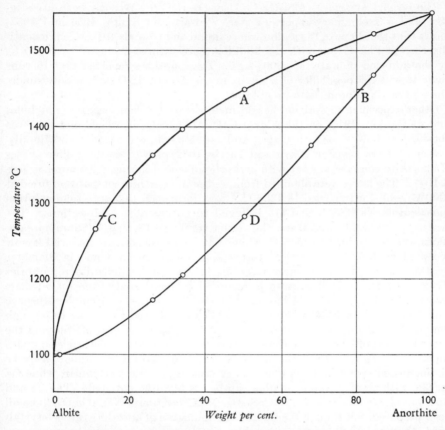

Fig. 47. Equilibrium diagram of the plagioclase felspars (after Bowen, 1913).

reverse zoning where the crystals become more calcic outwards is not rare. The problems of such zoning in plagioclase felspar were discussed by Phemister (1934) in terms of the relief of pressure consequent upon eruption allowing periodic accession of hot magma into higher chambers where crystals are forming. Hills (1936), however, favoured a diffusion-supersaturation theory to account for oscillatory-normal zoning, while the escape of volatiles, the presence of other mineral constituents and a sudden release of pressure were suggested as contributory factors to reverse and oscillatory-reverse zoning (see also Homma, 1932). The occasional oscillatory zoning in the plagioclase of the primary precipitate material of the Skaergaard intrusion, east Greenland, has been described by Carr (1954), who considered that a full oscillation of zoning was achieved during a complete circulation of the crystal around the magma chamber, the reversal being correlated with a relief in pressure on the ascent of the crystal which caused instability and the resorption of its outermost sodic layers. Excellent examples of oscillatory zoning in plagioclase phenocrysts with generally up to about twenty major zones are figured by Leedal (1952) from trondhjemite-porphyrites; one crystal had over a hundred zones.

The ternary system $NaAlSi_3O_8$–$CaAl_2Si_2O_8$–H_2O has recently been investigated and a preliminary report (Yoder, Stewart and Smith, 1956 and 1957) shows that the shape of the region where liquid and crystals are stable is essentially that of Fig. 47 but with the liquidus temperatures depressed over 300°C. by the addition of water at 5000 bars. These authors reported that in runs made to test the possibility of a solvus in the Ab–An–H_2O system only single-phase crystalline products were obtained.

Other experimental work on the end-members of the plagioclase series includes that of Rankin (1915) on the system CaO–Al_2O_3–SiO_2 in which anorthite was obtained at 1550°C. as lath-shaped and tabular twinned crystals, and the discovery by L. B. Wyckoff (Davis and Tuttle, 1952) of two new crystalline phases of anorthite composition but with orthorhombic and hexagonal symmetry (see p. 104). The latter were obtained from a glass of anorthite composition fused at 2000°C. and slowly cooled to 1250°C.: both forms can take into solid solution considerable $NaAlSi_3O_8$ and are believed to be unstable modifications. The melting point of the natural anorthite (An_{98}) of Table 18, anal. 7 (Subramaniam, 1956) was determined as 1548°C. while that for pure synthetic material is now accepted as 1553°C. Anorthite forms spherulites up to 4 cm. in diameter by the attack of lime-bearing slags on fireclay and sillimanite refractories (Hugill, 1944), while bytownite is recorded in fused shale from an oil-shale retort (Phemister, 1942). Albite has likewise been reported from glass-furnace vaults (Belyankin, 1934) where its low 2V was believed to be due to its high temperature of formation. Goldsmith (1950), with the object of studying the exact location of Al and Si in the structure, has prepared synthetic felspars with Ga substituting for Al and Ge substituting for Si. Al and Si cannot easily be distinguished structurally as their X-ray scattering power is similar, while Ga (or Ge) with greater atomic number can be readily differentiated. The Ga and Ge equivalents of albite, *i.e.* $NaGaSi_3O_8$, $NaAlGe_3O_8$ and $NaGaGe_3O_8$, have all been prepared, but though the Ga and Ge analogues of anorthite can be crystallized, they are unstable or metastable. Intermediate compounds were, however, prepared, and the melting diagram for the system $CaAl_2Si_2O_8$–$CaGa_2Si_2O_8$ has the unusual feature of a very close approach to a straight line solid solution, the melting interval being so small that it cannot be detected within experimental error. Synthetic albite and its production has been described by, among others, Greig and Barth (1938), Tuttle and Bowen (1950), Wilson (1950), Schairer and Bowen (1956) and MacKenzie (1957), and is more fully discussed in the section on alkali felspars.

Among other experimentally investigated systems containing a plagioclase field perhaps the most important is the ternary system $CaMgSi_2O_6$(diopside)–$CaAl_2Si_2O_8$(anorthite)–$NaAlSi_3O_8$(albite) (Bowen, 1915). Diopside with albite or anorthite was believed originally to form binary eutectics, but a re-investigation of the diopside–anorthite system, as part of the system $CaSiO_3$–$CaMgSi_2O_6$–

CaAl$_2$Si$_2$O$_8$ (Osborn, 1942), has indicated that the diopside–anorthite relationship may not be completely binary, probably because the diopside present contains a small amount of Al occupying Mg and Si positions in the structure. In the ternary system there is only one boundary curve separating the plagioclase and diopside fields (see also Bowen, 1928). The results of the relationships shown in this ternary system are that plagioclase of a given composition crystallizes at an appreciably lower temperature from a melt containing diopside, and the temperature at which the melt becomes completely crystalline also is lowered. The system NaAlSi$_3$O$_8$(albite)–CaSiO$_3$(wollastonite)–NaAlSiO$_4$ (nepheline) (Foster, 1942) also yielded plagioclase. More recently the liquidus diagram for the CaMgSi$_2$O$_6$(diopside)–CaAl$_2$Si$_2$O$_8$(anorthite)–water system (Yoder, 1954) has shown that, at 5000 bars water vapour pressure, the composition of the eutectic is shifted from 42 weight per cent. to about 73 per cent. An, and the eutectic temperature is lowered to 1095°C. A hypothetical ternary diagram for the system nepheline–anorthite–albite has been given by Greig and Barth (1938), using the previously determined equilibrium diagrams for albite–anorthite (Bowen, 1913), nepheline, carnegieite–anorthite (Bowen, 1912) and nepheline, carnegieite–anorthite–albite (Greig and Barth, *loc. cit.*). The system albite–anorthite–sphene was investigated by Prince (1943) who showed that in the binary system albite–sphene there is a break in the liquidus curve at 92·5 per cent. albite, while in the system anorthite–sphene the eutectic composition is at 37 per cent. anorthite, at a temperature of 1301°C.

Experimental investigations of systems involving only the anorthite molecule of the plagioclase felspars include the anorthite–forsterite–silica system described by Andersen (1915b), which has an anorthite–SiO$_2$ eutectic at 1353°C. with composition anorthite 52 per cent., an anorthite–forsterite–SiO$_2$ eutectic at 1222°C. with anorthite 50·5 per cent., forsterite 23·6, SiO$_2$ 25·9, and a reaction point at 1260°C. Other experimentally determined systems having an anorthite field include:

CaAl$_2$Si$_2$O$_8$–BaAl$_2$Si$_2$O$_8$	Ginzberg, 1915
CaAl$_2$Si$_2$O$_8$–CaTiO$_3$	Nisioka, 1935
CaAl$_2$Si$_2$O$_8$–CaSiO$_3$–NaAlSiO$_4$	Gummer, 1943
CaAl$_2$Si$_2$O$_8$–Ca$_2$Al$_2$Si$_2$O$_7$–NaAlSiO$_4$	Goldsmith, 1947
CaAl$_2$Si$_2$O$_8$–CaMgSi$_2$O$_6$–Mg$_2$SiO$_4$	Osborn and Tait, 1952
CaAl$_2$Si$_2$O$_8$–Ca$_2$MgSi$_2$O$_7$	De Wys and Foster, 1956
CaAl$_2$Si$_2$O$_8$–CaMgSi$_2$O$_6$–Ca$_2$MgSi$_2$O$_7$	De Wys and Foster, 1958
CaAl$_2$Si$_2$O$_8$–KAlSi$_2$O$_6$–SiO$_2$	Schairer and Bowen, 1947

The experimentally determined diagram for the CaAl$_2$Si$_2$O$_8$(anorthite)–KAlSi$_2$O$_6$(leucite)–SiO$_2$ system (Schairer and Bowen, 1947), gives a form for the orthoclase–anorthite relationship which differs from that earlier postulated by Bowen (1928) by having a eutectic rather than a reaction relation. The KAlSi$_3$O$_8$(orthoclase)–CaAl$_2$Si$_2$O$_8$(anorthite)–H$_2$O system has been investigated by Yoder, Stewart and Smith (1956, 1957) and a projection of this system at 5000 bars shows that, at that particular pressure, the maximum amount of CaAl$_2$Si$_2$O$_8$ in solid solution with KAlSi$_3$O$_8$ at 850°C. is less than 3 wt. per cent., and the maximum amount of KAlSi$_3$O$_8$ in solid solution with CaAl$_2$Si$_2$O$_8$ at

850°C. is less than 5 wt. per cent. Some compositions in the system $CaO-Al_2O_3-SiO_2-H_2O$ investigated in the range 400°–900°C. and 5000–42,000 bars H_2O pressure by Pistorius *et al.* (1962) show the phase assemblage boundary of the reaction anorthite + corundum + water = zoisite + sillimanite : the assemblage anorthite + quartz + water is stable at H_2O pressures below 12,000 bars at 800°C. and 14,000 bars at 400°C. In addition to the $CaAl_2Si_2O_8-NaAlSiO_4$ system described by Bowen (1912), the relations between anorthite and nepheline were discussed by Eitel *et al.* (1930) who prepared a large number of compounds with other alkalies in place of Na, and rare-earths in place of Al.

Experimental investigations of systems involving only the albite molecule of the plagioclase felspars include the determination of the system $NaAlSi_3O_8$ (albite)–Fe_2SiO_4(fayalite), which has a eutectic at 84 per cent. albite at a temperature of 1050°C. (Bowen and Schairer, 1936). The $NaAlSiO_4$(nepheline, carnegieite)–$NaAlSi_3O_8$(albite) system was investigated by Greig and Barth (1938) : they found the eutectic at 76 wt. per cent. albite at 1068°C., and, as noted earlier, considered that slight solid solution of nepheline in albite could probably occur. The system $NaAlSiO_4-NaAlSi_3O_8-H_2O$ has been investigated by MacKenzie (1954) who found that the minimum melting composition and temperature under a water vapour pressure of 1000 bars was $Ab_{72}Ne_{28}$ at 780°C., compared with $Ab_{76}Ne_{24}$ at 1068°C. in the "dry" system. Small crystals of nepheline could be distinguished in a preparation of composition $Ab_{95}Ne_5$ crystallized at 700°C., so that at this temperature the amount of solid solution of nepheline in the albite phase must be extremely small. A theoretical discussion of the $NaAlSiO_4-NaAlSi_3O_8-H_2O$ system is given by Morey (1957). Yoder and Weir (1951) considered the thermal expansion and compressibility data for albite, together with nepheline and jadeite, and on thermodynamical grounds suggested that jadeite should be the stable form in the reaction $NaAlSi_3O_8 + NaAlSiO_4 = 2NaAl(SiO_3)_2$. The binary system $NaAlSi_3O_8$(albite)–Al_2O_3(corundum) has been investigated by Schairer and Bowen who reported (1956) that it has a binary eutectic at 1108°C. of composition $Ab_{98.5}$. The system $NaAlSi_3O_8-LiAlSiO_4-H_2O$ was studied at 2000 bars H_2O pressure and temperatures below 900°C. by Stewart (1960) : no measurable substitution of Li for Na in albite was observed.

Goranson (1938) studied the $NaAlSi_3O_8$(albite)–H_2O system and was able to show that the liquidus of albite is lowered by over 300°C. at 3000 bars water vapour pressure. A theoretical explanation of this depression of the melting point of albite, and the solubility of water in the silicate melt of this system, has been given by Wasserburg (1957) who showed that these relationships are governed, to a good approximation, by the perfect solution law, the solution being between oxygen atoms in the water and the bridging oxygen atoms in the silicate. The stability relations of some minerals in the $Na_2O-Al_2O_3-SiO_2-H_2O$ system were examined by Sand *et al.* (1957) over the temperature range 250°–700°C. with water pressures of 15,000 lb./in.², and high-temperature albite was obtained. Wyllie and Tuttle (1961) have demonstrated that in the system albite–water the addition of NH_3 raises and HF lowers the beginning of melting of albite. Further work on systems with $NaAlSi_3O_8$ and water, particularly that of Bowen and Tuttle (1950) on the system $NaAlSi_3O_8-KAlSi_3O_8-SiO_2$, is discussed in the section on alkali felspars.

Further experimental work on plagioclase felspars includes that of Eskola *et al.* (1935) who contrived an experimental illustration of the spilite reaction by heating either synthetic anorthite, or natural basic plagioclase, with SiO_2 and water in a bomb, together with Na_2CO_3 and $NaHCO_3$, the plagioclase being thereby albitized. Pure albite was obtained at 264°–331 °C. and oligoclase-andesine at 360°–550 °C.

Thermochemistry. The thermochemistry of the plagioclase felspars has been investigated by White (1919) who determined the specific heats for varying temperature intervals for albite, andesine and anorthite, and by Kracek and Neuvonen (1952) who performed heats of solution (decomposition) measurements in 20 per cent. HF at 74·7 °C. for a series of analysed plagioclases, several of the analyses of which are given in Tables 12–18. The latter authors found that, as expected from structural considerations, rather than the simple continuous solid solution series found at the liquidus, these natural plagioclases fall into three groups, with divisions 0–30 mol. per cent. An (+ve.ΔH of formation), 30–65 mol. per cent. An (ΔH of formation values characteristic of mechanical mixtures of the two solid solution limits) and 65–100 mol. per cent. An (−ve.ΔH of formation). The latent heats of melting for albite and anorthite were calculated by Bowen (1913), and have been calculated also by Kracek and Neuvonen (1952) from their heats of solution measurements: the latent heat of melting of albite thus appears to be $\simeq 50$ cal./g. while that of anorthite is relatively more uncertain but probably $\simeq 65$ cal./g. The heat of inversion of low-temperature natural albite to high-temperature albite is 13 cal./g. (Kracek and Neuvonen, *loc. cit.*).

The d.t.a curves of some plagioclase felspars were examined by Köhler and Wieden (1954) who found sharp endothermal peaks at 820 °C. and 780 °C. for albite from Rischuna, Switzerland, and for anorthite from Pesmeda, Italy, respectively. These peaks are correlated with the change to the high-temperature form. Less well-defined endothermal peaks were obtained for oligoclase and labradorite, but it was concluded that for all the felspars examined some change occurs at between 780° and 820 °C.

Clouded plagioclases. Some plagioclases appear clouded due to the presence of numerous minute dark particles distributed throughout the crystals. This clouding is distinct from the turbidity due to alteration caused by the development of kaolinite or sericite and is due to the presence of iron-bearing minerals, typically magnetite, ilmenite, or haematite, but also spinel, garnet, biotite, rutile or hornblende. MacGregor (1931) attributed such clouding to the exsolution of iron ore, originally contained in the plagioclase in solid solution, due to thermal metamorphism. This view was criticized by Joplin (1935) and the various theories to account for clouded plagioclase have been reviewed by Poldervaart and Gilkey (1954). In particular, apart from the exsolution theory, it sometimes has been stated that the iron-bearing material has been introduced into the crystal after its formation: a further discussion on the significance and origin of clouded plagioclase will be found in the section on paragenesis.

Alteration. The plagioclase felspars are susceptible to changes under the action of hydrothermal solutions, the more sodic varieties being more stable than those richer in the anorthite molecule. Among alteration products recorded are montmorillonite (Tomlinson and Meier, 1937) where the plagioclase of a gabbro has been altered by magnesian solutions from an adjoining pyroxenite mass, scapolite (*e.g.* Lacroix, 1916), various zeolites including analcite, natrolite, heulandite, scolecite (*e.g.* M'Lintock, 1915), and thomsonite (Caillère, 1942) together with prehnite and other calcium-rich minerals in garnetized gabbros or dolerites. The albitization of more basic plagioclase is also a well-known phenomenon, while the plagioclase in gabbro and anorthosite from deep-sea bores has been reported to show alteration to orthoclase along cracks (Mellis, 1952).

Considerable experimental work has been performed on the alteration of plagioclase. Smirnov (1915) investigated the action of humus at room temperature and of pure water in an autoclave at 151°–158°C. on albite, oligoclase and anorthite: the alkalies and calcium were readily leached out, silica was somewhat less easily dissolved, while the alumina was relatively resistant to solution. Graham (1949) reported that the weathering rates, as indicated by released sodium and calcium, followed the calcium content; anorthite weathered most readily while albite was little affected by the action of hydrogen clay. Thugutt (1935) heated labradorite in a closed tube with water, when Na, Ca and Si were taken into solution, the Na/Ca ratio being twice as great in the solution as in the fresh felspar: by this method albite was found to be relatively more soluble than labradorite. Anorthite treated with HCl at 320°–330°C. was reported to have given kaolin (Schwarz and Trageser, 1933), see also Wichers *et al.* (1944): Norton (1941), however, recorded the formation of montmorillonite or beidellite from anorthite and CO_2-charged water vapour at elevated pressures and temperatures. The solubility of anorthite at 300 bars pressure at 200°–350°C. was measured by Frederickson and Cox (1954b): afwillite and xonotlite develop at higher temperatures. The action of solutions on albite has been studied by many authors: it was reported by Stephenson (1916) to be not appreciably affected by water but decomposed by alkaline solutions to form analcite, with the separation of silica. Norton (1939) recorded the reaction of finely ground albite with CO_2-charged water at 300°C. to form beidellite, while Gruner (1944) was able to obtain almost complete breakdown of powdered albite on heating with various amounts of KCl and $Al(OH)_3$ in $N/10$ HCl to yield kaolinite, pyrophyllite, and small amounts of boehmite. Frederickson and Cox (1954a) suspended crystals of albite in an autoclave with pure water at 200°–350°C. and 300 bars pressure and obtained the breakdown of the crystals into both ions and silicate fragments: much of the material was reduced to particles having colloidal dimensions which constituted an alumina-silica gel, and which subsequently formed crystals of a zeolite (probably analcite). These authors suggested the possibility that fragments of silicate structures, ranging up to 1000 unit cells in size, might be transported through rocks giving rise to local segregations or banding. Morey and Chen (1955) also investigated the action of hot water alone on albite at various pressures and temperatures: at 350°C. and 5000 lb./in.^{2} a large amount of analcite was formed, together with some boehmite, and the original grains of Amelia County albite (see Table 13) were coated with a white powder. The latter proved to be largely muscovite with some paragonite, the muscovite having been derived from the relatively small proportion of K_2O in this albite. In an experiment with albite at 100°C. the dissolved material had a molecular ratio of $Na_2O : Al_2O_3 : SiO_2$ of 2·35 : 1 : 13·57 (see also Morey and Fournier, 1961). Hydrolysis equilibria involving albite and its decomposition products in an aqueous chloride environment at elevated temperatures and pressures have been investigated by Hemley *et al.* (1961). At high temperatures

(> 400°C., 15,000 lb./in.² total pressure) albite is altered to paragonite plus quartz, which may become converted to pyrophyllite; at lower temperatures corresponding reactions are the decomposition of albite to montmorillonite and the alteration of montmorillonite to kaolinite. Brindley and Radoslovich (1956) studied the attack of $N/10$ HCl on albite from Amelia County and from Auburn, Maine, under hydrothermal conditions at about 280° and 430°C.: albite flakes were changed mainly to boehmite with occasional hydralsite ($2Al_2O_3 \cdot 2SiO_2 \cdot H_2O$), while powdered albites gave boehmite, kaolinite and hydralsite. The pH of powdered albite in CO_2-free water was measured by Stevens (1934) as 9·4–9·8, though later Umegaki (1938) using pure distilled water reported a range of pH of from 8·46 for albite to 9·78 for anorthite. The hydration of the plagioclase felspars and their surface chemistry has been discussed by DeVore (1956).

OPTICAL AND PHYSICAL PROPERTIES

The optical properties of the plagioclases are directly related to their albite–anorthite ratios. The relief and birefringence are both low and similar to those of quartz, but although the birefringence is rather irregularly variable the refractive indices increase steadily with increasing anorthite content and can be used to determine the composition of the plagioclase. The perfect {001} and good {010} cleavages, together with a systematic variation in the optic orientation within the series, allow the extinction angles to be used to determine the albite–anorthite ratio, and particular use is made of these in conjunction with the multiple albite twinning with composition plane (010). The optic axial angle for natural low-temperature plagioclase varies from approximately $2V_\alpha$ 75° through 90° to $2V_\gamma$ 75° but changes sign three times in the series, and is of less diagnostic value. Other properties varying with the composition and used for determining the plagioclases include the specific gravity, and the birefringence in sections of known orientation.

Refractive indices. The discovery of the close relationship between the chemical composition and refractive indices of the plagioclase felspars has been recognized as one of the early triumphs of modern mineralogy. With the increasing amount of optical data available on analysed material determinative charts using the refractive indices have been constructed by several authors: amongst recent examples are those by Calkins and Hess (Kennedy, 1947), Chayes (1950) γ-index only, Crump and Ketner (Emmons, 1953), Hess (Subramaniam, 1956) for the more calcic plagioclases, and Smith (1957) for both natural and heated plagioclase felspars. Chayes (1952) reported on measurements given for analysed samples in the literature over the previous half-century and subjected the data to extensive numerical analysis. He was thus able to give five equations covering the three refractive indices over the whole range, with discontinuities at $An_{66 \cdot 1}$ for α and $An_{30 \cdot 4}$ for γ: Chayes also listed the indices α, β and γ calculated from these equations for 5 wt. per cent. increments of anorthite. His determinative chart for the plagioclase series is given in Fig. 48: it is important to note that the measurement of the refractive indices must be accurate to $\pm 0 \cdot 001$ to obtain an accuracy of ± 2 per cent. An. The curves given by Chayes differ slightly from those of Crump and Ketner (Emmons, 1953), and the two sets of refractive indices values have been further discussed by Chayes (1954), who although believing the differences hardly large enough to be of practical concern, considered the discrepancy to lie more probably in the index measurements of Crump and Ketner, rather than in the chemical analyses or the determinative chart. Chayes (1952) also considered the possibility of breaks in the series, but concluded that optical continuity was not disproved by the data.

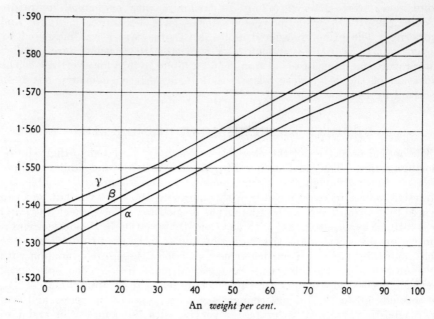

FIG. 48.   Determinative chart for the plagioclase series (after Chayes, 1952).

The refractive indices of high-temperature plagioclases vary slightly from those of the normal low-temperature series, see Table 19. Smith (1957) investigated ten samples of chemically analysed natural plagioclases whose optical properties were accurately known, and heated them either in the dry way or hydrothermally until their X-ray powder diffraction patterns showed

Table 19.   INDICES OF REFRACTION OF NATURAL AND SYNTHETIC PLAGIOCLASE END-MEMBERS (Chayes, 1952).

	α	β	γ
[1] Natural low-temperature albite	1·5274	1·5314	1·5379
Synthetic high-temperature albite	1·527	1·532	1·534
[1] Natural anorthite	1·5768	1·5846	1·5903
Synthetic orthorhombic $CaAl_2Si_2O_8$	1·553	1·580	1·584
Synthetic hexagonal $CaAl_2Si_2O_8$		(ω) 1·585	(ϵ) 1·590

[1] Values calculated from the equations used to construct the determinative chart.

that they had inverted to the "maximum" high-temperature forms. The optical properties were then measured again using the same methods (giving an accuracy of ± 0.0004 for refractive indices and ± 0.0002 for birefringence): the data thus obtained are shown in Fig. 49. Smith (*loc. cit.*) noted that the difference in the α index between high- and low-temperature forms is very slight: measurements of α will thus give a very reliable estimate of the composition of a plagioclase regardless of its structural state throughout the entire composition

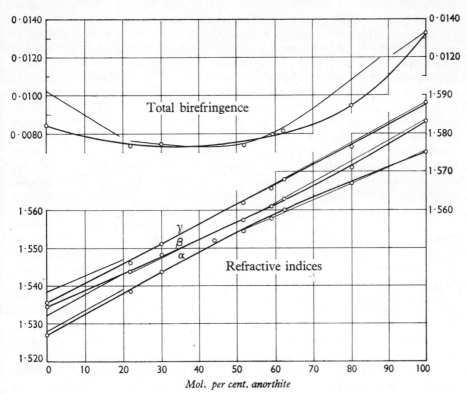

FIG. 49. Refractive indices and birefringence of plagioclases in the low- and high-temperature modifications. Light lines are for natural plagioclase from large plutonic intrusions and the circles and heavy lines represent the same plagioclases after they had been inverted to the "maximum" high-temperature modifications by heating (after J. R. Smith, 1957).

range (for plagioclases more calcic than An_{20} any of the three refractive indices may be used). If the composition is thus determined the structural state may be indicated by X-ray methods (p. 102) or by the optic axial angle.

Although a discussion on techniques is out of place here it is appropriate to mention briefly the various methods used to determine refractive indices. An approximation for the refractive indices of the more sodic plagioclases may be made in thin section by observing the Becke line on boundaries with quartz (ω 1·544, ϵ 1·553), or with the mounting medium where its refractive index is reliably known (that of Canada Balsam may vary from 1·532 to 1·542 depending on age and method of preparation). In this way it may be possible to place a plagioclase more sodic than about An_{48} into one of five compositional sub-divisions (*cf.* Chudoba, 1933).

The normal immersion method using sodium light is relatively rapid and is capable of giving sufficient accuracy of refractive indices of the plagioclase series for normal purposes. When working with cleavage fragments two varieties may be recognized : the perfect basal cleavage {001} and the slightly less perfect cleavage parallel to {010} give fragments lying on a cleavage plane displaying the two orientations illustrated in Fig. 54. The somewhat rect-angular fragments lying on the {001} cleavage have the {010} cleavage almost vertical and show the multiple albite twin lamellae parallel to {010} under crossed polarizers. Fragments lying on the {010} cleavage have a more angular outline due to the intersection of the perfect {001} cleavage with the poor {100} parting at about 64° and no albite twins are visible. The lower refractive indices obtainable from either of these cleavage fragments do not normally differ appreciably, and are also close to the true α refractive index, so that it is usually sufficiently accurate to determine the lower refractive index on an {001} or {010} cleavage flake and to plot this on the α curve to determine the plagioclase composition. The single variation method was applied to the plagioclase series by Tsuboi (1923b) with a later modification (Tsuboi, 1934) : this method uses the dispersion of the refractive indices of plagioclase in cleavage flakes parallel to {001} or {010} in conjunction with an immersion medium the dispersion of which is known. The refractive indices are compared, using a monochromator, until matching is obtained between the felspar and the immersion medium. Further data on dispersion are given by Leisen (1934). Details of the double variation procedure, using variation both in wavelength and temperature, have been given by Emmons (1929a); see also Crump and Ketner (Emmons, 1953).

Larsen (1909) recorded the refractive indices of six synthetic glasses in the albite–anorthite series. From this data it is possible to estimate the composition of natural plagioclase felspars by melting a small amount of material, quenching the molten charge to a glass, and determining the refractive index of the glass. Apart from other advantages the refractive index of an isotropic glass is more easily determined than the refractive index for a known orientation in a triclinic mineral. More reliable data on the refractive indices of plagioclase glasses have been given by Schairer *et al.* (1956), by using the higher purity of the modern chemical constituents of the glasses and the greater number of samples available. The curve of Schairer *et al.*, for which the refractive indices were measured to ± 0.001, is reproduced in Fig. 50. The procedure recommended by Foster (1955) involves the wrapping of a small portion of felspar in a piece of thin platinum foil, and holding it for several minutes in the hottest part of a blow-pipe flame, preferably using an oxygen-gas blowpipe. The heat-treated platinum-wrapped sample is then quenched to a glass to avoid possible crystal-lization, the glassy charge is broken free from the platinum, and its refractive index is measured using immersion media. An alternative technique using fusion of a small flake of plagioclase at the tip of an electrode from which a discharge is passing was described by Gradwell (1958). Advantages claimed for this method (Foster, *loc. cit.*) include lack of any uncertainty as to the optical orientation of the grain, a rate of change in refractive index with composition approximately twice as great as in the indices for crystalline plagioclase felspars, and its ability to give the average plagioclase composition for material with strong zoning or with exsolution intergrowths. The refractive indices are rather similar for orthoclase and albite glasses (1·487 and 1·489 respectively) so that the presence of even substantial amounts of the orthoclase molecule has little effect on the determination of the anorthite content: furthermore the original structural state of the plagioclase is of no consequence. The method does, however, call for a reasonable degree of purification of the felspar prior

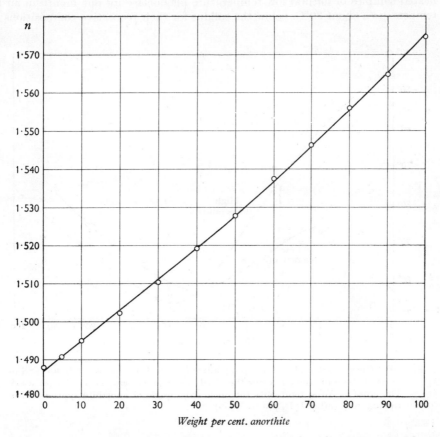

Fig. 50. Refractive indices of glasses of plagioclase compositions (after Schairer *et al.*, 1956).

to fusion, although using the technique outlined by Gradwell (*loc. cit.*) it is possible to select from a thin section a flake free from inclusions. The possibility that the alkali elements might be lost during such high temperature fusions has been discounted by the results of Dawson and Maxwell (1958).

Optic axial angle and optic sign. The 2V of plagioclases for the normal low-temperature series is always large (> 75°), the optic sign being (+) for albite, changing to (−) in the more calcic oligoclase range, becoming (+) again for most andesines and labradorites and reverting to (−) in bytownite and anorthite. Graphs relating 2V to the composition of the plagioclase series have been given by Calkins and Hess (Kennedy, 1947), Poldervaart (1950), Crump and Ketner (Emmons, 1953) and Smith, J. R. (1956). Tuttle and Bowen (1950) showed that high-temperature synthetic albite had $2V_\alpha$ 45° and that this change of optic axial angle and sign from $2V_\gamma$ 83° to $2V_\alpha \simeq 45°$ could also be induced by heating natural Amelia albite at 1080°C. for three weeks. Further results were obtained by heating natural low-temperature plagioclases of various known compositions (Tuttle and Bowen, *loc. cit.*, Fig. 4; Smith, J. R., 1956). The latter author heated samples of natural low-temperature plagioclase for one month in air at temperatures about 30°C. below the solidus for their respective compositions in

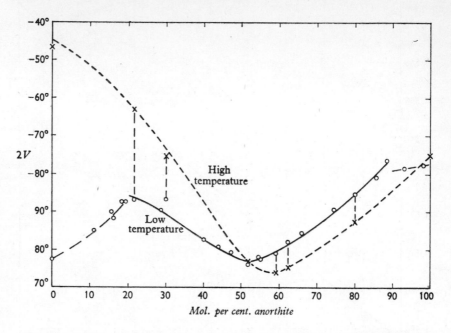

Fig. 51. Optic axial angles of low-temperature natural plagioclases (circles) and of some of the same samples after they had been heated near the solidus (crosses). The cross at An$_{100}$ represents the optic axial angle of anorthite synthesized in the dry way (after J. R. Smith, 1956).

the binary system $NaAlSi_3O_8$–$CaAl_2Si_2O_8$, converting them to the high-temperature form. The data thus obtained, together with the values for the plagioclases in their low-temperature state, are plotted in Fig. 51. In addition to the above mentioned change in 2V at the sodic end of the series, it will be seen that there is a difference of approximately 7° between the 2V of high- and low-temperature forms between An$_{60}$ and An$_{90}$.

In general the use of 2V and/or optic sign of a plagioclase alone is not recommended as a determinative technique: if, however, the composition is known from refractive index measurement or other methods, it may then be possible to determine the thermal state of the mineral by reference to its optic axial angle.

Optic orientation. The optic orientation varies very considerably with the composition (Fig. 52). In low-temperature albite the optic axial plane is approximately perpendicular to z, but in the more calcic plagioclases it tilts over (Fig. 53) until in anorthite it is almost parallel to z. For high-temperature albite the optic axial plane is approximately parallel to x. The positions of the optic axes for light of different colours at various compositions have been measured by Tsuboi (1923a, b) and Chudoba (1925, 1927).

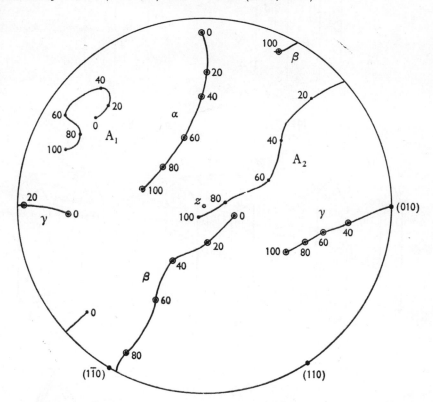

FIG. 52. Stereographic projection of the optic elements of plagioclase on a plane normal to z showing the two optic axes A_1 and A_2, and α, β and γ (after Duparc and Reinhard, 1924).

Extinction angles. Although the optic orientation alone, unless universal stage methods are employed, is not used directly to determine plagioclase compositions, the variation in the optic orientation causes the extinction angles on {001} or {010} cleavage fragments to vary systematically with composition. Determinative curves for use with this method are given in Fig. 54. The extinction angles are measured from the fast vibration direction (α') to the cleavage trace, the sign convention being shown in Fig. 54.

Extinction angles in conjunction with twinning. In thin sections, where the minerals are randomly oriented rather than lying on a good cleavage, plagioclases with an orientation suitable for the determination of their composition by the measurement of extinction angles may be recognized by the occurrence and sharpness of the twin composition planes.

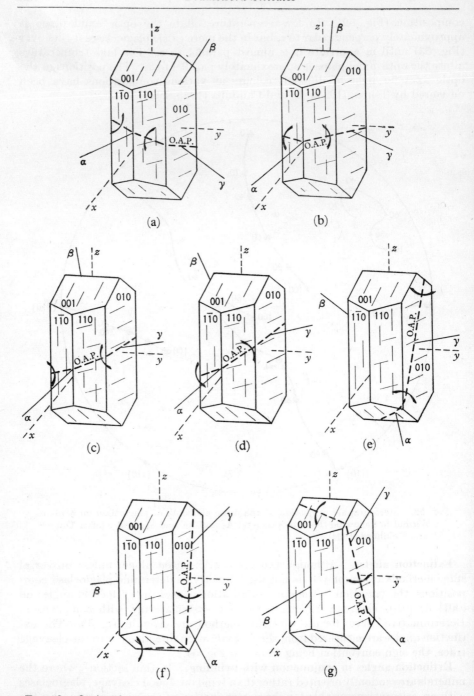

FIG. 53. Optic orientation of the plagioclase felspars: (a) high-albite; (b) low-albite; (c) oligoclase; (d) andesine; (e) labradorite; (f) bytownite; (g) anorthite.

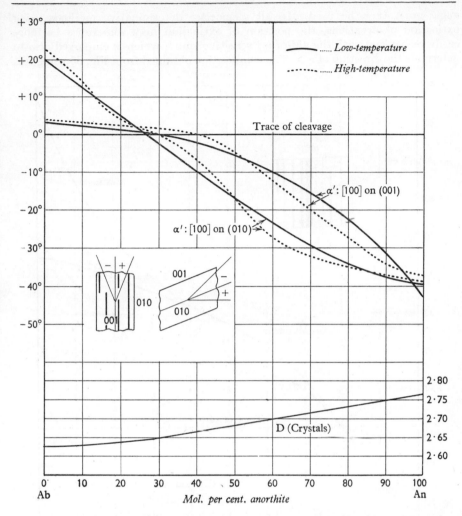

FIG. 54. Extinction angles (to α′) on plagioclase cleavage flakes parallel to (001) and (010); specific gravity of plagioclase grains.

The maximum extinction angles of albite twins in sections normal to {010} or in the so-called symmetrical zone are diagnostic (Fig. 55). In thin section the alternate twin lamellae give symmetrical extinction angles on either side of the twin plane. Such sections may be recognized by the sharpness of the composition plane between albite twin lamellae, which should show no lateral movement when the microscope focus is raised or lowered, by the equal interference colours of the twin lamellae when the twin plane is parallel to the vibration directions of the polarizers, and by adjacent lamellae giving equal extinction angles on either side of the twin plane. Values which show more than a 5 per cent. divergence in the extinction angles for the adjacent twin lamellae should be discarded, lesser variations may be averaged: it is essential to take measurements from several (6–12) suitable grains, and the highest symmetrical extinction angle must then be used. In all plagioclase determinative methods using extinction observations, the position of extinction may sometimes be more easily recognized with the aid of a "sensitive tint", which is employed also to determine the direction of α'. The composition obtained from Fig. 55 using this

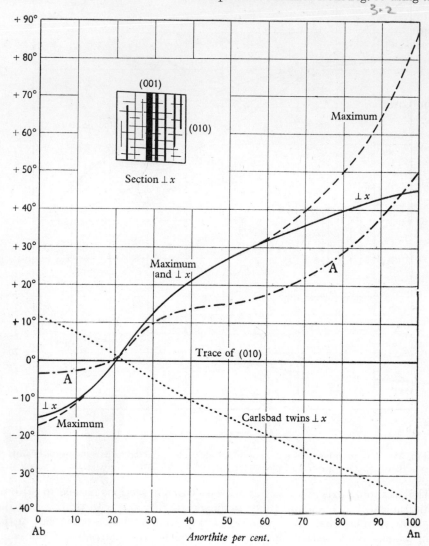

Fɪɢ. 55. Extinction angles (with respect to α') in the "symmetrical zone" and in sections normal to x (see text p. 139).

method is non-unique in that albite and sodic oligoclase may give similar values to calcic oligoclase and andesine: the refractive indices will generally eliminate this ambiguity, otherwise a combined twin method may be used. The latter method makes use of the difference in the extinction of the albite and Carlsbad twins for two individuals related by the Carlsbad law, this difference being given by the dotted curve (A) of Fig. 55: for Ab_{100} to Ab_{24} the maximum difference does not exceed $5°$, while from Ab_{25} to Ab_{50} it rises from $6°$ to $16°$. It is, however, important to be sure that the additional twinning is according to the Carlsbad law and not, for example, Ala B twinning which also has its composition plane parallel to (010): this may be ensured by the precautions outlined in the section below on the use of combined albite-Carlsbad twins.

The extinction angle in sections normal to x is also diagnostic, and varies approximately $1°$ for each 1 per cent. An from An_0 to An_{70} and then by about $\frac{1}{2}°$ for each 1 per cent. An to An_{100}. The composition of the plagioclase can thus be obtained from only one suitable section, *i.e.* it is not necessary to measure the maximum extinction angle for a large number of sections. Such sections are normal to both the $\{001\}$ and $\{010\}$ cleavages, they show the albite twin lamellae on $\{010\}$, the $\{001\}$ cleavage forms an angle of $86°$ with the $\{010\}$ cleavage and albite twin lamellae, and the sections tend to show almost square outlines (Fig. 55).

Extinction angles of combined Carlsbad and albite twins in the symmetrical zone normal to $\{010\}$ have a relationship which enables their measurement on a single section to be sufficient to determine the plagioclase composition, though such sections are sometimes rare. The determinative curves (Fig. 56) are those of Calkins and Hess (Kennedy, 1947). The mean of the two extinction angles on the portions related by the albite law, measured from α' to $\{010\}$, are plotted in conjunction with the extinction angle from α' to $\{010\}$ for the second half of the Carlsbad twin (if the second portion also shows albite twinning the mean extinction angle is again used). Suitable sections may be recognized by the fact that when the trace of the twin plane is oriented at $45°$ to the vibration directions of the polarizers, the albite twinning disappears and the crystal appears to be a simple Carlsbad twin; when the trace of the twin plane is parallel to the vibration directions of the polarizers both albite and Carlsbad twins disappear, or are almost invisible. As will be seen from Fig. 56 (for alternative forms of which see Poldervaart, 1950; Tröger, 1952) this method is of variable accuracy according to the composition, since where the two curves tend to run parallel a small difference in extinction angle corresponds to a relatively large difference in the anorthite content.

As noted in the section on chemistry, compositional zoning is fairly common in plagioclase, and due to the change in optic orientation with composition this zoning may be visible under crossed polarizers. An estimate of the composition of the various zones may be obtained from their respective extinction angles.

Extinction angles in conjunction with birefringence. A method using the polarizing microscope together with a Berek compensator and claimed to allow the estimation of the An content of plagioclase to within 2 per cent. from measurements on the position of the trace of the albite twin plane, the extinction angles for the two adjacent twin lamellae, and the ratio of their birefringences, has been described by Nieuwenkamp (1948). Details of this method, together with the necessary charts, are also given by Winchell and Winchell (1951). Other procedures involving the extinction angles and relative birefringences of albite twins have been given by Cesàro (1916), and more recently by Lafitte (1950, 1951) and by Tobi (1961). The latter methods make use of quartz (or other uniaxial minerals of constant optical properties) in proximity to the plagioclase to determine the thickness and hence the birefringence of the plagioclase. This makes use of a diagram relating the birefringence of quartz for progressive inclinations of the optic axis to the plane of the section (this inclination being derived with sufficient accuracy from the interference figure).

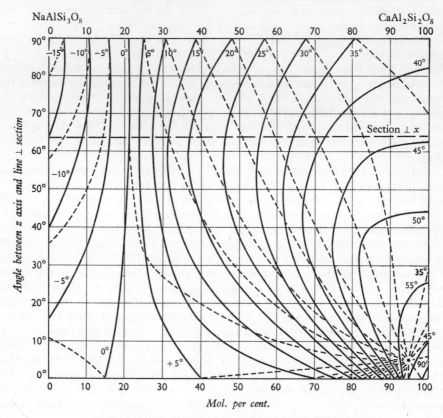

Solid curves for individual A, broken curves for individual B

FIG. 56. Variation of extinction angles of combined Carlsbad-albite twins in the plagioclase series (after Calkins and Hess, *in* Kennedy, 1947).

Universal stage methods. A full description of methods of determining plagioclase compositions and twin laws by means of the universal microscope stage is beyond the scope of this text, but the more important references on the subject are listed here. The three most comprehensive accounts written in English are those of Chuboda (1933), Emmons (1943) and Turner (1947), the first and last dealing with the 4-axis universal stage while the memoir of Emmons deals with the 5-axis stage earlier devised by that author (Emmons, 1929b). The work by Chudoba deals specifically with the zonal method (Rittmann, 1929), which is quicker than the Fedorov–Nikitin method, and gives results which compare tolerably well with those obtained by the more complete study: a further advantage is its applicability to small twin lamellae and microliths—it is of most use for compositions more sodic than An_{60}. The paper by Turner presents a concise account of the procedure of Nikitin (1936) for the determination of plagioclase, with special reference to the ambiguous cases at the sodic and calcic ends of the plagioclase series: a series of graphs are given with the optical data from the comprehensive coloured plate of Nikitin (*loc. cit.*) allowing twin laws and anorthite content to be determined simultaneously. Slemmons (1962) has substituted for the curves of Turner (*loc. cit.*) new curves for both low-temperature and high-temperature plagioclase, and the procedure for determining the twin law has been modified. These new curves in addition to giving the composition of the plagioclase will usually indicate also whether a given specimen has high-temperature, low-temperature, transitional or combined optical properties. A classical earlier description of the principles and applications of the universal stage to the determination of plagioclases is given by Duparc and Reinhard (1923), see also Reinhard (1931). An extension of Emmons' 5-axis stage methods allowing the determination of the crystallographic directions without any intermediary graphic constructions has been described by Zavaritsky (1942, 1943).

The discrepancies sometimes observed between points plotted from data measured with the universal stage and the standard curves were noted by Barber (1936a) who considered that physical conditions, especially temperature, prevailing at the time of crystallization were probably responsible for the observed variations. Later workers have shown that there are considerable variations in optical orientation between low- and high-temperature plagioclases, the differences being most marked at the sodic end and decreasing towards An_{70}. Köhler (1941) described a method of determining plagioclases by measuring the angles between equivalent optical directions in related twin lamellae: the optical orientations of two related twin lamellae are plotted on a stereographic projection parallel to (010) and the angles $\alpha\alpha'$ and $\gamma\gamma'$ are measured across (010), while $\beta\beta'$ is the supplement of the appropriate angle measured across (010). The several measurements should be mutually consistent, but for high-temperature plagioclases inconsistent results were obtained using curves from Reinhard's data. Köhler (*loc. cit.*), Tertsch (1941, 1942, 1943, 1944), Scholler (1942) and Oftedahl (1944) have all extended the data on high-temperature variations in optical orientation, and useful summaries have been given by Wenk (1945) and by Köhler (1949): see also Reynolds (1952). A compilation of previous data together with many new determinations was made by van der Kaaden (1951) who was not able, however, to accept the high-temperature optics of Tertsch, as much larger optical deviations obtained by later workers indicated that equilibrium was not reached in Tertsch's synthetic preparations. More recent papers reviewing the data and presenting further observations are those by Bradley (1953) and Muir (1955). A modification of the zonal method and its use for the distinction between high- and low-temperature plagioclases has been described by Rittmann and El-Hinnawi (1961).

Specific gravity. The specific gravities of albite and anorthite were determined by Ahlers (1924) as 2·611 and 2·752 respectively, while Chudoba (1936) after reviewing earlier results gave values of 2·618 for albite and 2·758 for anorthite (microcline 2·558) and tables of specific gravities for each 10 per cent. variation in composition from Ab_0 to Ab_{100}, and with Or_0 to Or_{20}, assuming straight line relationships. Poldervaart (1950) and Tröger (1952) both show a slightly curved relationship for this property between 2·625 for albite and 2·760 for anorthite (Fig. 54). Poldervaart (*loc. cit.*) also illustrates the straight line relationship for the specific gravities of plagioclase glasses from 2·38 for albite glass to 2·70 for anorthite glass (*cf.* Larsen, 1909). In view of the difficulties usually experienced in obtaining accurate values for mineral specific gravities, and since an accuracy of $\pm 0\cdot01$ will give only approximately ± 7 per cent. An content (or ± 3 per cent. for the glasses), its use as a determinative property is not recommended. The specific gravity of a Norwegian bytownite (2·71 at 20°C., 2·61 for its glass at 20°C.) at its melting point of approximately 1480°C. was calculated to be 2·63, and the specific gravity of the glass at its melting point was 2·52 (Dane, 1941).

Infra-red absorption spectra. Hunt *et al.* (1950) first determined the infra-red spectra of albite, oligoclase, and anorthite, and these spectra were found to show a marked difference in the number and positions of the absorption bands. Thompson and Wadsworth (1957) later obtained infra-red patterns for 18 plagioclases of known composition and were able to show a systematic variation in the wavelength of the absorption bands with chemical composition. The band in the 15·4–16·2 micron region is particularly useful in this respect and does not appear to be influenced by the high- or low-temperature history of the sample : a definite structural change is indicated at about An_{31-33}.

The effect of heat on optics. The variation of optical properties for plagioclase crystallized at high temperatures was noted by Belyankin (1934) who reported albite, from a glass-furnace vault, with $2V_\alpha 31°$–$34°$. A systematic experimental investigation on the effect of heat on natural albite, andesine, labradorite and anorthite was carried out by Barber (1936b) who heated these materials to 1000°C. for 200–500 hours and was able to report only minor shifts in the position of the (010) pole, determined on the universal stage, and variations in 2V only within the limits of experimental error (*cf.* Barth, 1931). Later, Spencer (1937) found that on heating Amelia albite for 300 hours at 1075°C. $2V_\alpha$ became 35°–60°, the specimen showed a uniform extinction of 8° on (010), the position of the optic axial plane changed considerably, and the specific gravity fell by 0·006. Later investigations by Köhler (1941), Scholler (1942) and Tertsch (1942) using universal stage techniques on heated specimens have been discussed in a previous section. The conversion of low-temperature plagioclases into the high-temperature form by heating was also carried out by Tuttle and Bowen (1950) who gave details of the optical orientation of high-temperature albite : further work on the optics of heated plagioclases includes that by Muir (1955) and Smith, J. R. (1956).

Miscellaneous physical properties. The linear thermal expansion of plagioclases was measured by Kôzu and Ueda (1933) who used analysed specimens of albite, oligoclase, andesine, and anorthite, and investigated the expansion in three mutually perpendicular directions. The volume thermal expansion of albite is the greatest, with 2·96 per cent. at 1000°C., falling to 1·96 per cent. for oligoclase and 1·45 per cent. for anorthite. Anorthite was also investigated by Rigby and Green (1942) who showed it to have a well-defined maximum coefficient of expansion at about 820°C. The hardness of the plagioclase series was investigated by Holmquist (1914).

Aventurine felspars in the albite, oligoclase, and labradorite ranges were investigated by Andersen (1915a) who reported reflecting lamellae of haematite (which disappear on heating to 1235°C.) parallel to {112} and {150}, causing aventurization on {001} and {010} respectively. Aventurine inclusions of metallic copper in colourless transparent labradorite have also been recorded (Andersen, 1917). The colours sometimes shown by labradorite were investigated by Lord Rayleigh (1923) who described the diffuse strongly coloured reflection as coming from a plane at approximately 15° from (010) and 84° from (001): with side illumination a patchy structure was seen, the colours perhaps being due to an interference phenomenon. Bøggild (1924) also considered this feature, which he called *labradorescence* as distinct from aventurism. He distinguished the sky-blue *peristerite* schiller effects (see section on morphology and twinning) from the brilliant coloured reflections of labradorite. In the latter case the colours were again attributed to an interference effect, but from enclosed lamellae of a substance with a refraction near that of the plagioclase; no reflecting lamellae were detected microscopically. The phenomenon of labradorescence, however, has not been conclusively explained.

Colour. Plagioclase is usually colourless when entirely fresh but typically has a white appearance due to incipient alteration. Other colourations sometimes found are generally due to inclusions: for example, anorthite crystals several inches in length in xenoliths (Thomas, 1922) are pink or blue from enclosed sillimanite or corundum (sapphire), while the bytownite of a contaminated eucrite from Carlingford, Eire, is so full of iron ore as to be almost black in hand specimen (Nockolds, 1938); the same effect may also be seen in the labradorite of anorthosite from the Egersund area of Norway in which the coarse plagioclase crystals are very dark grey to black in colour and can be seen in thin section to be crowded with iron ore inclusions. Although less commonly fluorescent than potassium felspar, plagioclase sometimes shows this property, as for example the plagioclase in a quartz diorite from the Vosges which has a raspberry-red fluorescence in ultra-violet light (Gagny, 1957). Low-temperature albite containing inclusions of uraninite which are surrounded by prominent extinction haloes in the albite has been described from the Cloncurry District of Queensland (McAndrew, 1957). These haloes are due to radiation damage of the albite by α-particle bombardment and in them $2V_\alpha$ is 61°, compared with $2V_\gamma$ 77° for the normal albite, and a 48° rotation of the optical indicatrix has taken place. It is considered that this radiation damage is likely to be associated with the dislocation of oxygen atoms from the $(Si,Al)O_4$ tetrahedra or with rearrangement of $Na(K,Ca)$.

DISTINGUISHING FEATURES

In thin section the plagioclase felspars may be distinguished by their low relief, lack of colour, low birefringence, and the biaxial character of their interference figure. The albite twinning on {010} giving rise to lamellae of different birefringence is characteristic: in its absence, or in a section approaching parallelism to {010}, the presence of a good cleavage may distinguish it from quartz and the refractive indices may distinguish it from the potassium felspars. In thin section, if untwinned plagioclase is thought to be present, it may be advantageous to stain the potassium felspars, using sodium cobaltinitrite (Rosenblum, 1956). Although cordierite sometimes shows twinning and occurs in transparent grains with similar optical characters, its tendency to form yellowish alteration products may distinguish it. The distinction of untwinned plagioclase from quartz relies on the lack of cleavage in the latter, together with its uniaxial character and generally fresher and clearer appearance. Methods for rapid distinction of untwinned plagioclase from quartz with the universal stage are given by Dodge (1936), Doeglas (1940) and Gilbert and Turner (1949). Although the sodic plagioclases are insoluble in most acids, beyond about An$_{50}$ they begin to be attacked by HCl, and anorthite is entirely decomposed by HCl with the separation of gelatinous silica.

The determination of individual plagioclases within the series is covered mainly by the previous section dealing with optical properties: reference should also be made to the structural section for determinative methods using X-ray powder diffraction patterns. In general the determination of a refractive index is recommended, or the determination of the refractive index of the plagioclase glass. In thin section, in the absence of universal stage techniques, an extinction angle method giving a unique solution is to be preferred, such as the method using combined albite–Carlsbad twinning. For zoned crystals the measurement of the refractive index of the glass is a convenient method to obtain the bulk composition while the composition of individual zones may be estimated by a study of their extinction angles. The measurement of 2V on slightly zoned crystals will tend to give too high an An content as the 2V is usually measured at the centre of a grain. An indication of the thermal history of the material may be obtained from the 2V curves of Fig. 51 if the composition of the plagioclase also is determined by other techniques. The small amount of the orthoclase molecule occurring in most plagioclases does not appear to affect their optical properties, but if more than 10 per cent. Or is present the optical properties may be appreciably altered (Chudoba and Engels, 1937).

PARAGENESIS

Volcanic rocks. Plagioclase is the most abundant mineral of many basalts, occurring both as phenocrysts and in the groundmass. In lavas belonging to a differentiation series the more calcium- and more sodium-rich plagioclase is usually only weakly zoned, but in the plagioclases of intermediate composition the zoning frequently extends over a wide range, and is often oscillatory in character. In many basalts, as in the early primary precipitation felspars of plutonic rocks, the composition of the wide homogeneous core of the plagioclase phenocrysts is bytownite. These cores usually are surrounded by narrow zones of more sodium-rich plagioclase the compositional range of which may exceed 40 per cent. of the anorthite molecule. Plagioclase of anorthitic composition is reported in the basalts, as well as in the early segregations of the basaltic magmas, represented by olivine eucrite and allivalite cognate ejecta, of the Hakone volcano and adjacent areas (Kuno, 1950). Such calcium-rich compositions are rare in basalts, and a statistical study of the plagioclase phenocrysts in the lavas of the San Juan region (Larsen and Irvine, 1938) showed that the composition of the plagioclase phenocrysts varies from An$_{83}$ to An$_{11}$. The average composition of the phenocrysts in these basalts is An$_{70}$, and in the siliceous rhyolites is An$_{27}$; plagioclase phenocrysts richer in sodium than An$_{20}$ are uncommon. The proportion of plagioclase phenocrysts is low in these basalts, high in the andesites and quartz latites, and low in the siliceous rhyolites.

In the olivine basalt–trachyte province of central Victoria (Edwards, 1938) the plagioclase phenocrysts in the basalts are rarely more calcium-rich than An_{52}; those of the groundmass vary between An_{60} and An_{25}. From a study of the fractionation stages of the Hawaiian lavas, Wager (1956) has shown that the albite content (normative molecular albite to normative molecular albite+ anorthite) varies from 38·8 to 60·6 per cent. in the early fractionation stages, from 58·7 to 79·3 per cent. in the late fractionation stages, and from 92 to 100 per cent. in the later differentiates. There is considerable evidence that the plagioclase phenocrysts in some lavas did not crystallize from the magma in which they were extruded. The wide cores, frequently of bytownite, indicate slow crystallization and settling into the magma which finally consolidated to form the lavas, and their composition is rich in calcium in relation to the overall composition of the rock. Thus in the pyroxene andesites of the San Juan region the composition of the plagioclase phenocrysts is An_{60}, and in the siliceous rhyolites, An_{27}. Larsen and Irvine (1938) have shown that in these lavas there is little relationship between the anorthite content of the plagioclase phenocrysts and either the normative composition of the plagioclase of the rock, or of the groundmass.

Plutonic rocks. Anorthite is not a common constituent of plutonic rocks, but has been described from olivine norite (Table 18, anal. 3), from troctolite associated with normal gabbros containing labradorite (Table 18, anal. 4), and as phenocrysts in dolerite (Table 18, anal. 2). The plagioclase An_{98} of some of the anorthosite bands in the layered complex of Sittampundi (Subramaniam, 1956b) are the most calcium-rich felspars that have been described. As these rocks have been strongly metamorphosed they may not be directly comparable with the felspar-rich bands of other layered complexes. In many plutonic rocks the first felspar to crystallize is bytownite. Thus the mean composition of the unzoned crystals, and the cores of the zoned plagioclase (Table 17, anal. 12), in the layered ultrabasic rocks of Rhum (Brown, 1956) is Ab_{85}. In this and other basic and ultrabasic complexes the plagioclase of the felspar-rich layers, representing an accumulation of primary precipitate felspar, is well formed and free from conspicuous zoning. Where the plagioclase occurs in olivine-rich layers containing no primary precipitate plagioclase, but has crystallized from interprecipitate liquid, the texture is often poikilitic, and the crystals show an appreciable range in zonal composition. Plagioclase compositions comparable with those in the Rhum allivalites has been described from the layered rocks of the Stillwater complex (Table 17, anals. 9, 13). The plagioclase of the lower layered rocks of the Great Dyke of Southern Rhodesia (Hess, 1950) is An_{76}, and in the upper group, An_{44}. Similar variations in the composition of plagioclase occur in many differentiated sills, thus the cores of the plagioclase of the Basistoppen Raft sill, east Greenland (Hughes, 1956), vary from An_{76} in the basal picrite to An_{45} in the upper pigeonitic gabbros.

In the strongly fractionated layered Skaergaard intrusion, east Greenland (Wager and Deer, 1939), the plagioclase of the chilled margin is moderately strongly zoned, and the average composition about An_{60}. The composition of the plagioclase in the lowest exposed rocks of the layered series is An_{61}, the composition becoming more sodium-rich (Table 15, anals. 7, 10) in the more highly differentiated rocks, and reaching An_{30} in the fayalite ferrogabbro. The zoning of the primary precipitate felspars in these rocks, apart from zoning resulting from the crystallization of the interprecipitate liquid, is not more than six or seven per cent. of the anorthite molecule. At least at one horizon in the layered series a small proportion of the primary precipitate felspar shows oscillatory normal zoning (Carr, 1954). In these crystals as many as three reversals occur, the magnitude of which is estimated as three per cent. anorthite, and the overall range in composition is six per cent. anorthite. Carr has suggested that the simple normal zoning shown by the majority of the crystals is the result of increasing hydrostatic pressure. The number of reversals is thus correlated with the number of times the crystal was carried round in the magma before its final accumulation at the base of the convecting magma.

The felspars of the calc-alkaline rock series include almost the whole range of plagioclase compositions. The most calcic plagioclase in the rocks of the Southern California batholith (Larsen, 1948) has a composition $Or_{0.6}Ab_{5.8}An_{93.6}$ (range An_{85}–An_{95}) and occurs in a hornblende gabbro; the plagioclase is An_{45} in a quartz biotite norite, and $Or_{3.4}Ab_{78.3}An_{18.3}$ in the granodiorite. The composition of the plagioclase varies sympathetically with the composition of the rock, and the anorthite content may be correlated with the $(\frac{1}{3}SiO_2 + K_2O - FeO - MgO - CaO)$ values of the associated rocks. The percentage of modal plagioclase varies from 60 per cent. in the gabbros to 50 per cent. in the granodiorites, and decreases to less than 20 per cent. in the plagioclase-poor granites. In this rock series the intensity of the plagioclase zoning is greatest in the more acid rocks. In many complexes with calc-alkaline affinities the plagioclase in the basic rocks is less rich in calcium than those of the Southern California batholith; thus the composition of the plagioclase in the gabbros of the Garabal Hill–Glen Fyne complex (Nockolds, 1941) varies between An_{63} and An_{53}, is An_{42} to An_{27} in the diorites, and An_{20} in the granodiorite.

Pegmatites. The plagioclase in pegmatites is generally albite (Table 12 anals. 1, 3: Table 13, anals, 1–9) or oligoclase (Table 14, anals. 1, 5, 6, 14). The albite of many pegmatites shows no evidence of transitional states between the low- and high-temperature forms. The albite variety pericline, however, common in alpine veins, sometimes associated with adularia, and formed at low temperatures, shows indications of crystallization in an intermediate- or high-temperature form. Its partial transformation to the stable low-temperature form may be due (MacKenzie, 1957) to the lack of sufficient energy, at the low water pressures and low temperatures of crystallization, to promote ordering of the aluminium and silicon atoms. Similar reasons have been suggested by Laves (1952) to explain the variations in the crystallography and optical properties of adularia.

Anorthosites. The plagioclase felspars of the anorthosites vary widely in composition. In many anorthosite masses the plagioclase is in the andesine-labradorite range (Table 15, anal. 14; Table 16, anals. 6 and 13). The composition of the plagioclase in the typical anorthosites of the Adirondacks (Buddington, 1939) varies between An_{38} and An_{50}, and in those of the Bergen Arc from An_{30} to An_{52} (Kolderup and Kolderup, 1940). The plagioclase of the small anorthosite–gabbro mass at Kadavur (Subramaniam, 1956a) is An_{50}–An_{58}, and of the anorthosites of the Ahvenisto massif (Savolahti, 1956) An_{53}–An_{58}. The plagioclase in some of the west Greenland anorthosites is richer in calcium than is usual in large masses of these rocks, e.g. Qaqortorssuaq (Ellitsgaard-Rasmussen and Mouritzen, 1954) An_{60}–An_{80}, and Buksefjorden, An_{70}–An_{80}

(Sørensen, 1955). The plagioclase of the Bönskar anorthosite in Sweden (Lundegårdh, 1941) is calcium bytownite, $An_{85.8}$ (Table 17, anal. 14).

Spilites. Albite is the most distinctive mineral of the spilites and, together with the high sodium content of the rocks, is the most characteristic feature of these basic lavas. In some spilites relict labradorite or andesine occurs enclosed within albite, and this relationship is considered as evidence that the present composition of the plagioclase is the result of a late magmatic metasomatic process by which rocks that crystallized as normal basalts have been modified by albitization to form spilites. In some spilites the presence of vesicles containing albite and albite veinlets is regarded as additional evidence of sodium metasomatism. It has been demonstrated by Eskola *et al.* (1935) that in a closed system anorthite reacts with sodium carbonate solution and silica, at temperatures below approximately 330°C. and at 220 atmospheres pressure, to give albite and calcite. In this reaction the formation of albite from basic plagioclase takes place without any appreciable volume change, thus sodium and silicon must enter the calcium-rich plagioclase and calcium and aluminium must be removed:

$$CaNaAl_3Si_5O_{16} + Na^+ + Si^{+4} \rightarrow 2NaAlSi_3O_8 + Ca^{+2} + Al^{+3}$$

In other spilites there is no textural evidence that the albite is not a product of normal magmatic crystallization from residual igneous liquids derived from magmas originally of olivine basalt or tholeiitic composition. Battey (1956) has described a suite of spilitic rocks from North Island, New Zealand, which represents a fairly complete range of petrographic types of decreasing basicity, the more siliceous of which are transitional in composition to the associated keratophyres. The plagioclase of the spilites is a fresh and unaltered low-albite developed in curved growth forms and as forked and hollow microliths. Battey concluded that the albite is a product of magmatic crystallization in a highly hydrous environment in which the early plagioclase reacted continuously with the liquid and thus became progressively enriched in sodium. The calcium released in the reaction enters into the formation of the associated clinopyroxene. Crystallization from volatile-rich basic magma has also been put forward to explain the texture and mineralogy of the albite diabase and albitite sills in the Enontekiö and Kittilä areas, Finland (Meriläinen, 1961).

In a recent study of the spilite problem, Nicholls (1958) has questioned the view that all these rocks are wet basalts derived by modification of the normal course of crystallization by unusual concentration of volatiles. Nicholls suggested that certain features of the lower spilites of the Builth volcanic series owe their origin to the immiscible separation, during the consolidation of the magma, of a liquid phase rich in volatiles, Ca, Mg and Fe, from a silicate residual magmatic liquid enriched in Na and Si. The separation of the two fractions is believed to have been sufficiently rapid to ensure that the build-up of sodium was not prevented by the crystallization of felspar, and the late liquids of the silicate "line of descent" were sufficiently rich in sodium to effect the conversion of the albite-oligoclase in the less metasomatized rocks to albite in the strongly metasomatized spilites.

Sodium metasomatism. The formation of adinoles, essentially albite (Ab_{100-95})–quartz rocks with some calcite and ankerite, from argillaceous sediments, is due to sodium metasomatism. Such a transformation of slates to adinoles has been described by Agrell (1939). The transformation is effected essentially by the fixation of sodium and silica from metasomatic fluids, probably derived from, and identical with, the autolytic liquids which albitized, carbonated and chloritized the associated albite dolerites. Metasomatic albite porphyroblasts are found in some keratophyres, and are distinguished from the earlier magmatic plagioclase by their water-clear appearance and chequer structure (Battey, 1955). This later development of alkali felspar, under relatively low-temperature conditions, is due to recrystallization, and the internal migration of alkalies and silica, and leads to the formation of both sodium- as well as potassium-rich modifications of the original rocks (see alkali felspar paragenesis, p. 79). Phenocrysts of perthite in some New Brunswick, Canada, porphyries have been converted to chess-board albite during the chlorite to low biotite-grade regional metamorphism of these rocks (Starkey, 1959). Transitional stages in the transformation are preserved and are represented by crystals consisting of patches of chequer albite and patches of small irregularly shaped grains of albite together with smaller crystals of potassium felspar. The albite crystals in the latter patches occur in two orientations which are coincident with those of the two sets of chess-board twins in the areas of chess-board albite. The autometamorphism of a basalt in which the early formed calcic plagioclase has been transformed to a sodium felspar, by the action of a residual hydrous solution, rich in alkalies, carbonate and silica, has been described by Tomkeieff (1941):

$$CaAl_2Si_2O_8 + (Na,K)_2CO_3 + 4SiO_2 \rightarrow 2(Na,K)AlSi_3O_8 + CaCO_3$$

Sodium metasomatism also occurs on a regional scale. The injection of the pre-orogenic Alpine granite gneisses by later granites is accompanied commonly by albitization and results in important changes in the mineralogy of the earlier granites. The typical granite gneiss consists of some 40 per cent. plagioclase (An_{12-27}), 30 per cent. microperthite and 30 per cent. quartz; the albitized gneisses 60 per cent. albite, 10 per cent. microperthite, 10 per cent. quartz and 10 per cent. muscovite (Bearth, 1948). The transformation of quartz–chlorite–muscovite phyllites to albite porphyroblast schists in the Stavanger area has been described by Goldschmidt (1921). Here the transformation is due essentially to the metasomatic introduction of sodium derived from the associated trondjhemitic intrusions. It is significant that both chequer albite and myrmekite (see alkali felspar paragenesis) are common in the igneous rocks, confirming the presence of late-stage, sodium-rich liquids. The transformation of slates and phyllites to mica schist and, with increasing regional metamorphism, to albite schists and gneisses is widespread in the Cowal area, Argyllshire, Scotland (Bailey, 1923). In this area the development of albite on a regional scale is unrelated to any surface evidence of igneous activity. The albitization of the original pelitic and semipelitic sediments is considered to result from the local migration of sodium, derived intraformationally from authigenic albite. In many of these rocks the paratectonic growth of the albite is illustrated by the presence of rotated inclusions in the albite porphyroblasts.

Metamorphic rocks. Albite is a very abundant constituent of the schists and some of the dolomites and limestones of the Glenarm series of Pennsylvania and Maryland (Cloos and Hietanen, 1941), in which it occurs both as porphyroblasts and as small crystals in the finer-grained areas of the rocks. Inclusions in the porphyroblasts show crystallographic orientation. Their disposition in straight and S-shaped rows, indicate that the albite recrystallized during the movements associated with the metamorphism. Reversed zoning is shown by the plagioclase of the Wissahickon schist, a core of albite (An_5) being followed by a zone of oligoclase composition (An_{16}), a zone of albite, a further zone of oligoclase, and a rim of albite. It is probable that the zoning is due to variations in temperature and pressure during the growth of the felspar, the albite centres recrystallizing at lower temperatures early in the metamorphism, and the oligoclase during two periods of higher temperature. Albite porphyroblasts in which the S-shaped inclusions are more abundant in the centre than at the periphery, and which are not continuous with the S-surfaces of the surrounding matrix, have been described by Hutton (1940) in some of the albite–epidote–chlorite schists of western Otago, New Zealand. Hutton concluded that they represent a relict structure, and that the growth of the porphyroblasts occurred after the cessation of the deforming movement, and are the result of post-tectonic recrystallization.

Felspathic sandstones may be transformed into rocks of granodioritic or granitic composition by the formation of plagioclase derived from the influx of sodium-rich solution. A number of stages in such a transformation, described either as granitization or felspathization, may be distinguished. An example of a felspathized arkose has been described by Coombs (1950). The felspathization here begins with the enlargement of the clastic oligoclase (An_{25}) by the growth of authigenic rims of albite. More intense felspathization is accompanied by an increase in the grain size of the plagioclase due to the encroachment of the newly formed albite into the areas of the cement. In the most advanced stage of felspathization the larger plagioclase porphyroblasts increase in size until further growth is inhibited by the mutual interference of other enlarging crystals of plagioclase and quartz. Simultaneously the detrital cores are modified by the development of patches of albite within the kernels of the original oligoclase.

The formation of plagioclase in boudins and veins in amphibolites has been investigated by Reitan (1956). The composition of the plagioclase in the boudins (An_{32}–An_{27}) is similar to that of the main amphibolite plagioclase (An_{30}–An_{27}); in the vein pegmatite the plagioclase is An_{20}. The composition of these pegmatites remote from the low temperature region of the $KAlSiO_4$–$NaAlSiO_4$–SiO_2 system, and their isolated location enclosed within amphibolite, suggest that they are not derived by either magmatic or hydrothermal crystallization. The pegmatites are located at sites of low pressure associated with fracturing and shearing, and their origin may be related to the intergranular diffusion of ions, during the regional metamorphism, towards the areas of lowest pressure. The compositional difference between the plagioclase of the veins and boudins is explained on the assumption that the calcium is less mobile than the sodium ion, the earlier formed plagioclase being more albitic than that formed later during the regional metamorphism. This relationship is in accord with the field observations, since the shear zones of low pressure, caused by the bending of the amphibolite bands and occupied by vein pegmatite plagioclase (An_{20}), developed prior to the rupturing and formation of the boudins, in which the composition of the plagioclase is An_{29}.

The composition of the plagioclase felspars of basic igneous rocks under the varying conditions of regional metamorphism was investigated by Wiseman

(1934) in his study of the progressive metamorphism of epidiorites. In the chlorite and biotite zones of regional metamorphism albite is the stable plagioclase in such associations as chlorite–biotite–epidote–albite amphibolite and chlorite–albite schist.   Phillips (1930) also has reported that, within the chlorite zone, the plagioclase of the rocks of the Green Beds does not contain more than 3 or 4 per cent. anorthite. In both the epidiorites and the Green Beds the anorthite molecule does not enter the plagioclase structure in notable quantities until the garnet zone.   In the low grade regionally metamorphosed epidiorites the anorthite molecule of the plagioclase, together with the original pyroxene, enters partially or wholly into the formation of an aluminous chlorite and an amphibole: epidote also is produced during this reaction:

$$3CaAl_2Si_2O_8 + CaO + H_2O \rightarrow 2Ca_2Al_3Si_3O_{12}(OH)$$
$$4CaAl_2Si_2O_8 + H_2O \rightarrow 2Ca_2Al_3Si_3O_{12}(OH) + Al_2O_3 + 2SiO_2$$

In the garnet and higher zones the calcium content of the plagioclase increases, and is accompanied by a diminution in the amount of epidote which reacts with the sodium felspar to form more calcium-rich plagioclase.   In the kyanite zone the plagioclase is andesine or sodium labradorite.   During retrograde metamorphism the process is reversed, and the sheared margins of some high grade amphibolites are transformed to calcite–chlorite–hornblende–epidote–albite rocks.   A study by Engel and Engel (1960) of the Adirondack paragneisses also has shown that there is a correlation between the anorthite content of the plagioclase of these rocks and their metamorphic grade, and in particular that oligoclase is the characteristic plagioclase in the metamorphic argillaceous sandstones belonging to the upper amphibolite or higher facies.

Rosenqvist (1952) discussed the general problem of the stability of the felspars in relation to metamorphic facies, and placed the division between the greenschist and saussurite facies[1] at the transition of albite to oligoclase according to the reaction:

albite + zoisite $\rightleftharpoons$ oligoclase + water

Fyfe *et al.* (1958) have suggested that the boundary between the greenschist and the almandine amphibolite facies can be more precisely drawn between albite (An_{0-7}) and oligoclase (An_{15-30}), and base this division on the absence, in low to medium grade schists, of plagioclase between An_7 and An_{15} in composition. Thus Waard (1959) has demonstrated the presence of a sharp break, from medium albite to medium oligoclase compositions, in the plagioclase of both the basic and pelitic schists of the Usu massif, Timor, while the scarcity of plagioclase in the range An_{10} to An_{20}, in the rocks of a progressively metamorphosed terrain in New England, has previously been reported by Lyons (1955).   This gap in the composition of plagioclases in regionally metamorphosed rocks has been correlated with the unmixed constitution (discrete submicroscopic lamellæ of compositions An_{1-5} and An_{20-25} respectively) of these plagioclases (Christie, 1959; Rutland, 1961; Noble, 1962; see also Brown, 1960).   The more calcium-rich phase of such felspars is unstable in the presence of water and excess calcium, and the reaction calcic plagioclase$\rightleftharpoons$albite + epidote takes place when the temperature reaches the point at which the velocity of the reaction attains a

[1] Rosenqvist's saussurite facies is not universally accepted but is approximately equivalent to the epidote–amphibolite facies of other workers.

geologically finite rate. The lower limit of the amphibolite facies, in rocks of basic, semipelitic and quartzo-felspathic composition, can thus be delineated by the transition from assemblages containing low-temperature albite to assemblages containing low-temperature plagioclase with the intermediate structure (Noble, 1962).

Where rocks of the amphibolite facies are subjected to a further increase in confining pressures and to a moderate increase in temperature, conditions of the granulite facies are reached; a characteristic reaction of the boundary conditions may be represented by the equation:

$$\underset{\text{amphibole}}{Ca_2Mg_3Al_4Si_6O_{22}(OH)_2} + SiO_2 \rightarrow \underset{\text{anorthite}}{2CaAl_2Si_2O_8} + \underset{\text{orthopyroxene}}{3MgSiO_3} + H_2O$$

The plagioclase felspars of the intermediate and acid rocks of the granulite facies commonly have compositions in the sodic andesine range. In the charnockite series, for example, the majority of the plagioclases have compositions An_{30} to An_{35} (Howie, 1955), although in some of the more basic rocks labradorite occurs. Antiperthitic plagioclases are common in rocks of the granulite facies and are occasionally present in volcanic rocks. Although many such plagioclases have originated by exsolution of a potassium felspar phase, antiperthites of replacement origin also occur. These are distinguished from exsolution antiperthites by a higher potassium content than is possible in plagioclase felspar, and by the presence of potassium felspar blebs of greater size, erratic distribution, and more irregular shape than those in exsolution antiperthite.

Rocks of the amphibolite facies affected by increasing temperature and decreasing pressure develop typical associations of thermal metamorphism and are included in the pyroxene hornfels facies. A characteristic association of the amphibolite facies is biotite–hornblende–plagioclase, and of the pyroxene hornfels facies, biotite–pyroxene–plagioclase. Hornblende is unstable in the pyroxene-hornfels facies and plagioclase is one of the breakdown products. This reaction may be expressed by the equation:

$$\underset{\text{amphibole}}{NaCa_2Mg_3Fe^{+2}Al_3Si_6O_{22}(OH)_2} + 4SiO_2 \rightarrow \underbrace{NaAlSi_3O_8 + CaAl_2Si_2O_8}_{\text{plagioclase}}$$

$$+ \underset{\text{diopside}}{CaMgSi_2O_6} + \underset{\text{orthopyroxene}}{Mg_2FeSi_3O_9} + H_2O$$

An anorthite (An_{90})–epidote–garnet hornfels in regional metamorphic rocks has been described by Coetzee (1941).

Plagioclase felspar is not stable in the pressure–temperature environment of the eclogite facies. The bulk chemical composition of rocks belonging to this facies is very restricted and they consist essentially of omphacite pyroxene and pyrope-almandine garnet. In the eclogites the albite component may be considered to enter into the composition of the pyroxene, and the reaction represented as:

$$\underset{\text{albite}}{NaAlSi_3O_8} + \underset{\text{olivine}}{(Mg,Fe)_2SiO_4} \rightarrow \underbrace{NaAlSi_2O_6 + 2(Mg,Fe)SiO_3}_{\text{omphacite}}$$

Similarly the anorthite component of the plagioclase may be considered to enter into the composition of the garnet:

$$CaAl_2Si_2O_8 + (Mg,Fe)_2SiO_4 \rightarrow Ca(Mg,Fe)_2Al_2Si_3O_{12}$$
$$\text{anorthite} \qquad \text{olivine} \qquad\qquad \text{garnet}$$

$$CaAl_2Si_2O_8 + 2MgSiO_3 \rightarrow CaMg_2Al_2Si_3O_{12} + SiO_2$$
$$\text{anorthite} \qquad \text{orthopyroxene} \qquad \text{garnet}$$

An investigation by Sen (1959) has shown that the content of potassium in plagioclase is related to its temperature of formation, and is not related to either the Ab–An ratio of the plagioclase or to the availability of potassium at the time of its crystallization. Sen gives the average content of $KAlSi_3O_8$ in 25 plagioclases from rocks of the amphibolite facies as 0·9 weight per cent. (range 0·6 to 2·3 per cent.), that of 26 plagioclases from rocks of the granulite facies as 4·0 weight per cent. (range 0·6 to 7·6 per cent.), and that of 11 plagioclases from volcanic rocks as 6·5 weight per cent. (range 4·4 to 11·5 per cent.; plagioclase of anorthite composition excluded).

Plagioclase is an important product of the thermal metamorphism of impure limestones. The calcium-sodium plagioclase and grossular are formed from the reaction of the earlier formed zoisite and albite, together with calcite and quartz (Hutchison, 1933):

$$NaAlSi_3O_8 + 2Ca_2Al_3Si_3O_{12}(OH) + CaCO_3 + SiO_2$$
$$\text{albite} \qquad\qquad \text{zoisite}$$

$$\rightarrow NaAlSi_3O_8 + 3CaAl_2Si_2O_8 + CaSiO_3 + CaO + H_2O + CO_2$$

$$\rightarrow NaCa_2Al_5Si_7O_{24} + Ca_3Al_2Si_3O_{12} + H_2O + CO_2$$
$$\text{plagioclase} \qquad\qquad \text{grossular}$$

The plagioclase of thermally metamorphosed impure arenaceous sediments arises mainly from the recrystallization of detrital felspar in markedly greater quantities than in the metamorphosed argillaceous sediments.

In some rocks the plagioclase felspars have a clouded appearance which is distinct from the frequent turbidity shown by felspars affected by weathering or hydrothermal alteration. The clouding of plagioclase has been attributed to thermal metamorphism (MacGregor, 1931) and clouded felspars are observed frequently in rocks within metamorphic aureoles. Poldervaart and Gilkey (1954) have examined the problem of clouding in felspars and list examples in which causes other than thermal metamorphism are more probable. The clouding is due to the presence of minute dark particles, variously described as dust-like specks, short rods and needles. Identification of the particles is difficult but generally they are considered to be iron oxide. The particles may have been derived from the exsolution of Fe^{+3}, originally substituting for Al, in the felspar structure, or may have been introduced into the crystal subsequent to its crystallization. Poldervaart and Gilkey concluded that both processes have operated, the slight clouding being associated with the exsolution of iron from the structure, and the more intense clouding with diffusion of extraneous material into the crystal after its formation. They report that strong clouding is restricted to plagioclases of intermediate composition. At low temperatures such plagioclases may consist of submicroscopic mixtures of two phases, and the innumerable surfaces of discontinuity provide access to the diffusion of the clouding material.

Sedimentary rocks. Sodium felspar is a common authigenic mineral, forming contemporaneously with sedimentation, as well as by replacement of detrital and precipitated material. In accordance with the chemical relationships of the alkali felspars, and their crystallization at the temperatures of the earth's surface and at moderate depths, authigenic albite generally shows greater purity than the magmatic and metamorphic sodium felspars, and compares in composition with some pegmatite minerals. Authigenic plagioclase is non-perthitic and the potassium felspar rarely exceeds 3 mol. per cent. The calcium content of authigenic albite is generally even lower, and the usual upper limit is approximately 0·3 per cent., equivalent to 1 mol. per cent. $CaAl_2Si_2O_8$. The authigenic albite from a limestone (Table 12, anal. 12), however, is exceptional in its content both of potassium and calcium. Much authigenic sodium felspar is low-albite, but varieties intermediate between low- and high-temperature albite are known (Baskin, 1956). In some sediments the replacement origin of authigenic albite is demonstrated by the development of idiomorphic crystals in cavities, and by the replacement of fossils. Straaten (1948) has reported albite containing inclusions parallel to structures typical of brachiopod shells. In other sediments the interlocking fabric indicates that the sodium felspar may be of indigenous origin, formed by the partial solution of detrital grains under pressure at points of contact, and precipitated at places of lower pressure in voids. Much of the authigenic albite shows simple growth twins, and is free of multiple twin lamellae.

An interesting occurrence of albite and analcite in a sodium-rich altered tuff, in Jurassic limestone, has been described by Gulbrandsen and Cressman (1960). The relict shard texture of the rock indicates that it was originally a fine-grained vitric tuff, and the presence of albite and analcite in the form of shards indicates that both minerals formed after deposition of the pyroclastic material. Although textural evidence of the order in which the analcite and albite crystallized is lacking, Gulbrandsen and Cressman consider that analcite formed first, probably as the product of a reaction between volcanic glass and sea water during diagenesis. From the stratigraphical evidence the temperature of formation of the albite from analcite is believed to be below 200°C.

Meteorites. Calcium plagioclase occurs in some stony meteorites, and although some variation may occur in a single specimen (Game, 1957) the composition is commonly bytownite (Table 17, anal. 10). From the differing responses to heat treatment of individual grains from the same meteorite it is inferred that their cooling history has not been identical.

REFERENCES

Adamson, O. J., 1942. Minerals of the Varuträsk pegmatite. XXXI. The feldspar group. *Geol. För. Förh., Stockholm*, vol. 64, p. 19.

Agrell, S. O., 1939. The adinoles of Dinas Head, Cornwall. *Min. Mag.*, vol. 25, p. 305.

Ahlers, L., 1924. Über die Dichte von Quartz, Orthoklas, Albit und Anorthit. *Zeit. Krist.*, vol. 59, p. 293.

Andersen, O., 1915a. On aventurine feldspar. *Amer. Journ. Sci.*, ser. 4, vol. 40, p. 351.

—— 1915b. The system anorthite–forsterite–silica. *Amer. Journ. Sci.*, ser. 4, vol. 39, p. 407.

—— 1917. Aventurine labradorite from California. *Amer. Min.*, vol. 2, p. 91.

Azzini, F., 1933. Adularia e albite di Val Devero (Ossola). *Atti Accad. Sci. Veneto-Trentino–Istriana*, vol. 23, p. 45 (M.A. 5–366).

Bailey, E. B., 1923.   The metamorphism of the south-west Highlands.   *Geol. Mag.*, vol. 60, p. 317.

Barber, C. T., 1936a.   The Tertiary igneous rocks of the Pakokku District and the Salingyi Township of the Lower Chindwin District, Burma, with special reference to the determination of the felspars by the Federoff Method.   *Geol. Surv. India.*, *Mem. 68*, pt. 2.

—— 1936b.   The effect of heat on the optical orientation of plagioclase felspars. *Min. Mag.*, vol. 24, p. 343.

Barth, T. F. W., 1931.   Permanent changes in the optical orientation of feldspars exposed to heat.   *Norsk. Geol. Tidssk.*, vol. 12, p. 57.

Baskin, Y., 1956.   A study of authigenic feldspars.   *Journ. Geol.*, vol. 64, p. 132.

Battey, M. H., 1955.   Alkali metasomatism and the petrology of some keratophyres. *Geol. Mag.*, vol. 92, p. 104.

—— 1956.   The petrogenesis of a spilitic rock series from New Zealand.   *Geol. Mag.*, vol. 93, p. 89.

Bearth, P., 1948.   Über Albitisierung im Altkristallin des Monte Rosa.   *Schweiz. Min. Petr. Mitt.*, vol. 28, p. 140.

Beder, R., 1927.   Sobre una andesina procedente de Alta Gracia (provincia de (Córdoba).   *Bol. Acad. Nac. Cienc. Argentina*, vol. 30, p. 1 (M.A. 3–494).

—— and **Jakob, J.**, 1932.   Über einen Andesin von Alta Gracia, Provinz Córdoba, Argentinien.   *Schweiz Min. Petr. Mitt.*, vol. 12, p. 247.

Belyankin, D. S., 1934.   Albite from Druzhnaya Gorka Works having a small angle of optical axes.   *Doklady Acad. Sci. USSR*, vol. 3, p. 651 (M.A. 6–294).

Bøggild, O. B., 1924.   On the labradorization of the feldspars.   *K. Danske Vidensk. Selskab, Math.-fys. Meddel.*, vol. 6, no. 3 (M.A. 2–492).

Bowen, N. L., 1912.   The binary system $Na_2Al_2Si_2O_8$ (nephelite, carnegieite)-$CaAl_2Si_2O_8$ (anorthite).   *Amer. Journ. Sci.*, 4th ser., vol. 33, p. 551.

—— 1913.   The melting phenomena of the plagioclase feldspars.   *Amer. Journ. Sci.*, 4th ser., vol. 35, p. 577.

—— 1915.   The crystallization of haplobasaltic, haplodioritic, and related magmas. *Amer. Journ. Sci.*, 4th ser., vol. 40, p. 161.

—— 1928.   *The evolution of the igneous rocks.*   Princeton.

—— and **Schairer, J. F.**, 1936.   The system albite–fayalite.   *Proc. Nat. Acad. Sci.*, vol. 22, p. 345.

—— and **Tuttle, O. F.**, 1950.   The system $NaAlSi_3O_8$–$KAlSi_3O_8$–H_2O.   *Journ. Geol.*, vol. 58, p. 489.

Bown, M. G. and **Gay, P.**, 1958.   The reciprocal lattice geometry of the plagioclase felspar structures.   *Zeit. Krist.*, vol. 111, p. 1.

Bradley, O., 1953.   An investigation of high-temperature optics in some naturally occurring plagioclases.   *Min. Mag.*, vol. 30, p. 227.

Bradley, J. E. S. and **Bradley, O.**, 1956.   A first attempt at a determination of felspars by activation analysis.   *Min. Mag.*, vol. 31, p. 164.

Brindley, G. W. and **Radoslovich, E. W.**, 1956.   X-ray studies of the alteration of soda feldspar.   *Proc. 4th Nat. Conference on Clays and Clay Minerals* (U.S.A.), p. 330.

Brousse, R., 1961.   Minéralogie et pétrographie des roches volcaniques du massif du Mont-Dore (Auvergne).   I.   Les minéraux.   II.   Pétrographie systematique. *Bull. Soc. franç. Min. Crist.*, vol. 84, p. 131.

Brown, G. M., 1956.   The layered ultrabasic rocks of Rhum, Inner Hebrides. *Phil. Trans. Roy. Soc. London*, vol. 240, B, p. 1.

Brown, W. L., 1960.   The crystallographic and petrologic significance of peristerite unmixing in the acid plagioclases.   *Zeit. Krist.*, vol. 113, p. 330.

Buddington, A. F., 1939.   Adirondack igneous rocks and their metamorphism. *Mem. Geol. Soc. Amer.*, no. 7.

Caillère, S., 1942. Sur un nouvel example d'altération de l'anorthite en une variété calcique de thomsonite. *Bull. Soc. franç. Min.,* vol. 65, p. 14.

Calkins, F. C., 1917. A decimal grouping of the plagioclases. *Journ. Geol.,* vol. 25, p. 157.

Campbell Smith, W., Bannister, F. A. and **Hey, M. H.,** 1944. Banalsite, a new barium felspar from Wales. *Min. Mag.,* vol. 27, p. 33.

Carmichael, I. S. E., 1960. The feldspar phenocrysts of some Tertiary acid glasses. *Min. Mag.,* vol. 32, p. 587.

Carr, J. M., 1954. Zoned plagioclases in layered gabbros of the Skaergaard intrusion, east Greenland. *Min. Mag.,* vol. 30, p. 367.

Cesàro, G., 1916. Emploi des plages normales à l'indice moyen et des plages perpendiculaires à une axe optique dans la détermination des plagioclases. *Bull. Soc. franç. Min.,* vol. 39, p. 38.

Chandrasekhar, S., 1957. Ph.D thesis, University of Cambridge.

Chao, S. H. and **Taylor, W. H.,** 1940. Isomorphous replacement and superlattice structures in the plagioclase felspars. *Proc. Roy. Soc.,* vol. 176, A, p. 76.

Chayes, F., 1950. On the relation between anorthite content and γ-index of natural plagioclase. *Journ. Geol.,* vol. 58, p. 593.

—— 1952. Relations between composition and indices of refraction in natural plagioclase. *Amer. Journ. Sci.,* Bowen vol., p. 85.

—— 1954. A test of the revised determinative chart for plagioclases. *Amer. Journ. Sci.,* vol. 252, p. 172.

—— 1958. A possible explanation of the δ_c separations in intermediate plagioclase. *Acta Cryst.,* vol. 11, p. 323.

—— and **Robbins, C. R.,** 1953. Anorthite content of low-temperature plagioclase. *Ann. Rep. Dir. Geophys. Lab., Carnegie Inst. Washington Yr. Bk.,* No. 52, p. 46.

Christie, O. H. J., 1959. Note on the equilibrium between plagioclase and epidote. *Norsk Geol. Tidsskr.,* vol. 39, p. 268.

Chudoba, K., 1925. Die Dispersion der Plagioklase. Albit und Anorthit. *Sitz. Akad. Wiss. Wien, Math-Nat. Kl.,* Abt. 1, vol. 134, p. 159 (M.A. 3–420).

—— 1927. Zur Dispersion der Plagioklase. *Fortschr. Min. Krist. Petr.,* vol. 11, p. 49.

—— 1933. *The determination of the feldspars in thin section* (Translated by **W. Q.** Kennedy). Murby, London.

—— 1936. Dichte und chemische Zusammensetzung der Plagioklase auf ternärer Grundlage. *Centr. Min., Abt. A,* p. 1.

—— and **Engels, A.,** 1937. Der Einfluss der Kalifeldspatkomponente auf die Optik der Plagioklase. III. Die optische Orientierung kalifeldspathaltiger Plagioklase. *Centr. Min., Abt. A,* p. 129.

Claisse, F., 1950. A rontgenographic method for determining plagioclases. *Amer. Min.,* vol. 35, p. 412.

Cloos, E. and **Hietanen, A.,** 1941. Geology of the "Martic Overthrust" and the Glenarm series in Pennsylvania and Maryland. *Geol. Soc. Amer., Special Paper* No. 35.

Coetzee, C. B., 1941. An anorthite–epidote–garnet–hornfels from Namaqualand, South Africa. *Min. Mag.,* vol. 26, p. 134.

Cole, W. F., Sörum, H. and **Taylor, W. H.,** 1951. The structures of the plagioclase felspars. I. *Acta Cryst.,* vol. 4, p. 20.

Coombs, D. S., 1954. The ferriferous orthoclase of Madagascar. *Min. Mag.,* vol. 30, p. 409.

Coombs, H. A., 1950. Granitization in the Swank arkose near Wenatchee Washington. *Amer. Journ. Sci.,* vol. 248, p. 369.

Dane, E. B., Jr., 1941.　Densities of molten rocks and minerals.　*Amer. Journ. Sci.,* vol. 239, p. 809.

Davis, G. L. and Tuttle, O. F., 1952.　Two new crystalline phases of the anorthite composition, $CaO.Al_2O_3.2SiO_2$.　*Amer. Journ. Sci.,* Bowen vol., p. 107.

Dawson, K. R. and Maxwell, J. A., 1958.　Possible loss of sodium and potassium during fusion of plagioclase feldspars.　*Canadian Min.,* vol. 6, p. 288.

Day, A. L. and Allen, E. T., 1905.　The isomorphism and thermal properties of the feldspars.　*Carnegie Inst. of Washington, Publ. No.* 31.

DeVore, G., 1956.　Surface chemistry as a chemical control on mineral association.　*Journ. Geol.,* vol. 64, p. 31.

De Wys, E. C. and Foster, W. R., 1956.　The binary system anorthite $(CaAl_2Si_2O_8)$–åkermanite $(Ca_2MgSi_2O_7)$.　*Journ. Amer. Ceram. Soc.,* vol. 39, p. 372.

—— —— 1958.　The system diopside–anorthite–åkermanite.　*Min. Mag.,* vol. 31, p. 736.

Divljan, S., 1960.　The results of field and laboratory studies of aventurine plagioclases from some Norwegian pegmatites.　*Rept. 21st. Intern. Geol. Congr., Norden,* Part 17, p. 94.

Dodge, T. A., 1936.　A rapid microscopic method for distinguishing quartz from untwinned oligoclase–andesine.　*Amer. Min.,* vol. 21, p. 531.

Doeglas, D. J., 1940.　Reliable and rapid method for distinguishing quartz and untwinned feldspar with the universal stage.　*Amer. Min.,* vol. 25, p. 286.

Donnay, G., 1952.　Hexagonal $CaAl_2Si_2O_8$.　*Acta Cryst.,* vol. 5, p. 153.

—— and **Donnay, J. D. H.,** 1952.　The symmetry change in the high-temperature alkali–feldspar series.　*Amer. Journ. Sci.,* Bowen volume, p. 115.

Donnay, J. D. H., 1943.　Plagioclase twinning.　*Bull. Geol. Soc. Amer.,* vol. 54, p. 1645.

Duparc, L. and Gysin, M., 1926.　Sur la composition et les propriétés optiques de quelques plagioclases.　*Schweiz. Min. Petr. Mitt.,* vol. 6, p. 255.

—— and **Reinhard, M.,** 1923.　Les méthodes de Féderof et leur application à la détermination des plagioclases.　*Schweiz. Min. Petr. Mitt.,* vol. 3, p. 1.

—— —— 1924.　La détermination des plagioclases dans les coupes minces.　*Soc. Phys. et Hist. nat. Genève,* vol. 40.

Edwards, A. B., 1938.　The tertiary rocks of central Victoria.　*Quart. Journ. Geol. Soc.,* vol. 94, p. 243.

Eitel, W., Herlinger, E. and Tromel, G., 1930.　Zur Kristallchemie der Aluminosilicate Beziehungen der Anorthitgruppe zur Gruppe des Nephelins.　*Naturwiss.,* vol. 18, p. 469.

Ellitsgaard-Rasmussen, K., and Mouritzen, M., 1954.　An anorthosite occurrence from west Greenland.　*Meddel. fra Dansk Geol. Foren.,* Bd. 12, p. 436.

Emmons, R. C., 1929a.　The double variation method of refractive index determination. (Second paper).　*Amer. Min.,* vol. 14, p. 414.

—— 1929b.　A modified universal stage.　*Amer. Min.,* vol. 14, p. 441.

—— 1943.　The universal stage (with five axes of rotation).　*Mem. Geol. Soc. Amer.,* no. 8.

—— 1953.　Selected petrogenic relationships of plagioclase.　*Mem. Geol. Soc. Amer.,* no. 52.

—— 1955.　Plagioclase silica.　*Bull. Geol. Soc. Amer.,* vol. 66, p. 1061.

—— and **Gates, R. M.,** 1939.　New method for the determination of feldspar twins.　*Amer. Min.,* vol. 24, p. 577.

—— and **Mann, V.,** 1953.　A twin zone relationship in plagioclase feldspar, *in* Selected petrogenic relationships of plagioclase.　*Mem. Geol. Soc. Amer.,* no. 52, p. 41.　Editor.　R. C. Emmons.

Engel, A. E. J. and **Engel, C. G.**, 1960. Progressive metamorphism and granitization of the major paragneiss, northwest Adirondack Mountains, New York: Part II: Mineralogy. *Bull. Geol. Soc. Amer.*, vol. 71, p. 11.

Ernst, E. and **Nieland, H.**, 1934. Plagioklase von Linosa, ein Beitrag zur Anemousit-frage. *Min. Petr. Mitt. (Tschermak)*, vol. 46, p. 93.

Eskola, P., Vuoristo, U. and **Rankama, K.**, 1935. An experimental illustration of the spilite reaction. *Compt. Rend. Soc. géol. Finlande*, no. 9.

Fischer, H., 1925. Über die optischen Eigenschaften des Albits. *Zeit. Krist.*, vol. 61, p. 226.

Foster, W. R., 1942. The system $NaAlSi_3O_8$–$CaSiO_3$–$NaAlSiO_4$. *Journ. Geol.*, vol. 50, p. 152.

—— 1955. Simple method for the determination of the plagioclase feldspars. *Amer. Min.*, vol. 40, p. 179.

Frederickson, A. F. and **Cox, J. E.**, 1954a. Solubility of albite in hydrothermal solutions. *Amer. Min.*, vol. 39, p. 738.

—— —— 1954b. The decomposition products of anorthite attacked by pure water at elevated temperature and pressure. *Proc. 2nd Conf. Clays and Clay Mins.*, *Nat. Acad. Sci.*, *Nat. Res. Council*, Publ. 327, p. 111.

Fyfe, W. S., Turner, F. J. and **Verhoogen, J.**, 1958. Metamorphic reactions and metamorphic facies. *Geol. Soc. Amer.*, Mem. 73.

Gagny, C., 1957. Caractère particulier de la fluorescence des feldspaths dans certains granites des Vosges. *Bull. Soc. franç. Minér. Crist.*, vol. 80, p. 546.

Game, P. M., 1949. Plagioclases from Sultan Hamud, Kenya. *Min. Mag.*, vol. 28, p. 682.

—— 1957. Plagioclases from the Juvinas meteorite and from allivalite from the Isle of Rhum. *Min. Mag.*, vol. 31, p. 656.

Gay, P., 1953. The structures of the plagioclase felspars. III. An X-ray study of anorthites and bytownites. *Min. Mag.*, vol. 30, p. 169.

—— 1954. The structures of the plagioclase felspars. V. The heat treatment of lime-rich plagioclases. *Min. Mag.*, vol. 30, p. 428.

—— 1956a. The structures of the plagioclase felspars. VI. Natural intermediate plagioclases. *Min. Mag.*, vol. 31, p. 21.

—— 1956b. A note on albite twinning in plagioclase felspars. *Min. Mag.*, vol. 31, p. 301.

—— and **Taylor, W. H.**, 1953. The structures of the plagioclase felspars. IV. Variations in the anorthite structure. *Acta Cryst.*, vol. 6, p. 647.

—— and **Smith, J. V.**, 1955. Phase relations in the plagioclase felspars: composition range An_0 to An_{70}. *Acta Cryst.*, vol. 8, p. 64.

—— and **Bown, M. G.**, 1956. The structures of the plagioclase felspars. VII. The heat treatment of intermediate plagioclases. *Min. Mag.*, vol. 31, p. 306.

Gilbert, C. M. and **Turner, F. J.**, 1949. Use of the universal stage in sedimentary petrography. *Amer. Journ. Sci.*, vol. 247, p. 1.

Ginzberg, A. S., 1915. On some artificial bariumalumosilicates. Collection of scientific papers dedicated to F. Y. Levison-Lessing, Petrograd (M.A. 2–153).

Goldschmidt, V. M., 1921. Geologisch-Petrographische Studien in *Hochgebirge des Sudlichen Norvegens*. vol. 5, p. 84.

Goldsmith, J. R., 1947. The system $CaAl_2Si_2O_8$–$Ca_2Al_2SiO_7$–$NaAlSiO_4$. *Journ. Geol.*, vol. 55, p. 381.

—— 1950. Gallium and germanium substitutions in synthetic feldspars. *Journ. Geol.*, vol. 58, p. 518.

—— and **Laves, F.**, 1955. Cation order in anorthite ($CaAl_2Si_2O_8$) as revealed by gallium and germanium substitutions. *Zeit. Krist.*, vol. 106, p. 213.

—— —— 1956. Crystallisation of metastable disordered anorthite at "low temperatures". *Zeit. Krist.*, vol. 107, p. 369.

Goodspeed, G. E., 1937. Development of plagioclase porphyroblasts. *Amer. Min.,* vol. 22, p. 1133.

Goodyear, J. and **Duffin, W. J.,** 1954. The identification and determination of plagioclase felspars by the X-ray powder method. *Min. Mag.,* vol. 30, p. 306.
—— —— 1955. The determination of composition and thermal history of plagioclase by the X-ray powder method. *Min. Mag.,* vol. 30, p. 648.

Gorai, M., 1951. Petrological studies on plagioclase twins. *Amer. Min.,* vol. 36, p. 884.

Goranson, R. W., 1938. Silicate–water systems. Phase equilibria in the NaAl-Si$_3$O$_8$–H$_2$O and KAlSi$_3$O$_8$–H$_2$O systems at high temperatures and pressures. *Amer. Journ. Sci.,* 5th ser., vol. 35, p. 71.

Gradwell, R., 1958. A simple fusion method for determination of plagioclase feldspar from thin section. *Amer. Min.,* vol. 43, p. 368.

Graham, E. R., 1949. The plagioclase feldspars as an index to soil weathering. *Proc. Soil Sci. Soc. Amer.,* vol. 14, p. 300.

Greig, J. W. and **Barth, F. W.,** 1938. The system, Na$_2$O·Al$_2$O$_3$·2SiO$_2$(nephelite, carnegieite)–Na$_2$O·Al$_2$O$_3$·6SiO$_2$(albite). *Amer. Journ. Sci.,* 5th ser., vol. 35, p. 93.

Gruner, J. W., 1944. The hydrothermal alteration of feldspars in acid solutions between 300°C. and 400°C. *Econ. Geol.,* vol. 39, p. 578.

Gulbrandsen, R. A. and **Cressman, E. R.,** 1960. Analcime and albite in altered Jurassic tuff in Idaho and Wyoming. *Journ. Geol.,* vol. 68, p. 458.

Gummer, W. K., 1943. The system CaSiO$_3$–CaAl$_2$Si$_2$O$_8$–NaAlSiO$_4$. *Journ. Geol.,* vol. 51, p. 503.

Guppy, E. M., 1931. Chemical analyses of igneous rocks, metamorphic rocks and minerals. *Mem. Geol. Surv. Great Britain.*

Gysin, M., 1925. Sur la présence de la macle de l'acline A dans les plagioclases. *Schweiz. Min. Petr. Mitt.,* vol. 5, p. 128 (M.A. 3–520).

Harada, Z., 1948. Chemical analyses of Japanese minerals (II). *Journ. Fac. Sci. Hokkaido Univ.,* ser. IV, vol. 7, p. 143.
—— 1954. Chemical analyses of Japanese minerals (III). *Journ. Fac. Sci. Hokkaido Univ.,* ser. IV, vol. 8, p. 289.

Hemley, J. J., Meyer, C. and **Richter, D. H.,** 1961. Some alteration reactions in the system Na$_2$O–Al$_2$O$_3$–SiO$_2$–H$_2$O. *U.S. Geol. Surv., Prof. Paper* 424-D, p. 338.

Hess, H. H., 1950. Vertical mineral variation in the Great Dyke of Southern Rhodesia. *Trans. Geol. Soc. S. Africa,* vol. 53, p. 159.

Hills, E. S., 1936. Reverse and oscillatory zoning in plagioclase felspars. *Geol. Mag.,* vol. 73, p. 49.

Hoel, A. and **Schetelig, J.,** 1916. Nephelin-bearing pegmatitic dykes in Seiland. *Festskrift, Amund Helland,* p. 110 (M.A. 1–282).

Holmquist, P. J., 1914. Die Schliefhärte der Feldspäte. *Geol. För. Förh. Stockholm,* vol. 36, p. 401.

Homma, F., 1932. Über das Ergebnis von Messungen an zonaren Plagioklasen aus Andesiten mit Hilfe des Universaldrehtisches. *Schweiz. Min. Petr. Mitt.,* vol. 12, p. 345.

Howie, R. A., 1955. The geochemistry of the charnockite series of Madras, India. *Trans. Roy. Soc. Edin.,* vol. 62, p. 725.

Hughes, C. J., 1956. Geological investigations in east Greenland Part VI. A differentiated basic sill enclosed in the Skaergaard intrusion, east Greenland, and related sills injecting the lavas. *Meddel. om Grøn.,* Bd. 137, no. 2.

Hugill, W., 1944. The spherulitic crystallization of anorthite. *Trans. Brit. Ceram. Soc.,* vol. 43, p. 90.

Hunt, J. M., Wisherd, M. P. and **Bonham, L. C.,** 1950. Infrared absorption spectra of minerals and other inorganic compounds. *Anal. Chem.,* vol. 22, p. 1478.

Hutchinson, A. and **Campbell Smith, W.,** 1912. On sericite from North Wales and on penninite and labradorite from Ireland. *Min. Mag.*, vol. 16, p. 264.

Hutchison, A. G., 1933. The metamorphism of the Deeside Limestone, Aberdeenshire. *Trans. Roy. Soc. Edin.*, vol. 57, p. 557.

Hutton, C. O., 1940. Metamorphism in the Lake Wakatipu region. *New Zealand Dept. Sci. and Industrial Res., Geol. Mem.,* no. 5.

Jackson, E. D., 1961. X-ray determinative curve for some natural plagioclases of composition An_{60-85}. *U.S. Geol. Surv., Prof. Paper* 424, p. 286.

Joplin, G. A., 1935. A note on the origin of basic xenoliths in plutonic rocks, with special reference to their grain-size. *Geol. Mag.*, vol. 72, p. 227.

Kaaden, G. van der, 1951. Optical studies on natural plagioclase feldspars with high- and low-temperature-optics. *Diss. Univ. Utrecht.*

Kempster, C. J. E., 1957. Summarised proceedings of a conference on X-ray analysis—Cardiff, April, 1957. *Journ. Appl. Physics*, vol. 8, p. 427.

—— **Megaw, H. D.** and **Radoslovich, E. W.,** 1960. The structure of anorthite. *Acta Cryst.*, vol. 13, p. 1003 (abstract only).

Kennedy, G. C., 1947. Charts for correlation of optical properties with chemical composition of some common rock-forming minerals. *Amer. Min.*, vol. 32, p. 561.

Köhler, A., 1923. Zur Bestimmung der Plagioklase in Doppelzwillingen noch dem Albit und Karlsbadergesetz. *Min. Petr. Mitt. (Tschermak)*, vol. 36, p. 42.

—— 1941. Die Abhängigkeit der Plagioklas-optik vom vorangegangenen Wärmeverhalten. (Die Existenz einer Hoch- und Tieftemperaturoptik). *Min. Petr. Mitt (Tschermak)*, vol. 53, p. 24.

—— 1949. Recent results of investigations on the feldspars. *Journ. Geol.*, vol. 57, p. 592.

—— and **Wieden, P.,** 1954. Vorläufige Versuche in der Feldspatgruppe mittels der DTA. *Neues Jahrb. Min., Monat.*, p. 249.

Kolderup, C. F. and **Kolderup, N. H.,** 1940. Geology of the Bergen arc system. *Bergens Museums Skrifter*, no. 20.

Kôzu, S. and **Ueda, J.,** 1933. Thermal expansion of plagioclase. *Proc. Imp. Acad. Tokyo*, vol. 9, p. 262 (M.A. 5–350).

Kracek, F. C. and **Neuvonen, K. J.,** 1952. Thermochemistry of the plagioclase and alkali feldspars. *Amer. Journ. Sci.*, Bowen vol., p. 293.

Kuno, H., 1950. Petrology of Hakone volcano and the adjacent areas, Japan. *Bull. Geol. Soc. Amer.*, vol. 61, p. 957.

Lacroix, A., 1916. Sur la caractéristique chimique de la dipyrisation des plagioclases des ophites des Pyrénées. *Bull. Soc. franç. Min.*, vol. 39, p. 74 (M.A. 2–227).

Lafitte, P., 1950. Série d'abaques permettant la détermination rapide des feldspaths maclés albite. *Bull. Soc. franç. Min. Crist.*, vol. 73, p. 425.

—— 1951. Mesure précise de la biréfringence d'une section de minéral dans une lame mince. Application à la détermination rapide des feldspaths calcosodiques. *Bull. Soc. franç. Min. Crist.*, vol. 74, p. 495.

Larsen, E. S., Jr., 1909. The relation between the refractive index and the density of some crystallized silicates and their glasses. *Amer. Journ. Sci.*, ser 4, vol. 28, p. 263.

—— 1948. Batholith and associated rocks of Corona, Elsinore, and San Luis Rey Quadrangles, Southern California. *Mem. Geol. Soc. Amer.*, no. 29.

—— and **Draisin, W. M.,** 1948. Composition of the minerals in the rocks of the southern California batholith. *Rep. Internat. Geol. Congr. (18th, Gt. Britain)* pt. 2, p. 66.

—— and **Irving, J.,** 1938. Petrologic results of a study of the minerals from the Tertiary volcanic rocks of the San Juan Region, Colorado. 7. The plagioclase feldspars. *Amer. Min.*, vol. 23, p. 227.

Laves, F., 1952. Phase relations of the alkali feldspars. *Journ Geol.*, vol. 60, p. 436.

—— 1954. The coexistence of two plagioclases in the oligoclase compositional range. *Journ. Geol.*, vol. 62, p. 409.

—— and **Goldsmith, J. R.**, 1954a. Discussion on anorthite superstructure. *Acta Cryst.*, vol. 7, p. 31.

—— —— 1954b. Long-range–short-range order in calcic plagioclases as a continuous and reversible function of temperature. *Acta Cryst.*, vol. 7, p. 465.

—— —— 1954c. On the use of calcic plagioclases in geologic thermometry. *Journ. Geol.*, vol. 62, p. 405.

—— —— 1955. The effect of temperature and composition on the Al–Si distribution in anorthite. *Zeit. Krist.*, vol. 106, p. 227.

—— and **Schneider, T.**, 1956. Ueber den rhombischen Schnitt in sauren Plagioklasen. *Schweiz. Min. Petr. Mitt.*, vol. 36, p. 622.

Le Bas., M. J., 1955. Magmatic and amygdaloidal plagioclases. *Geol. Mag.*, vol. 92, p. 291.

Leedal, G. P., 1952. The Cluanie igneous intrusion, Inverness-shire and Ross-shire. *Quart. Journ. Geol. Soc.*, vol. 108, p. 35.

Leisen, E., 1934. Beitrag zur Kenntnis der Dispersion der Kalknatronfeldspäte. *Zeit. Krist.*, vol. 89, p. 49.

Lundegårdh, P. H., 1941. Bytownit aus Anorthosit von Bonskär im nördlichen Teil der Stockholmer Schären und seine Beziehungen zu verschiedenen Feldspatsbestimmungskurven. *Bull. Geol. Inst. Univ. Upsala*, vol. 28, p. 415.

Lyons, J. B., 1955. Geology of the Hanover quadrangle, New Hampshire–Vermont. *Bull. Geol. Soc. Amer.*, vol. 66, p. 105.

McAndrew, J., 1957. Natural radiation damage in albite. *Amer. Journ. Sci.*, vol. 255, p. 715.

Macdonald, G. A., 1942. Potash-oligoclase in Hawaiian lavas. *Amer. Min.*, vol. 27, p. 793.

MacGregor, A. G., 1931. Clouded felspars and thermal metamorphism. *Min. Mag.*, vol. 22, p. 524.

MacKenzie, W. S., 1954. The system $NaAlSiO_4$–$NaAlSi_3O_8$–H_2O. (*Annual Rep. Director Geophys. Lab.*). *Carnegie Inst. Washington, Yr. Book*, no. 53, p. 119.

—— 1957. The crystalline modifications of $NaAlSi_3O_8$. *Amer. Journ. Sci.*, vol. 255, p. 481.

Meen, V. B., 1933. A description of a few plagioclases. *Univ. Toronto Studs., Geol. Ser.*, no. 35, p. 37.

Megaw, H. D., 1957. Summarised proceedings of a conference on X-ray analysis—Cardiff, April, 1957. *Journ. Appl. Physics*, vol. 8, p. 427.

—— 1959. Order and disorder in the feldspars, I. *Min. Mag.*, vol. 32, p. 226.

—— 1960a. Order and disorder. I. Theory of stacking faults and diffraction maxima. *Proc. Roy. Soc.*, A, vol. 259, p. 59.

—— 1960b. Order and disorder. II. Theory of diffraction effects in the intermediate felspars. *Ibid.*, p. 159.

—— 1960c. Order and disorder. III. The structure of the intermediate plagioclase felspars. *Ibid.*, p. 184.

Mellis, O., 1952. Replacement of plagioclase in deep-sea deposits. *Nature*, vol. 169, p. 624.

Meriläinen, K., 1961. Albite diabases and albitites in Enontekiö and Kittilä, Finland. *Bull. Comm. géol. Finlande*, No. 195.

Miller, F. S., 1935. Anorthite from California. *Amer. Min.*, vol. 20, p. 139.

M'Lintock, W. F. P., 1915. On the zeolites and associated minerals from the Tertiary lavas around Ben More, Mull. *Trans. Roy. Soc. Edinburgh*, vol. 51, p. 1.

Morey, G. W., 1957. The system water–nepheline–albite: a theoretical discussion. *Amer. Journ. Sci.,* vol. 255, p. 461.

—— and **Chen, W. T.,** 1955. The action of hot water on some feldspars. *Amer. Min.,* vol. 40, p. 996.

—— and **Fournier, R. O.,** 1961. The decomposition of microcline, albite and nepheline in hot water. *Amer. Min.,* vol. 46, p. 688.

Muir, I. D., 1955. Transitional optics of some andesines and labradorites. *Min. Mag.,* vol. 30, p. 545.

Musgrave, R. N., 1882. Analysis of beautifully crystallised albite from the same locality (near Amelia C.H., Va). *Chemical News,* vol. 46, p. 204.

Němec, D., 1954. Reciprocal oriented overgrowth of plagioclase and potash felspars (2). *Acta Acad. Sci Čechoslovenicae, Basis Brunensis,* vol. 26, No. 6, 52 pp. (M.A. 13–402).

Nicholls, G. D., 1958. Autometasomatism in the Lower Spilites of the Builth volcanic series. *Quart. Journ. Geol. Soc.,* vol. 114, p. 137.

Nieuwenkamp, W., 1948. *Stereograms for the determination of plagioclase feldspars in random sections.* Spectrum, New York, Utrecht and Brussels.

Nikitin, W., 1936. *Die Fedorow-Methode.* Borntraeger, Berlin.

Nisioka, U., 1935. The equilibrium diagram of the system $CaO.Al_2O_3.2SiO_2$–$CaO.TiO_2$. *Sci. Rep. Tôhoku Univ.,* ser. 1, vol. 24, p. 707.

Noble, D. C., 1962. Plagioclase unmixing and the lower boundary of the amphibolite facies. *Journ. Geol.,* vol. 70, p. 234.

Nockolds, S. R., 1938. Contributions to the petrology of Barnavave, Carlingford, I.F.S. 3: On some hybrids from the E. and S.E. slopes of Barnavave Mountain. *Geol. Mag.,* vol. 75, p. 469.

—— 1941. The Garabal Hill–Glen Fyne igneous complex. *Quart. Journ. Geol., Soc.,* vol. 96, p. 451.

Norton, F. H., 1939. Hydrothermal formation of clay minerals in the laboratory. *Amer. Min.,* vol. 24, p. 1.

—— 1941. Hydrothermal formation of clay minerals in the laboratory, Part II. *Amer. Min.,* vol. 26, p. 1.

Oftedahl, C., 1944. High temperature optics in plagioclases of the Oslo region. *Norsk. Geol. Tidssk.,* vol. 24, p. 75.

Osborn, E. F., 1942. The system $CaSiO_3$–diopside–anorthite. *Amer. Journ. Sci.,* vol. 240, p. 751.

—— and **Tait, D. B.,** 1952. The system diopside–forsterite–anorthite. *Amer. Journ. Sci.,* Bowen vol., p. 413.

Pagliani, G., 1937. L'albite delle druse del granito di Baveno. *Atti Soc. Ital. Sci. Nat. Milano,* vol. 76, p. 331 (M.A. 7–294).

Perrier, C., 1930. Sul plagioclasio di una plumasite di Val Sabbiola e sulla teoria della deformazioni ioniche. *Boll. R. Ufficio Geol. Italia,* vol. 55, no. 6 (M.A. 5–69).

Phemister, J., 1934. Zoning in plagioclase felspar. *Min. Mag.,* vol. 23, p. 541.

—— 1942. Note on fused spent shale from a retort at Pumpherston, Midlothian. *Trans. Geol. Soc. Glasgow,* vol. 20, p. 238.

Phillips, F. C., 1930. Some mineralogical and chemical changes induced by progressive metamorphism in the Green Bed group of the Scottish Dalradian. *Min. Mag.,* vol. 22, p. 239.

Pistorius, C. W. F. T., Kennedy, G. C. and **Sourirajan, S.,** 1962. Some relations between the phases anorthite, zoisite and lawsonite at high temperatures and pressures. *Amer. Journ. Sci.,* vol. 260, p. 44.

Poldervaart, A., 1950. Correlation of physical properties and chemical composition in the plagioclase, olivine, and orthopyroxene series. *Amer. Min.,* vol. 35, p. 1067.

11—R.F.M. IV.

Poldervaart, A. and **Gilkey, A. K.**, 1954. On clouded plagioclase. *Amer. Min.*, vol. 39, p. 75.

Prince, A. T., 1943. The system albite–anorthite–sphene. *Journ. Geol.*, vol. 51, p. 1.

Raman, C. V., **Jayaraman, A.** and **Srinivasan, T.**, 1950. The structure and optical behaviour of the Ceylon moonstones. *Proc. Ind. Acad. Sci.*, vol. 32A, p. 123.

Rankin, G. A., 1915. The ternary system CaO–Al$_2$O$_3$–SiO$_2$. *Amer. Journ. Sci.*, 4th ser., vol. 39, p. 1.

Rayleigh, Lord, 1923. Studies of iridescent colour, and the structure producing it— III. The colours of labrador felspar. *Proc. Roy. Soc. London*, vol. 103, A, p. 34.

Reinhard, M., 1931. *Universal Drehtischmethoden*. Basle.

Reitan, P., 1956. Pegmatite veins and the surrounding rocks. I. Petrography and structure. *Norsk. Geol. Tidsskrift*, Bd. 36, p. 213.

Reynolds, D. L., 1952. The difference in optics between volcanic and plutonic plagioclases, and its bearing on the granite problem. *Geol. Mag.*, vol. 89, p. 233.

Ribbe, P. H., 1960. An X-ray and optical investigation of the peristerite plagioclases. *Amer. Min.*, vol. 45, p. 626.

Rigby, G. R. and **Green, A. T.**, 1942. The thermal expansion of some calcareous and magnesian minerals. *Trans. Brit. Ceram. Soc.*, vol. 41, p. 123.

Rittmann, A., 1929. Die Zonenmethode. Ein Beitrag zur Methodik der Plagioklasbestimmung mit Hilfe des Theodolithtisches. *Schwiez. Min. Petr. Mitt.*, vol. 9, p. 1.

—— and **El-Hinnawi, E. E.**, 1961. The application of the zonal method for the distinction between low- and high-temperature plagioclase feldspars. *Schweiz. Min. Petr. Mitt.*, vol. 41, p. 41.

Rosenblum, S., 1956. Improved technique for staining potash feldspars. *Amer. Min.*, vol. 41, p. 662.

Rosenqvist, I.Th., 1952. The metamorphic facies and the felspar minerals. *Universitetet i Bergen. Årbok Naturvitenskapelig rekke*, Nr. 4.

Rutland, R. W. R., 1961. Discussion. The control of anorthite content of plagioclase in metamorphic crystallization. *Amer. Journ. Sci.*, vol. 259, p. 76.

Sand, L. B., **Roy, R.** and **Osborn, E. F.**, 1957. Stability relations of some minerals in the Na$_2$O–Al$_2$O$_3$–SiO$_2$–H$_2$O system. *Econ. Geol.*, vol. 52, p. 169.

Savolahti, A., 1956. On the petrology of the Ahvenisto area. Age relation of the gabbro–anorthosite complex and the crystallisation of rapakivi. *Bull. Comm. géol. Finlande*, no. 174.

Schairer, J. F. and **Bowen, N. L.**, 1947. The system anorthite–leucite–silica. *Bull. Soc. géol. Finlande*, No. 140, p. 67.

—— —— 1956. The system Na$_2$O–Al$_2$O$_3$–SiO$_2$. *Amer. Journ. Sci.*, vol. 254, p. 129.

—— **Smith, J. R.** and **Chayes, F.**, 1956. Refractive indices of plagioclase glasses. *Annual Rep. Director Geophys. Lab., Carnegie Inst. Washington, Yr. Book*, No. 55, p. 195.

Schneider, T. R., 1957. Röntgenographische und optische Untersuchung der Umwandlung Albit-Analbit-Monalbit. *Zeit. Krist.*, vol. 109, p. 245.

Scholler, H., 1942. Versuche zur Temperaturabhängigkeit der Plagioklasoptik. *Min. Petr. Mitt. (Tschermak)*, vol. 53, p. 180.

Schwarz, R. and **Trageser, G.**, 1933. Über die künstliche Umwandlung von Feldspat in Kaolin. *Zeit. anorg. Chem.*, vol. 215, p. 190.

Sen, S. K., 1959. Potassium content of natural plagioclases and the origin of antiperthites. *Journ. Geol.*, vol. 67, p. 479.

Seto, K., 1923. Chemical study of some felspars. *Sci. Rep. Tôhoku Univ., Japan*, ser. 3, vol. 1, p. 219.

Simpson, E. S., 1948. *Minerals of Western Australia,* vol. 1. Perth (Govt. Printer).

Slemmons, D. B., 1962. Determination of volcanic and plutonic plagioclases using a three- or four-axis universal stage. *Geol. Soc. Amer. Special Paper* No. 69.

Smirnov, V. P., 1915. *On the question of the influence of humus compounds on the character of the weathering of aluminosilicates.* Kharkov (M.A. 2–377).

Smith, J. R., 1956. Effects of heating natural plagioclases. (*Annual Rep. Director Geophys. Lab.*). *Carnegie Inst. Washington, Yr. Book,* No. 55, p. 188.

—— 1957. Optical properties of heated plagioclases (*Annual Rep. Director Geophys. Lab.*). *Carnegie Inst. Washington, Yr. Book,* No. 56, p. 216.

—— and **Yoder, H. S., Jr.,** 1956. Variations in X-ray powder diffraction patterns of plagioclase feldspars. *Amer. Min.,* vol. 41, p. 632.

Smith, J. V., 1956. The powder patterns and lattice parameters of plagioclase felspars. I. The soda-rich plagioclases. *Min. Mag.,* vol. 31, p. 47.

—— 1958. The effect of composition and structural state on the rhombic section and pericline twins of plagioclase felspars. *Min. Mag.,* vol. 31, p. 914.

—— and **Gay, P.,** 1958. The powder patterns and lattice parameters of plagioclase felspars. II. *Min. Mag.,* vol. 31, p. 744.

Smythe, J. A., 1924. Minerals of the north country. Silicates. *The Vasculum,* Newcastle-upon-Tyne, vol. 10, p. 66.

Solodovnikova, L. L., 1935. Beiträge zum Studium von Feldspäten aus Pegmatitgängen Nord-Kareliens. *Trav. Inst. Lomonossoff Géochem. Crist. Min., Acad. Sci. USSR* (M.A. 7–179).

Sørensen, H., 1955. Anorthosite from Buksefjorden, west Greenland. *Meddel. fra Dansk Geol. Foren.,* Bd. 13, p. 31.

Sörum, H., 1951. Studies on the structures of plagioclase felspars. *Kgl. Norske Vid. Selsk. Skrifter.* No. 3, p. 1.

—— 1953. The structures of the plagioclase felspars. II. *Acta Cryst.,* vol. 6, p. 413.

Spence, H. S., 1932. *Feldspar.* Dept. Mines, Mines Branch, Ottawa, no. 731.

Spencer, E., 1925. Albite and other authigenic minerals in limestone from Bengal. *Min. Mag.,* vol. 20, p. 365.

—— 1930. A contribution to the study of moonstone from Ceylon and other areas and of the stability-relations of the alkali-felspars. *Min. Mag.,* vol. 22, p. 291.

—— 1937. The potash–soda–felspars. I. Thermal Stability. *Min. Mag.,* vol. 24, p. 453.

Starkey, J., 1959. Chess-board albite from New Brunswick, Canada. *Geol. Mag.,* vol. 96, p. 141.

Stephenson, A. E., 1916. Studies in hydrothermal alteration. Part I. The action of certain alkaline solutions on feldspars and hornblende. *Journ. Geol.,* vol. 24, p. 180 (M.A. 2–216).

Stevens, R. E., 1934. Studies on the alkalinity of some silicate minerals. *U.S. Geol. Surv., Prof. Paper* 185–*A*, p. 1.

Stewart, D. B., 1960. The system $LiAlSiO_4–NaAlSi_3O_8–H_2O$ at 2000 bars. *Rept. 21st. Intern. Geol. Congr., Norden,* Part 17, p. 15.

Straaten, L. M. J. U. van, 1948. Note on the occurrence of authigenic feldspar in non-metamorphic sediments. *Amer. Journ. Sci.,* vol. 246, p. 569.

Subramaniam, A. P., 1956a. Petrology of the anorthosite-gabbro mass at Kadavur, Madras, India. *Geol. Mag.,* vol. 93, p. 287.

—— 1956b. Mineralogy and petrology of the Sittampundi complex, Salem district, Madras State, India. *Bull. Geol. Soc. Amer.,* vol. 67, p. 317.

Takéuchi, Y. and **Donnay, G.,** 1959. The crystal structure of hexagonal $CaAl_2Si_2O_8$. *Acta Cryst.,* vol. 12, p. 465.

Takubo, J., 1941. *Mem. Fac. Sci., Kyôto Univ.,* B, vol. 16, p. 121 (quoted from Harada, 1948).

Taylor, W. H., Darbyshire, J. A. and **Strunz, H.,** 1934. An X-ray investigation of the felspars. *Zeit. Krist.,* vol. 87, p. 464.

Tertsch, H., 1941. Die optische Orientierung des Hochtemperatur-Anorthites. *Min. Petr. Mitt. (Tschermak),* vol. 53, p. 50.

—— 1942. Zur Hochtemperaturoptik basischer Plagioklase. *Min. Petr. Mitt. (Tschermak),* vol. 54, p. 193.

—— 1943. Optische Orientierung albitnaher getemperter Plagioklase. *Akad. Wiss. Wien.,* p. 1.

—— 1944. Ergänzungen zur Hochtemperatur-Optik der Plagioklase. *Neues Jahrb. Min., Monat., Abt. A,* p. 274.

Terzaghi, R. D., 1940. The rapakivi of Head Harbor Island, Maine. *Amer. Min.,* vol. 25, p. 111.

Thomas, H. H., 1922. On certain xenolithic Tertiary minor intrusions in the Island of Mull (Argyllshire). *Quart. Journ. Geol. Soc.,* vol. 78, p. 229.

Thompson, C. S. and **Wadsworth, M. E.,** 1957. Determination of the composition of plagioclase feldspars by means of infrared spectroscopy. *Amer. Min.,* vol. 42, p. 334.

Thugutt, S. J., 1935. Sur les produits d'hydrolysê du labrador volhynien de Horoszki. *Arch. Min. Tow. Nauk. Warsaw,* vol. 11, p. 20 (M.A. 6–240).

Tobi, A. C., 1961. The recognition of plagioclase twins in sections normal to the composition plane. *Amer. Min.,* vol. 46, p. 1470.

Tomkeieff, S. I., 1941. Metasomatism in the basalt of Haddenrig quarry near Kelso and the veining of the rocks exposed there. *Min. Mag.,* vol. 26, p. 45.

Tomlinson, W. H. and **Meier, A. E.,** 1937. On the origin of montmorillonite. *Amer. Min.,* vol. 22, p. 1124.

Tröger, W. E., 1952. *Tabellen zur optischen Bestimmung der gesteinsbildenden Minerale.* Stuttgart.

Tsuboi, S., 1923a. Optical dispersion of three intermediate plagioclases. *Min. Mag.,* vol. 20, p. 93.

—— 1923b. A dispersion method of determining plagioclases in cleavage-flakes. *Min. Mag.,* vol. 20, p. 108.

—— 1934. A straight-line diagram for determining plagioclases by the dispersion method. *Japanese Journ. Geol. Geogr.,* vol. 11, p. 325.

—— 1935. Petrological notes (1)–(10). *Japanese Journ. Geol. Geogr.,* vol. 12, p. 110.

Tunell, G., 1952. The angle between the a-axis and the trace of the rhombic section on the {010}-pinacoid in the plagioclases. *Amer. Journ. Sci.,* Bowen vol., p. 547.

Turner, F. J., 1947. Determination of plagioclase with the four-axis universal stage. *Amer. Min.,* vol. 32, p. 389.

—— 1951. Observations on twinning of plagioclase in metamorphic rocks. *Amer. Min.,* vol. 36, p. 581.

Tuttle, O. F. and **Bowen, N. L.,** 1950. High-temperature albite and contiguous feldspars. *Journ. Geol.,* vol. 58. p. 572.

Umegaki, Y., 1938. Über die bei der Hydrolyse der Plagioklase und einiger Karbonatmineralien nachgewiesene wasserstoffion-Konzentration. *Mem. Coll. Sci. Kyoto Univ.,* ser. B., vol. 14, p. 141 (M.A. 7–445).

Vorobieva, O. A., 1934. On one plagioclase pegmatite. *Trav. Inst. Pétrogr. Acad. Sci. USSR,* no. 6, p. 45 (M.A. 6–418).

Waard, D. de, 1959. Anorthite content of plagioclase in basic and pelitic schists as related to metamorphic zoning in the Usu massif, Timor. *Amer. Journ. Sci.,* vol. 257, p. 553.

Wager, L. R., 1956. A chemical definition of fractional stages as a basis for comparison of Hawaiian, Hebridean and other basic lavas. *Geochim. et Cosmochim. Acta.*, vol. 9, p. 217.

—— and **Deer, W. A.**, 1939. Geological investigation in east Greenland, Part III. The petrology of the Skaergaard intrusion, Kangerdlugssuaq, east Greenland. *Meddel. om Grøn.*, Bd. 105, Nr. 4.

—— and **Mitchell, R. L.**, 1951. The distribution of trace elements during strong fractionation of basic magma—a further study of the Skaergaard intrusion, east Greenland. *Geochim. et Cosmochim. Acta.*, vol. 1, p. 129.

Walker, T. L., 1932. Plagioclase in graphic granite. *Univ. Toronto Studs., Geol. Ser.*, no. 32, p. 11.

—— and **Parsons, A. L.**, 1927. A re-examination of bytownite and huronite. *Univ. Toronto Studs., Geol. Ser.*, no. 24, p. 5.

Washington, H. S. and **Wright, F. E.**, 1910. A feldspar from Linosa and the existence of soda anorthite (carnegieite). *Amer. Journ. Sci.*, 4th ser., vol. 29, p. 51.

Wasserburg, G. J., 1957. The effect of H_2O in silicate systems. *Journ. Geol.*, vol. 65, p. 15.

Wenk, E., 1945. Kritischer Vergleich von Anorthitbestimmungen an Plagioklasen. *Schweiz. Min. Petr. Mitt.*, vol. 25, p. 349.

White, W. P., 1919. Silicate specific heats. Second series. *Amer. Journ. Sci.*, 4th ser., vol. 47, p. 1.

Wichers, E., Schlecht, W. G. and **Gordon, C. L.**, 1944. Preparing refractory oxides, silicates, and ceramic materials for analysis by heating with acids in sealed tubes at elevated temperatures. *Journ. Research, Nat. Bur. Standards U.S.A.*, vol. 33, p. 451 (M.A. 10–298).

Wilson, G., 1950. An experimental synthesis of quartz, albite and analcite. *Geol. Mag.*, vol. 87, p. 41.

Winchell, A. N. and **Winchell, H.**, 1951. *Elements of optical mineralogy. Part II. Descriptions of minerals* (4th edit.) Wiley, New York.

Wiseman, J. D. H., 1934. The central and south-west Highland epidiorities: A study in progressive metamorphism. *Quart. Journ. Geol. Soc.*, vol. 90, p. 354.

Wyllie, P. J. and **Tuttle, O. F.**, 1961. Experimental investigation of silicate systems containing two volatile components. Part II. The effects of NH_3 and HF, in addition to H_2O, on the melting temperatures of albite and granite. *Amer. Journ. Sci.*, vol. 259, p. 128.

Yagi, K., 1949. *Journ. Japanese Assoc. Min. Petr. Econ. Geol.*, vol. 33, p. 13 (Quoted from Harada, 1954).

Yoder, H. S., Jr., 1954. The system diopside–anorthite–water (Annual Rep. Director Geophys. Lab.). *Carnegie Inst. Washington, Yr. Book*, No. 53, p. 106.

——, **Stewart, D. B.** and **Smith, J. R.**, 1956 (1957). Ternary feldspars (Annual Rep. Director Geophys. Lab.). *Carnegie Inst. Washington, Yr. Book*, No. 55 (56), p. 190 (206).

—— and **Weir, C. E.**, 1951. Change of free energy with pressure of the reaction nepheline + albite = 2 jadeite. *Amer. Journ. Sci.*, vol. 249, p. 683.

Yoshiki, B. and **Matsumoto, K.**, 1951. High-temperature modification of barium-feldspar. *Journ. Amer. Ceram. Soc.*, vol. 34, p. 283.

Zavaritsky, A. N., 1942. A new diagram for the determination of plagioclase twins. *Doklady Acad. Sci. USSR*, vol. 36, p. 14.

—— 1943. The further step in the application of the universal stage (on the fiftieth anniversary of the Fedorov method). *Mém. Soc. Russe Min.*, vol. 72, p. 93 (M.A. 10–164).

Barium Felspars

Celsian
Hyalophane

$Ba[Al_2Si_2O_8]$
$(K,Na,Ba)[AlSi_3O_8]$

MONOCLINIC $(+)$ OR $(-)$

	Celsian[1]	Hyalophane[1]
α	1·579–1·587†	1·520–1·542
β	1·583–1·593	1·524–1·545
γ	1·588–1·600	1·526–1·547
δ	0·009–0·013	0·005–0·010
$2V_\gamma$	83–92°	101–132°
$\alpha:z$	3–5°	0–20° $(\alpha:x)$
O.A.P.	(010), $\beta=y$	$\perp$(010), $\gamma=y$
Dispersion:	—	$r>v$
D	3·10–3·39	2·58–2·82
H	6–6½	6–6½
Cleavage:	{001}Perfect, {010}good, {110}poor.	{001}Perfect, {010} good.
Twinning:	Carlsbad, Manebach, Baveno laws.	
Colour:	Colourless, white, or yellow; colourless in thin section.	
Unit cell:	a (Å) 8·627	8·52§
	b (Å) 13·045	12·95
	c (Å) 2 × 7·204	7·14
	β 115·2°	≃116°
	Z 8	4
Space group	$I2_1/c$	—

The barium ion is present in small quantities in the great majority of felspars, and only rarely occurs as a major constituent. In general, felspars are considered here as barium varieties when their barium content is in excess of approximately 2 per cent. BaO. Relatively pure barium felspar, in which the $BaAl_2Si_2O_8$ molecule is greater than 90 per cent. is described as celsian; this felspar can be regarded chemically as a barium-anorthite in which most of the Ca is replaced by Ba. Hyalophane, the first barium felspar to be described (Sartorius von Walterhausen, 1855) is the name given to those felspars usually

---

[1] The optical properties of kasoite, calciocelsian and other intermediate barium felspars are given in Table 23.
† Refractive indices of synthetic $BaAl_2Si_2O_8$ (Eskola, 1922).
§ See Table 21.

rich in the $KAlSi_3O_8$ molecule, and in which the content of $BaAl_2Si_2O_8$ is generally less than 30 per cent. Barium felspars which are essentially of plagioclase compositions with some 10 to 20 per cent. $BaAl_2Si_2O_8$ are described as barium-plagioclase, and those in which $BaAl_2Si_2O_8$ is dominant over $CaAl_2Si_2O_8$ content as calciocelsian. Felspars with a content of between 50 and 90 per cent. of the celsian molecule are exceedingly rare. It may be that there are two barium-rich felspar series, an alkali felspar–hyalophane–celsian series, and a plagioclase–calciocelsian–celsian series. It is not possible, however, from the data available, to evaluate the validity of such a division, for although there is considerable evidence of a wide range of replacement in the alkali felspar-celsian series there is a conspicuous lack of analyses in the range Cn_{50} to Cn_{90}, and for barium plagioclase, data are extremely scanty. As far as the barium-rich alkali felspars are concerned (Table 22, anals. 3, 4, 5, 6), there is much to favour the view that they are members of the four component system $KAlSi_3O_8$, $NaAlSi_3O_8$, $CaAl_2Si_2O_8$ and $BaAl_2Si_2O_8$.

STRUCTURE

Taylor, Darbyshire and Strunz (1934) showed that barium felspars are structurally very similar to potassium felspars and suggested that orthoclase ($KAlSi_3O_8$) and celsian ($BaAl_2Si_2O_8$) form an isomorphous series, with hyalophane as an intermediate member. In the hyalophane studied, approximately one third of the large cation sites were occupied by barium and two thirds by potassium ($Ba_{1/3}K_{2/3}Al_{4/3}Si_{8/3}O_8$), charge balance being maintained by the appropriate replacement of Si by Al. Hyalophane was stated to have monoclinic symmetry and celsian was described as triclinic but pseudo-monoclinic. Gay (1956) showed that the cell of celsian resembles that of anorthite in that a number of weak reflections of the (b) type (p. 96) indicate a body centred cell with doubled c dimension. (Further additional weak reflections given by primitive anorthite are not observed for celsian). Cell parameters of orthoclase, celsian and an hyalophane (approximately Cn_{30}) are compared among others in Table 21.

A detailed structure determination carried out by Newnham and Megaw (1960) shows that celsian is truly monoclinic, with space group $I2_1/c$. There is a considerable degree of ordering of Si and Al amongst the tetrahedral sites, of a type different from that found in either microcline or low-albite. The manner of ordering, with Si and Al occupying alternate tetrahedral sites, appears to confirm the ideas of Loewenstein (1954) about "aluminium avoidance".

X-ray powder studies of the potassium–barium felspar series (Vermaas, 1953) suggest that a break occurs at about Cn_{40}–Cn_{45}. The barium content of hyalophanes (Cn_0–Cn_{40}) can be estimated by measurement of the separation of suitable pairs of peaks on X-ray powder patterns. Relatively few specimens have been found with Cn > 40 per cent. (apart from the nearly pure celsian end-member), so that the possibility of further complexities of structure within the range Cn_{40}–Cn_{100} cannot be ruled out. Vermaas shows that the hyalophanes studied are closely similar to low-temperature forms of potassium felspar rather than the high-temperature form (sanidine).

Another crystalline form of $BaAl_2Si_2O_8$, the mineral paracelsian, was first described by Spencer (1942). X-ray structural studies (Smith, 1953) show that paracelsian is monoclinic (pseudo-orthorhombic) with $a \sin \beta$ 9·076, b 9·583, $c \sin \beta$ 8·578 Å, β 90°±0·5°, space group $P2_1/a$, 4($BaAl_2Si_2O_8$) per unit cell. The structure of paracelsian is similar to that of danburite, $CaB_2Si_2O_8$: both have similar chains of tetrahedra, $(Si,Al)O_4$ or $(Si,B)O_4$, to those found in the felspar structures (p. 8, Fig. 2) but the chains are linked in a different manner. The close relation between the paracelsian and celsian structures is revealed when alternative cell descriptions are used. Thus Table 20 compares cell parameters using for celsian the larger parameter c' (*cf.* Fig. 3, p. 9) and for paracelsian the repeat distances along [011] and [0$\bar{1}$1], instead of c and b.

Table 20. COMPARISON OF CELSIAN, PARACELSIAN AND BANALSITE LATTICES WITH APPROPRIATE CHOICE OF CELL EDGES

Celsian $BaAl_2Si_2O_8$		Paracelsian $BaAl_2Si_2O_8$		Banalsite $BaNa_2Si_4Al_4O_{16}$	
a Å	8·63	a	8·58	a	8·50
b Å	13·05	[011]	13·2	[011]	12·99
c' Å	13·28	[0$\bar{1}$1]	13·2	[0$\bar{1}$1]	12·99
β'	99°	β	90°	β	90°
α'	90°	[011]:[0$\bar{1}$1]	93·6°	[011]:[0$\bar{1}$1]	100°

No conclusions can be drawn from the results of the structure determination regarding the distribution of Si and Al atoms in paracelsian. Some ordering of these atoms may or may not be responsible for the slight deviation from orthorhombic symmetry. Paracelsian can be changed readily to celsian by heating.

The mineral banalsite (Campbell Smith *et al.*, 1944) has a body-centred orthorhombic cell with a 8·50, b 9·97, c 2×8·36 Å, and Z=4. The doubled c parameter and body-centring is again evident only by virtue of some weak reflections. It seems likely that the structure of banalsite is similar to that of paracelsian, and its possible relation to the felspar structure is also indicated by suitable choice of cell (Table 20). The [011] and [0$\bar{1}$1] repeat distances for banalsite given in the table are obtained assuming an undoubled c parameter. In view of its structural features and chemical composition ($BaNa_2Al_4Si_4O_{16}$), banalsite cannot be regarded as a felspar mineral.

Another form of $BaAl_2Si_2O_8$ is found in the synthetic high-temperature celsian (Ito, 1950) which is hexagonal, $C6/m\ mm$, with a 5·25, c 7·84 Å. It too changes to celsian on prolonged heating.

Table 21 lists cell parameters and structure types for barium felspars and for chemically and/or structurally related substances. Included in this table are orthorhombic and hexagonal forms of synthetic $CaAl_2Si_2O_8$. Hexagonal $CaAl_2Si_2O_8$ although not iso-structural with hexagonal $BaAl_2Si_2O_8$ has basically a similar structure in which pairs of sheets of (Si,Al)–O tetrahedra are linked directly by apical oxygen atoms. These double sheets are separated by planes of Ca (or Ba) atoms (Takéuchi and Donnay, 1959). The orthorhombic $CaAl_2Si_2O_8$ appears to be structurally unrelated to paracelsian. The labelling of cell edges in Table 21 differs from that given by the investigators in some cases, since an attempt is made to achieve correspondence between structurally similar crystallographic directions.

Table 21. CELL PARAMETERS OF BARIUM FELSPARS AND RELATED SUBSTANCES

		a Å	b Å	c Å	α	β	γ	crystal system	structure type
Celsian	$BaAl_2Si_2O_8$	8·627	13·045	$2 \times 7·204$	—	115·2°	—	monoclinic	felspar
Hyalophane	$BaK_2Al_4Si_4O_{16}$	8·52	12·95	7·14	—	$\simeq$116°	—	monoclinic	felspar
Paracelsian	$BaAl_2Si_2O_8$	8·58	9·583	9·08	—	$\simeq$90°	—	monoclinic (pseudo-orthorhombic)	danburite
Banalsite	$BaNa_2Al_4Si_4O_{16}$	8·50	9·97	$2 \times 8·36$	—	—	—	orthorhombic	danburite?
Danburite	$CaB_2Si_2O_8$	7·72	8·75	8·01	—	—	—	orthorhombic	danburite
Synthetic	$BaAl_2Si_2O_8$	5·25	—	7·84	—	—	—	hexagonal	—
Anorthite	$CaAl_2Si_2O_8$	8·177	12·877	7·085	93·17°	115·85°	91·22°	triclinic	felspar
Synthetic	$CaAl_2Si_2O_8$	8·22	8·60	4·83	—	—	—	orthorhombic	—
Synthetic	$CaAl_2Si_2O_8$	5·10	—	$2 \times 7·36$	—	—	—	hexagonal	—
Orthoclase	$KAlSi_3O_8$	8·562	12·996	7·193	—	116·02°	—	monoclinic	felspar

Table 22. BARIUM

	1.	2.	3.	4.	5.	6.	7.	8.
SiO_2	61·15	61·17	57·80	59·85	44·6	55·10	34·74	38·48
TiO_2	—	—	0·17	tr.	—	—	—	—
Al_2O_3	20·58	20·35	21·55	20·64	33·0	23·20	31·20	23·61
Fe_2O_3	0·29	—	0·29	—	—	0·45	—	0·60
FeO	—	—	1·14	—	—	—	—	—
MnO	—	—	—	—	—	—	0·03	2·67
MgO	—	—	0·72	0·21	—	0·56	1·00	0·97
BaO	3·36	3·89	5·02	6·92	5·7	7·30	21·99	25·50
CaO	0·16	—	1·35	0·86	14·0	1·83	0·81	0·85
Na_2O	0·41	2·92	3·71	0·93	2·0	7·45	8·43	1·85
K_2O	13·87	11·52	8·00	11·07	0·7	0·83	0·66	5·10
H_2O^+	}0·30	—	}0·21	0·12	—	}3·72	}1·08	}0·98
H_2O^-		—		0·12	—			
Total	100·12	99·85	99·96	100·72	100·0	100·44	99·94	100·61
α	1·520–1·522	1·525	1·536	1·534	1·571	—	1·5695	1·564
β	—	1·530	1·542	1·538	1·580	—	1·5710	1·568
γ	1·526–1·528	1·532	1·546	1·540	1·585	—	1·5775	1·572
2V	75°(−)	62°(−)	48°(−)	78°(−)	78°(−)	—	41°(+)	80½°(−)
D	2·585	—	—	2·701	2·872	2·835	3·065	3·003

NUMBERS OF IONS ON

	1.	2.	3.	4.	5.	6.	7.	8.
Si	11·527	11·512	10·982	11·393	8·537	10·677	7·707	—
Al	4·573	4·515	4·826	4·631	7·456	5·299	8·160	—
Fe^{+3}	0·041	—	0·041	—	—	0·065	—	—
Ti	—	—	0·024	—	—	—	—	—
Mg	—	—	0·204	0·059	—	0·162	0·331	—
Fe^{+2}	—	—	0·181	—	—	—	—	—
Mn	—	—	—	—	—	—	0·005	—
Na	0·150	1·065	1·366	0·343	0·736	2·799	3·626	—
Ca	0·032	—	0·275	0·175	2·872	0·380	0·192	—
K	3·336	2·766	1·939	2·688	0·170	0·205	0·187	—
Ba	0·248	0·287	0·373	0·516	0·428	0·554	1·912	—
Z	16·14	16·03	16·05	16·02	15·99	16·04	15·87	—
X	3·77	4·12	4·16	3·78	4·21	4·10	6·25	—

Mol. %	Cn	6·6	7·0	9·0	13·6	10·2	13·5	—	49·8
	Or	88·5	67·2	46·6	71·1	4·1	5·0	—	32·4
	Ab	4·0	25·8	32·9	9·1	17·5	68·3	—	17·8
	An	0·9	—	11·5	6·2	68·2	13·2	—	—

1. Barium adularia, haematite deposit, Isagosawa mine, Iwaté Co., Iwaté Prefecture, Japan (Yoshimura & Shirôzu, 1953). Anal. H. Shirôzu.
2. Hyalophane, manganese deposit, Otjosondu, South-West Africa (Vermaas, 1953). Anal. C. F. J. van der Walt (Anal. recalc. free from impurities).
3. "Barium sanidine" mafic phonolite, Highwood Mountains, Montana (Larsen *et al.*, 1941).
4. Transparent, bluish-grey hyalophane, phlogopite–calcite veins in pyroxene–amphibole gneiss, Slyud-yanka, Transbaikalia, Siberia (Kalinin, 1939). Anal. P. V. Kalinin.
5. Barium plagioclase felspar, with quartz, clinozoisite, hornblende and sphene, Broken Hill district, New South Wales (Nockolds & Zies, 1933). Anal. E. G. Zies (Anal. recalc, free from impurities).
6. Barium plagioclase (Des Cloizeaux, 1877) (Includes volatile matter 3·72).
7. Banalsite, Benallt magnanese mine, Rhiw, Lleyn Peninsula, Caernarvonshire (Campbell Smith *et al.* 1944). Anal. M. H. Hey.
8. Impure kasoite (potassium celsian ?), manganese deposit, Kaso mine, 25 km. W. of Utunomyia, Totiki Prefecture, Japan (Yosimura, 1936). Anal. T. Yosimura (Contains 5% rhodonite and 3% rhodo-chrosite).

FELSPAR ANALYSES

9.	10.	11.	12.	13.	14.	15.	
42·0	35·1	33·9	33·20	32·68	33·01	32·01	SiO_2
—	—	—	—	0·08	tr.	—	TiO_2
25·8	26·8	25·6	25·20	27·28	27·16	25·02	Al_2O_3
—	—	—	2·24	0·40	0·28	0·54	Fe_2O_3
—	—	—	—	—	—	—	FeO
—	—	—	—	0·13	tr.	—	MnO
—	—	—	—	0·26	0·14	tr.	MgO
25·8	35·8	37·7	38·62	38·94	38·53	41·68	BaO
4·0	—	—	0·12	0·08	0·06	0·60	CaO
0·3	—	—	0·12	0·00	0·15	—	Na_2O
1·4	2·3	—	0·52	0·18	0·54	—	K_2O
—	—	—	—	0·08	0·05	—	H_2O^+
—	—	—	—	0·05	0·00	—	H_2O^-
99·3	100·0	97·6	100·02	100·31	99·92	99·85	Total
1·572	1·579	1·584	1·593	1·580	1·5702	(ω 1·573)	α
—	1·583	1·589	1·599	—	1·5824	—	β
1·584	1·588	1·596	1·608	1·590	1·5869	—	γ
76°(−)	88°(−)	≃90°	85°(+)	—	50°35′	—	2V
—	3·1–3·2	—	—	3·31	3·29	3·303	D

THE BASIS OF 32(O)

9.	10.	11.	12.	13.	14.	15.	
9·256	8·441	8·486	8·223	8·037	8·112	8·139	Si
6·700	7·600	7·553	7·357	7·908	7·868	7·500	Al
—	—	—	0·418	0·074	0·052	0·103	Fe^{+3}
—	—	—	—	0·015	—	—	Ti
—	—	—	—	0·095	0·052	—	Mg
—	—	—	—	—	—	—	Fe^{+2}
—	—	—	—	0·027	—	—	Mn
0·132	—	—	0·058	—	0·070	—	Na
0·944	—	—	0·032	0·021	0·016	0·163	Ca
0·397	0·705	—	0·164	0·056	0·169	—	K
2·227	3·373	3·698	3·748	3·752	3·710	4·153	Ba
15·96	16·04	16·04	16·00	16·03	16·03	15·74	Z
3·70	4·08	3·70	4·00	3·95	4·02	4·32	X
60·2	82·7	—	93·6	95·0	92·4	96·2	Cn
10·7	17·3	—	4·1	1·4	4·2	—	Or — Mol. %
3·6	—	—	1·5	—	1·7	—	Ab
25·5	—	—	0·8	3·6	1·7	3·8	An

9. Calciocelsian, "The Piggery", Broken Hill, New South Wales (Segnit, 1946).   Anal. E. R. Segnit.
10. Celsian, light-coloured gneiss, "The Piggery", Broken Hill, New South Wales (Segnit, 1946).   Anal. E. R. Segnit (Anal. recalc. to 100·0).
11. Celsian, moraine rock, Alaska range, Alaska (Schaller, 1929).   Anal. W. T. Schaller (Includes insol. 0·4).
12. Celsian, manganese deposit, Otjosondu, South-West Africa (Vermaas, 1953).   Anal. C. F. J. van der Walt (Anal. recalc. free from impurities).
13. Celsian, Benallt manganese mine, Rhiw, Lleyn Peninsula, Caernarvonshire (Spencer, 1942).   Anal. H. Bennett (Includes SO_3 0·15).
14. Paracelsian, Benallt manganese mine, Rhiw, Lleyn Peninsula, Caernarvonshire (Spencer, 1942).   Anal. H. Bennett (2V quoted from Smith, 1953).
15. Artificial, high-temperature (hexagonal) celsian (Yoshiki & Matsumoto, 1951).

CHEMISTRY

Although barium has a higher charge, its ionic radius is very close to that of potassium and it commonly replaces potassium to a greater or lesser extent, and also calcium and sodium. Chemical analyses of barium felspars are listed in Table 22. Additional analyses are quoted by Yosimura (1939) but many of the earlier analyses are of material containing a large proportion of impurities: with the exception of the material (anal. 8) termed kasoite by Yosimura (1936), such analyses have been omitted from Table 22.

Celsian ($BaAl_2Si_2O_8$) may be regarded as chemically equivalent to a barium-anorthite, though typically it has a considerable amount of the orthoclase molecule in solid solution and the amount of sodium usually is low. Calcio-celsian, a variety with 25 per cent. of the anorthite molecule, was reported by Segnit (1946), see Table 22, anal. 9. Kasoite, described as a new mineral by Yosimura (1936), appears to be a potassium-bearing celsian, but no analysis of pure material is available. *Paracelsian*, the orthorhombic phase, is less common: analyses indicate that its composition is usually fairly near to that of the end-member, $BaAl_2Si_2O_8$ (*e.g.* Table 22, anal. 14). It was first described by Tacconi (1905) who gave its formula as $Ba_3Al_8Si_8O_{31}$, but it is now known to be polymorphous with celsian, though not strictly a felspar.

Hyalophane generally has 5–30 per cent. of the celsian molecule present and can be considered chemically as a mixture of the celsian and potassium felspar molecules, generally with a small amount of sodium felspar molecule also present. Strandmark (1903) noted a gap between hyalophanes high in Ba and the celsians proper. Kasoite reduces this gap somewhat, and more recently Vermaas (1953) has reported two intermediate felspars of composition Cn_{55} and Cn_{50}: unfortunately insufficient material was available for more than a determination of their BaO contents, but they would appear to go considerably further towards the known celsian field, and it now seems probable that chemically there is a complete series from the alkali felspars to celsian.

Barium-bearing plagioclase felspars are rather more rare and show a range of composition. The material of Table 22, anal. 6, reported by Des Cloizeaux (1877) approximates to a barium-oligoclase in composition, while the barium plagioclase described by Nockolds and Zies (1933) is equivalent to a barium-bytownite (Table 22, anal. 5). A "barium-albite" has been recorded by Yosimura (1939) on the basis of recalculation of an analysis of manganhedenbergite containing only this mineral as an impurity, though its calculated composition, $Or_{42}Ab_{44}Cn_{14}$, places it in the alkali felspar field.

Banalsite ($BaNa_2Al_4Si_4O_{16}$) was described by Campbell Smith *et al.* (1944): although bearing some family resemblance to the felspars, it is orthorhombic and structurally not a member of the felspar group.

Artificial barium felspars were first prepared by Fouqué and Michel-Lévy (1880) who produced celsian synthetically by fusing a mixture of the oxides: later preparations were carried out by Dittler (1911), Ginzberg (1915) and Eskola (1922), the latter using a barium vanadate flux. Ginzberg gave the melting point of $BaAl_2Si_2O_8$ as 1640°C. (by extrapolation) and recorded a eutectic at 1323°C. with 50 per cent. of $BaAl_2Si_2O_8$ and of $CaAl_2Si_2O_8$. The high-temperature hexagonal modification of $BaAl_2Si_2O_8$ was obtained by Weyberg (1904) by fusing kaolin with $BaCl_2$, and this "barium nepheline" was also crystallized by Ginzberg (1915) who obtained in addition hexagonal mixed crystals with 15 per cent. $KAlSi_3O_8$. Dittler and Lasch (1930) synthesized hexagonal plates of $BaAl_2Si_2O_8$ up to 10 mm. across by sintering and fusing mixtures of the oxides: this pure high-temperature celsian had a melting point of 1715 °C. Hexagonal mixed crystals of high-temperature celsian–"orthoclase" containing up to 30 per cent. $KAlSi_3O_8$ were also crystallized. High-temperature celsian has also been recorded from a lead slag (Faber, 1935), and has been formed by striking an electric arc in a mixture of $BaCO_3$ and kaolin (Yoshiki and Matsumoto, 1951) giving hexagonal plates (Table 22, anal. 15): for the latter material dilatometer and specific heat determinations showed the reversible monoclinic–hexagonal change at 300°C. Yoshiki and Matsumoto also record the formation of a coating of low-temperature celsian on the clay pots in the manufacture of barium-rich optical glasses.

OPTICAL AND PHYSICAL PROPERTIES

The barium felspars show a wide range in optical and physical properties, and increasing contents of barium are associated with higher refractive indices and

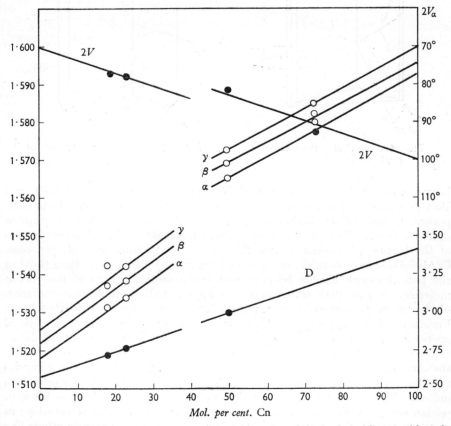

FIG. 57. Variation of the optical properties and density of the barium felspars with mol. per cent. (Or+Ab+Ne+Ks) to Cn (after Yosimura, 1939).

higher specific gravities. Yosimura (1939) has presented graphically the variation of the refractive indices, optic axial angle, extinction angles $\alpha:z$ and $\gamma:x$ on (010), and specific gravity with the chemical composition expressed as the mol. ratio (Or+Ab+Ne+Ks) : Cn, and has suggested that for most of the barium felspars the relationships are linear. His data for birefringence, refractive indices, optic axial angle and extinction angle indicate a break in the series at approxmately 40 per cent. celsian (BaO 16 per cent.). Yosimura's data for the γ-index and 2V are shown in Fig. 57 in which the values for most of the minerals detailed in Table 22 are also given. The present uncertainty,

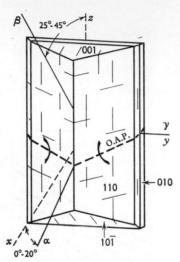

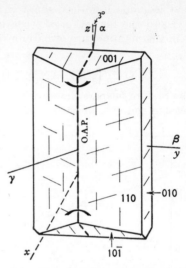

Fig. 58. Optical orientation of hyalophane.

Fig. 59. Optical orientation of celsian.

however, concerning the existence of a complete series between $KAlSi_3O_8$ and $BaAl_2Si_2O_8$, as well as the presence of variable amounts of the anorthite component in some of the barium felspars, make the use of such a diagram of doubtful value. The effect of the anorthite molecule on the refractive indices of the barium plagioclase (Table 22, anal. 5) containing 68 mol. per cent. $CaAl_2Si_2O_8$ is most notable, the indices being some 0·045 greater than those of the potassium-rich barium felspars with comparable amounts of the celsian molecule. Segnit (1946) stated that there appears to be no continuous variation of the optical properties between pure $KAlSi_3O_8$ and pure $BaAl_2Si_2O_8$ felspar. Vermaas (1953) also considered that a reliable variation diagram of the optical properties of the barium felspars cannot be compiled from the available data.

The optical orientation of hyalophane (Fig. 58) is similar to that of adularia, the optic axial plane is perpendicular to (010), and γ parallel to the y crystal axis, but compared with the potassium felspars the mineral has higher refractive indices. The values of the optic axial angle are more variable than those of celsian but are always lower and negative. The crystal habit is variable; in some crystals the forms developed are similar to those of adularia, in others like orthoclase.

In celsian (Fig. 59) the optic axial plane is parallel to (010) with $\beta=y$. The extinction angle $\alpha:z$ is $-3°$, that of $\gamma:x$ has been reported to be between $27°$ and $30°$. The refractive indices are a little higher than those of anorthite, and Eskola (1922) gives γ 1·600 for the pure synthetic mineral. The abnormally high indices (γ 1·608) of the Otjosondu celsian are associated with an unusually high content of Fe^{+3}. The optic axial angle is close to $90°$, with values of $2V_y$ between $83°$ and $92°$. Spencer (1942) reported two habits, short stout prismatic crystals with adularia habit showing twinning according to the Manebach and Baveno laws, and acicular prisms with Carlsbad twinning.

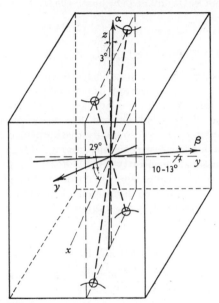

Fig. 60. Optical orientation of kasoite
(after Yosimura, 1939).

The kasoite (Fig. 60) described by Yosimura (1939) has an adularia-type crystal habit, is untwinned and shows {001} perfect, {010} distinct, and {110} weak, cleavages. The optical orientation is similar to that of celsian, the optic plane being parallel to (010), β parallel (or nearly so) to y and the extinction angle $\alpha:z=-3°$; the mineral is optically negative with $2V_\alpha$ 80·5°. In addition to kasoite there are a few other barium felspar compositions and refractive indices which are intermediate between the normally accepted ranges for hyalophane and celsian. The data for these minerals are not included in the table at the beginning of this section because of the uncertainty concerning their relationships with hyalophane and celsian, but are given separately in Table 23. The optical and physical properties of paracelsian (Table 22, anal. 14), the pseudo-ortho-rhombic $BaAl_2Si_2O_8$, are α 1·5702, β 1·5824, γ 1·5869 (Na); α 1·5634, β 1·5793, γ 1·5843 (Li); α 1·5734, β 1·5867, γ 1·5901 (Tl); $2V_\alpha$ 50° 35′, cleavage {110}, twinning {100} simple, {201} lamellar, colourless to white, D 3·29–3·31, H ⩽ 6 (Spencer, 1942).

Table 23. INTERMEDIATE BARIUM FELSPARS

	Mol. % Cn	α	β	γ	$\gamma:x$	$2V_\alpha$
1.	49·8	1·564	1 568	1·572	28–29°	80·5°
2.	50	1·555	1·562	1·564	—	43°
3.	55	1·565	1·572	1·574	—	40°
4.	60·2	1·572	—	1·584	29°	76°

1. Kasoite (Table 22, anal. 8); 2. and 3. Intermediate barium felspars, compositions calculated from BaO content (Vermaas, 1953); 4. Calciocelsian (Table 22, anal. 9).

DISTINGUISHING FEATURES

Celsian is distinguished from all plagioclase felspars by its higher refractive indices, and from all plagioclase except anorthite by its much higher density and absence of multiple twinning. Compared with the alkali felspars the refractive indices and density of celsian are very much higher. Barium plagioclase and hyalophane are not so easily distinguished from normal plagioclase and potassium-rich felspar respectively, and a determination of the barium content may be necessary for positive identification. In general, however, barium plagioclase may be distinguished from normal plagioclase by the higher density, and the more barium-rich hyalophanes (BaO > 3·5 weight per cent.) distinguished from alkali felspars by the higher refractive indices and density of the former.

PARAGENESIS

The barium felspars have a very restricted paragenesis and most of them occur in association with manganese deposits. Barium felspars are the most characteristic minerals in the manganese deposit of the Kaso Mine, Japan (Yosimura, 1939). At this locality the sequence of crystallization of the barium felspars is approximately one of decreasing barium and increasing potassium content. There is also a regular relationship between the ratio Na:K and the mol. per cent. celsian, the range being from 1·25 at $Cn_{73.3}$ to 0·14 at $Cn_{18.5}$. Celsian also occurs in knebelite masses, in which it sometimes replaces the manganese-rich olivine, and also as relict crystals in rhodochrosite ore. Kasoite (Table 22, anal. 8) is found as monomineralic veinlets and in coarse crystalline aggregates with iron-rich rhodonite. Hyalophanes containing between 18·5 and 25·8 mol. per cent. $BaAl_2Si_2O_8$ occur in veins with manganese-rich tremolite, rhodonite, rhodochrosite and spessartine. Some of the hyalophane is considered by Yosimura to be derived from kasoite by a process in which the kasoite is modified by the addition of silicon and potassium. A barium-rich alkali felspar containing 14 mol. per cent. $BaAl_2Si_2O_8$ occurs as a minor constituent in a manganhedenbergite vein.

In the manganese ores of Otjosondu, South-West Africa, celsian (Table 22, anal. 12) is associated with a fine-grained vredenburgite($2Mn_3O_4 \cdot 2Fe_2O_3$)–garnet rock; the hyalophane (anal. 2) is found in a rock consisting mainly of the manganese-rich garnet calderite, and also occurs as small veinlets in the garnet. Two barium felspars, containing 50 and 55 per cent. $BaAl_2Si_2O_8$, in rocks composed of braunite ($Mn^{+2}Mn_6^{+}4O_8SiO_4$), garnet and hollandite ($Ba_{\leq 2}$ Mn_8O_{16}), also occur at this locality (Vermaas, 1953). At the Benallt manganese mine at Rhiw in North Wales (Spencer, 1942) celsian (Table 22, anal. 13) and paracelsian (anal. 14) occur in a band in shales and sandstones associated with beds of manganese ore, and it is possible that the barium felspars were formed as the result of metamorphism by a dolerite sill. Barium-rich felspars including celsian, calciocelsian, hyalophane and barium-plagioclase have been described from lenses and streaks in acid gneiss at Broken Hill, New South Wales (Nockolds and Zies, 1933; Segnit, 1946). The celsian (Table 22, anal. 10) is associated with plagioclase ($Ab_{18}An_{82}$) and the calciocelsian (anal. 9) with plagioclase (An_{88} to An_{90}), quartz and biotite. The hyalophane occurs in a rock consisting almost entirely of felspar, the hyalophane and plagioclase ($Ab_{30}An_{70}$) being in roughly equal amounts; some of the plagioclase forms patches of fine irregular intergrowths in the hyalophane. The barium plagioclase (Table 22, anal. 5) is associated with quartz, clinozoisite and sphene.

A barium-rich sanidine (Table 22, anal. 3) occurs in the analcite phonolite from the Highwood Mountains, Montana (Larsen *et al.*, 1941), as phenocrysts which commonly exhibit several narrow oscillatory zones, and in the ground-mass: some of the analcite is resorbed and replaced by the barium-sanidine. At Slyudyanka, Siberia, hyalophane (Table 22, anal. 4) occurs in phlogopite-calcite veins in a pyroxene–amphibole gneiss, and it has been found in coarse grey crystals in zoned pegmatic apatite-bearing veins in Pre-Cambrian gneisses at Nisikkatch Lake, Saskatchewan (Hogarth, 1957). An extensive list of celsian, paracelsian and hyalophane localities is given by Spencer (1942).

REFERENCES

Campbell Smith, W., Bannister, F. E. and **Hey, M. H.,** 1944. Banalsite, a new barium-felspar from Wales. *Min. Mag.*, vol. 27, p. 33.
Cole, W. F., Sörum, H. and **Kennard, O.,** 1949. The crystal structures of orthoclase and sanidinised orthoclase. *Acta Cryst.*, vol. 2, p. 280.
—— —— and **Taylor, W. H.,** 1951. The structures of the plagioclase felspars. I. *Acta Cryst.*, vol. 4, p. 20.
Davis, G. L. and **Tuttle, O. F.,** 1952. Two new crystalline phases of the anorthite composition, $CaO.Al_2O_3.2SiO_2$. *Amer. Journ. Sci.*, Bowen vol., p. 107.
Des Cloizeaux, A., 1877. *Min. Petr. Mitt. (Tschermak)*, p. 99.
Dittler, E., 1911. Ueber das Verhalten des Orthoklas zu Andesin und Celsian und über seine Stabilität in küntslichen Schmelzen. *Min. Petr. Mitt. (Tschermak)*, vol. 30, p. 118.
—— and **Lasch, H.,** 1930. Synthetische Untersuchungen über die Mischkristall-bildung des Barium- und Strontiumfeldspates mit Orthoklas. *Akad. Wiss. Wien, Matt.-nat. Kl.*, p. 201 (M.A. 5–102).
Donnay, G., 1952. Hexagonal $CaAl_2Si_2O_8$. *Acta Cryst.*, vol. 5, p. 153.
Dunbar, C. and **Machatschki, F.,** 1930. Structure of danburite, $CaB_2Si_2O_8$. *Zeit. Krist.*, vol. 76. p. 133.
Eskola, P., 1922. The silicates of strontium and barium. *Amer. Journ. Sci.*, ser. 5, vol. 4, p. 331.
Faber, W., 1935. Die Mineralien der Bleischlacken. *Chemie der Erde*, vol. 10, p. 67 (M.A. 6–355).

Fouqué, F. and **Michel-Lévy, A.**, 1880. Sur la production artificielle de feldspaths à base de baryte, de strontiane et de plomb, correspondant à l'oligoclase, au labrador et à l'anorthit; étude des propriétés optiques de ces minéraux. *Bull. Soc. Min. Franç.*, vol. 3, p. 124.

Gay, P., 1956. A note on celsian. *Acta Cryst.*, vol. 9, p. 474.

Ginzberg, A. S., 1915. On some artificial bariumalumosilicates. *Collection of scientific papers dedicated to F. Y. Levison-Lessing*, Petrograd (M.A. 2–153).

Hogarth, D, D., 1957. The apatite-bearing veins of Nisikkatch Lake, Saskatchewan. *Canadian Min.*, vol. 6, p. 140.

Ito, T., 1950. *X-ray studies on polymorphism.* Maruzen Co. Ltd., Tokyo.

Kalinin, P. V., 1939. Hyalophane from the Slyudyanka river. *Doklady Acad. Sci. USSR*, vol. 23, p. 163.

Larsen, E. S., Hurlbut, C. S., Jr., Griggs, D. and **Burgess, C. H.**, 1941. Igneous rocks of the Highwood Mountains, Montana. *Bull. Geol. Soc. Amer.*, vol. 52, p. 1733.

Loewenstein, W., 1954. The distribution of aluminium in the tetrahedra of silicates and aluminates. *Amer. Min.*, vol. 39, p. 92.

Newnham, R. E. and **Megaw, H. D.**, 1960. The crystal structure of celsian (barium felspar). *Acta Cryst.*, vol. 13, p. 303.

Nockolds, S. R. and **Zies, E. G.**, 1933. On a new barium plagioclase felspar. *Min. Mag.*, vol. 23, p. 448.

Sartorius von Waltershausen, W., 1855. Ein Beitrag zur näheren Kenntniss des Dolomits in den Walliser Alpen. *Ann. Phys. Chem.* (*Poggendorf*), vol. 94, p. 115.

Schaller, W. T., 1929. The properties and associated minerals of gillespite. *Amer. Min.*, vol. 14, p. 319.

Segnit, E. R., 1946. Barium-felspars from Broken Hill, New South Wales. *Min. Mag.*, vol. 27, p. 166.

Smith, J. V., 1953. The crystal structure of paracelsian, $BaAl_2Si_2O_8$. *Acta Cryst.* vol. 6, p. 613.

Spencer, L. J., 1942. Barium-felspars (celsian and paracelsian) from Wales. *Min. Mag.*, vol. 26, p. 231.

Strandmark, J. E., 1903. Bidrag till kännedomen om celsian och andra baryt-fältspater. I. Celsian. *Geol. För. Förh.*, Stockholm, vol. 25, p. 289.

Tacconi, E., 1905. Di un silicato di alluminio e bario dei calcefiri di Candoglia in valle de Toce. *Rend. R. Inst. Lombardo Sci. Lett. Milano*, ser. 2, vol. 38, p. 636 (Min. Mag. 14–406).

Takéuchi, Y. and **Donnay, G.**, 1959. The crystal structure of hexagonal $CaAl_2Si_2O_8$. *Acta Cryst.*, vol. 12, p. 465.

Taylor, W. H., Darbyshire, J. A. and **Strunz, H.**, 1934. An X-ray investigation of the felspars. *Zeit. Krist.*, vol. 87, p. 464.

Vermaas, F. H. S., 1953. A new occurrence of barium-feldspar at Otjosundu, South-West Africa, and an X-ray method for determining the composition of hyalophane. *Amer. Min.*, vol. 38, p. 845.

Weyberg, Z., 1904. On barium and strontium nephelines. *Bull. Univ. Varsovie*, vol. 4, p. 1.

Yoshiki, B. and **Matsumoto, K.**, 1951. High-temperature modification of barium feldspar. *Journ. Amer. Ceramic Soc.*, vol. 34, p. 283.

Yosimura, T., 1936. On barium felspars from the Kaso mine, Tochigi Prefecture, Japan. *Journ. Geol. Soc. Japan*, vol. 43, p. 877 (M.A. 6–489).

—— 1939. Studies on the minerals from the manganese deposit of the Kaso mine, Japan. *Journ. Fac. Sci. Hokkaido Univ.*, ser. 4, vol. 4, p. 313.

Yoshimura, T. and **Shirozu, H.**, 1953. Bariumadularia from the Isagosawa mine, Iwate prefecture, Japan. *Proc. 7th Pacific Sci. Congr.* (*Auckland and Christchurch meeting*), Part 2, p. 206 (M.A. 14–50).

SILICA MINERALS

Quartz, Tridymite, Cristobalite

SiO_2

	QUARTZ	TRIDYMITE	CRISTOBALITE
	Trigonal (+)	Orthorhombic (+)	Tetragonal? (−)
	ω 1·544	α 1·471–1·479	ϵ 1·484
	ϵ 1·553	β 1·472–1·480	ω 1·487
		γ 1·474–1·483	
	δ 0·009	0·002$_5$–0·004	0·003
$2V_\gamma$		66°–90°	
Orientation:		O.A.P. (100), $\alpha = y$	
D	2·65	2·27	2·33
H	7	7	6–7
Cleavage:	none	poor prismatic cleavage	none
Twinning:	(1) Twin axis z	common on {110}	Spinel-type twins on {111}.
	(2) Twin plane {11$\bar{2}$0}		
	(3) Twin plane {11$\bar{2}$2}		
	Twinning rarely seen in thin section.		
Colour:	Colourless, white, or variable; black purple, green, etc.	Colourless or white.	Colourless, white or yellowish.
	Colourless in thin section		
Unit cell:	a (Å) 4·913	9·88	4·97
	b (Å)	17·1	
	c (Å) 5·405	16·3	6·92
	c/a 1·1001		1·395
	Z 3	64	8
Space group:	$P3_121$ or $P3_221$	$Fmm, Fmmm$ or $F222$	$P4_121$ or $P4_321$

Insoluble in acids except HF. Soluble in molten Na_2CO_3.

Quartz is one of the most abundant minerals and occurs as an essential constituent of many igneous, sedimentary and metamorphic rocks. It is also found as an accessory mineral, and as a secondary mineral in veins and meta-somatic deposits. The origin of the name quartz has been discussed by Tomkeieff (1942): it appears to have replaced the name crystal or rock crystal for this mineral towards the end of the 18th century, though references to

"quaertz" are known from 1505 onwards.   It may have been derived from the
Saxon word "Querkluftertz", or cross-vein-ore, which could easily have become
condensed to Querertz and then to quartz: this hypothesis is supported by the
old Cornish name for crystalline silica of "cross-course-spar".   See also Taube
(1944).

Tridymite occurs in cavities in siliceous volcanic rocks and also may be found
disseminated through such rocks: it may be produced by the late-stage action of
hot gases.   It is often found in threefold groups of twins or trillings and the
name is from the Greek *tridumos*, threefold, in allusion to this habit.

Cristobalite is also found in siliceous volcanic rocks and in cavities in these
rocks, and is often associated with tridymite.   The name is after the locality
Cerro San Cristobal, near Pachuca, Mexico.

The modifications and temperature ranges of stability of the silica minerals
are as follows (*cf*. Sosman, 1927):

α-Quartz: stable at atmospheric temperatures and up to 573°C.

β-Quartz: stable from 573°C. to 870°C.   Can exist metastably above 870°C.

δ-Quartz: a supposed non-piezoelectric form of quartz formed below $-183 \cdot 5$°C.
        (Osterberg, 1936; Balamuth *et al*., 1936).

α-Tridymite: can exist at atmospheric temperatures and up to 117°C. but is not
        the stable form in this range.

β_1-Tridymite: can exist between 117° and 163°C. but is not the stable form in
        this range.

β_2-Tridymite: can exist above 163°C. and is the stable form from 870° to 1470°C.;
        above 1470°C. it can exist but is unstable: melts at 1670°C.

α-Cristobalite: can exist at atmospheric temperatures and up to 200°–275°C.
        but is not the stable form in this range.

β-Cristobalite: can exist above 200°–275°C. and is stable from 1470° to its
        melting point, 1713°C.

Keatite (silica K): a high-pressure synthetic phase, not yet found in nature,
        produced at 380°–585°C. and 5000–18,000 lb./in.^{2} pressure.   Stability
        range unknown (Keat, 1954; Sosman, 1954).

Coesite (silica C): a high-pressure phase, produced at 500°–800°C. and 35,000
        atmos. pressure (Coes, 1953; Sosman, 1954)   Found in rocks subjected to
        the impact of large meteorites.

Amorphous silica: quartz crystals shock-loaded to 360–600 kilobars become
        amorphous to X-ray diffraction and have n 1·46, D 2·22.   This amorphous
        state is less dense and stable than coesite but more stable than quartz (De
        Carli and Jamieson, 1959).

Silica O: common at room temperatures in synthetic products, and repre-
        sents a solid solution series from SiO_2 towards $LiAlO_2$ (Roy, 1959).

Stishovite: a high density form of silica, D 4·3, synthesized at 160,000 atmo-
        spheres and > 1200°C.; recognized in Meteor Crater, Arizona (Stishov and
        Popova, 1961; Chao *et al*., 1962).

Melanophlogite: a low-temperature cubic polymorph, *a* 13·402Å, Z 48, D 2·05
        (Skinner and Appleman, 1962).

Silica glass (vitreous silica; lechatelierite): can exist at room temperatures and
        up to 1000°C. when its rate of crystallization rapidly increases.   It is an
        unstable glass at all temperatures below 1713°C.

Cryptocrystalline silica (chalcedony): compact varieties containing minute crystals of quartz with submicroscopic pores.

It should be noted that the nomenclature here used is that of α for a lower temperature phase and β for a higher temperature phase. The convention of α for low-temperature forms is followed in modern mineralogical texts (*e.g.* Hey, 1955) though it should be noted that at one time in recent years the Geophysical Laboratory of the Carnegie Institute of Washington, and others, unfortunately used exactly the reverse convention. Four different notations for polymorphic modifications exist (*cf.* Boldyrev, 1936) and to avoid confusion the lengthier though more precise method of using the prefixes high- and low- is sometimes preferable.

STRUCTURE

The three principal crystalline forms of SiO_2 (quartz, tridymite and cristobalite) have quite distinct crystal structures, each with a well defined field of stability under equilibrium conditions. The transformations from one to another are, however, somewhat sluggish, so that the higher temperature forms, cristobalite and tridymite, can exist metastably below their inversion temperatures. Each of the three, quartz, metastable tridymite and metastable cristobalite, has furthermore a low- and high-temperature modification designated α- and β- respectively. The six structures are described below, the form with highest symmetry for each pair being dealt with first: cell parameters are listed in Table 24. In each case the structure is built from SiO_4 tetrahedra which are

Table 24. SYMMETRY AND CELL PARAMETERS OF FORMS OF SILICA

Form of SiO_2	System	Space Group	a Å	b Å	c Å	Remarks
α-Quartz	Trigonal	$P3_121$ or $P3_221$	4·913	—	5·405	At 25°C., Swanson *et al.*, 1954.
β-Quartz	Hexagonal	$P6_222$ or $P6_422$	5·01	—	5·47	Wyckoff, 1926.
α-Tridymite	Orthorhombic (pseudo-hexagonal)	?	9·88	17·1 ($\simeq \sqrt{3}a$)	16·3	Gibbs, 1927 (Lukesh, 1942, gives c 81·57 Å).
β-Tridymite	Hexagonal	$P6_3/m\,mc$	5·03	—	8·22	Gibbs, 1927.
α-Cristobalite	Tetragonal (pseudo-cubic)	$P4_121$ or $P4_321$	4·9715	—	6·9193	At 22°C., Jay, 1944.
β-Cristobalite	Cubic	$Fd3m$	7·13	—	—	At 290°C., Wyckoff, 1925.

Synthetic SiO_2	System	Space Group	a Å	b Å	c Å	β	Reference
Silica C	Monoclinic	$C2/c$	7·17	12·38	7·17	120°	Zoltai & Buerger, 1959.
Silica K	Tetragonal	$P4_121$ or $P4_321$	7·46	—	8·60	—	Shropshire *et al.*, 1959.

linked by sharing each of their corners with another tetrahedron. In the three-dimensional framework thus formed every silicon has four oxygens and every oxygen has two silicons as nearest neighbours.

β-**Quartz** (the structure of which was determined by Bragg and Gibbs, 1925, and by Wyckoff, 1926) has hexagonal symmetry and belongs to the enantio-

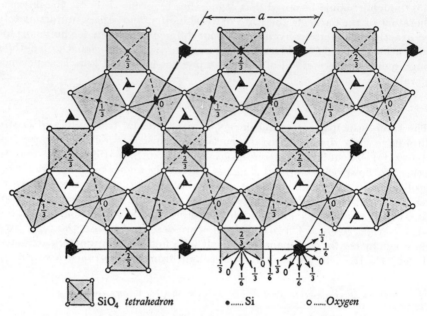

FIG. 61.   Structure of β-quartz projected on (0001).

morphous crystal class 622. Its space group is $P6_222$ or $P6_422$ for right- and left-handed crystals respectively, and there are $3SiO_2$ per unit cell. A projection of the ideal structure on the basal plane (0001) is shown in Fig. 61.

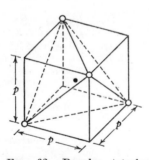

FIG. 62.   Regular tetrahedron inscribed in cube.

SiO_4 tetrahedra may be regarded as based on a cube of side p with silicon at its centre and oxygens at four of its eight corners (Fig. 62). When viewed along diad axes they appear as squares which are shaded in Fig. 61; lower edges of tetrahedra are shown by a broken line while upper edges are solid. Tetrahedra are grouped to form regular hexagonal and trigonal helices, and their heights (referred to their Si atoms) are expressed as fractions of the c repeat distance. In the ideal structure built from regular tetrahedra the height of the cell $c = 3p$ and the side $a = p(1 + \sqrt{3})$ so that c/a should be 1·098. In the actual structure of β-quartz the tetrahedra need not be completely regular but need only have three diad axes in order to conform with the space group symmetry; the observed value of c/a is 1·092. In addition to vertical screw hexad and screw triad axes the structure has vertical and horizontal diads and screw diads, the latter being shown only in the bottom right corner of Fig. 61.   An illustration of the structure showing 3_2 and 6_2 helices projected on to $(11\bar{2}0)$ is given in Fig. 63.   The structure possesses neither mirror planes nor centres of symmetry and so it has right- and left-handed forms.   If the height markings 1/3 and 2/3 in Fig. 61 were interchanged this would transform it to the structure of opposite

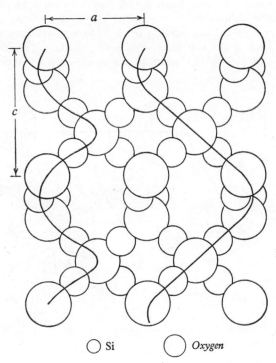

FIG. 63.   β-quartz: projection on $(11\bar{2}0)$, showing 3_2 and 6_2 helices of …Si–O–Si–O… (after Gibbs, 1926).

"hand".   The cell parameters obtained by Wyckoff (1926) are listed in Table 24, but somewhat different values (a 5·11 Å, c 5·37 Å) were found by Bradley and Grim (1951) for a synthetic β-quartz which they prepared by firing montmorillonite at 1000°C.

α-Quartz has trigonal symmetry, belongs to the enantiomorphous crystal class 32, and its space group is $P3_121$ or $P3_221$ according to its right- or left-handedness.   Its structure was among the first to be investigated by X-ray methods (Bragg, 1914) and received attention from many other workers before it was determined by Gibbs (1926).   More detailed studies were subsequently carried out by Wei (1935), and Machatschki (1936), and Fourier methods were applied by Brill *et al.* (1942).   A detailed analysis of the atomic co-ordinates and thermal motions in α-quartz has been made by Young and Post (1962). The structure is illustrated by an (0001) projection in Fig. 64 and by comparison with Fig. 61, the differences between α- and β-quartz may be discerned.   Again there are three SiO_2 per cell, but the silicon atoms in α-quartz no longer occupy the special positions $(\frac{1}{2},0,0)$, $(0,\frac{1}{2},\frac{2}{3})$, $(\frac{1}{2},\frac{1}{2},\frac{1}{3})$ and are instead at $(x,0,0)$, $(0,x,\frac{2}{3})$, $(\bar{x},\bar{x},\frac{1}{3})$ where $x=0\cdot465$.   Since their z coordinates are unchanged, the relation to β-quartz can be described approximately as a rotation of the tetrahedra about the screw triad axis of about 7°.   The screw triad axes remain as before but the screw hexads of β-quartz become screw triads in α-quartz.   The oxygens of tetrahedra are also in different positions so that they no longer lie in coplanar pairs at levels $c/6$ above and below the silicon atoms.   Other losses of symmetry elements in passing from β- to α-quartz are vertical diads, three horizontal diads and three horizontal screw diads.   The SiO_4 tetrahedra are not regular, and satisfy the space group symmetry by possessing only a

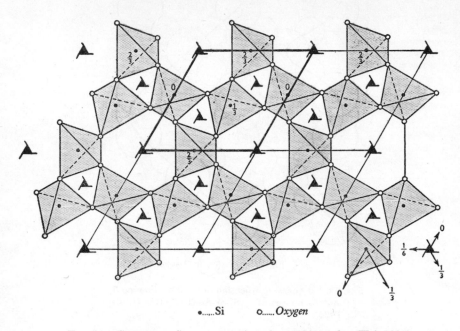

●......Si   o......*Oxygen*

FIG. 64.   Structure of α-quartz projected on (0001) (after Wei, 1935).

diad axis.   Like β-quartz, α-quartz has neither mirror planes nor centres of symmetry and therefore shows enantiomorphism.   In α-quartz the directions parallel to the x, y and u axes are of a polar character whereas in β-quartz they are perpendicular to diad axes and so are non-polar.   The twinning of both α- and β-quartz and its relation to structure have been discussed by Bragg and Gibbs (1925) and by Bragg (1937).

When the structures of α- and β-quartz are compared it is seen that the α–β transformation is one of relatively minor atomic movements involving no breakage of Si–O bonds or interchange of atoms.   By contrast with tridymite and cristobalite, quartz has a very densely packed arrangement of tetrahedra, and the disposition of its oxygen ions is not related to either hexagonal or cubic close packing.

The cell parameters of α-quartz have been measured for many specimens and by many workers. For some time the constancy of values obtained for quartz from different localities led to its use as a standard for the calibration of X-ray powder cameras. The extreme values obtained in accurate experiments differ by about 0·001 Å in *a* and 0·0005 Å in *c* but the majority of results lie within a range of about 0·01 per cent. Even so, this is greater than the experimental error reasonably attainable in powder methods, so that for the most accurate work a quartz standard is not recommended (Keith, 1950). A selection of accurate values obtained for quartz at 18°C. is given in Table 25.

Table 25. α-QUARTZ; ACCURATE CELL PARAMETERS (18°C.)

Specimen	*a* Å	*c* Å	*c/a*	Reference
Synthesized at 290°C.	4·913124	5·404714	1·100056	Keith, 1950.
Synthesized at 380°C.	4·912734	5·404425	1·100083	Keith, 1950.
Natural, Brazil.	4·912488	5·404228	1·10010	Keith, 1950.
Natural.	4·91278	5·404164	1·10002	Bradley & Jay, 1933.
Natural, Brazil.	4·91310	5·40460	1·10004	Lipson & Wilson, 1941.
Natural, Lake Toxaway.	4·913	5·405	1·1001	Swanson *et al.*, 1954.

Variations in the lattice parameters have been attributed to the presence of foreign ions, the presence of lattice defects (vacancies) and the influence of temperature and pressure at the time of crystallization. Sabatier and Wyart (1954) found that parameters of synthetic quartzes are scarcely affected by physical conditions of crystallization whereas they are markedly affected by traces of sodium impurity. Keith (1950), however, had found that synthetic crystals grown at higher temperatures have smaller cell parameters and larger axial ratios. Differences of cell parameters are accompanied by small differences of the α–β inversion temperature (Keith and Tuttle, 1952) and it is likely that both variations are associated with solid solution of impurity ions. Jay (1933) investigated the thermal expansion of quartz by the X-ray powder method and showed that the expansion coefficient increases more rapidly at higher temperatures, the rate of increase approaching infinity at the inversion temperature.

Quantitative determination of quartz in a mixture of minerals is often required, and X-ray methods for achieving this have been described, *e.g.* Carl, 1947; Gordon *et al.*, 1952; Gordon and Harris, 1956.

β-tridymite is hexagonal, $P6_3/m\ mc$, with *a* 5·03 Å, *c* 8·22 Å and $4SiO_2$ in the unit cell. The structure was determined by Gibbs (1927) using a specimen which had been derived from α-tridymite by heating. The structure is best regarded as formed by the linkage of sheets parallel to (0001), one of which is illustrated in Fig. 65. The sheet is formed by an open network of SiO_4 tetrahedra, sharing oxygens to form six-membered rings. The triangular bases of all tetrahedra lie in the (0001) plane but their apices point alternately in opposite directions. Successive parallel sheets of tetrahedra share apical oxygens and

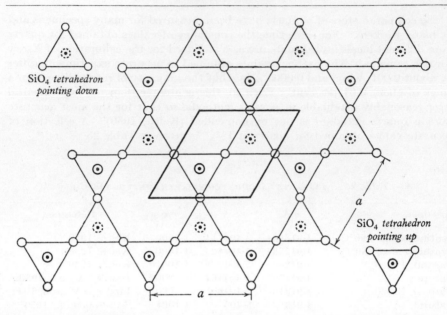

FIG. 65.   A single sheet of the β-tridymite structure viewed along the z axis.   Unit cell outlined.

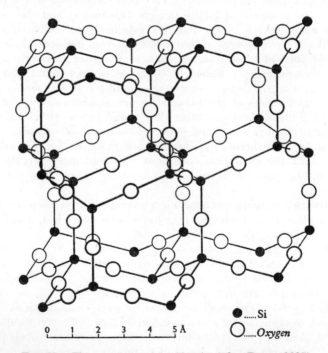

FIG. 66.   The structure of β-tridymite (after Bragg, 1937).

are related by mirror planes passing through them so that the silicons and basal oxygens of a downward pointing tetrahedron in one sheet lie directly above those of an upward pointing tetrahedron in the sheet below. A perspective view of the structure is shown in Fig. 66. In the ideal structure the c axis will be four times the height of a tetrahedron standing on its base, and the a axis twice the tetrahedral edge, so that c/a should be $2\sqrt{\frac{2}{3}}$ ($=1\cdot633$): the values quoted above give $c/a=1\cdot634$. In the actual structure the SiO_4 tetrahedra are not necessarily regular but since the silicon atoms lie on inverse hexad axes the tetrahedron must have a triad axis parallel to z. Passing through the centres of the six-membered rings of tetrahedra are vertical screw hexad axes and passing through each basal oxygen are vertical screw diads. In addition to the

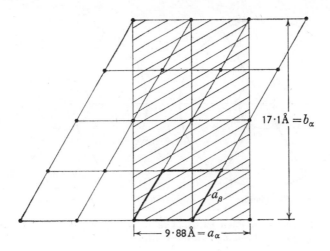

Fig. 67. Showing the relationship between the unit cells of α- and β-tridymite.

horizontal mirror plane the structure has vertical mirror and glide planes and it is centro-symmetric. Minor deviations from the ideal structure which are possible (still conforming to the space group symmetry) have not been fully investigated.

α-tridymite is orthorhombic with a 9·88 Å, b 17·1 Å, c 16·3 Å (Gibbs, 1927). The space group cannot be given with certainty but provided that the C face is centred this cell is approximately related in a simple way to that of β-tridymite (Fig. 67). Since $b \simeq a\sqrt{3}$ the cell is ortho-hexagonal and the lattice could also be described by the hexagonal cell with a 9·88 Å and c 16·3 Å; these parameters are approximately twice those of β-tridymite. The structure of α-tridymite has not been determined in detail but it is thought to involve relatively slight changes from the high-temperature form analogous to those relating α- to β-quartz. One specimen of α-tridymite was found to have the orthorhombic cell a 9·91 Å, b 17·18 Å, c 81·57 Å and space group $Fmmm$ or $F222$, and another has approximately half of the above c value (Lukesh, 1942). Unlike quartz, tridymite has a very open structure containing channels through which quite large ions could pass, and in which even very large ions could be trapped in the process of crystallization.   The specimen which has c 81·57 Å was found to contain a considerable amount of impurity which probably exists as foreign ions occupying cavities within the SiO_2 framework.   The precise location of such ions may determine the variable nature of a super-cell based upon the simple cell of β-tridymite.

The work of Fenner (1913) showed that there is a third form of tridymite to which α-tridymite transforms at 117°C.   Fenner called this a second β-form, but Gibbs (1927) suggested that it is structurally more closely related to the α-form, and that the three forms of tridymite should be called α, α′ and β.

β-cristobalite is cubic with cell edge $a \simeq 7 \cdot 13$ Å.   Its structure (idealized structure determined by Wyckoff, 1925) may be described by analogy with

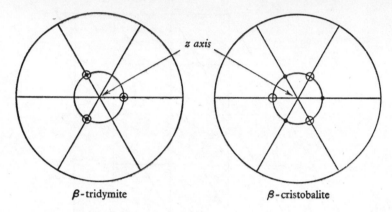

β-tridymite   β-cristobalite

FIG. 68.   Poles represent locations of six basal oxygens with reference to the oxygen bridging two tetrahedra.

that of β-tridymite since it is based upon similar sheets of six-membered rings of SiO_4 tetrahedra.   Tetrahedra in successive sheets are again linked by Si–O–Si bonds which are normal to (0001) but the basal oxygens of a tetrahedron, instead of being directly superimposed, are rotated by 60° with respect to those of the tetrahedron below it.   With reference to the apical oxygens which join successive sheets, the basal oxygens are disposed as illustrated in the stereograms of Fig. 68.   Thus as far as the oxygen layers are concerned, although these are not densely packed, their relationship in tridymite and cristobalite is similar to hexagonal and cubic close packing respectively.   The two structures are also similar to those of wurtzite and sphalerite respectively.   The repeat distance perpendicular to (0001) in cristobalite is the height of six tetrahedra instead of four as in tridymite.   The idealized structure of β-cristobalite has in fact cubic symmetry ($Fd3m$) and can alternatively be described with a cubic cell containing $8SiO_2$.   From this point of view the structure may be likened to that of diamond, with silicon atoms occupying the positions of carbons, and an oxygen at the mid-point of each Si–Si join (Fig. 69).

The idealized structure described above is not in fact possible since it involves an exceptionally small Si–O distance.   Barth (1932) suggested small deviations in both Si and O positions which result in a change of symmetry from

Fd3m to *P2₁3*. Re-examination of the structure by single-crystal methods, however (Nieuwenkamp, 1937), supported the space group *Fd3m*. This work suggested that the silicon atoms are ideally located but that either each oxygen is rotating about the Si–Si axis in a circle of radius 0·4 Å centred on its ideal position, or the oxygen atoms are statistically distributed throughout the structure among several points on such circles. For natural specimens of cristobalite various values of *a* have been given but they lie within the range 7·13–7·17 Å (at 500°C.). Synthetic β-cristobalite, however, has *a* 7·031₇ Å at 275°C. and 7·044 Å at 400°C. (Lukesh, 1942). The differences may be attributed to impurities in natural specimens, since cristobalite, like tridymite, has a very open structure which can easily accommodate foreign ions.

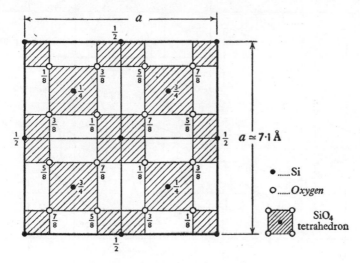

FIG. 69. Idealized structure of β-cristobalite projected on to (001).

α-cristobalite is tetragonal with $a \simeq 4\cdot97$ Å, $c \simeq 6\cdot92$ Å. The primitive unit cell ($P4_12_1$) is illustrated by a projection on (001) in Fig. 70. Its lattice may alternatively be described by a *C* face-centred cell which has $a' = \sqrt{2} \times 4\cdot97$ (= 7·03 Å) and which is pseudo-cubic. With reference to this cell the essential similarities and small differences between α- and β-cristobalite can be clearly seen. The structure determination (Nieuwenkamp, 1935b) shows that silicons and oxygens are moved from their ideal positions, and since the triad axes are no longer present the cubic symmetry is lost, but screw tetrad axes parallel to *z* remain. The contrast between the very open structures of tridymite and cristobalite on the one hand and the dense structure of quartz on the other is very marked. Buerger (1935) suggests that the open structures are kept open by thermal agitation at high temperatures, and that their persistence at lower temperatures owes much to the supporting influence of foreign ions. The introduction of foreign cations into structural cavities is probably accompanied by the charge balancing substitution of Al for Si. The extreme case of regular substitution of half of the Si atoms by Al, and introduction of an equal number of Na atoms, results in the formation of nepheline, $NaAlSiO_4$, the structure of which closely resembles that of tridymite with half of its voids filled by Na ions. Similarly, the regular filling of half the voids of cristobalite gives the higher temperature form of $NaAlSiO_4$, carnegieite. The structure of this mineral is similar to that of cristobalite and it too has α- and β-modifications. There can be no quartz structure for $NaAlSiO_4$ since quartz has no voids for the accommodation of Na ions. Moreover because quartz has such a closely packed structure, foreign ions of any sort cannot easily be enclosed and its chemical

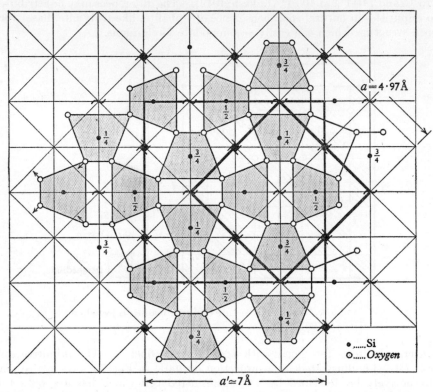

Fig. 70. Structure of α-cristobalite projected on (001), showing the primitive tetragonal unit cell (thick outline), and the C face-centred tetragonal (pseudo-cubic) cell. SiO_4 tetrahedra are shaded.

purity is very high. While transformations from α- to β-forms for each of the three SiO_2 minerals involve only minor atomic movements, the changes between quartz, tridymite and cristobalite are more disruptive. The change from quartz to a higher temperature form must involve the breaking of Si–O bonds and the migration of both Si and O atoms in several directions. The change from tridymite to cristobalite similarly involves the breaking of bonds and changing the disposition of nearest neighbours, but since both have similar layer units (parallel to (0001) in tridymite and (111) in cristobalite), this could be achieved with more restricted atomic movements. A stage in the structural transition could be visualized where some of the fundamental "layers" are joined as in tridymite and some as in cristobalite, a random mixture of the two behaving as a two-dimensional crystal of cristobalite. This arrangement has been reported for cristobalite specimens which give a cross-grating X-ray diffraction pattern instead of the more usual three-dimensional crystal pattern (Nieuwenkamp, 1935a). X-ray powder patterns and cell sizes for three purified cristobalites are given by Tokuda (1960).

Coesite is monoclinic $C2/c$, a 7·17, b 12·38, c 7·17 Å, β 120° (the y axis projection is dimensionally hexagonal). The structure contains four-membered rings of SiO_4 tetrahedra, some parallel to (010) and others parallel to (001), and their three-dimensional linkage is in some ways similar to that in the felspars (Zoltai and Buerger, 1959).

Keatite is tetragonal $P4_12_1$ or $P4_32_1$, with a 7·46, c 8·61 Å, $Z=12$, D calc. 2·502. The structure contains fourfold spirals of SiO_4 tetrahedra which share corners. These spirals are linked together by additional tetrahedra each of which shares its corners with tetrahedra in four different spirals.

CHEMISTRY

Quartz. The composition of quartz is normally close to 100 per cent. SiO_2. In chemical analyses showing small amounts of other oxides, etc. (see Table 27) these oxides are generally due either to small inclusions of other minerals or to the liquid infillings in cavities within the quartz. It is possible, however, that a limited amount of substitutional solid solution may occur. Ge is one probable element for solid solution in quartz and Al must be considered a possibility for this role. Bray (1942) has reported that all the quartz from certain Colorado igneous rocks, ranging from Pre-Cambrian to Tertiary in age, contain Al. The substitution of Li+Al for Si may also occur: this possibility and the results of spectrographic analysis on pure clear quartz were discussed by Keith and Tuttle (1952), who reported trace amounts (about 0·1 p.p.m.) of Fe, Mg, Al, Ca, Li, Na and K in apparently pure quartz: B was also recorded for two samples (approximately 0·1–0·2 p.p.m.). Frondel and Hurlbut (1955) in a determination of the atomic weight of Si by precision measurements on colourless, transparent, natural quartz of optical quality, investigated its chemistry: the results, together with those for coloured varieties of quartz are given in Table 26. As remarked earlier the interpretation of quartz analyses in general, but particularly with regard to the alkali values, is complicated by the frequent occurrence in quartz of minute cavities containing entrapped liquid. For

Table 26. Chemical analyses of quartz samples

	Li_2O	Na_2O	K_2O	Al_2O_3	Fe_2O_3	MnO_2	TiO_2
Colourless	0·0005	0·0004	0·0002	0·0008	0·0000	0·00002	0·0001
Smoky	0·0004	0·0000	0·0000	0·0008	0·0005	0·00002	0·0002
Rose	0·0038	0·0011	0·0001	0·0001	0·0003	0·00005	0·0015
Rose	0·0038	0·0104	0·0010	0·0004	0·0006	0·00004	0·0011
Amethyst	—	—	—	0·0004	0·0216	0·00000	0·0004

Alkalies flame photometrically by R. B. Ellestad: Ti, Mn, Fe and Al by J. A. Maxwell (Frondel & Hurlbut, 1955).

colourless quartz of optical quality these may be presumed to be at a minimum, and the substitution of Al^{+3} for Si^{+4} appears to be accompanied by an introduction of the smallest alkali ions Li^+ and Na^+ into interstitial sites in the amount needed for valency balance.

The variation in the isotope abundances of silicon in quartz was investigated by Reynolds and Verhoogen (1953) who showed that the $^{28}Si/^{30}Si$ ratio varies only slightly, increasing from pegmatite quartz to vein quartz and to geyserite. Allenby (1954) showed that the $^{28}Si/^{30}Si$ ratio increased from 29·68 for low-temperature quartz, to 29·75–29·86 for high-temperature quartz, and had a value of 20·10 in siliceous sinter: see also Grant (1954). The isotope composition of the oxygen of quartz was investigated by Silverman (1951) who found that the $^{16}O/^{18}O$ ratio is lower in silica deposited from sea water.

Tridymite. The compositions of all natural tridymites appear to depart in varying degrees from 100 per cent. SiO_2. The more open structure of tridymite evidently can house easily the relatively large ions of the alkali and alkaline earth groups, the Si^{+4} ion being replaced readily by Al^{+3} in tetrahedral

Table 27. SILICA MINERAL ANALYSES

	1.	2.	3.	4.	5.	6.	7.
SiO_2	99·79	(99·78)	99·53	99·00	(95·1)	(95·1)	98·40
TiO_2	0·048	0·015	—	—	0·26	0·28	—
Al_2O_3	0·042	—	0·02	—	2·4	2·70	0·35
Fe_2O_3	0·007	0·07	0·05	—	0·36	0·25	—
FeO	—	0·04	0·05	0·36	—	—	0·68
MnO	0·009	—	—	0·02	0·003	0·000₅	—
MgO	0·008	0·09	—	—	0·3	0·03	—
CaO	0·010	—	—	—	0·4	0·2	0·85
Na_2O	—	—	—	—	0·80	0·67	—
K_2O	—	—	—	—	0·37	0·75	—
H_2O^+	—	—	0·20	0·39	—	—	—
H_2O^-	—	—	0·13	—	—	—	—
Total	99·92	100·00	99·98	99·77	99·99	99·98	100·48
β	—	—	—	—	1·478	1·478	1·477 (*n*)
δ	—	—	—	—	—	—	0·001
D	—	—	—	—	—	—	2·354

1. Rose quartz (242 g.), Brazil (Vultée, 1955) (Includes PbO 0·006).
2. Quartz (5 g.), garnetiferous leptynite, Pallavaram, Madras (Howie, unpublished).
3. Quartz, Miyamori village, Kamihei county, Iwaté Pref., Japan (Yagi, 1950).
4. Quartz crystals, Railway Block Chrome Mine, Selukwe, Southern Rhodesia (Golding, 1936).
5. Tridymite, in andesite, Cerro San Cristobal, Pachuca, Mexico (Mason, 1953). Spectrographic anal. R. K. Leininger.
6. Tridymite, in trachyte, near Lyttleton, New Zealand (Mason, 1955). Spectrographic anal. R. K. Leininger.
7. White asbestiform cristobalite, blast-furnace producing slag-wool (Pehrman, 1948) (Includes C 0·20).

co-ordination (*cf.* Buerger, 1954). Barth and Kvalheim (1944) described a tridymite-like mineral in a lava from Deception Island which had a composition taken to indicate that it contained 5 per cent. nepheline in solid solution, and the name christensenite was proposed for minerals in the supposed series tridymite–nepheline: more recent work by Mason (1953), however, has confirmed the presence of Al and Na in tridymite from the type locality in Mexico (Table 27, anal. 5) and under these circumstances the name christensenite is probably superfluous. A tridymite variant from Plumas Co., California, contains impurities and has a composition approximating to $NaCaAl_3Si_{15}O_{36}$ (Lukesh and Buerger, 1942). A further example of tridymite from small cavities, probably gas vesicles, in a trachytic dyke near Lyttleton, New Zealand (Table 27, anal. 6) has been described by Mason (1955): when the analysis of this material is recalculated in terms of atomic percentages the charge deficit caused by the replacement of Si^{+4} by Al^{+3} is seen to be approximately balanced by the introduction of $Ca^{+2}+Na+K$. As remarked by Mason (1953), in view of the ability of the tridymite structure to accommodate foreign ions it is unlikely that pure SiO_2 will crystallize in the tridymite structure in any natural environment where foreign ions are universally present.

Cristobalite. Cristobalite also has a very open structure compared with that of quartz, and the tridymite type of chemical replacement evidently can take place, the deficiency in charge following the replacement of Si^{+4} by Al^{+3} being balanced by the introduction of alkali and alkaline earth ions. As in the case of tridymite, no analyses of cristobalite show it to have 100 per cent. SiO_2: the original analysis (vom Rath, 1887) gave only 91·0 per cent. SiO_2, but some gangue was present. An analysis of fibrous cristobalite produced artificially in a blast-furnace is given in Table 27, anal. 7.

The SiO_2 system. The relations between the several forms of silica were established in the classic paper by Fenner (1913) which laid a sound foundation for the eventual study of all silicate systems. The stability relations of the silica minerals are illustrated in Fig. 71 in which temperature is plotted against vapour pressure. The vapour pressures have not been measured for these minerals, but as vapour pressure rises with temperature and the vapour pressure of an unstable form is higher than that of a stable form, the vapour pressures readily illustrate the relations between the stable and unstable modifications. Fenner (*loc. cit.*) found that the inversion relations between α- and β-quartz, between quartz and tridymite, and between tridymite and cristobalite were enantiotropic. The velocities of the two latter transformations are very slow and often Ostwald's rule is followed, *i.e.* an unstable form does not pass directly into the most stable form, but the action progresses through successive steps and intermediate phases appear which eventually reach the stage of greatest stability. Fenner gives as an example a heating experiment in which tridymite was partially converted to cristobalite although the temperature in all parts of the crucible was maintained within the tridymite stability range—"a result which at first sight seems impossible". In the laboratory it is necessary to use fluxes to promote the rather sluggish transformations and Fenner used sodium tungstate in this way: this technique may lead to a contamination of the silica modifications giving rise to variable or inconsistent optical properties for the tridymite or cristobalite thus obtained. Sosman (1927) gave a very full and complete review of the various silica minerals (see also Flörke, 1955).

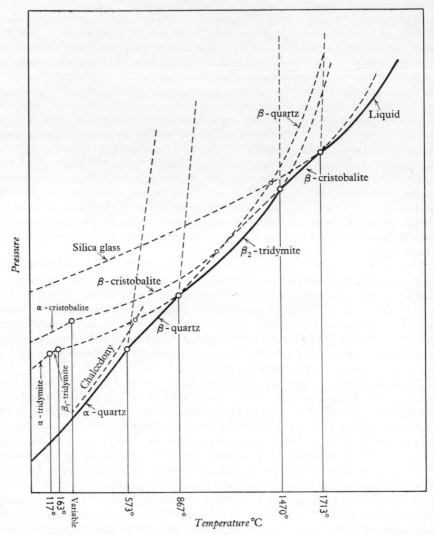

Fig. 71. The stability relations of the silica minerals (after Fenner, 1913).

Synthesis of quartz. Quartz has been produced synthetically for over a century: Schafhäutl (1845) produced microscopic crystals of quartz of hexagonal appearance by heating freshly precipitated silica for eight days, while Daubrée (1860) heated glass tubes in water in an autoclave and obtained a kaolin-like mass in which doubly-terminated perfect quartz crystals were embedded. The first relatively large crystals were produced by Spezia (1900) using a technique based on the fact that quartz is more soluble in a solution of sodium metasilicate at temperatures above 300°C. than below it. Similar methods were used by Wooster and Wooster (1946), and modern requirements of high-grade quartz for piezoelectric uses in the control of oscillators in high-frequency transmitters has led to an intensification of research into its synthetic production. A general account of the experimental work connected with the production of large single crystals has been given by Walker (1950). The latter author described the production of quartz crystals of up to 312 g. grown in one month in a vertical autoclave 12 inches in length, with a temperature gradient from 400°C. at the bottom to 380°C. at the top, containing a solution of Na_2CO_3 or NaOH, quartz fragments, and suspended seed plates cut parallel to (10$\bar{1}$1). Brown *et al.* (1952) have reported the hydrothermal production of synthetic quartz crystals of up to 150 g. with physical properties which compare with those of high-quality natural quartz: the only means of distinguishing the synthetic and natural materials is the non-susceptibility of the synthetic quartz to darkening by X-ray irradiation. The stable growth forms of synthetic quartz have been discussed by Brown *et al.* (*loc. cit.*) and by Butuzov and Ikornikova (1956). Experiments to determine the effect of pressure and temperature on the rate of formation of quartz from silicic acid were carried out by Carr and Fyfe (1958) who found that quartz did not appear in significant quantities until the two other phases, cristobalite and keatite had formed. The formation rate is influenced much more by pressure than by temperature, a pressure increase of 1000 bars favouring the attainment of equilibrium more than a temperature increase of 100°C.: these authors also discussed a possible mechanism of induced nucleation. The deliberate incorporation of selected impurities in synthetic quartz crystals during growth has been studied by Stanley and Theokritoff (1956) to determine their effect on growth rate, quality and properties of the quartz. Eleven ions in various states were added but only Al and Ge were found incorporated in the structure in "radio-grade" crystals. Boron appeared to affect the growth rate while a crystal containing Ag had a rose colour.

Coesite, a dense high pressure phase, was first synthesized by Coes (1953) from dry Na_2SiO_3, with $(NH_4)HPO_4$ or another mineralizer, at 35,000 atmospheres pressure. It is not attacked by HF, but is dissolved and volatilized in fused $(NH_4)HF_2$. Coesite has also been synthesized in well crystallized idiomorphic transparent plates with a maximum size of 0·7 mm. by subjecting amorphous silica to temperatures between 450° and 600°C. and pressures of 26,000 to 38,000 atmospheres (Khitarov *et al.*, 1957). The quartz–coesite stability relations were investigated later by MacDonald (1956), Dachille and Roy (1959) and by Boyd and England (1960), at temperatures of 400°–800°C. and pressures up to 80,000 bars: in terms of the estimated thermal gradient of the Earth, quartz should invert to coesite at a depth of between 60 and 100 kilometres. Keatite, a less dense high-pressure phase, was produced from silica gel, with water and a very small amount of alkali, in an autoclave at 5000–18,000 lb./in.^{2} and at 380°–585°C. (Keat, 1954): it is soluble in cold HF.

The α–β quartz inversion. The low–high inversion of quartz was first noted by Le Chatelier (1889) and has been investigated by Wright and Larsen (1909) who gave the transformation temperature as 575°C., while Sosman (1927) using the work of Bates and Phelps (1921) gave 573°C. for the rising temperature inversion. The effect of pressure on the inversion has been investigated by Gibson (1928) who showed that at 3000 bars the inversion point is raised to 644°C.: similarly Yoder (1950) found that at 1000 bars it was at 599°C. and at 10,000 bars it was raised to 815°C.; *i.e.* the inversion temperature is raised approximately 1°C. by each 40 bars of pressure.

The possibility of finding a variation in the temperature of the α–β quartz inversion dependent on the previous thermal history and conditions of crystallization of the quartz was first discussed by Fenner (1913, p. 377). Later Tuttle (1949a) found that the α–β inversion temperature (about 573°C.) varied as much as 1·90°C., the temperature of the inversion varying inversely with the temperature of formation: its use as a geological thermometer was thus suggested. Keith and Tuttle (1952) reported on the inversion temperatures of some 250 quartz specimens and found that over 95 per cent. of all natural specimens inverted within a range of 2·5°C. The variations are believed to be due to the solid solution of small amounts of ions other than Si^{+4} and O^{-2}, which in turn is influenced by the temperature of growth. Thus the inversion temperature can be used as an indication of the relative temperature of formation of samples of quartz which crystallized in similar chemical environments. Keith and Tuttle note that there are numerous exceptions to this relationship and that the temperature differences in the inversion can generally be taken to indicate only that the quartz is in some way different, *i.e.* the inversion in most cases can be used only as a "finger-print" method of comparing quartz from various sources and for the study of zoning within rock masses. Tuttle and England (1955) investigated the system SiO_2–H_2O, and showed that at water vapour pressures above approximately 1400 bars quartz melts directly to a hydrous liquid (see also Tuttle and Bowen, 1958, p. 31).

Solubility of quartz. Experiments with super-critical steam have shown that it dissolves silica and can transport it (Nieuwenburg and Blumendahl, 1931; Gillis, 1933; Nieuwenburg and Zon, 1935). More recently solubility measurements in the system SiO_2–H_2O have been carried out by Kennedy (1950), and by Morey and Hesselgesser (1951): the latter authors' determinations in a specially designed continuous flow apparatus gave the solubility of quartz as 1 g. per million g. water at 400°C. and 500 lb./in.^{2}, and 2596 g. per million g. water at 500°C. and 1500 lb./in.^{2}; see also Tuttle and England (*loc. cit.*). The solubility of quartz in pure water at elevated temperatures and pressure was also investigated by Frederickson and Cox (1954) who concluded that silica "dissolves" or disintegrates to give a colloidal suspension. Their experimental results were critically examined by Fyfe (1955) and by Mosebach (1957). The thermodynamic functions connected with the equilibria between quartz and aqueous solutions saturated with monosilicic acid have been calculated by Greenberg (1957).

The solution mechanism of low-temperature quartz was reviewed by Mosebach (1957) who considered that at elevated temperatures and pressures it corresponds to a bimolecular heterogeneous gas reaction. Solubility measurements performed by Holt and King (1955) were taken to indicate that an incomplete monolayer normally exists on quartz surfaces which is more soluble than the rest: it is thought to be silicic acid. O'Connor and Buchanan (1956) interpreted the electrokinetic properties of quartz in terms of the ionization of such a surface layer of silicic acid, the surface charge being considerably influenced by cation exchange in suitable circumstances. Similarly Richardson and Waddams (1955) reported ammonium molybdate reactive (AMR) silica believed to have been derived from the surface of quartz particles. The solubility of quartz in pure water, after removal of a 300 Å disturbed surface area by washing in HF solution, was determined to be $1·09 \times 10^{-3}$ mole/kg. at 100°C., extrapolation to 25°C. giving $1\cdot8\times10^{-4}$ mole/kg. (Lier *et al.*, 1960): both solution and crystallization are accelerated several orders of magnitude by NaOH or NaCl solutions.

Synthesis and experimental work involving tridymite. Considerable work on the production of synthetic tridymite and on its inversion points was carried out by Fenner (1913) and its experimentally determined fields of stability are shown in Fig. 71. The melting point of a natural tridymite was later established as being at $1670°\pm10°C$. (Ferguson and Merwin, 1918). Artificial tridymite is also of common occurrence in slags, glasses and silica bricks, and as one phase in many experimentally investigated systems involving SiO_2. Papailhau (1957) has shown that in the presence of fluorides and carbonates of sodium and potassium, at elevated temperatures, a gel of silica recrystallizes readily to form tridymite: likewise Fenner earlier used sodium tungstate as a flux. Carr and Fyfe (1958), however, crystallized amorphous silica at various pressures and temperatures and reported that tridymite was not formed in any experiments in sufficient quantity to yield an X-ray pattern, though cristobalite, keatite and quartz were obtained. Similarly Tokuda (1957) crystallized "amorphous" silica to the tridymite structure, but noted that this structure was not formed when alkali ions were absent. An investigation of the system SiO_2–H_2O (Tuttle and England, 1955) showed that at water vapour pressures above approximately 400 bars tridymite melts directly to a hydrous liquid: at pressures above approximately 1400 bars it is not formed as a stable phase.

There is thus some evidence that pure tridymite probably has never been prepared "dry" from quartz or cristobalite and although it can be produced from "amorphous" silica or from cristobalite under hydrothermal conditions its formation is difficult (*cf.* Roy, 1956). It appears then that tridymite crystallizes most readily from alkali-containing systems. Two forms of tridymite, named tridymite-M (metastable) and tridymite-S (stable), were prepared by Hill and Roy (1958) from transistor-grade silicon using only pure water as a flux: they reported that the two forms are related to each other by a very sluggish monotropic transformation.

Synthesis and experimental work involving cristobalite. Many of the earlier laboratory investigations on the production and stability field of cristobalite were performed by Fenner (1913), who also investigated the variable temperature of the α–β inversion. He was able to prepare cristobalite by heating silica glass or precipitated silica without a flux at 1300° to 1400°C. Later Greig *et al.* (1933) showed that minute crystals of cristobalite were formed on the walls of an evacuated tube of silica glass in which rock fragments wrapped in platinum foil were heated at 700°–1200°C., this transference of silica being brought about by the volatiles present in the rock. The same effect was obtained by heating evacuated tubes of silica glass containing a trace of water. The effect of various catalysts in promoting the normally sluggish inversion of quartz→tridymite→cristobalite was examined by Taylor and Lin (1941), who found that even $0\cdot1$ per cent. of alkali oxides or fluorides accelerated the inversion. Likewise Wyart (1943) when treating powdered silica glass with distilled water at 374°C. and 200 bars obtained minor amounts of cristobalite, but with the addition of $0\cdot01$ g. mol. KOH per litre the whole of the glass was converted into cristobalite. The hydrothermal reaction between dilute solutions of calicum hydroxide and silica glass at 400°C. and 340 atmospheres pressure has also, by continued reaction with the xonotlite formed, produced both α- and finally β-cristobalite (Corwin *et al.*, 1957). Using powdered silicic acid with water at pressures of 15,000 to 59,000 lb./in.[2] and temperatures of 330° to 440°C., Carr and Fyfe (1958) found that cristobalite was in all cases the first phase to form (it later became converted to keatite and then quartz).

Thus cristobalite can be synthesized from silica glass or silicic acid without the presence of alkali solutions or other mineralizers, though the presence of water is a considerable advantage. It is also produced artificially in silica bricks (*e.g.* Belyankin and Kaznakova, 1934), glasses, slags (Table 27, anal. 7), calcined flint, and in synthetic systems *e.g.* Li_2SiO_3–$LiAlSi_2O_6$–SiO_2 (Roy and Osborn, 1949). The melting point of cristobalite was accurately determined by Greig (1927) as $1713° \pm 5°C$. Its solubility at 400°C. under 480 bars water vapour pressure was 1050 mg./kg. of water vapour. In an investigation of the system SiO_2–H_2O (Tuttle and England, 1955) it was shown that the liquidus of cristobalite is considerably lowered by water vapour under pressure.

Thermal properties of quartz. The d.t.a. curve for quartz was first obtained by Fenner (1913) and many later workers have also investigated the differential thermal effects of this mineral, *e.g.* Berkelhamer (1944) and Grimshaw *et al.* (1948). A review of the whole field of quartz d.t.a. work, including techniques and methods for the quantitative determination of quartz, is given by Grimshaw and Roberts (1957). The dominant feature of the quartz d.t.a. curve is the endothermic reaction due to the α–β inversion at approximately 573°C. Accurate work by Keith and Tuttle (1952), with an error of measurement for the thermal peak of $\pm 0.1°C$., showed that the inversion temperature of natural samples varied over a range of 38°C., though over 95 per cent. of the natural quartzes inverted within a range of 2·5°C. Keith and Tuttle point out that although the d.t.a method does not give the equilibrium inversion temperature directly, it probably lies somewhere in the range between the temperatures of completion of the thermal effect on heating and on cooling. For pure quartz, the inversion temperature on heating lies in the range 573·3° to 573·6°C., and 573·3° to 574·0°C. on cooling: for the highly pure optical quality quartz investigated by Frondel and Hurlbut (1955) the inversion temperature as determined by Keith was 573·3°C. on both the heating and cooling cycles. The quartz–tridymite inversion was placed at 870°C. by Fenner (1913): a later determination by Kracek (1939) gave its temperature as $867° \pm 3°C$. The influence of pressure on the temperature of the β-quartz→tridymite inversion was calculated by Moseman and Pitzer (1941) and determined directly at up to 1000 bars by Tuttle and Bowen (1958). The latter pressure raises the inversion temperature approximately 180°C. (Fig. 72), and extrapolation of this curve to higher temperatures indicates that quartz will melt directly to a liquid at moderate pressures (∼5000 bars). Using the slope of the quartz–tridymite inversion temperature versus pressure curve Tuttle and Bowen calculated the heat of transformation to be 560 cal./mole. (compared with the value of 120 ± 50 cal./mole. calculated by Moseman and Pitzer).

Keith and Tuttle (*loc. cit.*) and other workers have demonstrated that as little as 5 per cent. of quartz in a mixture may be detected by d.t.a. methods, and Grimshaw *et al.* (1948) have shown that pure quartz may be estimated in mixtures containing upwards of 10 per cent., with a precision of about ± 1 per cent. The quartz content of some quartzites as estimated by the thermal methods, however, is much lower than that anticipated from the total silica content : this is possibly due to the presence of non-crystalline silica.

The thermal conductivity of quartz at 0°C. has been determined as $27\cdot3 \times 10^{-3}$ cal./cm. sec.°C. parallel to the z axis and $16\cdot3$ perpendicular to this axis (Birch and Clark, 1940). The linear thermal expansion of quartz has been determined by Sosman (1927) and by Rosenholtz and Smith (1941) : in addition to a change due to the α–β inversion at 573°C. Rosenholtz and Smith found a second change at 872°C. in all specimens cut perpendicular to the z axis,

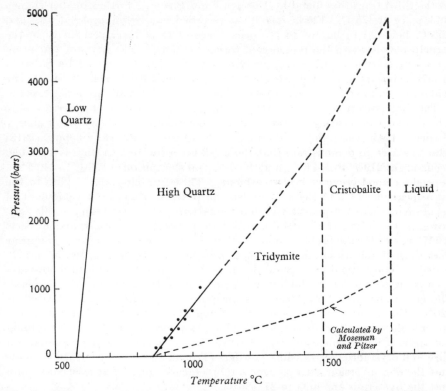

FIG. 72. Pressure–temperature diagram for SiO_2 (after Tuttle and Bowen, 1958).

corresponding to the quartz–tridymite inversion (some sections cut parallel to z, however, showed a sudden acceleration in the rate of contraction at $830° \pm 2$°C.).

Thermal properties of tridymite. The thermal investigation of tridymite was first undertaken by Fenner (1913) who reported two weak but distinct peaks on the d.t.a. curve at approximately 117° and 163°C. corresponding to the $\alpha \rightarrow \beta_1$ transition and the $\beta_1 \rightarrow \beta_2$ transition respectively ; the inversions on cooling were noted as being not very rapid. Further investigations were carried out by Tool and Insley (1938) and by Lukesh and Buerger (1942) : see also Bellanca (1943). At the relatively low temperatures of these inversions the samples cool so slowly that the thermal effects may be difficult to detect : the techniques recommended are discussed by Grimshaw and Roberts (1957). The latter authors also note that there is some evidence to indicate that the inversions of tridymite are liable to variations, possibly due to impurities : if the impurities increase greatly in amount the double inversion may be replaced by a single one.

Moseman and Pitzer (1941), using heat content capacity measurements, distinguished a possible third tridymite inversion ($\beta_2{\to}\beta_3$) at around 225°C. although they were unable to explain this in terms of probable or even improbable impurities. Later Austin (1954) who determined the coefficients of linear thermal expansion for the three forms of tridymite, reported a further change in the expansion coefficient at 210°C. which was believed to correspond to the third transition found by Moseman and Pitzer : a further smaller change took place at 475°C. Flörke (1955) has recorded small d.t.a. peaks at 235° and 255°C. believed to be due to the occurrence of three-layer periodicity in the structure, related to the presence of foreign cations. The heats of transition for $\alpha{\to}\beta_1$ tridymite and $\beta_1{\to}\beta_2$ tridymite have been determined by Sabatier (1957), using d.t.a. methods, as 0·43 cal./g. and 0·23 cal./g. respectively. The tridymite–cristobalite inversion takes place at 1470°C. at atmospheric pressure.

Thermal properties of cristobalite. The inversion from α- to β-cristobalite which occurs on heating is sharp but is accompanied by a very small energy change. Its investigation by thermal methods was pioneered by Fenner (1913) who was able to demonstrate that the $\alpha{\to}\beta$ inversion temperature is variable, occurring at 219·7° to 274·6°C., and the $\beta{\to}\alpha$ transformation at 198·1° to 240·5°C., depending upon previous heat-treatment. This variability also applies to the d.t.a. peak height and the area under the peak, so that the development of accurate methods for quantitative determinations has not yet been possible : see, however, Grimshaw *et al.* (1948) and Bellanca (1943). Grimshaw and Roberts (1957), reviewing the problem, note that from experimental data it would appear that all the impurities so far tested, which include Al, Fe, Ti, Ca, Mg, K and Na added as oxides, tend to increase the inversion temperature of cristobalite and thus point to a greater solubility in the β than in the α form of this mineral. The minimum inversion temperature for pure cristobalite is now indicated as 220°C., the highest so far encountered being 277°C. for material crystallizing under high-temperature conditions with long exposure to furnace slag containing a variety of ions (Grimshaw *et al.*, 1948). Microcalorimetric investigations on pure well crystallized cristobalite powders (Trömel and Kriesement, 1959) show that the α–β inversion extends over a temperature range of at least 10°C. and that the hysteresis amounts to 27°–36°C.

The inversion on cooling of isotropic β-cristobalite to birefringent α-cristobalite takes place readily if the crystals are free but may be arrested if they are embedded in opal (Greig, 1932; Sosman, 1932). The inversion of β-quartz to β-cristobalite takes place at 1027°C. but this reaction is metastable below 650 atmospheres (Moseman and Pitzer, 1941).

Alteration. Quartz is one of the most stable minerals, and in addition to being resistant chemically to most attacking solutions its hardness and lack of cleavage help it to resist many of the other agencies of weathering. Tridymite and cristobalite can exist only metastably at ordinary temperatures, and thus paramorphs of one form of silica after another are relatively common, with quartz most typically occurring after cristobalite or tridymite. Tridymite occurring in an inclusion in hornblende andesite (Staudt, 1925) is reported to have been corroded and surrounded by a fringe of alkali felspar with sometimes only a small core of tridymite remaining. The micro-etching or "frosting" of quartz grains by carbonate replacement has been described by Walker (1957). The replacement of quartz by orthoclase has been recorded in a quartzite adjacent to a copper ore body (Stringham, 1953): the crystal structure of the quartz has governed the position of the felspar replacement, resulting in partially replaced quartz grains which show crystallographic outlines. When quartz is very finely powdered its density has been reported to have been reduced by as much as 10 per cent., *e.g.* Tammann and Moritz (1934), and the possibility of a change in the crystallographic nature of the mineral has been critically examined by Dempster and Ritchie (1953). The latter authors were able to show that the apparent loss of density of quartz is due to the formation of a surface layer of non-quartz material (*cf.* the silicic acid layer or kaolin-type mineral layer believed to occur when quartz is agitated with water, p. 196): this surface layer of non-quartz siliceous material does not give the thermal effects of quartz, and leads to apparently low results in the quantitative determination of quartz as compared with those values obtained by chemical and other methods.

OPTICAL AND PHYSICAL PROPERTIES

Quartz. Careful determinations of the refractive indices of quartz show little variation from the values obtained for pure clear material (ω 1·544, ϵ 1·553), and these values have been suggested for use as standards (Anderson and Payne, 1940). Formulae for the refractive indices of quartz in the visible, ultra-violet, and infra-red regions were given by Coode-Adams (1927, 1928), *e.g.* for the ordinary ray

$$\omega^2 = 3{\cdot}53445 + \frac{0{\cdot}008067}{\lambda^2 - 0{\cdot}0127493} + \frac{0{\cdot}002682}{\lambda^2 - 0{\cdot}000974} + \frac{127{\cdot}2}{\lambda^2 - 108}$$

Barbaron (1948) showed that the refractive indices and the birefringence decrease very slightly with increase in temperature, *e.g.* for λ 5460 Å, at $-200\,°$C. $\omega = 1{\cdot}55724$, $\delta = 0{\cdot}00939$; and at $+50\,°$C. $\omega = 1{\cdot}55552$, $\delta = 0{\cdot}00915$. A relationship giving the dispersion of the double refraction in quartz was presented by Havelock (1929), and many accurate observations of the dispersion of this property were recorded by Harris (1929). The double refraction perpendicular to the optic axis was examined for a range of 4°C. near the temperature of the α–β quartz inversion by Steinwehr (1938), leading him to suggest the existence of two additional modifications of quartz between the α and β forms. The most accurate measurements of the refractive indices of optical quartz of known purity are probably those of Frondel and Hurlbut (1955) who, using a 60° prism and the method of minimum deviation, obtained values for λ 589·29mμ of ω 1·544258, ϵ 1·553380, referred to 18°C. Earlier high-precision determinations, including measurements on left- and right-handed crystals of quartz, have been reviewed at length by Sosman (1927). The infra-red absorption spectrum of quartz was investigated by Drummond (1936) and by Stein (1939). The latter author reported that quartz shows strong dichroism over the range 12 to 20μ, and that over the range 15 to 18μ the refractive indices show marked dispersion, as does the birefringence. More recently the variation in absorption strength in the region of 3μ has been shown, by comparisons between normal crystalline quartz and irradiated crystals, to be associated with imperfections in the crystal (Mitchell and Rigden, 1957), while Keller and Pickett (1949) have shown that for 2–15μ quartz of various types shows a characteristic curve, with slight variations for chalcedony, chert and flint: opal gives indications of the presence of OH and H_2O.

Plane-polarized light travelling through quartz along the optic axis may be considered as advancing as two circularly-polarized waves of opposite sign and slightly different velocities: the two sets of waves recombine on emerging from the crystal to form a plane-polarized wave, with the plane of polarization rotated from its original position. This phenomenon is a result of the enantiomorphism of quartz (see structure section, p. 184): the angle of rotation, per mm. thickness, is called the rotatory power, and quartz is sometimes referred to as being "optically active". Determinations of the rotatory dispersion of quartz have been made by Lowry and Coode-Adams (1927) who gave a formula for expressing the relation between the angle of rotation and the wavelength: see also Bradshaw and Livens (1929) and Chandrasekhar (1957). Szivessy (1937) has shown that α-quartz is optically inactive in directions inclined at 56° 10′ to the optic axis. The temperature coefficient of rotation of quartz in the ultra-violet region was determined by Crook and Taylor (1947). The rotatory polarization of quartz may affect the interference figure seen in convergent light, so that for sections appreciably thicker than normal the central part of the black cross is faint or absent and the space within the inner ring may be brightly coloured, the colour changing if the polarizer is rotated. When thick sections of right- and left-handed quartz are superimposed the centre of the interference figure consists of a four-rayed spiral (Airy's spiral).

In some metamorphic rocks quartz develops undulatory extinction due to strain, and in such quartz fine lamellae may occur which have been attributed to translation gliding. The orientation of these lamellae has been studied by Fairbairn (1941) who found that for quartz in a highly deformed micaceous quartzite 80 per cent. of the poles of the lamellae lay between 7° and 36° from the z crystallographic axis. Ingerson and Tuttle (1945) confirmed this observation, and concluded that the orientation of the lamellae is controlled almost entirely by the stress pattern which determined the (quartz) fabric-axes in the rock. Since the orientation of the z axes also is controlled partly by this pattern there is an indirect relation between the lamellae and the structure of the quartz. Undulatory extinction and deformation lamellae in quartz have also been investigated by Sander (1930) and by Riley (1947). Ingerson and Tuttle reported that the lamellae have a slightly higher refractive index than the rest of the grain, though Griggs and Bell (1938) and Fairbairn reached the opposite conclusion. Griggs and Bell produced undulatory extinction in quartz using pressures of about 138,000 atmospheres, the optic axis being displaced by 2°–7°. They showed a striking correlation between Sander's observed quartz maxima in tectonites and the experimental results which demonstrated the tendency of quartz to fracture into needles with boundary planes parallel to {0001}, {10$\bar{1}$0} and {10$\bar{1}$1}. Bailey *et al.* (1958) considered that quartz deformed plastically mostly by bend-gliding, one of the 3 (x, y or u) axes always being the major axis of bending. These authors explain undulatory extinction as being the optical expression of the results of bend-gliding and polygonization, the latter term being used for bent crystals transformed into a number of elongate relatively perfect crystallites inclined to one another at small angles and separated by regions of atomic misfit. In some instances quartz may show a distinctly biaxial character, with 2V as high as 10°. During later recrystallization the more obvious traces of internal strain are removed from individual quartz grains. For zoned smoky quartz, Dellwig and Hill (1960) reported that no crystal was found to be uniaxial throughout, a 2V of $7\frac{1}{2}$–8° being found in some smoky zones.

Twinning in quartz. Although twinning is rarely seen in thin sections of quartz-bearing rocks it is fairly common and may be observed frequently in hand specimens of well-developed crystals of quartz. Twinning may take place on several laws, the commonest being:

(a) Twin axis z, twin plane {10$\bar{1}$0}.   Dauphiné law.
(b) Twin plane {11$\bar{2}$0}.   Brazil law.
(c) Twin plane {11$\bar{2}$2}.   Japanese law.
(d) Twin plane {10$\bar{1}$1}.   Estérel law.
(e) Twin plane {10$\bar{1}$2}.   Sardinian law.
(f) Twin plane {11$\bar{2}$1}.   Breithaupt law.
(g) Combined Dauphiné-Brazil law.

(In the so-called Zinnwald twin of quartz the (10$\bar{1}$1) face of one crystal coincides with (10$\bar{1}$0) of another, such a relationship not being explicable by any operation of symmetry: Friedel, 1933).

By far the commonest twins are those on the Dauphiné, Brazil and Dauphiné-Brazil laws: none of these types of twinning can be detected optically in thin sections of the normal thickness. Because of the unsuitability of twinned quartz (particularly that twinned on the Dauphiné law) for use in quartz oscillator plates, a considerable volume of data on the frequency of twinning has been assembled: Hurlbut (1946) reported on 52,000 slices from 3015 crystals from 16 localities and found for relatively large crystals from pegmatites that about 80 per cent. were untwinned, while for the remainder Dauphiné twinning was more common than Brazil twinning. Gault (1949) determined the frequency of twin types for 1179 crystals from six localities and likewise reported the predominance of the Dauphiné and Dauphiné-Brazil twins: the relative frequency of the twin types was believed to reflect the conditions of growth and geological environment.

In Dauphiné twinning the composition plane is often irregular and the two portions of the crystal are of the same kind (both right-handed or both left-handed), but one is rotated 180° about z with respect to the other. Dauphiné twinning may be produced by the inversion on cooling through 573°C., and this phenomenon has been discussed by Mügge (1921), see also Pérez (1939) and Tzinzerling (1941, 1952). Thomas and Wooster (1951) have reported that Dauphiné twinning can be reduced or increased by twisting or bending at temperatures of 300°–600°C., or by maintaining a thermal gradient of a few degrees during cooling through the transition temperature, 573°C. This reversible increase of twinning under stress was termed piezocrescence. Small shifts are involved in the positions of the SiO_4 tetrahedra that link the two portions of a Dauphiné twin. The boundaries of some natural Dauphiné twins coincide with smoky areas, and when the crystals are re-inverted at 573°C. the original twin boundaries are approximately restored, but after exposure to

X-rays the original smoky and colourless areas are interchanged (Frondel, 1946: see also Armstrong, 1946). Frondel (1945b) has shown that Dauphiné twinning can be produced artificially, and also that Dauphiné twinned crystals may be largely "detwinned" by heating the quartz through the inversion point to β-quartz (in which state this twinning cannot exist by reason of symmetry) and controlling the cooling conditions so that re-inversion takes place from one centre rather than from many.

In twinning on the Brazil law the two individuals are of opposite kinds, one being right-handed, the other left-handed, with a face of the trigonal prism $\{11\bar{2}0\}$ (at 30° to the $\{10\bar{1}0\}$ prism face) as twin plane. Brazil law twin boundaries tend to be more regular than those for Dauphiné law twinning and in many cases are parallel to crystallographic directions. Twinning on this law is sometimes referred to as optical twinning, being visible optically, as opposed to the so-called electrical twinning on the Dauphiné law which reduces the piezoelectric activity of the crystal, though the term optical twinning should include all other known twin laws except the Dauphiné law. The combined Dauphiné-Brazil twin law is discussed at length by Gault (1949): twinning on this law may be more common than hitherto recognized.

Twinning on the Japanese law is less common: a review of the literature on this type of twin was given by Brauns (1919). Heide (1927) distinguished four varieties of Japanese twin, only one of which has the twin plane $(11\bar{2}2)$, and later Kôzu (1952) distinguished ten types of these twins. Twinning on the Japanese law is often combined with that on Dauphiné or Brazil laws. Twins on the Estérel law are somewhat rare, they have been reported in a paramorph of α-quartz after β-quartz from a phenocryst in hornblende–riebeckite–anorthoclase liparite (Tomita, 1932), and also in quartz from certain quartz porphyries (Lemmlein, 1940): in the latter material regular intergrowths of quartz also occur in a similar fashion to the Wheal Coates twin law described by Drugman (1927) with twin-plane $\{21\bar{3}1\}$. Other rare varieties of twinning in quartz are described by Zyndel (1914), Friedel (1923) and by Drugman (*loc. cit.*); the latter author has also described in detail the twin laws of β-quartz.

The piezoelectric property of quartz. The discovery that quartz developed an electric potential across the end of the polar (x, y, u) axes when subjected to properly directed pressure was made by P. and J. Curie (1880) and it was later suggested that such crystals would become mechanically deformed if subjected to an electrical field: this converse piezoelectric effect was experimentally verified by the Curies. The effect was first applied to control vacuum tube oscillators by Cady (1922) who applied the alternating electric potential generated by a vacuum tube radio circuit to a quartz plate, cut to a particular size and mounted so that one of its natural frequencies of mechanical vibration coincided with the oscillations of the circuit, thus stabilizing and controlling the frequency of transmission or reception. The excellency of quartz for use in frequency control lies also in the large values of Q in quartz resonators, Q being a measure of the relative efficiency of transfer of energy back and forth between strain and motion (*i.e.* Q is the ratio of energy stored to energy dissipated per cycle: Van Dyke, 1945). Quartz resonators not only have the highest values of Q known, but they exceed by a hundredfold those for the best of other measured elastic substances. The history of the development of the use of the piezoelectric property of quartz has been fully documented by Vigoureux (1931),

Scheibe (1938) and Frondel (1945a), the latter contribution being part of a Symposium[1] on quartz oscillator-plates. A detailed description of the piezo-electric property of quartz is also given by Sosman (1927).

The simplest form of piezoelectric plate made from quartz is one cut per-pendicular to an axis of twofold symmetry (an "electric axis") and with its long dimension perpendicular to the z axis of the quartz, the so-called X-cut. In practice, however, it is important to consider also the mechanical properties of the quartz, and modern techniques choose specific orientations to take advantage of the compensating effects between the temperature coefficients of the several elastic properties which play a part in the vibration (Van Dyke, 1945).

Osterberg and Cookson (1935) reported that β-quartz, above the transition temperature of around $573\,°C.$, showed a greater piezoelectric effect than that of low-temperature or α-quartz. At $847\,°C.$ the material was, however, no longer piezoelectric.

Enantiomorphism of quartz. Quartz is enantiomorphous and simple crystals are either right- or left-handed. The convention used by mineralogists is that in a right-handed crystal the face $(11\bar{2}1)$ of the trigonal bipyramid, if present, lies to the right of the $(10\bar{1}0)$ face lying below the predominant positive rhombohedron $(10\bar{1}1)$: the trigonal trapezohedron $\{51\bar{6}1\}$ may also be present. In a left-handed crystal the equivalent forms are $\{2\bar{1}\bar{1}1\}$ and $\{6\bar{1}\bar{5}1\}$. In many crystals, however, only the hexagonal prism $\{10\bar{1}0\}$ and the complementary rhombohedra $\{10\bar{1}1\}$ and $\{01\bar{1}1\}$ are present. The relative frequency of right- and left-handed quartz crystals has been investigated by several workers, *e.g.* Trommsdorff (1937) and Hurlbut (1946), and the results for several thousand crystals indicate that statistically it is a matter of chance whether a crystal is right- or left-handed, there being a close approximation to 50 per cent. of each in the samples.

The colour of quartz. Quartz occurs in colourless, yellow, grey-brown to black, pink, and violet varieties, the coloured varieties being called citrine, smoky quartz, rose quartz and amethyst respectively. The cause of some of these colours was investigated by Holden (1925) and the irradiation colours of quartz have been discussed in some detail by Przibram (1956).

Citrine may owe its colour to a submicroscopic distribution of colloidal ferric hydroxide (Holden, 1923). On heating it is bleached, while radium irradiation gives it the appearance of smoky quartz: amethyst may be converted to citrine by heating to about $500\,°C.$ The colour of rose quartz has been ascribed to manganese (Holden, 1924), and can be imitated by the addition of $0·01$ per cent. MnO to amorphous silicon hydroxide. Holden also recorded, however, that in a pink quartz the colour was due to microscopic haematite inclusions, while for a rose quartz with a bluish tinge, containing inclusions of fine needles of rutile, TiO_2 amounted to $0·029$ per cent. (*cf.* Table 26, p. 191, where the rose varieties show notably higher TiO_2 contents than the other specimens). Rose quartz can be decolorized at approximately $575\,°C.$ and when exposed to radium radiation it becomes smoky. Petrun (1955) has suggested that rose quartz represents metamorphosed amethyst, boron possibly being the cause of the coloration.

Amethyst is decolorized on heating to about $290\,°C.$, but after heating to

[1] *Amer. Min.*, 1945, vol. 30, pp. 205–468.

550°–560°C. a yellow-brown colour may develop on cooling. The bleached amethyst can be coloured purple again with radium irradiation. Absorption spectra for amethyst have been determined by Vedeneeva (1940), Bappu (1952) and Cohen (1956a). Vedeneeva suggested that the colour is due to highly dispersed Fe^{+3} inclusions, the charge being neutralized by exposure to radio-activity. This is in agreement with the results of Holden (1925), and of Frondel and Hurlbut (1955), who found that Mn and Ti were present in only small amounts which did not vary with the colour, while in amethyst free from visible inclusions Fe_2O_3 varied with the colour from 0·007 to 0·14 per cent. (*cf.* Table 26, p. 191). Some amethyst from Montezuma, Brazil, is made green by heat treatment: the purple colour is bleached and the green residual tint is due to a separate green phase, possibly chlorite (Cohen, 1956a). The inclusion of iron in quartz crystals grown from NaOH or Na_2CO_3 solutions is prevented by the formation of aegirine, but ferrous or ferric iron may be introduced into quartz grown from K_2CO_3 solutions if Mn or Be is also present (Ballman, 1961), and give green and yellow coloured bands. The Be^{+2} may replace Si^{+4}, with Fe^{+2} or Fe^{+3} being added to balance the loss of charge, giving a stuffed derivative (Roy, 1961).

Smoky quartz becomes colourless at temperatures between 200° and 300°C.: the colour may be reproduced by irradiation. Free or reduced Si has been suggested as the colouring agent (a brown silicon monoxide is known—Przibram, 1956): the small amounts of Fe, Ti and Mn reported bear no relationship to the depth of colour. Holden (1925) considered that the free silicon ions were gener-ated by the action of radioactivity, and that the smoky colour was due to the scattering of light by these ions. Chentzova and Vedeneeva (1952) have postulated that the colour may be due to the formation of absorption centres formed by the accumulation of electrons ejected from atoms by the action of ionizing radiation: their electroconductivity experiments suggest that the impurities are of the nature of cations, which may be subject to displacements of the order of 2 Å at 300°–500°C. Smoky quartz in which the colour is due to particular electronic distributions within the SiO_2 structure must be distinguished from black or grey quartz varieties which owe their colour to some other strongly absorbing impurity. Boyle (1953) has reported black and grey quartz owing its colour primarily to carbon or graphite distributed along planes or disseminated in the medium-grained quartz: sulphides, tourmaline or other dark minerals may also be responsible for the dark colour of some quartz.

The colour centres of smoky quartz have been considered by Cohen (1956b) to be associated with an impurity which was believed to be aluminium. The locations of foreign atoms in the quartz structure were later investigated by considering the variation in the axial ratio and increment ratio $\left(\dfrac{\Delta a}{a} \Big/ \dfrac{\Delta c}{c}\right)$: the predominance of interstitial rather than substitutional impurites gives a greater relative increase in the a dimension (Cohen and Sumner, 1958). X-ray irradiation frequently causes colourless optical-grade quartz to become brownish-black or smoky. Wide variation occurs in the amount of darkening caused in different crystals by the same amount of X-ray irradiation, and this most probably indicates imperfection in some of the crystals. Armstrong (1946) found a positive correlation between the amount of darkening and the ease with which crystals resume their former structures after heating to 600°C. The effects of heat treatment on the kinetics of coloration of quartz are considered also by Paige (1957), who in addition explains radiation bleaching by both X-rays and neutrons by considering the dependence of the occupancy of one electron or hole trap on other traps (see also Bass, 1957).

In the greyish blue and blue quartz of some rocks, typically of the granulite facies, the greyish blue colour may be due to needles of rutile (Vultée, 1955; Vultée and Leitz, 1956): Jayaraman (1939) reported blue quartz to contain 0·014–0·030 per cent. TiO_2, and to have abundant needles of rutile, while the depth of the blue colour was proportional to the amount of colloidal TiO_2 shown as a brownish yellow turbidity (*cf.* Watson and Beard, 1917, who showed blue quartz to contain 0·069 per cent. TiO_2 and 0·539 per cent. Fe_2O_3).[1]

Asterism in rose quartz is due to rutile needles. Eppler (1958), in discussing the physical conditions necessary, states that chatoyancy and asterism are due to the conical reflection of light on very fine, thin, elongated inclusions oriented parallel to each other and which follow only one direction: the elongated inclusions must be thin enough to produce the conical reflection of light in a similar way to its production on very thin cylinders. Quartz showing a brilliant green iridescence at normal incidence of sunlight, changing to bluish violet at oblique incidence, has been reported by Raman (1950), who attributed this phenomenon to a sub-surface layer of lamellae of Brazil twinning of right- and left-handed quartz.

Inclusions in quartz. Inclusions may take the form of small flakes or needles of other minerals, such as the rutile needles mentioned above, or haematite, tourmaline, or goethite, or liquid inclusions which may sometimes contain also either a gas phase or small crystals of such material as sylvine and halite. In recent years attempts have been made to determine the temperature of formation of individual quartz specimens, by determining the temperature at which the bubbles disappear from liquid inclusions: Ingerson (1947), for example, found that bubbles in quartz from pegmatites disappeared at 100°–182°C., and correcting for pressure, calculated the temperature of formation to be not greater than 250°C. Bailey (1949) found, however, that the results obtained in this way might vary as much as 163°C. for adjacent inclusions, and considered that none of the observed liquid inclusions were primary. Likewise Cameron *et al.* (1953) concluded that it was not possible by this method to estimate the temperature of formation: a range of 124° to 292°C. was obtained in one crystal. Peach (1951), using a decrepitation method, obtained values for the temperature of crystallization of pegmatite quartz as 450°–550°C. and a pressure of about 3000 bars.

The composition of the liquid in inclusions in quartz containing in addition halite and sylvine was determined approximately by Lemmlein and Klevtzov (1955) by microscopical observations during heating and cooling of the quartz, while Umova *et al.* (1957) investigated the composition of gaseous inclusions in quartz and found a great variation in their composition. Tuttle (1949b) has shown that planes of secondary liquid inclusions, continuous through adjacent quartz grains, are related to the foliation and folding of the rocks over wide areas.

The density of quartz. Ahlers (1924), defining density as the ratio of the weight of 1 ml. of mineral at 0°C. *in vacuo* to the weight of 1 ml. of water at 4°C.

[1] Blue quartz owing its colour to tiny needles of tourmaline has been reported by Parker (*Amer. Min.*, 1961, vol. 47, p. 1201).

in vacuo, obtained a density for quartz of $2 \cdot 6507 \pm 0 \cdot 0003$, and Anderson and Payne (1940) took as a standard value the density of quartz $D_4^{15} = 2 \cdot 651$. Earlier work included determinations on various national standards of mass, such as that on two perfect cubes of quartz, of 4 cm. and 5 cm. edge (Macé de Lépinay *et al.*, 1910), which gave an average result of $2 \cdot 65062$: individual measurements had a precision of the order of $0 \cdot 000002$ and probably include the best determinations yet made on any crystalline substance. For the colourless and flawless crystal of optical grade quartz from Arkansas (Table 26) Frondel and Hurlbut (1955) obtained an average value of $2 \cdot 64847$ g./cm.^{3} at 25°C., while flawless smoky quartz had a density of $2 \cdot 64849$ g./cm.^{3} at 25°C. Sosman (1927) gives the most probable value for the density of a randomly selected, natural, colourless quartz crystal of optical grade as $2 \cdot 6506 \pm 0 \cdot 0001$ g./cm.^{3} at 0°C. and atmospheric pressure ($2 \cdot 6483 \pm 0 \cdot 0001$ g./cm.^{3} at 25°C.).

Tammann and Moritz (1934) have reported that when a coarse quartz powder is very finely powdered in an agate mortar with a force of 20 kg. a strong yellow-red luminescence is observed. This triboluminescence has been recorded also by Inoue *et al.* (1939).

When quartz is subjected to fast neutron irradiation in a pile the density may be reduced to $2 \cdot 26$ (Klemens, 1956), and this may be explained on the basis of disordered regions within the crystal which are under compression until the number of such regions is sufficiently large for the stresses in the crystal to be relieved by plastic flow (the quartz becoming isotropic and having the X-ray pattern of a glass). At an intermediate stage, with doses in excess of 8×10^{19} neutrons/cm.^{2}, the inhomogeneous shear strain induced by the large anisotropic expansions may be shown by the extreme skewing of the $22\bar{4}0$ reflection (Wittels, 1957).

Other properties of quartz. Quartz, like calcite, is one of the few natural anisotropic materials available in a high state of purity in relatively large crystals, and as such has been used by physicists for many experimental determinations of various properties. Many such measurements are more appropriately discussed in texts on solid state physics. Among those, however, which are of interest to mineralogists is the hardness (Mohs' scale 7) which, as given by the load divided by the area of indentation, has Knoop values in the range 640–900 according to the crystallographic orientation (Winchell, 1945), or for a load of 50 gms. a Vickers hardness of 1103 perpendicular to z and 1260 parallel to z (Taylor, 1949). The linear compressibility of a rod cut from quartz has been determined by Bridgman (1949) for pressures up to 30,000 bars, while the complete determination of the six elastic constants of quartz was performed by Rao (1945). The relative elasticity compared with steel (at 92) was determined to be $95\frac{1}{2}$ for a prism face and $> 93\frac{1}{2}$ for a pyramid face of quartz (Johannsen and Phemister, 1925). The thermal conductivity of quartz at 0°C. has been determined as $27 \cdot 3 \times 10^{-3}$ cal./cm. sec. °C. parallel to the z axis and $16 \cdot 3$ perpendicular to this axis (Birch and Clark, 1940). The linear and volume coefficients of expansion and the change in axial ratios for temperatures up to 800°C. were measured and calculated by Kôzu and Takané (1929); see also p. 185). The dielectric constant of quartz has been given as $6 \cdot 53$ by Rosenholtz and Smith (1936), though Rao (1947) lists values around $4 \cdot 50$ for colourless and smoky quartz and $4 \cdot 98$–$5 \cdot 40$ for amethyst. Many other determinations of these and other physical properties of quartz are given by Sosman (1927).

Shubnikov (1930) has shown that the feeble cleavage of quartz on {10Ī1} may be made visible by striking a basal section with a steel point, followed by suitable regrinding and etching of the surface. Murdoch and Webb (1938) reported lamellar quartz with parting in three directions, this structure being thought to be due to the replacement of the lamellae of a triclinic felspar by single quartz crystals. A large clear crystal of quartz with all three {10Ī0} cleavages clearly developed has been recorded by Drugman (1939). A form of quartz termed royite was described by Sharma (1940) as occurring with normal quartz along sandstone joints as brownish black flattened prisms forming radial groups and having good prismatic and rhombohedral cleavage. Massive colourless quartz from California which breaks parallel to rhombohedral faces has been described by Haldén (1955). Quartz deformation was investigated experimentally by Griggs and Bell (1938), who found that quartz immersed in Na_2CO_3 solution heated to 450°C. ruptured at 4000 atmospheres pressure, and that the ruptured fragments were true cleavage fragments, with rhombohedral, prismatic or basal bounding planes. Further experimental work on the anisotropy of fracture in quartz was performed by Bloss (1957) who considered that a definite crystallographic control of fracture was indicated: fragments lying with their optic axis at around 52° to the normal to the plane of rest were taken to indicate cleavage parallel to the {10Ī1}*r* and {01Ī1}*z* rhombohedra of low-quartz and to the corresponding unit pyramid of high-quartz, while prismatic cleavage was seen to be next in importance.

Chalcedony. The compact varieties of silica grouped together as chalcedony are composed of minute crystals of quartz with submicroscopic pores. The colour and texture vary considerably according to the impurities present but in general such materials may be sub-divided into chalcedony, in which the colour is fairly uniform, and agate, in which the colour is arranged in bands or concentric zones. The terms chert and flint are used for opaque dull-coloured or black chalcedony and in common usage chert is taken as the name for this material when it occurs in stratified or massive form in rocks, while the term flint is normally restricted to dark chalcedony occurring in nodular form in a rock matrix, particularly in the Chalk.

Although earlier considered to be a mixture of quartz and mainly amorphous hydrated silica (opal), chalcedony is believed now to consist essentially of a network of microcrystalline quartz with a large number of micropores (Midgley, 1951). X-ray evidence shows that the quantity of opal, if any, in chalcedony and flint, must be considerably less than 10 per cent., although to account for the accepted values for density and refractive index more than 10 per cent. of opal would be required. The work of Midgley also demonstrated that flint commonly has more than 1·0 per cent. water and has α 1·537, γ 1·540, while chalcedony has less than 1·0 per cent. water and has α 1·534, γ 1·539. Folk and Weaver (1952) have recorded, by electron microscopy, pores of 0·1 micron diameter in chert, such micropores being the cause of the lower specific gravity and refractive indices. The common brown or yellow colour of chalcedony seen using the optical microscope is due to the scattering of light from these micropores. The physical properties of flint have also been studied in detail by Weymouth and Williamson (1951) and a further study of chalcedony was made by Pelto (1956) who listed evidence that such material is essentially microcrystalline quartz with submicroscopic pores: heat effects near the α–β inversion

14—R.F.M. IV.

temperature of quartz are masked by the strained condition of this material. Specimens of chalcedony with D 2·625 gave an X-ray powder photograph identical with that of quartz (Kolaczkowska, 1936) and had cell dimensions *a* 4·728 Å, *c* 5·285 Å. X-ray and optical investigations were also carried out by Novák (1947) who found in chalcedony that quartz needles are usually elongated parallel to the *z* axis but may be in random orientation (see also Lemmlein, (1946): quartzine with *a* 4·916, *c* 5·412 Å and lutecite with *a* 4·909, *c* 5·425 Å were both identified as α-quartz. The red opaque massive form of chalcedony is sometimes called jasper, the colouring here being due to iron-bearing impurities, but this name has also been applied to impure opaque microcrystalline silica with a yellow, brown or grey colour. The physical properties and the origin of agate have been discussed by Farrington (1927). For further details on the various coloured, banded or opaque varieties of chalcedony reference may be made to Sosman (1927).

The artificial production of chalcedony was reported by White and Corwin (1961) from the treatment of silica glass or cristobalite in the presence of hydrothermal solutions at moderate temperature and pressure. In general no conversion took place in slightly acid solutions but complete rapid conversion occurred in slightly alkaline solutions.

Opal. The hydrous cryptocrystalline or collodial form of silica, opal, may be colourless, milky white, yellow, red, green, blue or black. In precious opal a play of delicate colours is observed and the commoner varieties of opal also show a rather pearly reflection or opalescence. Opal has a composition of $SiO_2 . nH_2O$, with the water content around 6 to 10 per cent. in precious opal. The optical properties were investigated by Baier (1932) who found that the iridescence was due to a series of reflections from ultramicroscopic laminae arranged with hexagonal symmetry: he considered that these were due to some form of calcite residue in a gel of silicic acid. Other authors have considered that the solidified gel contains a variable amount of water and that, on cooling, the gel assumes the form of a series of extremely thin films which differ slightly in their refractivity (Smith, G. F. H., 1958). At the surface of each film interference takes place, the colour produced being more uniform if the films are spaced evenly apart. Some non-iridescent opals are believed to contain cracks filled with air, with the result that the light is totally internally reflected. If such types are immersed in water the iridescence is developed and this variety has been called hydrophane. Many observations were made by Kokta (1930) for opals (homogeneous on microscopical examination) and showed a linear relation between the amount of water and both the refractive index and specific gravity within the ranges H_2O 9·16 to 3·55 per cent., *n* 1·441 to 1·459, and D 2·008 to 2·160. A similar investigation by Taliaferro (1935) showed in addition that on heating slowly between 120° and 350°C. there is an initial increase in *n* and D up to a transition point (1·6–2·8 mols. H_2O) after which they decrease, and in completely dehydrated material these values are less than those of the original material. X-ray powder photographs of opal show faint patterns of β-cristobalite, and Raman and Jayaraman (1953) have suggested that a periodic interstratification of α-cristobalite (*n* 1·484, D 2·32) and β-cristobalite (*n* 1·468, D 2·27) may be present.

Tridymite. The refractive indices reported for tridymite show some slight variation, and the differences presumably are related to deviations from pure

SiO$_2$; for synthetic material Fenner (1913) obtained the values α 1·469, γ 1·473, 2V 35·5°. Other values include the determinations of Heide (1923) on meteoritic tridymite which gave α 1·471, β 1·472, γ 1·474, 2V$_\gamma$ 76$\frac{1}{4}$°, D 2·267, H 6$\frac{1}{2}$; Durrell (1940) on tridymite in andesite, α 1·478, β 1·479, γ 1·481 (δ 0·0025), 2V 66° to 90°; while the tridymite from the type area and from New Zealand (both containing appreciable alkalies—Table 27, anals. 5 and 6) have β 1·478 (Mason, 1953). The optic axial plane is (100), with $\alpha = y$, $\beta = x$ and $\gamma = z$.

Twinning is fairly common and gives rise to wedge-shaped crystals of two or more individuals: the twin plane has been given as {10$\bar{1}$6} using the original hexagonal indices of vom Rath (1874). This twin law also gives rise to the trillings from which tridymite derives its name. Twinning on {30$\bar{3}$4} is also recorded, sometimes in combination with the previous law: repeated twins also may occur. The density of synthetic tridymite is 2·270 g./cm.^{3} (Fenner, 1913), while values of 2·277 and 2·28 are recorded for natural material (Rosický, 1928; Mallard, 1890). X-ray powder data are given by Clark (1946).

Cristobalite. The refractive indices reported for cristobalite vary slightly but it is not possible at present to relate the variation to any chemical deviation from pure SiO$_2$. The relief is moderate with the mean refractive index around 1·485, and the birefringence is weak. On artificial crystals Fenner (1913) determined the refractive indices as ϵ 1·484, ω 1·487, while natural material (Ōhashi, 1936) had ϵ 1·482, ω 1·489. Cristobalite in silica bricks has been reported to be practically isotropic with refractive index 1·487–1·492 (Belyankin and Kaznakova, 1934). It has been suggested that cristobalite formed by direct inversion of quartz below 147°C. is almost isotropic while cristobalite formed above 1600°C. is noticeably birefringent: it may well be, however, that the material formed on inversion from quartz is so fine-grained and microcrystalline that it appears as an apparently isotropic mass, or alternatively it may be metastable cubic β-cristobalite with n 1·486. Interpenetrant spinel-type twins on {111} are fairly common (*e.g.* Murdoch 1942), and complex and repeated twinning have also been reported. Fenner (1913) recorded repeated spinel-type twins in synthetic cristobalite.

The density of synthetic material prepared by Fenner was 2·333 g./cm.^{3}, while for natural material the values reported range from 2·32 (Weil, 1925) to 2·36 (Rogers, 1922). The X-ray powder data for α-cristobalite are given by Jay (1944) and by Clark (1946).

Coesite. Synthetic coesite has α 1·590, γ 1·604, 2V$_\gamma$ 54°; Knoop harness 1200 (quartz 820), D 3·01 (Coes, 1953): it is thus notably denser and harder than quartz. Khitarov *et al.* (1957) give values α 1·594, γ 1·597, 2V 61°. Coesite differs from the other silica minerals in being unattacked by HF.

DISTINGUISHING FEATURES

Quartz is most readily distinguished by its lack of colour, cleavage and visible twinning, and by its low relief and weak birefringence. It is typically fresh and unaltered and is unattacked by acids except HF, and in hand specimen often has a distinctive crystal habit and vitreous lustre: its hardness and lack of cleavage easily distinguish it from calcite. In thin section its uniaxial figure distinguishes it from cordierite or the felspars, and in addition the alkali felspars normally have lower refractive indices and often lower birefringence. Beryl and scapolite differ in being length-fast and optically negative, while nepheline is also negative, gelatinizes with acids and is rarely completely clear.

Wright and Larsen (1909) suggested various criteria for distinguishing natural α-quartz from that formed originally above 573 °C. Frondel (1945b) critically examined these suggestions; he considered that experimental observations greatly increased the uncertainty attending their application, and showed that there are numerous exceptions to most of the criteria. He was able, however, to suggest that threefold symmetry in the distribution of the Dauphiné or Brazil twinning, as revealed by etching, or in distribution of colour or inclusions, would seem to indicate that the quartz did not crystallize above 573 °C.

Tridymite and cristobalite may be identified by their moderate relief, their refractive indices of 1·47–1·49 being considerably less than that of Canada Balsam. The twinning of tridymite and the wedge-shaped grains are characteristic: in the absence of twinning it may be necessary to determine the refractive indices of isolated grains. The refractive indices of tridymite are lower than those of cristobalite and the optic signs for these two minerals are opposite.

PARAGENESIS

Quartz. Next to the felspars, quartz is the most abundant mineral in the Earth's crust. It is a common constituent in many igneous, sedimentary and metamorphic rocks, and also occurs as secondary material often forming a cementing medium in sediments.

Igneous rocks. Quartz is an important constituent of igneous rocks. In granites, microgranites, adamellites, etc., it typically forms shapeless grains but it may show euhedral outlines in the fine-grained, rapidly cooled rhyolites, pitchstones and quartz porphyries, although in some of these rocks such as porphyritic pitchstone the quartz phenocrysts may suffer later magmatic corrosion.

As noted in the section on chemistry, inversion temperatures of natural quartzes which crystallized in chemically similar environments are considered to be inversely related to growth temperatures: this may be related also to the ability of the structure to accept certain foreign ions at higher temperatures. On a chart of the inversion-break on heating against that on cooling, rhyolitic quartz and granitic quartz show a statistical grouping into separate areas (Fig. 73). The most probable explanation is that the quartz of many granites crystallized during the low temperature late stages of magmatic activity: quartz from granites of metasomatic origin might, however, be expected to exhibit similar differences from that of rhyolite. A study of 25 specimens of quartz from the Beinn an Dubhaich, Skye, granite (Tuttle and Keith, 1954) has shown that they have inversion characteristics resembling those from rhyolites, and that the quartz from this particular Tertiary granite has undergone little recrystallization and has retained the inversion characteristics of primary crystallization from a magma.

In the igneous rocks of intermediate acidity the amount of quartz is less than in those of granitic composition, and in basic rocks it usually amounts to less than 5 per cent. though it is more abundant in some quartz dolerites and similar rock types. Quartz is incompatible with nepheline and the other felspathoids on chemical grounds and is thus absent from the under-saturated igneous rocks. Quartz and olivine in the normal compositional range do not occur together as a stable association, though quartz and the more fayalitic olivines can exist in equilibrium and may be found together in acid vugs, pegmatites, ferrogabbros and iron-rich dolerites. Quartz xenocrysts are sometimes found in basic lavas, and the various reaction phenomena which they exhibit have been described by Lacroix (1893). The quartz is often surrounded by a zone of pyroxene, and on the inner side of this zone the quartz may be replaced by glass, both at the

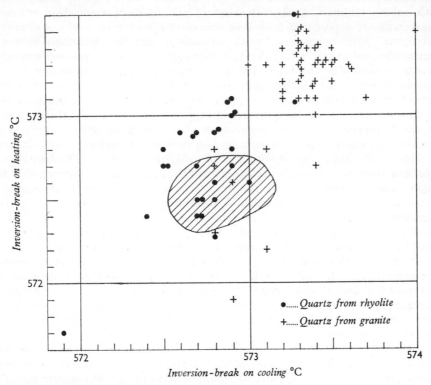

FIG. 73. The α–β inversion of quartz from granites and rhyolites (after Keith and Tuttle, 1952). The 25 specimens of quartz from the Beinn an Dubhaich granite, Skye, have inversion temperatures which all fall in the shaded area.

margin and in a series of vein-like channels. Holmes (1936) studied quartz xenocrysts in alkaline basic and ultrabasic lavas from Uganda and showed that the glass resulted from the transfusion of quartz by the introduction of various constituents in proportions different from those in which they were probably present in the magmatic part of the lava : the chief oxides introduced were Al_2O_3 K_2O and H_2O. Stages in the assimilation of quartzite xenoliths by a granodiorite have been described by Muir (1953).

In granite pegmatites quartz crystals may sometimes reach large dimensions : well-formed crystals up to 1400 lb. have been recorded (Hess, 1925 : Palache, 1932). Anhedral individuals of even greater size forming so-called massive quartz commonly occur in crystals weighing several tons (Jahns, 1953): a milky white crystal 3·5 m. long and 1·6 m. in diameter, estimated to weigh 13 tons, has been reported from Siberia (Komarov, 1951) where large quartz crystals are not uncommon in the weathered granite.

Quartz is a common constituent of hydrothermal veins and probably owes its name to its common occurrence with the z axis inclined at a high angle to the walls of such veins (see p. 180). The various habits of quartz in veins have been investigated, and the lamellar or platy variety sometimes considered to be pseudomorphous after calcite is believed to be the result of primary intergrowth with calcite (Morgan, 1925). Because of the frequent association of vein quartz with ore deposits the genesis of vein quartz has been the subject of much discussion. Many suggestions have been made of a genetic relationship between pegmatites and quartz veins; the differences between these types of occurrence have been summarized by Jahns (1955). Furnival (1939), after examining many references, concluded that no occurrence of a body of quartz undoubtedly formed by the action of magmatic processes (*i.e.* by direct crystallization from an igneous magma) had been described in geological literature. Quartz veins appear to represent a lower temperature of emplacement than that for pegmatites, and when felspars are present also they are characteristically adularia or albite. The approximate solubility of quartz in near-neutral hydrothermal solutions along a steep geothermal gradient has been calculated by Smith, F. G. (1958), who considered that for the formation of vein quartz it is unnecessary to postulate that the hydrothermal vein-forming solutions were alkaline. He considered the solubility in neutral and acid solutions to be both independent of alkalinity-acidity and large enough to be significant, and calculated that if quartz is deposited to fill a vein during a 10° drop in temperature near 500°C. a minimum of $1\frac{1}{2}$ tons of solution must flow through the fissure for every pound of quartz deposited. Likewise, if a sedimentary quartz-bearing rock is metamorphosed at 500°C. and loses 2 per cent. of its weight as a water solution saturated with silica (real loss of silica 0·01 per cent. of the original rock), a cubic kilometre of rock on metamorphism could provide the silica for about 200,000 tons of vein quartz.

In the well-known Minas Gerais area of Brazil, which has provided considerable quantities of clear single crystals of quartz, the main sources are not pegmatites but quartz veins or flat-lying blanket deposits of milky quartz roughly parallel to the enclosing sediments (Stoiber *et al.*, 1945). The clear crystals usually occur in vugs or pockets, and appear to have formed later than the milky quartz. The quartz occurs in all sizes from the most minute to crystals weighing over five tons, while the ratio of milky quartz to clear quartz crystals has been estimated variously at 10,000 to 1 and 1000 to 1.

Sedimentary rocks. Because of its chemical and physical resistance to corrosion quartz is an abundant detrital mineral and becomes concentrated during sedimentary processes to give rise to sands and sandstones of various types. Secondary quartz is often deposited around pre-existing grains (of quartz or other minerals) and is a common cementing material in sediments. In some relatively porous sandstones the secondary quartz may be deposited in crystallographic continuity with the detrital quartz, the boundary between the two generations of silica being visible only by the occasional presence of a rim o⁶ iron-staining on the detrital grain. The behaviour of silica in the sedimentary cycle was discussed by Siever (1957) who gave the probable solubility of quartz in water at 25°C. as between 7·25 and 14 p.p.m., and that of amorphous silica as 160 p.p.m. He considered that although some inorganic precipitation of silica may take place, the major mechanism of silica precipitation at the earth's surface is biochemical.

Authigenic quartz sometimes occurs in limestones (Babukov 1919; Black, 1949) where it may form well-developed crystals, and small doubly terminated crystals of quartz have been found embedded in limonite in a ferruginous sandstone replacing dolomite (Oder, 1929). In some oolites, quartz fragments occur as nuclei, and examples are known where the quartz grains have become enlarged by secondary silica and transgress across the calcareous boundaries (Henbest, 1945). The Little Falls dolomite of New York has yielded particularly fine quartz crystals known as "Herkimer diamonds".

The compact microcrystalline varieties of silica—chert, flint, agate, jasper, etc.—consist essentially of a fine network of quartz with a large number of micropores (Midgley, 1951; Pelto, 1956: see also p. 209). Chalcedony encrusted with quartz has been reported from geodes by Lemmlein (1946) who discussed the relative orientation of quartz crystals in these two habits (see also Novák, 1947).

Metamorphic rocks. Quartz is a common mineral in many metamorphic rocks, occurring in the metamorphosed equivalents of quartz-bearing sediments and igneous rocks. Although in the low grades of metamorphism quartz may survive unchanged, in the higher grades it undergoes recrystallization with concomitant increase in grain size. In addition much quartz is developed by the release of SiO_2 in reactions taking place during metamorphism. The orientation of quartz grains in metamorphic rocks may yield important evidence as to the previous history of these rocks. Iiyama (1954) has shown that the quartz formed at higher metamorphic grades has lower inversion points than that formed at lower grades.

Some quartz veins in metamorphic rocks may have been derived by metamorphic differentiation. Chapman (1950) reported quartz veins in staurolite–mica schist and suggested that silica was transferred in solution from the schist, the process being aided by differential compression due to folding. Quartz veins or bands are often associated with serpentinites and related ultrabasic rocks. A possible mechanism for the release of silica in such environments is represented by the following equation:

$$Mg_3Si_2O_5(OH)_4 + 3CO_2 \rightarrow 3MgCO_3 + 2SiO_2 + 2H_2O$$
$$\text{serpentine} \qquad\qquad \text{magnesite}$$

Farquhar (1958) has suggested that silica bands in serpentinite lenses in Kenya may result from the alteration of the peridotite to serpentinite by silica derived from a basement complex during regional metamorphism. Diamonds from the diamond-bearing breccias of Diamantina, Brazil (Draper, 1923), were reported to be occasionally intersected by minute veins of quartz.

Quartz has been recorded from meteoric stones, a section of the St. Mark's stone showing an aggregate of quartz granules, one with a good hexagonal outline, embedded in the metallic phase (Merrill, 1924).

Quartz intergrowths. Intergrowths of quartz and other minerals are fairly common, particularly those of quartz and potassium felspar as in graphic or micrographic granite, and quartz and plagioclase (myrmekite) in association with potassium felspar: for a fuller discussion of these two intergrowths reference should be made to the section on felspars (pp. 75–77). Such intergrowths are common in many types of acid igneous and metamorphic rocks; particular mention may be made of the intimately intergrown quartz and felspar typical of many granophyres. A detailed investigation of the graphic structure of pegmatites with reference to the quartz and its orientation was carried out by Fersman (1915). Intergrowths of quartz and cassiterite in regular orientation were reported by Ramdohr (1923) and of quartz and black tourmaline by New-house and Holden (1925). Non-oriented intergrowths of quartz may sometimes occur due to the release of SiO_2 in a metamorphic reaction: garnets, for example, frequently contain small blebs of quartz, one possible reaction being

$$CaAl_2Si_2O_8 + FeMgSi_2O_6 \rightarrow CaFeMgAl_2Si_3O_{12} + SiO_2$$
$$\text{anorthite} \qquad \text{orthopyroxene} \qquad \text{garnet} \qquad \text{quartz}$$

Pseudomorphs. The occurrence of quartz as pseudomorphs after the higher temperature forms of SiO_2, tridymite and cristobalite, is fairly common. The crystal outlines are often sufficiently well preserved for the identity of the original mineral to be established (Van Valkenburg and Buie, 1945; Ray, 1947; Wager *et al.*, 1953). Quartz has also been reported to occur as a pseudomorph after crocidolite (Lingen, 1918) and fibrous actinolite (Thiesmeyer, 1937).

Tridymite. The typical occurrence of tridymite is in acid volcanic rocks such as rhyolite, obsidian, trachyte, andesite and dacite; it also occasionally occurs in basalts. In such rocks it is often found in cavities and may be associated with such minerals as sanidine, and less frequently, augite or fayalite. Lacroix (1905) found that rocks collected from Mt. Pelée soon after the eruptions contained no tridymite, but that this mineral began to appear in the volcanic rocks of this centre about six months later. Rogers (1928), in a review of the silica minerals, doubted whether tridymite ever crystallized even as a late magmatic mineral, and considered it to be a "metamorphic" mineral in terms of pneumatolytic metamorphism. He recorded a rhyolitic obsidian from California which grades through spherulitic obsidian and dense devitrified obsidians to tridymite–felspar rocks, the metamorphic agent here being hot gases. Likewise Ustiev (1934) attributed the formation of tridymite in vesicles in dacite to the action of magmatic volatiles. Tridymite has been recorded as an abundant mineral in some of the rhyolitic tuffs of the Tertiary volcanic rocks of the San Juan region, Colorado (Larsen *et al.*, 1936), where in part it forms the binder for the tuffs and formed after the tuff was deposited. In the rhyolites and quartz latites of this region tridymite is the chief silica mineral and many of the rocks contain as much as 25 per cent. tridymite.

Tridymite may occur in meteorites (*e.g.* Heide 1923; Foshag, 1938; Hess and Henderson, 1949) and is a fairly common constituent of highly metamorphosed impure sandstones: Lacroix (1946) described laths of tridymite in the glassy base of a volcanic xenolith representing a completely fused quartzose sediment. A sandstone in contact with basic dykes has been described (Osborne, 1948) in which the quartz grains are surrounded by a fringe of tridymite: in the presence of vitrified felspar whole grains of quartz have been converted to tridymite. Other occurrences of tridymite in metamorphosed arkoses adjacent to basic igneous intrusions have been noted by Harker (1932, p. 68), Black (1954) and

Wyllie (1959), while phenocrysts of tridymite inverted to quartz have been recorded in granophyre from Skye (Wager *et al.*, 1953): the latter authors suggest that the criss-cross texture of the acicular quartz found in the high ferrogabbros and the andesine andesite of the Skaergaard intrusion, east Greenland (Wager and Deer, 1939), may represent inverted tridymite.

The geological interpretation of the occurrence of tridymite in rocks in terms of the temperature and pressure of its crystallization is fraught with difficulty. Although many authors have used tridymite as an indicator of fairly high temperature, and also of relatively low pressures (Black, 1954), it is well to remember the statement by Fenner (1913) that "emphasis should be laid upon the fact that the presence of cristobalite or tridymite in a rock does not necessarily imply that at the time of formation of these minerals the temperature was above the respective inversion-points (1470° and 870°)". Fenner pointed out that in certain circumstances SiO_2 may form in a modification that is not the stable one for the prevailing temperature and pressure conditions.

Cristobalite. Like tridymite, cristobalite is typically a mineral of volcanic rocks, where it may occur in cavities, often in association (metastable) with tridymite. It has been found in hollow spherulites (lithophysae) in obsidian and in rhyolite, trachyte, andesite, dacite and olivine basalt. It is often a late product of crystallization, sometimes replacing tridymite, and may also be associated with anorthoclase, chlorite and even calcite. Cristobalite has been found in octahedral crystals in gas cavities in auganite (Ōhashi, 1936) and this rock also contains cristobalite as idiomorphic microphenocrysts, elongated streaks, and mesostasis between the lath-shaped plagioclase of the groundmass. In the San Juan lavas of Colorado (Larsen *et al.*, 1936) cristobalite occurs as rounded spherulites or crystals projecting from the walls of larger gas cavities: it is the most common silica mineral in the gas cavities of basaltic lavas, but in the San Juan rocks is very rare in the cavities of the rhyolites. Larsen *et al.* considered that cristobalite formed in the dense parts of the groundmass when crystallization was rapid and not assisted by "mineralizers", while in the larger gas cavities it formed by gas transfer after solidification of the groundmass. In the dacites and andesites of the Mariana Islands, Schmidt (1957) has recorded silica-rich glass together with quartz, tridymite, cristobalite, chalcedony and opal.

Cristobalite is also known from thermally metamorphosed sandstones and from sandstone xenoliths in basaltic or other basic rocks, where the sandstone has been converted into buchite, *e.g.* at Arkhara, U.S.S.R. (Petrov and Finko, 1957). Both cristobalite and tridymite are found in a metamorphosed lithomarge (porcellanite) block in the olivine dolerite plug of Tievebulliagh, Northern Ireland (Agrell and Langley, 1958).

The material known as "lussatite" which occurs in association with serpentinites has been shown to be cristobalite (Novák, 1932, 1947; see also Laves, 1939). Cristobalite has also been recorded in a similar occurrence as brown crusts in veins of magnesite with gymnite (Kratovchíl, 1947), and has been reported from samples of bentonite and fuller's earth (Gruner, 1940). Myers and Peck (1925) found that sand grains adhering to the exterior of a fulgurite, in a New Jersey sand pit, have a centre of quartz bordered by cristobalite.

The occurrence of cristobalite in opal has been recognized from X-ray powder patterns and such material is usually in the high-temperature, β-cristobalite, form (Levin and Ott, 1932; Greig, 1932). The inversion to α-cristobalite on cooling presumably has been arrested due to the crystals being embedded in a glass or colloidal matrix. Raman and Jayaraman (1953) reported X-ray patterns from a fire-opal which showed some evidence for the occurrence of both α- and β-cristobalite, which they postulated might exist in a periodic inter-stratification.

Paramorphs of quartz after cristobalite are fairly common in vesicles in volcanic rocks, *e.g.* Van Valkenburg and Buie (1945) described twinned octahedra of cristobalite, some of which had inverted to quartz, perched on fibres of mordenite in a vesicular basalt from the Deccan volcanics. Paramorphs of cristobalite supposedly after tridymite have been recorded in trachyte from the French Puys (Bentor, 1941).

As noted above for tridymite, the ability of cristobalite to occur as an unstable form, outside its equilibrium field, means that no definite conclusions normally can be drawn as to conditions at its time of deposition.

Coesite. As this recently discovered SiO_2 polymorph was known from synthetic work to be stable at high pressures it was thought that in nature it might be found in eclogitic rock types. It has not so far been recognized in such rocks, but has been discovered, in coexistence with quartz and fused silica glass, in sheared porous sandstone at Meteor Crater, Arizona (Chao *et al.*, 1960), where it was presumably developed by the shock wave generated by the impact of the meteorite. It has also been reported in similarly "shocked" granite and pumaceous tuff near the rim of the Rieskessel crater, Bavaria (Pecora, 1960).

REFERENCES

Agrell, S. O. and **Langley, J. M.**, 1958. The dolerite plug at Tievebulliagh, near Cushendall, Co. Antrim. Part (I): The thermal metamorphism. *Proc. Roy. Irish Acad.*, vol. 59, B, p. 93.

Ahlers, L., 1924. Über die Dichte von Quarz, Orthoklas, Albit und Anorthit. *Zeit. Krist.*, vol. 59, p. 293.

Allenby, R. J., 1954. Determination of the isotopic ratios of silicon in rocks. *Geochim. et Cosmochim. Acta*, vol. 5, p. 40.

Anderson, B. W. and **Payne, C. J.**, 1940. The constancy of quartz and other minerals. *Gemmologist*, vol. 9, pp. 93 and 119.

Armstrong, E., 1946. Relation between secondary Dauphiné twinning and irradia-tion-coloring in quartz. *Amer. Min.*, vol. 31, p. 456.

Austin, J. B., 1954. The coefficient of linear thermal expansion of tridymite. *Journ. Amer. Chem. Soc.*, vol. 76, p. 6019.

Babukov, G. Z., 1919. On a find of minute crystals of rock-crystal in non-meta-morphic limestones of South Russia. *Bull. Reg. Mus. Indus. & Agric. Rostov on Don*, pt. 1, p. 41 (M.A. 2–71).

Baier, E., 1932. Die Optik der Edelopale. *Zeit. Krist.*, vol. 81, p. 183.

Bailey, S. W., 1949. Liquid inclusions in granite thermometry. *Journ. Geol.*, vol. 57, p. 304.

—— **Bell, R. A.** and **Peng, C. J.**, 1958. Plastic deformation of quartz in nature. *Bull. Geol. Soc. Amer.*, vol. 69, p. 1443.

Balamuth, L., Rose, F. and **Quimby, S. L.**, 1936. Note on δ quartz. *Physical Rev.*, vol. 49, p. 703.

Ballman, A. A., 1961. The growth and properties of colored quartz. *Amer. Min.*, vol. 46, p. 439.

Bappu, M. K. W., 1952. Spectroscopic study of amethyst quartz in the visible region. *Indian Journ. Phys.*, vol. 26, p. 1.

Barbaron, M., 1948. Constantes optiques du quartz à basse temperature. *Compt. Rend. Acad. Sci. Paris*, vol. 226, p. 1443.

Barrer, R. M., 1946. Preparation of synthetic quartz. *Nature*, vol. 157, p. 734.

Barth, T. F. W., 1932. The cristobalite structure: I High-cristobalite. II Low-cristobalite. *Amer. Journ. Sci.*, ser. 5, vol, 23, p. 350; vol. 24, p. 97.

—— and **Kvalheim, A.**, 1944. *Scientific results of the Norwegian Antarctic expeditions 1927–1928.* No. 22.

Bass, M. N., 1957. Effects of gamma irradiation on physical properties of minerals. *Amer. Min.*, vol. 42, p. 100.

Bates, F. J. and **Phelps, F. P.**, 1921. The new fixed point on the thermometric scale. *Phys. Rev.*, vol. 18, p. 115.

Bellanca, A., 1943. Identificazione e dosaggio delle modificazioni polimorfe dei minerali delle rocce mediante l'analisi termica. (Nota I). Natura e dosaggio della sillice non combinata nelle ftaniti. *Periodico Min. Roma*, vol. 13, p. 277 (M.A. 9–156).

Belyankin, D. S. and **Kaznakova, N. G.**, 1934. On the question of cristobalite. *Trav. Inst. Pétrogr. Acad. Sci. URSS*, no. 6, p. 361 (M.A. 7–138).

Bentor, Y., 1941. Sur quelques minéraux des laves de la Chaîne des Puys. *Compt. Rend. Acad. Sci. Paris*, vol. 213, p. 289.

Berkelhamer, L. H., 1944. (The differential thermal analysis of quartz). *Rep. Invest. U.S. Bur. Mines*, no. 3763.

Birch, F. and **Clark, H.**, 1940. The thermal conductivity of rocks and its dependencies upon temperature and composition. *Amer. Journ. Sci.*, vol. 238, pp. 529 and 613.

Black, G. P., 1954. The significance of tridymite in igneous and metamorphic petrogenesis. *Min. Mag.*, vol. 30, p. 518.

Black, W. W., 1949. An occurrence of authigenic felspar and quartz in Yoredale limestones. *Geol. Mag.*, vol. 86, p. 129.

Bloss, F. D., 1957. Anisotropy of fracture in quartz. *Amer. Journ. Sci.*, vol. 255, p. 214.

Boldyrev, A. K., 1936. Über die Bezeichung polymorpher Modifikationen. *Min. Petr. Mitt. (Tschermak)*, vol. 47, p. 517.

Boyd, F. R. and **England, J. L.**, 1960. The quartz–coesite transition. *Journ. Geophys. Research*, vol. 65, p. 749.

Boyle, R. W., 1953. On the colour of black and grey quartz from Yellowknife, Northwest Territories, Canada. *Amer. Min.*, vol. 38, p. 528.

Bradley, W. F. and **Grim, R. E.**, 1951. High temperature thermal effects of clay and related materials. *Amer. Min.*, vol. 36, p. 182.

—— and **Jay, A. H.**, 1933. Quartz as a standard for accurate lattice-spacing measurements. *Proc. Phys. Soc.*, vol. 45, p. 507.

Bradshaw, T. and **Livens, G. H.**, 1929. The formula for the optical rotatory dispersion of quartz. *Proc. Roy. Soc.*, A, vol. 122, p. 245.

Bragg, W. H., 1914. The X-ray spectra given by crystals of sulphur and quartz. *Proc. Roy. Soc.*, A, vol. 89, p. 575.

—— and **Gibbs, R. E.**, 1925. The structure of α- and β-quartz. *Proc. Roy. Soc.*, A, vol. 109, p. 405.

Bragg, W. L., 1937. *Atomic Structure of Minerals.* Cornell University Press.

Brauns, R., 1919. Einige Mitteilungen über Quartz. *Neues Jahrb. Min.*, p. 29.

Bray, J. M., 1942. Spectroscopic distribution of minor elements in igneous rocks from Jamestown, Colorado. *Bull. Geol. Soc. Amer.*, vol. 53, p. 765.

Bridgman, P. W., 1949. Linear compressions to 30,000 kg./cm.^{2}, including relatively incompressible substances. *Proc. Amer. Acad. Arts Sci.*, vol. 77, p. 187.

Brill, R., Hermann, C. and Peters, C., 1942. Röntgenographische Fouriersynthese von Quartz. *Annal. Phys. Lpz.*, vol. 41, p. 233.

Brown, C. S., Kell, R. C., Thomas, L. A., Wooster, N. and Wooster, W. A., 1952. The growth and properties of large crystals of synthetic quartz. *Min. Mag.*, vol. 29, p. 858.

Buerger, M. J., 1935. The silica framework crystals and their stability fields. *Zeit. Krist.*, vol. 90, p. 186.

—— 1954. The stuffed derivatives of the silica structures. *Amer. Min.*, vol. 39, p. 600.

Butuzov, V. P. and Ikornikova, N.Yu., 1956. The stable form of growth of crystals of artificial quartz. *Mém. Soc. Russe Min.*, vol. 85, p. 394.

Cady, W. G., 1922. The piezo-electric resonator. *Proc. Inst. Radio Engineers*, vol. 10, p. 83.

Cameron, E. N., Rowe, R. B. and Weis, P. L., 1953. Fluid inclusions in beryl and quartz from pegmatites in the Middletown district, Connecticut. *Amer. Min.*, vol. 38, p. 218.

Carl, H. F., 1947. Quantitative mineral analysis with a recording X-ray diffraction spectrometer. *Amer. Min.*, 1947, vol. 32, p. 508.

Carr, R. M. and Fyfe, W. S., 1958. Some observations on the crystallization of amorphous silica. *Amer. Min.*, vol. 43, p. 908.

Chao, E. C. T., Shoemaker, E. M. and Madsen, B. M., 1960. The first natural occurrence of coesite from Meteor Crater, Ariz. *Science*, vol. 132, p. 220.

—— Fahey, J. J., Littler, J. and Milton, D. J., 1962. Stishovite, SiO_2, a very high pressure new mineral from Meteor Crater, Arizona. *Journ. Geophys. Res.*, vol. 67, p. 419.

Chapman, C. A., 1950. Quartz veins formed by metamorphic differentiation of aluminous schists. *Amer. Min.*, vol. 35, p. 693.

Chandrasekhar, S., 1957. The optical rotatory dispersion of quartz. *Proc. Indian Acad. Sci.*, A, vol. 45, p. 147.

Chentzova, L. G. and Vedeneeva, N. E., 1952. The study of the nature of the coloration of smoky quartz on the basis of phenomena of thermal decolorization. *Trudy Inst. Cryst.*, no. 7, p. 159 (M.A. 12–596).

Clark, C. B., 1946. X-ray diffraction data for compounds in the system $CaO-MgO-SiO_2$. *Journ. Amer. Ceram. Soc.*, vol. 29, p. 25.

Coes, L., Jr., 1953. A new dense crystalline silica. *Science*, vol. 118, p. 131.

Cohen, A. J., 1956a. Color centers in the α-quartz called amethyst. *Amer. Min.*, vol. 41, p. 874.

—— 1956b. Anisotropic color centers in α-quartz. Part. I Smoky quartz. *Journ. Chem. Physics*, vol. 25, p. 908.

—— and Sumner, G. G., 1958. Relationships among impurity contents, color centers and lattice constants in quartz. *Amer. Min.*, vol. 43, p. 58.

Coode-Adams, W. R. C., 1927 (1928). The refractive index of quartz. *Proc. Roy. Soc.*, A, vol. 117 (121), p. 209 (476).

Corwin, J. F., Yalman, R. G., Edwards, J. W. and Shaw, E. R., 1957. Hydrothermal reactions under supercritical conditions. II. The reaction between calcium hydroxide and silica. *Journ. Physical Chem.*, vol. 61, p. 941.

Crook, A. W. and Taylor, A. M., 1947. Temperature coefficient of rotation of quartz in the ultra-violet region. *Nature*, vol. 160, p. 396.

Curie, J. and Curie, P., 1880. Développement, par pression, d'électricité polaire dans les cristaux hémièdres à faces inclinées. *Compt. Rend. Acad. Sci. Paris*, vol. 91, p. 294.

Dachille, F. and Roy, R., 1959. High-pressure region of the silica isotopes. *Zeit. Krist.*, vol. 111, p. 451.

Daubrée, A., 1860. *Études et expériences synthétiques sur le métamorphisme.* Paris.

De Carli, P. S. and **Jamieson, J. C.,** 1959. Formation of an amorphous form of quartz under shock conditions. *Journ. Chem. Phys.,* vol. 31, p. 1675.

Dellwig, L. F. and **Hill, W. E.,** 1960. Variations in interference figures in single crystals of zoned smoky quartz. *Amer. Min.,* vol. 45, p. 1116.

Dempster, P. B. and **Ritchie, P. D.,** 1953. Physicochemical studies on dusts. V. Examination of finely ground quartz by differential analysis and other physica methods. *Journ. Applied Chem.,* vol. 3, p. 182.

Draper, D., 1923. Additional evidence regarding the origin of the high level diamond-bearing breccias of Diamantina, Brazil. *Trans. Geol. Soc. S. Africa,* vol. 26, p. 7.

Drugman, J., 1927. On β-quartz twins from some Cornish localities. *Min. Mag.,* vol. 21, p. 366.

—— 1939. Prismatic cleavage and steep rhombohedral form in α-quartz. *Min. Mag.,* vol. 25, p. 259.

Drummond, D. G., 1936. The infra-red absorption spectra of quartz and fused silica from 1 to $7\cdot5\mu$. II. Experimental results. *Proc. Roy. Soc.,* A, vol. 153, p. 328.

Durrell, C., 1940. New data on the optical properties of tridymite. *Amer. Min.,* vol. 25, p. 202.

Eppler, W. F., 1958. Notes on asterism in corundum, rose quartz and almandine garnet and chatoyancy in beryl. *Journ. Gemmology,* 1958, vol. 6, p. 195.

Fairbairn, H. W., 1941. Deformation lamellae in quartz from the Ajibik formation, Michigan. *Bull. Geol. Soc. Amer.,* vol. 52, p. 1265.

Farquhar, O. C., 1958. Silica bands and serpentinite in the Taita hills, Kenya. *Bull. Geol. Soc. Amer.,* vol. 69, p. 1562 (abstract).

Farrington, O. C., 1927. Agate — physical properties and origin. *Field Museum of Nat. Hist., Chicago, Geology Leaflet 8.*

Fenner, C. N., 1913. Stability relations of the silica minerals. *Amer. Journ. Sci.,* 4th ser., vol. 36, p. 331.

Ferguson, J. B. and **Merwin, H. E.,** 1918. The melting points of cristobalite and tridymite. *Amer. Journ. Sci.,* ser. 4, vol. 46, p. 417.

Fersman, A. E., 1915. Graphic structure of pegmatites and the causes of its origin. *Bull. Acad. Imp. Sci., Petrograd.,* ser. 6, vol. 9, p. 1211 (M.A. 2–63).

Flörke, O. W., 1955. Strukturanomalien bei Tridymit und Cristobalit. *Ber. dtsch. keram. Ges.,* vol. 32, p. 369.

Folk, R. L. and **Weaver, C. E.,** 1952. A study of the texture and composition of chert. *Amer. Journ. Sci.,* vol. 250, p. 498.

Foshag, W. F., 1938. Petrology of the Pasamonte, New Mexico, meteorite. *Amer. Journ. Sci.,* ser. 5, vol. 35, p. 374.

Frederickson, A. F. and **Cox, J. E., Jr.,** 1954. Mechanism of "solution" of quartz in pure water at elevated temperatures and pressures. *Amer. Min.,* vol. 39, p. 886.

Friedel, G., 1923. Sur les macles du quartz. *Bull. Soc. franç. Min.,* vol. 46, p. 79.

—— 1933. Sur un nouveau type de macles. *Compt. Rend. Acad. Sci. Paris,* vol. 197, p. 103.

Frondel, C., 1945a. History of the quartz oscillator-plate industry, 1941–1944. *Amer. Min.,* vol. 30, p. 205.

—— 1945b. Secondary Dauphiné twinning in quartz. *Amer. Min.,* vol. 30, p. 447.

—— 1946. Secondary Dauphiné twinning in quartz produced by sawing. Irradiation of twinned quartz. *Amer. Min.,* vol. 31, p. 58.

—— and **Hurlbut, C. S., Jr.,** 1955. Determination of the atomic weight of silicon by physical measurements on quartz. *Journ. Chemical Phys.,* vol. 23, p. 1215.

Furnival, G. M., 1939. Notes on quartz "dikes". *Amer. Min.,* vol. 24, p. 499.

Fyfe, W. S., 1955. A discussion on "Mechanism of solution of quartz in pure water at elevated temperatures and pressures." *Amer. Min.,* vol. 40, p. 520.

Gault, H. R., 1949. The frequency of twin types in quartz crystals. *Amer. Min.,* vol. 34, p. 142.

Gibbs, R. E., 1926. Structure of α-quartz. *Proc. Roy. Soc.,* A, vol. 110, p. 443.

—— 1927. The polymorphism of silicon dioxide and the structure of tridymite. *Proc. Roy. Soc.,* A, vol. 113, p. 351.

Gibson, R. E., 1928. The influence of pressure on the high–low inversion of quartz. *Journ. Physical Chem.,* vol. 32, p. 1197.

Gillis, J., 1933. Vervluchtiging van SiO$_2$ en van koper in stoom. *Natuurwetensch. Tijds., Antwerp,* vol. 15, p. 153.

Golding, E., 1936. Chemical analyses of the rocks, ores and minerals of Southern Rhodesia. *S. Rhodesia Geol. Surv. Bull.,* no. 29.

Gordon, R. L., Griffin, O. G. and **Nagelschmidt, G.,** 1952. The quantitative determination of quartz by X-ray diffraction. *Safety in Mines Research Establishment, Research Report* No. 52.

—— and **Harris, G. W.,** 1956. Geiger-Müller counter equipment for quantitative X-ray diffraction analysis of powders. *Safety in Mines Research Establishment, Research Report* No. 138.

Grant, E. S., 1954. The geological significance of variations in the abundance of the isotopes of silicon in rocks. *Geochim. et Cosmochim. Acta,* vol. 5, p. 225.

Greenberg, S. A., 1957. Thermodynamic functions for the solution of silica in water. *Journ. Physical Chem.,* vol. 61, p. 196.

Greig, J. W., 1927. Immiscibility in silicate melts. *Amer. Journ. Sci.,* ser. 5, vol. 13, pp. 1 and 133.

—— 1932. The existence of the high-temperature form of cristobalite at room temperature and the crystallinity of opal. *Journ. Amer. Chem. Soc.,* vol. 54, p. 2846.

—— **Merwin, H. E.** and **Shepherd, E. S.,** 1933. Notes on the volatile transport of silica. *Amer. Journ. Sci.,* ser. 5, vol. 25, p. 61.

Griggs, D. and **Bell, J. F.,** 1938. Experiments bearing on the orientation of quartz in deformed rocks. *Bull. Geol. Soc. Amer.,* vol. 49, p. 1723.

Grimshaw, R. W. and **Roberts, A. L.,** 1957. The silica minerals, in *The differential thermal investigation of clays.* Min. Soc., London.

—— **Westerman, A.** and **Roberts, A. L.,** 1948. Thermal effects accompanying silica inversion. *Trans. Brit. Ceram. Soc.,* vol. 47, p. 269.

Gruner, J. W., 1940. Abundance and significance of cristobalite in bentonites and fuller's earths. *Econ. Geol.,* vol. 35, p. 867.

Haldén, G. H., 1955. Quasi-cleavable quartz. *Rocks and Minerals,* vol. 30, p. 38.

Harker, A., 1932. *Metamorphism.* Methuen, London.

Harris, F. C., 1929. The dispersion of double refraction in quartz. *Phil. Mag.,* ser. 7, vol. 7, p. 80.

Havelock, T. H., 1929. The dispersion of double refraction in quartz. *Proc. Roy. Soc.,* A, vol. 124, p. 46.

Heide, F., 1923. Der Meteorit von Grimma i.S. *Centralbl. Min.,* p. 69.

—— 1927. Die Japaner Zwillinge des Quarzes und ihr Auftreten im Quarzporphyr vom Saubach i. V. *Zeit. Krist.,* vol. 66, p. 239.

Henbest, L. G., 1945. Unusual nuclei in oolites from the Morrow Group, near Fayetteville, Arkansas. *Journ. Sed. Petr.,* vol. 15, p. 20.

Hess, F. L., 1925. The natural history of the pegmatites. *Eng. & Min. Journ.,* vol. 120, p. 289.

Hess, H. H. and **Henderson, E. P.,** 1949. The Moore County meteorite: a further study with comment on its primordial development. *Amer. Min.,* vol. 34, p. 494.

Hey, M. H., 1955. *An index of mineral species and varieties arranged chemically.* British Museum, London.

Hill, V. G. and Roy, R., 1958. Silica structure studies. VI. On tridymites. *Trans. Brit. Ceram. Soc.,* vol. 57, p. 496.

Holden, E. F., 1923. The color of three varieties of quartz. *Amer. Min.,* vol. 8, p. 117.

—— 1924. The cause of color in rose quartz. *Amer. Min.,* vol. 9, pp. 75 and 101.

—— 1925. The cause of color in smoky quartz and amethyst. *Amer. Min.,* vol. 10, p. 203.

Holmes, A., 1936. Transfusion of quartz xenoliths in alkali basic and ultrabasic lavas, south-west Uganda. *Min. Mag.,* vol. 24, p. 408.

Holt, P. F. and King, D. T., 1955. The chemistry of silica surfaces. *Journ. Chem. Soc.,* p. 773.

Hurlbut, C. S., Jr., 1946. Influence of twinning on the usability of quartz from various localities. *Amer. Min.,* vol. 31, p. 443.

Iiyama, T., 1954. High–low inversion point of quartz in metamorphic rocks. *Journ. Fac. Sci. Univ. Tokyo,* vol. 9, p. 193

Ingerson, E., 1947. Liquid inclusions in geologic thermometry. *Amer. Min.,* vol. 32, p. 375.

—— and Tuttle, O. F., 1945. Relations of lamellae and crystallography of quartz and fabric directions in some deformed rocks. *Trans. Amer. Geophys. Union,* vol. 26, p. 95.

Inoue, T., Kunitomi, M. and Shibato, E., 1939. Über Triboluminescenz. *Journ. Sci., Hirosima Univ.,* ser. A, vol. 9, p. 129.

Jahns, R. H., 1953. The genesis of pegmatites. I. Occurrence and origin of giant crystals. *Amer. Min.,* vol. 38, p. 563.

—— 1955. The study of pegmatites. *Econ. Geol.,* 50th Anniv. vol., p. 1105.

Jay, A. H., 1933. The thermal expansion of quartz by X-ray measurements. *Proc. Roy. Soc.,* A, vol. 142, p. 237.

—— 1944. The X-ray pattern of low temperature cristobalite. *Min. Mag.,* vol. 27, p. 54.

Jayaraman, N., 1939. The cause of the colour of the blue quartzes of the charnockites of south India and of the Champion gneiss and other related rocks of Mysore. *Proc. Indian Acad. Sci.,* A, vol. 9, p. 275.

Johannsen, A. and Phemister, T. C., 1925. A note on the elasticity of some minerals and its measurement. *Journ. Geol.,* vol. 33, p. 268.

Kaye, G. W. C. and Higgins, W. F., 1926. The thermal conductivity of vitreous silica, with a note on crystalline quartz. *Proc. Roy. Soc.,* A, vol. 113, p. 335.

Keat, D. D., 1954. A new crystalline silica. *Science,* vol. 120, p. 328.

Keith, H. D., 1950. The lattice-parameters of clear crystalline quartz. *Proc. Phys. Soc.,* B, vol. 63, p. 208.

Keith, M. L. and Tuttle, O. F., 1952. Significance of variation in the high–low inversion of quartz. *Amer. Journ. Sci.,* Bowen vol., p. 203.

Keller, W. D. and Pickett, E. E., 1949. Absorption of infrared radiation by powdered silica minerals. *Amer. Min.,* vol. 34, p. 855.

Kennedy, G. C., 1950. A portion of the system silica–water. *Econ. Geol.,* vol. 45, p. 629.

Khitarov, N. I., Slutzky, A. B. and Arsenieva, R. V., 1957. Synthesis and characteristics of coesite—the stable modification of silica at high pressures. *Geochemistry, Publ. Acad. Sci. USSR,* no. 8, p. 666 (M.A. 14–189).

Klemens, P. G., 1956. Density changes in irradiated quartz. *Phil. Mag.,* ser. 8, vol. 1, p. 938.

Kokta, J., 1930. On some physico-chemical properties of opal and their relation to artificially prepared amorphous silicic acid. *Rozpravy České Akad.,* vol. 40. no. 21 (M.A. 4–517).

Kolaczkowska, M., 1936. La cellule fondamentale du quartz et de la calcédoine. *Arch. Min. Tow. Nauk, Warsaw*, vol. 12, p. 82 (M.A. 6–410).

Komarov, O. P., 1951. On a new find of a gigantic quartz crystal. *Mém. Soc. Russe Min.*, vol. 80, p. 153.

Kôzu, S., 1952. Japanese twins of quartz. *Amer. Journ. Sci.*, Bowen vol., p. 281.

—— and **Takané, K.**, 1929. Influence of temperature on the axial ratio, the interfacial angle and the volume of quartz. *Sci. Rep. Tôhoku Univ.*, ser. 3, vol. 3, p. 239.

Kracek, F. C., 1939. Phase equilibrium relations in the system Na_2SiO_3–Li_2SiO_3–SiO_2. *Journ. Amer. Chem. Soc.*, vol. 61, p. 2863.

Kratovchíl, F., 1947. Contribution to the petrography of the crystallinicum of Bohemia. *Sborník Stát. Geol. Ústavu Repub. Česk.*, vol. 14, p. 449 (M.A. 10–439).

Lacroix, A., 1893. *Les enclaves des roches volcaniques.* Macon (p. 697).

—— 1905. Observation faites à la Montagne Pelée sur les conditions présidant à la production de la tridymite dans les roches volcaniques. *Bull. Soc. Franç. Min.*, vol. 28, p. 56.

Lacroix, A., 1946. Sur un nouveau cas de fomation de tridymite par fusion d'une enclave quartzique d'un volcan andésitique (Tanna des Nouvelles-Hébrides). *Compt. Rend. Acad. Sci. Paris*, vol. 223, p. 409.

Larsen, E. S., **Irving, J.**, **Gonyer, F. A.** and **Larsen, E. S., 3rd.**, 1936. Petrographic results of a study of the minerals from the Tertiary volcanic rocks of the San Juan region, Colorado. *Amer. Min.*, vol. 21, p. 679.

Laves, F., 1939. Über den Einfluss von Spannungen auf die Regelung von Quarz- und Cristobalit-Kristallchen im Chalzedon, Quartzin und Lussatit. *Naturwiss.*, vol. 27, p. 705.

Le Chatelier, H., 1889. Sur la dilatation du quartz. *Compt. Rend. Acad. Sci. Paris*, vol. 108, p. 1046; vol. 109, p. 264.

Lemmlein, G. G., 1940. On regular intergrowths of porphyry-quartz on (10Ī1) face. *Trav. Lab. Crist. Acad. Sci URSS*, no. 2, p. 123 (M.A. 9–211).

—— 1946. On the growth of quartz on chalcedony. *D. S. Belyankin jubilee vol.*, Acad. Sci. USSR, p. 130 (M.A. 11–66).

—— and **Klevtzov, P. V.**, 1955. Physico-chemical analysis of liquid inclusions in quartz containing small crystals of halite and sylvine. *Mém. Soc. Russe Min.*, ser. 2, vol. 84, p. 47 (M.A. 13–122).

Levin, I. and **Ott, E.**, 1932. The crystallinity of opals and the existence of high-temperature cristobalite at room temperatures. *Journ. Amer. Chem. Soc.*, vol. 54, p. 828.

Lier, J. P. van, **Bruyn, P. L. de** and **Overbeek, J. T. G.**, 1960. The solubility of quartz. *Journ. Phys. Chem.*, vol. 64, p. 1675.

Lingen, J. S. v.d., 1918. Notes on . . . (b) serpentine, malachite, and pseudomorph quartz. *Trans. Roy. Soc. S. Africa*, vol. 7, p. 59.

Lipson, H. and **Wilson, A. J. C.**, 1941. The derivation of lattice spacings from Debye-Scherrer photographs, *Journ. Sci. Instr.*, vol. 18, p. 144.

Lowry, T. M. and **Coode-Adams, W. R. C.**, 1927. Optical rotatory dispersion. Part III. The rotatory dispersion of quartz in the infra-red, visible and ultra-violet regions of the spectrum. *Phil. Trans. Roy. Soc.*, A, vol. 226, p. 391.

Lukesh, J. S., 1942. The size of the unit cell and coefficient of expansion of high-cristobalite. *Amer. Min.*, vol. 27, p. 22 (abstract).

—— and **Buerger, M. J.**, 1942. The tridymite problem. *Amer. Min.*, vol. 27, p. 143 (abstract).

MacDonald, G. J. F., 1956. Quartz-coesite stability relations at high temperatures and pressures. *Amer. Journ. Sci.*, vol. 254, p. 713.

Macé de Lépinay, J., Buisson, H. and Benoit, J. R., 1910.   Détermination du volume du kilogramme d'eau.   *Trav. Mém. Bur. Int. Poids et Mesures*, vol. 14.

Machatschki, F., 1936.   Die Kristallstruktur von Tiefquartz SiO_2 und Aluminium-orthoarsenat $AlAsO_4$.   *Zeit. Krist.*, vol. 94, p. 222.

Mallard, E., 1890.   Sur la tridymite et la Christobalite.   *Bull. Soc. Franç. Min.*, vol. 13, p. 161.

Mason, B., 1953.   Tridymite and christensenite.   *Amer. Min.*, vol. 38, p. 866.

—— 1955.   Notes on some New Zealand minerals.   *N.Z. Journ. Sci. & Technol.*, Sect. B, vol. 36, p. 557.

Merril, G. P., 1924.   Quartz in meteoric stones.   *Amer. Min.*, vol. 9, p. 112.

Midgley, H. G., 1951.   Chalcedony and flint.   *Geol. Mag.*, vol. 88, p. 179.

Mitchell, E. W. J. and Rigden, J. D., 1957.   The effects of radiation on the near infra-red absorption spectrum of α-quartz.   *Phil. Mag.*, ser. 8, vol. 2, p. 941.

Morey, G. W. and Hesselgesser, J. M., 1951.   The solubility of quartz and some other substances in superheated steam at high pressures.   *Trans. Amer. Soc. Mech. Engrs.*, vol. 73, p. 865.

Morgan, P. G., 1925.   The so-called "pseudomorphous" quartz of Tertiary gold–silver veins.   *Econ. Geol.*, vol. 20, p. 203.

Mosebach, R., 1957.   Thermodynamic behavior of quartz and other forms of silica in pure water at elevated temperatures and pressures with conclusions on their mechanism of solution.   *Journ. Geol.*, vol. 65, p. 347.

Moseman, M. A. and Pitzer, K. S., 1941.   Thermodynamic properties of the crystalline forms of silica.   *Journ. Amer. Chem. Soc.*, vol. 63, p. 2348.

Mügge, O., 1921.   Über Quarz als geologisches Thermometer und bie Bedeutung der Zuzammensetzungsfläche von Zwillingen.   *Centralblatt Min.*, p. 609 and p. 641.

Muir, I. D., 1953.   Quartzite xenoliths from the Ballachulish granodiorite.   *Geol. Mag.*, vol. 90, p. 409.

Murdoch, J., 1942.   Crystallographic notes: cristobalite, stephanite, natrolite.   *Amer. Min.*, vol. 27, p. 500.

—— and Webb, R. W., 1938.   Notes on some minerals from southern California.   *Amer. Min.*, vol. 23, p. 349.

Myers, W. M. and Peck, A. B., 1925.   A fulgurite from South Amboy, New Jersey.   *Amer. Min.*, vol. 10, p. 152.

Newhouse, W. H. and Holden, E. F., 1925.   Graphic intergrowths of quartz and black tourmaline from Maine.   *Amer. Min.*, vol. 10, p. 42.

Nieuwenburg, C. J. and Blumendal, H. B., 1931.   The pneumatolytic synthesis of silicates.   *Rec. Trav. Chim. Pays-Bas*, vol. 50, p. 129 and p. 989.

—— and Zon, P. M., 1935.   Semi-quantitative measurements of the solubility of quartz in super-critical steam.   *Rec. Trav. Chim. Pays-Bas*, vol. 54, p. 129.

Nieuwenkamp, W., 1935a.   Zweidimensionale Cristobalitkristalle.   *Zeit. Krist.*, vol. 90, p. 377.

—— 1935b.   Die Kristallstruktur des Tief-Cristobalits SiO_2.   *Zeit. Krist.*, vol. 92, p. 82.

—— 1937.   Über die struktur von Hoch-Cristobalit.   *Zeit. Krist.*, vol. 96, p. 454.

Novák, J., 1932.   Cristobalit ze serpentinů ze zápandí Moravy.   *Spisy Vydávané Přir. Fak. Masarykovy Univ.*, no. 153 (M.A. 5–476).

—— 1947.   Les modifications fibreuses de la silice.   *Bull. Soc. franç. Min.*, vol. 70, p. 238.

O'Connor, D. J. and Buchanan, A. S., 1956.   Electrokinetic properties and surface reactions of quartz.   *Trans. Faraday Soc.*, vol. 52, p. 397.

Oder, C. R. L., 1929.   Occurrence of doubly terminated quartz crystals in sandstone in the Shenandoah valley, Virginia.   *Amer. Min.*, vol. 14, p. 382.

Ōhashi, R., 1936.   Heating tests on cristobalite from Kosaka mine, Japan.   *Journ. Geol. Soc. Tokyo*, vol. 43, p. 453 (M.A. 6–374).

Osborne, G. D., 1948. Note on the occurrence of tridymite in metamorphosed Hawkesbury sandstone at Bundeena and West Pymble, Sydney district, New South Wales. *Journ. Roy. Soc., N.S.W.,* vol. 82, p. 309.

Osterberg, H., 1936. A new form of crystalline quartz at $-183\cdot5°C$. *Physical Rev.,* vol. 49, p. 552.

—— and **Cookson, J. W.,** 1935. Some piezoelectric and elastic properties of β-quartz. *Journ. Franklin Inst., Philadelphia,* vol. 220, p. 361.

Paige, E. G. S., 1957. The kinetics of colour centre formation in quartz. *Phil. Mag.,* ser. 8, vol. 2, p. 864.

Palache, C., 1932. The largest crystal. *Amer. Min.,* vol. 17, p. 362.

Papailhau, J., 1957. Sur la formation par voie thermique de tridymite et de cristobalite à partir de silice amorphe précipitée. *Compt. Rend. Acad. Sci. Paris,* vol. 245, p. 1443.

Peach, P. A., 1951. Geothermometry of some pegmatite minerals of Hybla, Ontario. *Journ. Geol.,* vol. 59, p. 32.

Pecora, W. T., 1960. Coesite craters and space geology. *Geotimes,* vol. 5, no. 2, p. 16.

Pehrman, G., 1948. Cristobalit aus einem Schmelzofen. *Bull. Geol. Inst. Univ. Upsala,* vol. 32, p. 475.

Pelto, C. R., 1956. A study of chalcedony. *Amer. Journ. Sci.,* vol. 254, p. 32.

Pérez, J. P., 1939. Macles du quartz α après un séjour temporaire sous la forme β. *Compt. Rend. Acad. Sci. Paris,* vol. 209, p. 173.

Petrov, V. P. and **Finko, V. I.,** 1957. Mullite and cordierite in sandstone xenoliths in basalts of the Zeisko-Bureinskaya depression. *Trans. Inst. Geol. of Oredeposits, Petr., Min. & Geochem.,* vol. 17, p. 11 (M.A. 14–298).

Petrun, V. F., 1955. On the question of the origin of the rose quartz of hydrothermal veins. *Mém. Soc. Russe Min.,* ser. 2, vol. 84, p. 191.

Przibram, K., 1956. *Irradiation colours and Luminescence.* London, Pergamon Press.

Raman, Sir C. V., 1950. Crystals of quartz with iridescent faces. *Proc. Indian Acad. Sci.,* A, vol. 31, p. 275.

—— and **Jayaraman, A.,** 1953. The structure of opal and the origin of its iridescence. *Proc. Indian Acad. Sci.,* A, vol. 38, p. 101.

Ramdohr, P., 1923. Eine orientierte Verwachsung von Zinnstein mit Quarz. *Centralblatt Min.,* p. 200.

Ramsdell, C. S., 1955. The crystallography of "coesite". *Amer. Min.,* vol. 40, p. 975.

Rao, B. R., 1945. Elastic constants of quartz. *Curr. Sci.,* vol. 14, p. 17.

Rao, D. A. A. S. Narayana, 1947. Dielectric constants of crystals. I. Different types of quartz. *Proc. Indian Acad. Sci.,* A, vol. 25, p. 408.

Ray, L. L., 1947. Quartz paramorphs after tridymite from Colorado. *Amer. Min.* vol. 32, p. 643.

Reynolds, J. H. and **Verhoogen, J.,** 1953. Natural variations in the isotopic constitution of silicon. *Geochim. et Cosmochim. Acta,* vol. 3, p. 224.

Richardson, E. and **Waddams, J. A.,** 1955. New observations on the interaction between quartz and water. *Research Correspondence, Suppl. to Research,* vol. 8, p. S21.

Riley, N. A., 1947. Structural petrology of the Baraboo quartzite. *Journ. Geol.,* vol. 55, p. 453.

Rogers, A. F., 1922. A new occurrence of cristobalite in California. *Journ. Geol.,* vol. 30, p. 211.

—— 1928. Natural history of the silica minerals [with 5 plates]. *Amer. Min.,* vol. 13, p. 73.

Rosenholtz, J. L. and **Smith, D. T.**, 1936.   The dielectric constant of mineral powders. *Amer. Min.*, vol. 21, p. 115.

—— —— 1941.   Linear thermal expansion and inversions of quartz, var. rock crystal. *Amer. Min.*, vol. 26, p. 103.

Rosický, V., 1928.   Die Drusenminerale des Andesites von Nezdenice in Mähren. *Festsch. V. Goldschmidt*, Heidelberg (M.A. 4–524).

Roy, R., 1956.   New data bearing on the crystal chemistry of the silica polymorphs. *Bull. Geol. Soc. Amer.*, vol. 67, p. 1730 (abstract).

—— 1959.   Silica O, a new form of silica. *Zeit. Krist.*, vol. 111, p. 185.

—— 1961.   Comment on "Growth and properties of colored quartz". *Amer. Min.*, vol. 46, p. 446.

—— and **Osborn, E. F.**, 1949.   The system lithium metasilicate–spodumene–silica. *Journ. Amer. Chem. Soc.*, vol. 71, p. 2086.

Sabatier, G., 1957.   Chaleurs de transition des formes de basse température aux formes de haute température du quartz, de la tridymite et de la cristobalite. *Bull. Soc. franç. Min. Crist.*, vol. 80, p. 444.

—— and **Wyart, J.**, 1954.   Variations des paramètres cristallins et de la température de transformation $\alpha = \beta$ dans des quartz de synthèse. *Compt. Rend. Acad. Sci. Paris*, 1954, vol. 239, p. 1053 (M.A. 12–499).

Sander, B., 1930.   *Gefügekunde der Gesteine.* Springer, Vienna.

Schafhäutl, C. E., 1845.   Gelehrte Anzeigen. *Akad. Wiss. Munchen*, vol. 20, p. 578.

Scheibe, A., 1938.   *Piezoelektrizatät des Quarzes.* Dresden and Leipzig.

Schmidt, R. G., 1957.   Geology of Saipan, Mariana Islands.   Part 2B.   Petrology of the volcanic rocks. *U.S. Geol. Surv., Prof. Paper 280*, p. 127.

Sharma, N. L., 1940.   Royite, a new variety of quartz, from the Jhaira coal-field. *Proc. Indian. Acad. Sci.*, B, vol. 12, p. 215.

Shropshire, J., **Keat, P. P.** and **Vaughan, P. A.**, 1959.   The crystal structure of keatite, a new form of silica. *Zeit. Krist.*, vol. 112, p. 409.

Shubnikov, A., 1930.   Über Schlagfiguren des Quarzes. *Zeit. Krist.*, vol. 74, p. 103.

Siever, R., 1957.   The silica budget in the sedimentary cycle. *Amer. Min.*, vol. 42, p. 821.

Silverman, S. R., 1951.   The isotope geology of oxygen. *Geochim. et Cosmochim Acta*, vol. 2, p. 26.

Skinner, B. J. and **Appleman, D. E.**, 1962.   Melanophlogite, a cubic polymorph of silica, *Geol. Soc. Amer.*, Program 1962 Ann. Meeting, p. 145A.

Smith, F. G., 1958.   Transport and deposition of the non-sulphide vein minerals. VI.   Quartz. *Canadian Min.*, vol. 6, p. 210.

Smith, G. F. H., 1958.   *Gemstones* (Revised by F. C. Phillips).   Methuen, London.

Sosman, R. B., 1927.   *The properties of silica.*   New York.

—— 1932.   The inversion of cristobalite. *Journ. Amer. Chem. Soc.*, vol. 54, p. 3015.

—— 1954.   New high-pressure phases of silica. *Science*, vol. 119, p. 783.

Spezia, G., 1900.   *Atti R. Accad. Sci. Torino*, vol. 34, p. 631.

Stanley, J. M. and **Theokritoff, S.**, 1956.   Incorporation of impurities in synthetic quartz crystals. *Amer. Min.*, vol. 41, p. 527.

Stein, W., 1939.   Über die optischen Eigenschaften des Quarzes bei den Wellenlängen 8–20μ. *Ann. Physik*, ser. 5, vol. 36, p. 462.

Steinwehr, H. E.v., 1938.   Umwandlung $\alpha = \beta$-quartz. *Zeit. Krist.*, vol. 99, p. 292.

Stishov, S. M. and **Popova, S. V.**, 1961.   New dense polymorphic modification of silica. *Geokhimiya*, vol. 10, p. 837.

Stoiber, R. E., **Tolman, C.** and **Butler, R. D.**, 1945.   Geology of quartz crystal deposits. *Amer. Min.*, vol. 30, p. 245.

Stringham, B., 1953.   Crystallographic control of replacement of quartz by feldspar. *Amer. Min.*, vol. 38, p. 834.

Swanson, H. E., Fuyat, R. K. and **Ugrinic, G. M.,** 1954.   Standard X-ray diffraction powder patterns.   *U.S. Nat. Bur. Standards, Circ. 539.*

Szivessy, G., 1937.   Neuere Untersuchungen über die optischen.   Erscheinungen be aktiven Kristallen.   *Fortschr. Min. Krist. Petr.,* vol. 21, p. 111.

Taliaferro, N. L., 1935.   Some properties of opal.   *Amer. Journ. Sci.,* ser. 5, vol. 30, p. 450.

Tammann, G. and **Moritz, G.,** 1934.   Die Dichteabnahme des Quartzes beim Reiken.   *Zeit. anorg. Chem.,* vol. 218, p. 267.

Taube, E., 1944.   Mining terms of obscure origins.   *Science* (Amer. Assoc. Adv. Sci.), vol. 58, p. 454.

Taylor, E. W., 1949.   Correlation of the Mohs's scale of hardness with the Vickers's hardness numbers.   *Min. Mag.,* vol. 28, p. 718.

Taylor, N. W. and **Lin, C-Y,** 1941.   Effect of various catalysts on conversion of quartz to cristobalite and tridymite at high temperatures.   *Journ. Amer. Ceram. Soc.,* vol. 24, p. 57.

Thiesmeyer, L. R., 1937.   Vein quartz pseudomorphs of cross-fibre asbestos in Virginia.   *Amer. Min.,* vol. 22, p. 701.

Thomas, L. A. and **Wooster, W. A.,** 1951.   Piezocrescence — the growth of Dauphiné twinning in quartz under stress.   *Proc. Roy. Soc.,* A, vol. 208, p. 43.

Tokuda, T., 1957.   Doubt about Fenner's phase diagram of the one component system SiO_2.   *Mem. Inst. Sci. & Ind. Res., Osaka Univ.,* vol. 14, p. 153.

—— 1960.   The X-ray powder patterns and the lattice constants of natural cristobalites.   *Min. Journ. (Japan),* vol. 3, p. 1.

Tomita, T., 1932.   The Esterel twin of porphyritic quartz in alkali-liparite from Dôgo, Oki-island, Japan.   *Japanese Journ. Geol. Geogr.,* vol. 9, p. 243.

Tomkeieff, S. I., 1942.   On the origin of the name "quartz".   *Min. Mag.,* vol. 26, p. 172.

Tool, A. Q. and **Insley, H.,** 1938.   Observations on crystalline silica in certain devitrified glasses.   *Journ. Res. Nat. Bur. Standards (U.S.A.),* vol. 21, p. 743.

Trömel, G. and **Kriesement, O.,** 1959.   The α–β cristobalite inversion.   *Tonindustr. Zeit.,* vol. 83, p. 118 (M.A. 14–404).

Trommsdorff, W. E., 1937.   Das Verhältnis der Anzahl der Linksquarze zu der Anzahl der Rechtsquarze in einer grosseren Menge von Quarzkristallen.   *Neues Jahrb. Min.,* Abt. A, Beil-Bd. 72, p. 464.

Tuttle, O. F., 1949a.   The variable inversion temperature of quartz as a possible geologic thermometer.   *Amer. Min.,* vol. 34, p. 723.

—— 1949b.   Structural petrology of planes of liquid inclusions.   *Journ. Geol.,* vol. 57, p. 331.

—— and **Bowen, N. L.,** 1958.   Origin of granite in the light of experimental studies in the system $NaAlSi_3O_8$–$KAlSi_3O_8$–SiO_2–H_2O.   *Mem. Geol. Soc. Amer.,* no. 74.

—— and **England, J. L.,** 1955.   Preliminary report on the system SiO_2–H_2O.   *Bull. Geol. Soc. Amer.,* vol. 66, p. 149.

—— and **Keith, M. L.,** 1954.   The granite problem: evidence from the quartz and feldspar of a Tertiary granite.   *Geol. Mag.,* vol. 91, p. 61.

Tzinzerling, E. V., 1941.   Quartz twinning control under $\alpha{\to}\beta$ conversion.   *Doklady Acad. Sci. USSR,* vol. 33, p. 365.

—— 1952.   The morphology of twins produced at $\beta{\to}\alpha{\to}\beta$-transformations of quartz.   *Trudy Inst. Cryst.,* no. 7, p. 81 (M.A. 12–557).

Umova, M. A., Glebov, R. T. and **Shibanov, P. N.,** 1957.   An investigation of the chemical composition of gaseous inclusions in quartz from different deposits.   *Doklady Acad. Sci. USSR,* vol. 112, p. 519.

Ustiev, E. K., 1934. On the tridymite dacite from volcanic region of Keli in the middle Caucasus. *Trav. Inst. Pétrogr. Acad. Sci. URSS*, no. 6, p. 159 (M.A. 7–50).

Van Dyke, K. S., 1945. The piezoelectric quartz resonator. *Amer. Min.*, vol. 30, p. 214.

Van Valkenburg, A., Jr. and **Buie, B. F.**, 1945. Octahedral cristobalite with quartz paramorphs from Ellora caves, Hyderabad State, India. *Amer. Min.*, vol. 30, p. 526.

Vedeneeva, N. E., 1940. On the nature of coloring of ameythyst. *Trav. Lab. Crist. Acad. Sci. URSS*, no. 2, p. 107 (M.A. 9–198).

Vigoureux, P., 1931. *Quartz Resonators and Oscillators.* London (H.M.S.O.).

vom Rath, G., 1874. *Ueber die Krystallisation, und Zwillingsbildungen des Tridymits.* Monat. Kon. Pr. Akad. Wiss, Berlin, p. 165.

—— 1887. Über Cristobalit vom Cerro S. Cristobal bei Pachuca (Mexico). *Neues Jahrb.* (1), p. 198.

Vultée, J. von, 1955. Über die orientierten Verwachsungen von Rutil in Quarz. *Neues Jahrb. Min., Abhandl.*, vol. 87, p. 389.

—— and **Leitz, J.**, 1956. Über die Rolle des Titans als Färbungsursache von Blau- und Rosenquarzen. *Neues Jahrb. Min., Monat.*, 3, p. 49.

Wager, L. R. and **Deer, W. A.**, 1939. Petrology of the Skaergaard intrusion, Kangerdlugssuaq, east Greenland. *Meddel. om Grønland*, vol. 105, no. 4.

—— **Weedon, D. S.** and **Vincent, E. A.**, 1953. A granophyre from Coire Uaigneich, Isle of Skye, containing quartz paramorphs after tridymite. *Min. Mag.* vol. 30, p. 263.

Walker, A. C., 1950. Growing piezoelectric crystals. *Journ. Franklin Inst.*, vol. 250, p. 481.

Walker, T. R., 1957. Frosting of quartz grains by carbonate replacement. *Bull. Geol. Soc. Amer.*, vol. 68, p. 267.

Watson, T. L. and **Beard, R. E.**, 1917. The color of amethyst, rose, and blue varieties of quartz. *Proc. U.S. Nat. Mus.*, vol. 53, p. 553 (M.A. 1–11).

Wei, P., 1935. The structure of α-quartz. *Zeit. Krist.*, vol. 92, p. 355.

Weil, R., 1925. Synthèse de la cristobalite par voie humide. *Compt. Rend. Acad. Sci. Paris*, vol. 181, p. 423.

Weymouth, J. H. and **Williamson, W. O.**, 1951. Some physical properties of raw and calcined flint. *Min. Mag.*, vol. 29, p. 573.

White, J. F. and **Corwin, J. F.**, 1961. Synthesis and origin of chalcedony. *Amer. Min.*, vol. 46, p. 112.

Wilson, A. J. C. and **Lipson, H.**, 1941. The calibration of Debye-Scherrer X-ray powder cameras. *Proc. Phys. Soc.*, vol. 53, p. 245.

Winchell, H., 1945. The Knoop microhardness tester as a mineralogical tool. *Amer. Min.*, vol. 30, p. 583.

Wittels, M. C., 1957. Structural behaviour of neutron irradiated quartz. *Phil. Mag.*, ser. 8, vol. 2, p. 1445.

Wooster, N. and **Wooster, W. A.**, 1946. Preparation of synthetic quartz. *Nature.* vol. 157, p. 297.

Wright, F. E. and **Larsen, E. S.**, 1909. Quartz as a geologic thermometer. *Amer. Journ. Sci.*, ser. 4, vol. 27, p. 421.

Wyart, J., 1943. Sur la cristallisation de la silice en présence de l'eau sous pression. *Bull. Soc. franç. Min.*, vol. 66, p. 479.

Wyckoff, R. W. G., 1925. Die Kristallstruktur von β-Cristobalit SiO_2 (bei hohen Temperaturen stabile Form). *Zeit. Krist.*, vol. 62, p. 189.

—— 1926. The crystal structure of the high temperature (β-) modification of quartz. *Amer. Journ. Sci.*, ser. 5, vol. 11, p. 101.

Wyllie, P. J., 1959. Microscopic cordierite in fused Torridonian arkose. *Amer. Min.*, vol. 44, p. 1039.

Yagi, K., 1950. Quoted from: Harada, S., 1954. Chemical analyses of Japanese minerals (III). *Journ. Fac. Sci. Hokkaido Univ.*, ser. IV, vol. 8, p. 300.

Yoder, H. S., Jr., 1950. High–low quartz inversion up to 10,000 bars. *Trans. Amer. Geophys. Union*, vol. 31, p. 827.

Young, R. A. and Post, B., 1962. Electron density and thermal effects in alpha quartz. *Acta Cryst.*, vol. 15, p. 337.

Zoltai, T. and Buerger, M. J., 1959. The crystal structure of coesite, the dense, high-pressure form of silica. *Zeit. Krist.*, vol. 111, p. 129.

Zyndel, F., 1914. Über Quartzzwillinge mit nichtparallelen Hauptaxen. *Zeit. Krist.*, vol. 53, p. 15.

NEPHELINE GROUP

Nepheline $\qquad\qquad\qquad\qquad\qquad\qquad\qquad$ $Na_3K[Al_4Si_4O_{16}]$
Kalsilite $\qquad\qquad\qquad\qquad\qquad\qquad\qquad\qquad$ $K[AlSiO_4]$

HEXAGONAL (−)

	Nepheline	Kalsilite
ϵ	1·526–1·542	1·532–1·537[1]
ω	1·529–1·546	1·538–1·543[1]
δ	0·003–0·005	0·005–0·006
Dispersion:	Weak	Weak
D	2·56–2·665	2·59–2·625[1]
H	$5\frac{1}{2}$–6	6
Cleavage:	$\{10\bar{1}0\}$, $\{0001\}$, poor.	$\{10\bar{1}0\}$, $\{0001\}$, poor.
Twinning:	$\{10\bar{1}0\}$, $\{33\bar{6}5\}$, $\{11\bar{2}2\}$.	
Colour:	Colourless, white, grey; colourless in thin section.	
Unit cell:		
a	$\simeq 10\cdot0$ Å	$\simeq 5\cdot2$ Å
c	$\simeq 8\cdot4$ Å	$\simeq 8\cdot7$ Å
Z	2	2
Space group:	$P6_3$	$P6_322$

Gelantinizes in strong HCl.

Nepheline and kalsilite are not isostructural, but both structures are based upon a tridymite-type framework in which approximately half of the silicon atoms are replaced by aluminium; the electrical neutrality is maintained by the presence of alkali atoms in the structural cavities. In addition to structural differences for different compositions, polymorphism is present over the greater part of the chemical range of the series. At the pure sodium end of the series low-temperature nepheline is the stable phase up to about 900°C., at which temperature it inverts to high-temperature nepheline; the latter inverts at 1254°C. to the high-temperature polymorph carnegieite. According to the tentative phase diagram by Tuttle and Smith (1958), Fig. 79, the temperature of both inversions is raised by the substitution of sodium by potassium; that of low- to high-temperature nepheline rises rapidly and reaches a maximum of 1248°C. at a composition Ne_{95} while in more potassium-rich nephelines the low-temperature phase inverts directly to carnegieite, the limiting composition of which is about Ne_{73}.

At the potassium end of the series, kalsilite inverts at approximately 850°C. to an orthorhombic phase, O_1. The relationships for compositions between

---

[1] A ferrian kalsilite described by Sahama (1954) has ϵ 1·550, ω 1·554, D 2·663 (see Table 30, anal. 5).

Ne_{30} and Ne_{10} are more complex and less precisely defined, but the occurrence of a second orthorhombic phase (O_2), tetrakalsilite, and trikalsilite has been confirmed. Kaliophilite, which has a similar compositional range to kalsilite, is probably a metastable phase at atmospheric pressure, and its relationships to kalsilite and to the other potassium-rich phases are not clearly understood.

A summary of the chemical and structural features of the various phases in the $NaAlSiO_4$–$KAlSiO_4$ system is presented in Table 28.

Solid solution of K in the nepheline structure is limited to about 25 mol. per cent. at ordinary temperatures, but the amount of solid solution increases with increasing temperature, and reaches about 70 per cent. at 1070°C. At the other end of the Na, K chemical series the amount of Na which can enter the kalsilite structure rises from zero to about 25 per cent. at 1070°C. (Fig. 79). Both nepheline and kalsilite solid solutions may be quenched to room temperature without unmixing.

Table 28. SYMMETRY AND LATTICE PARAMETERS OF PHASES IN THE $NaAlSiO_4$–$KAlSiO_4$ SYSTEM

	$NaAlSiO_4$ Weight %	Symmetry	Lattice parameters (Å)			Reference
			a	b	c	
Nepheline	100–30	Hexagonal	10·0	—	8·4	Smith and Tuttle (1957)
High-temperature nepheline	≃ 100	Orthorhombic	10·2	17·6	8·5	Smith and Tuttle (1957)
High-temperature nepheline	≃ 100	Hexagonal	10·0	—	8·3	Donnay *et al.* (1959)
Low-temperature carnegieite	100–90	?		?		—
High-temperature carnegieite	100–90	Cubic	7·3	—	—	Smith and Tuttle (1957)
Kalsilite	0–20	Hexagonal	5·2	—	8·7	Smith and Tuttle (1957)
Orthorhombic $KAlSiO_4(O_1)$	0–10	Orthorhombic	9·1	15·7	8·6	Smith and Tuttle (1957)
Orthorhombic $KAlSiO_4(O_2)$	≃ 15	Orthorhombic	8·9	10·5	8·5	Smith and Tuttle (1957)
Trikalsilite	≃ 30	Hexagonal	15·4	—	8·6	Sahama and Smith (1957)
Tetrakalsilite	≃ 25	Hexagonal	20·5	—	8·5	Smith and Tuttle (1957)
Natural kaliophilite	0–10	Hexagonal	26·9	—	8·5	Smith and Tuttle (1957)
Synthetic kaliophilite	0–10	Hexagonal	5·2	—	8·6	Smith and Tuttle (1957)

Nepheline is the most characteristic mineral of the alkaline rocks, and occurs as a primary phase in many plutonic, hypabyssal and volcanic rocks of extremely varied mineralogical and chemical composition. The composition of nepheline in plutonic rocks and nepheline gneisses is generally close to $Na_3KAl_4Si_4O_{16}$; in contrast, nephelines of volcanic rocks are commonly either more sodium- or more potassium-rich. The prefixes subpotassic, mediopotassic and perpotassic are used to describe nepheline solid solutions in which the numbers of potassium atoms replacing sodium (on the basis of 32 oxygens) are between 0 and 0·25, between 0·25 and 2·0, and between 2·0 and 4·73 respectively. Kalsilite is an important constituent of the groundmass of some potassium-rich lavas, but also occurs in complex nepheline–kalsilite phenocrysts of some less potassium-rich lavas; kalsilite is unknown in plutonic rocks.

Nepheline is named from the Greek *nephele*, a cloud, in allusion to the cloudy appearance developed by nepheline when immersed in strong acid. The name elaeolite (from the Greek *elaion*, oil) has also been used, and refers to the greasy lustre of the mineral; carnegieite, which does not occur as a natural mineral, is named after the Carnegie Institution of Washington. The name kalsilite refers to the chemical formula, KAlSi(lite).

STRUCTURE

Nepheline. The structure of nepheline is based on a tridymite-type framework (Schiebold, 1930) containing 32 oxygen atoms per unit cell, in which approximately half of the silicon atoms are replaced by aluminium (tridymite unit cell a 5·04, c 8·24 Å, nepheline unit cell $a \simeq 2 \times 5·0$, $c \simeq 8·4$ Å). In nepheline the tetrahedra with the apices pointing in one direction along the z-axis are occupied by silicon, while those which point in the opposite direction are occupied by aluminium; the resulting negative charge is balanced by alkali atoms occupying cavities in the framework (Fig. 74a). In nepheline of ideal composition, $Na_6K_2Al_8Si_8O_{32}$, the tridymite-type framework is distorted, and the alkali sites are of two different sizes. Two of the eight intraframework sites (Fig. 74b) have nine-fold oxygen co-ordination, their average cation–oxygen distance is 2·9 Å, and they are occupied by potassium (Buerger *et al.*, 1954; Hahn and Buerger, 1955). The six smaller sites have eight-fold oxygen co-ordination, the average cation–oxygen distance is 2·65 Å, and the sites are occupied by sodium. Some nephelines have less potassium than the ideal composition, and in these some of the larger voids are occupied by sodium; in other nephelines more than 1 in 4 of the voids may be occupied by potassium, and it is thus possible for both sites to admit either sodium or potassium atoms. Occupation of all the voids by potassium does not, however, occur, and the range of solid solution of potassium in the nepheline structure does not go beyond about Ne_{75} at ordinary temperatures. Calcium atoms are present in some nephelines but it is uncertain whether they are located in the larger or smaller voids, or are distributed between both.

Sahama (1958) has reported that a nepheline, composition 19·8 atomic per cent. K:(K+Na+Ca), from a cancrinite ijolite, Iivaara, northern Finland (Lehijärvi, 1956), in addition to giving the strong reflections on rotation and Weissenberg photographs corresponding to the usually accepted nepheline unit cell ($a \simeq 10$, $c \simeq 8·4$ Å), shows a pattern of weak extra reflections. These additional reflections indicate that the above cell is a pseudo-cell and that the true cell (also hexagonal) dimensions are a 17·4, $c \simeq 74$ Å. More recently McConnell (1962) has shown that similar additional maxima are present in nephelines of widely different composition and parageneses. On heating at temperatures above 200 °C. these maxima become diffuse, but are not completely removed by extended hydrothermal treatment at higher temperatures (*e.g.* 138 hours at 750°C. and P_{H_2O} of 1000 atmospheres). McConnell has interpreted the additional maxima in relation to a cell three times the volume of the Buerger unit cell, and considers that the true structure in the low-temperature state involves a statistical antisymmetry in respect of this large cell due to (Si, Al) ordering.

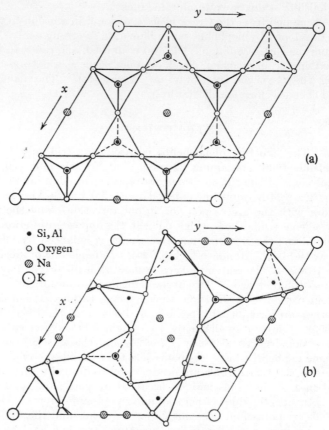

FIG. 74(a). Idealized structure of nepheline, $Na_3KAl_4Si_4O_{16}$, projected on the (0001) plane, based on the high-tridymite arrangement of tetrahedra. (b) Structure of nepheline, $Na_3KAl_4Si_4O_{16}$, projected on the (0001) plane (after Hahn and Buerger, 1955). Both figures show the linkage of SiO_4 and AlO_4 tetrahedra and the positions of K and Na ions.

Smith and Sahama (1954) have shown that for both natural and synthetic nepheline and nepheline solid solutions, the 2θ values of the $20\bar{2}2$ and $21\bar{3}0$ reflections vary systematically with the ratio $K:(K+Na+Ca)$. Compared with the curve of 2θ values against composition for synthetic nephelines, the curve for natural nephelines is displaced slightly in the direction of higher potassium content, the average deviation being 2 atomic per cent. $K:(K+Na+Ca)$. The following linear equations, calculated by the least-squares method, are given by Smith and Sahama for the determination of this ratio in natural nepheline solid solutions:

$21\bar{3}0$ reflection, 100 K : (K + Na)   9 to 25
$100\ K : (K + Na) = 61{\cdot}24 - 176{\cdot}3\ (2\theta_{Cu} - 27{\cdot}00°)$
$21\bar{3}0$ reflection, 100 K : (K + Na)   25–60
$100\ K : (K + Na) = 118{\cdot}02 - 77{\cdot}26\ (2\theta_{Cu} - 26{\cdot}00°)$
$20\bar{2}2$ reflection, 100 K : (K + Na)   9 to 25
$100\ K : (K + Na) = 117{\cdot}35 - 148{\cdot}1\ (2\theta_{Cu} - 29{\cdot}00°)$
$20\bar{2}2$ reflection, 100 K : (K + Na)   25 to 60
$100\ K : (K + Na) = 79{\cdot}94 - 88{\cdot}13\ (2\theta_{Cu} - 29{\cdot}00°)$

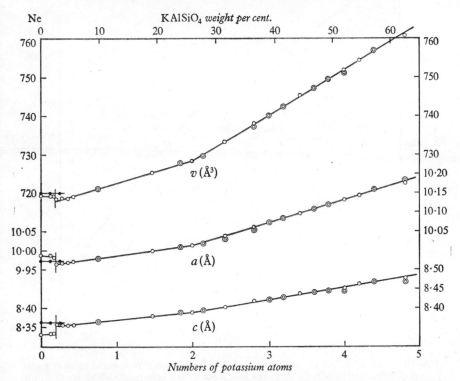

Fig. 75.   Cell dimensions of synthetic $Na_{8-x}K_xAl_8Si_8O_{32}$ nepheline solid solutions. The number of potassium atoms per cell, x, is given on the lower scale and the weight per cent. $KAlSiO_4$ on the upper scale of the abscissa. ● quenched high-temperature form; ○ low-temperature form; ⊚ data of Smith and Tuttle, 1957 (after Donnay *et al.*, 1959).

Tuttle and Smith (1958) have shown that there is a change in slope in the plot of the *a* and *c* nepheline solid solution parameters against the ratio Na:K, the change occurring at Na:K = 3:1 ($Ne_{72.9}$ $Ks_{27.1}$ weight per cent.). Tuttle and Smith correlated this discontinuity with the presence in sodium-rich nephelines of Na ions in some of the larger voids suitable for potassium, and the presence in potassium-rich nephelines of potassium ions in some of the smaller voids suitable for sodium.

Donnay *et al.* (1959) have also demonstrated that the substitution of Na by K ($Na_{8-x} K_x Al_8Si_8O_{32}$) is accompanied by an increase in both the a and c parameters. For compositions in which the value of x is between 0·25 and 2·0, the linear increase in cell volume is 5·82 Å³ per K ion, and between 2·0 and 4·73 it is 11·8 Å³ per K ion (Fig. 75). A sample of composition 62·5 weight per cent. $KAlSiO_4$ ($x=4·796$) gave a powder pattern which includes non-nepheline reflections. Because of the experimental uncertainty it was not possible to

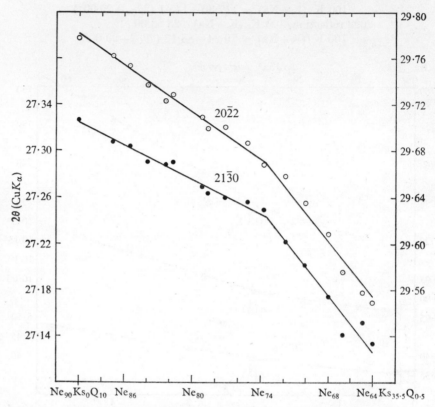

Fig. 76. Plot of values of $2\theta(CuK_\alpha)$ of the $21\bar{3}0$ and $20\bar{2}2$ reflections against composition of nephelines lying on the line joining the compositions $Ne_{90}Ks_0Q_{10}$ and $Ne_{64}Ks_{35·5}Q_{0·5}$ (after Hamilton and MacKenzie, 1960).

decide whether or not there is a singularity or discontinuity in the cell volumes for compositions from x 0 to 0·25. Smith and Tuttle (1957) had earlier noted that the a parameters of both dry and hydrothermally prepared $NaAlSiO_4$ are approximately 0·025 Å greater than the value extrapolated from the parameters of more potassium-rich nephelines. The use of the terms subpotassic, mediopotassic and perpotassic has been suggested by Donnay *et al.* (1959) to describe nepheline solid solutions in the compositional ranges $0 < x < 0·25$, $0·25 < x < 2·0$, and $2·0 < x < 4·73$.

Although Donnay *et al.* (1959) found that the lattice parameters of pure $NaAlSiO_4$ are virtually unaffected by omission solid solution ($Na_{8-y}\square_yAl_{8-y}$

$Si_{8+y}O_{32}$), Hamilton and MacKenzie (1960) have shown that changes in lattice parameters accompany the replacement of Al by Si and of Na by vacant sites in potassium-bearing nephelines having excess SiO_2. Thus the break in the lattice parameters with changing chemical composition for nephelines belonging to the system $NaAlSiO_4$–$KAlSiO_4$, demonstrated by Tuttle and Smith (1958), also occurs in nephelines the composition of which can only be precisely described with reference to the ternary system $NaAlSiO_4$–$KAlSiO_4$–SiO_2. The

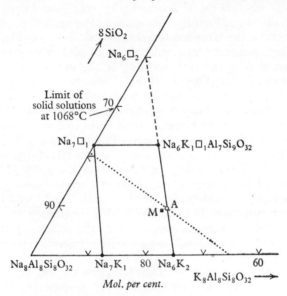

Fig. 77.   Diagram showing part of the system $NaAlSiO_4$
–$KAlSiO_4$–SiO_2; compositions are plotted on a
molecular per cent. basis.   Dotted line represents
approximately the limit of nepheline solid solutions
at 700°C.   The position of the break in the X-ray
determinative curve (Fig. 76), marked by the
point A, lies very close to the line representing six
of the eight alkali sites filled by Na atoms.   M is
the composition originally suggested by Morozewicz
for rock-forming nephelines (after Hamilton and
MacKenzie, 1960).

change in slope of the plot of 2θ ($21\bar{3}0$) and 2θ ($20\bar{2}2$) against composition (Fig. 76) occurs at $Ne_{73.5}Ks_{22.5}Q_{4.0}(Ne_{71.24}Ks_{19.59}Q_{9.17}$ molecular per cent.), a composition which may be expressed by the formula:

$$Na_{5.97}K_{1.64}\square_{0.39}Al_{7.61}Si_{8.39}O_{32}$$

It would thus appear that the change in lattice parameters occurs in omission solid solution nephelines when the six smaller voids are occupied by sodium atoms and when there are no sodium atoms in the larger voids suitable for potassium, *i.e.* omission substitution occurs only in relation to the large potassium sites (Fig. 77).

The double substitution, calcium replacing sodium and aluminium replacing silicon, $Na_{8-z}Ca_zAl_{8+z}Si_{8-z}O_{32}$, is accompanied by a linear increase in the cell volume of 2·2 $Å^3$ per calcium atom (Donnay *et al.*, 1959; see also Miyashiro and Miyashiro, 1954).

In the subpotassic compositional range nepheline occurs in both low- and high-temperature forms. Tuttle and Smith (1958) showed that dry and hydro-thermally prepared nephelines, Ne_{100}, differ in their response to differential thermal analysis; thus the dry synthesized material shows a reversible thermal effect at 850°C., whereas the hydrothermally synthesized nepheline does not. The effect of replacing sodium by potassium in the nepheline solid solution will probably be to raise the inversion temperature as shown in Fig. 79.

Evidence that nepheline can exist in low- and high-temperature forms has been obtained from the measurement of the unit cell dimensions of four synthetic nephelines with different thermal histories (Donnay, 1957; Donnay *et al.*, 1959). The high-temperature form was obtained by quenching a nepheline crystallized from a synthetic nepheline glass held at 1100°C. for six hours. The cell dimensions of the high-temperature form (considered by Donnay to be hexagonal, but possibly orthorhombic according to Tuttle and Smith, 1958)[1] are a 9·971, c 8·362 ± 0·005 Å, $c:a$ 0·8386; the average values for nine samples of the low-temperature form are a 9·986, c 8·330 ± 0·005 Å $c:a$ 0·8342.

Measurement of birefringence at different temperatures, and of thermal expansion, indicate the existence, in the medio- and perpotassic range of compositions, of two types of nepheline and a continuous gradation between them (Sahama, 1962). Sahama suggests that the difference between the two types is characteristic of a sluggish order–disorder transition probably associated with (Si,Al) distribution.

Carnegieite. The structure of high-temperature carnegieite (Barth and Posnjak, 1932) is based on a cristobalite-type framework; the symmetry is cubic, a 7·325 Å at 750°C., and the space group $P2_13$. The unit cell content of high-temperature carnegieite is $Na_4Al_4Si_4O_{16}$, and both silicon and aluminium are tetrahedrally co-ordinated. The sodium atoms occupy some of the voids in the framework and are in twelve-fold co-ordination. Low-temperature carnegieite is intimately twinned, and its symmetry is probably low; the lattice parameters and symmetry have not been determined. X-ray powder patterns of high- and low-temperature carnegieite are given by Smith and Tuttle (1957).

Kalsilite. The composition at which the change from the nepheline to the kalsilite structure takes place is not known precisely, but occurs in the range Ne_{30} to Ne_{20} (Tuttle and Smith, 1958). The structure has not been investi-gated in detail but is most probably based on a tridymite-type framework. The cell dimensions, $a \simeq 5·2$, $c \simeq 8·8$ Å, differ from those of nepheline, a 10·0, c 8·4 Å, as also does the space group, $P 6_322$, of kalsilite (Claringbull and Bannister, 1948). Thus for hydrothermally synthesized kalsilite, Ne_0, the cell dimensions are a 5·1597, c 8·7032 Å, and for kalsilite Ne_{10} are a 5·1485, c 8·6428 Å (Smith and Tuttle, 1957). The composition of the kalsilite solid solutions may be deter-mined from the equation:

$$100 \, K:(K+Na) = 100 - 227·27 \, (\Delta - 6·204)$$

where $\Delta = 2\theta_{(10\bar{1}2)} - 2\theta_{(10\bar{1}1)}$ for Cu$K\alpha$ radiation (Sahama *et al.*, 1956).

[1] Unlike that prepared by Donnay *et al.*, the high-temperature nepheline prepared by Tuttle and Smith was reported as non-quenchable.

Claringbull and Bannister (1948) have pointed out that for this structure the halved *a* parameter of kalsilite compared with that of nepheline implies that the Si and Al atoms are disordered. Smith and Sahama (1957) have reported variations in the intensities of reflections indicative of partial order in the kalsilite phase of a kalsilite–nepheline "microperthite". The unit cell of this kalsilite phase is at 30° to the normal 5·2 Å cell and the *a* repeat distance is thus 8·9 Å (*i.e.* $5·2\sqrt{3}$). The *c* parameter is unchanged and the symmetry of this cell remains hexagonal. Smith and Sahama have suggested that the prefixes *d-* and *o-* should be used to characterize the disordered (*a* 5·15 Å) and the ordered (*a* 8·9 Å) forms of kalsilite.

The lattice parameters of orthorhombic $KAlSiO_4$ were given as *a* 9·013, *b* 15·673, *c* 8·574 Å by Kunze (1954), and Smith and Tuttle (1957) have shown that the parameters of the pure $KAlSiO_4$ (O_1 phase) are larger than those of orthorhombic $KAlSiO_4$ in which some K is replaced by Na. A second orthorhombic phase (O_2), having the cell dimensions *a* 8·892, *b* 10·468, *c* 8·547 Å, was reported by Smith and Tuttle. The composition of the latter crystals is probably Ne_{15}: they were obtained by quenching charges of Ne_{20} composition heated above 1520°C.

The tetrakalsilite phase has cell parameters $a \simeq 20·5$, $c \simeq 8·5$ Å, and space group $P6_322$. The compositional range over which this phase can form is not known precisely but probably extends from approximately 5 to 30 weight per cent. $NaAlSiO_4$. Sahama and Smith (1957) have described a further (K, Na) $AlSiO_4$ mineral, trikalsilite (*a* 15·4, *c* 8·6 Å; space group probably $P6_3$). This phase, from a lava at Kabfumo, North Kivu, Congo, occurs in parallel growth with nepheline and its compositional range is probably similar to that of tetrakalsilite.

The X-ray powder pattern of the compound $\alpha\text{-}K_2O \cdot MgO \cdot 3SiO_2$, synthesized during an investigation of the system $K_2O–MgO–SiO_2$ (Roedder, 1951), is very similar to that of kalsilite.

Kaliophilite. The structure of kaliophilite has not been investigated in detail but cell dimensions (Table 28) have been determined by Gossner and Mussgnug (1930), Bannister and Hey (1931), Lukesh and Buerger (1942) and Smith and Tuttle (1957). The *a* (26·9 Å) dimension of kaliophilite is considerably greater than the *a* (5·2 Å) dimension of kalsilite, but is related to it by the factor $3\sqrt{3}$, *i.e.* it is three times the repeat distance in the direction at 30° to *x* in kalsilite. The number of formula units per unit cell is 54 (*i.e.* $54KAlSiO_4$). The *c* dimension is somewhat smaller than the *c* dimension of kalsilite and this may be caused by a slight flexing of the (Si,Al)–O–(Si,Al) linkages parallel to the *z* axis in kaliophilite (Claringbull and Bannister, 1948). The space group is $P6_322$, but Lukesh and Buerger have suggested that the symmetry may be orthorhombic and that the observed hexagonal symmetry may be due to twinning. Tilley and Henry (1953) have described a kaliophilite from the Alban Hills which gives anomalous X-ray reflections, and synthetically prepared crystals also differ from natural kaliophilite. Smith and Tuttle (1957) have suggested that the synthetic material is a disordered form of natural kaliophilite and that the anomalous natural kaliophilite described by Tilley and Henry represents an intermediate stage of ordering. X-ray powder data for natural and synthetic kaliophilite are given by Smith and Tuttle (1957).

CHEMISTRY

Analyses of 19 nephelines and the average composition of 16 nephelines from nepheline-syenites, together with the number of cations in the unit cells calculated on the basis of 32 oxygens, are given in Table 29. The generally accepted view that nephelines contain more silicon and less aluminium than is represented by the formula $NaAlSiO_4$ is confirmed by the number (8·01 to 8·88) of silicon atoms per formula unit present in the nephelines detailed in Table 29. The sum of the Si and Al atoms does not depart significantly from the ideal cell content of 16 atoms in tetrahedral co-ordination, a value that is approached even more closely if Fe^{+3} is assumed to be located in the tetrahedral positions of the tridymite-type framework; the average $\sum (Si + Al + Fe^{+3})$ of the nephelines in Table 29 is 15·99 atoms, and the greatest divergence from the ideal cell content of 16 is $\pm 0·12$ atoms. The excess of SiO_2 compared with the compositions of solid solutions between $NaAlSiO_4$ and $KAlSiO_4$ is shown also by the normative percentage of the sodium molecule (Ne), the potassium molecule (Ks) and SiO_2 (Q) in the analyses. It is apparent too that there is a significantly greater excess of SiO_2 in the more sodium- than in the more potassium-rich nephelines.

Although nepheline can take 35 mol. per cent. anorthite into solid solution (Bowen, 1912), most natural nephelines contain only relatively small amounts of calcium. In many the paucity of calcium can be correlated with the small content of calcium in the magmas from which the nephelines crystallized, but even nephelines formed in a calcium-rich environment do not in general contain appreciably greater amounts. This may be related either to the lesser solubility of calcium in the nepheline structure at the lower temperatures of crystallization of natural minerals, or to the entry of calcium preferentially into other phases crystallizing earlier or together with the nepheline.

Small amounts of Mg, Mn and Ti are reported in many nephelines, and in recalculating the analyses it has been assumed that these ions substitute for Na, K or Ca. On the assumption that in the ideal nepheline unit cell the number of (Si + Al) atoms is 16, and that the negative charge on the tridymite-type framework is balanced by the charge on the alkali atoms, $\sum R (= Na + K + 2Ca)$, which equals the number of aluminiums in the unit cell, Bannister and Hey (1931) expressed the nepheline formula as $(Na, K, \frac{1}{2}Ca)_n$ $[Si_{16-n}Al_nO_{32}]$ where n varies from 6·6 to 8·2. In natural nephelines n usually varies between 7 and 8 (for the minerals listed in Table 29, the range is from 7·08 to 8·12). Thus in some nephelines the intraframework cavities are not completely occupied.

Hahn and Buerger (1955) consider that the ideal composition of the unit cell is $Na_6K_2[Si_8Al_8O_{32}]$, but since the substitution of silicon by aluminium does not attain the ideal Si : Al ratio 1 : 1 they expressed the general nepheline formula as

$$A_yB_z[Si_{8+x}Al_{8-x}O_{32}]$$

where x is the deficiency of Al compared with the ideal unit cell content, and $y + z = 8 - x$, $y \leqslant 2$, $z \leqslant 6$. If divalent calcium substitutes for monovalent alkali atoms then the formula becomes

$$A_yB_zC_w[Si_{8+x}Al_{8-x}O_{32}]$$

where $y + z + 2w = 8 - x$, $y \leqslant 2$, $z \leqslant 6$ and $y + z + w \leqslant 8$.

In order to express vacancies in cation sites, Donnay *et al.* (1959) give the general nepheline formula as

$$K_xNa_yCa_z\square_{8-(x+y+z)}Al_{(x+y+2z)})Si_{16-(x+y+2z)}O_{32}$$

where $\square$ are the vacant sites.

Pure sodium nepheline exists in two forms; the low-temperature form is the stable phase from room temperature to approximately 900°C., at which temperature it inverts to the high-temperature form. The symmetry of low-temperature nepheline is hexagonal but there is some uncertainty as to the true symmetry of the high-temperature phase (see structure section).

Sodium nepheline inverts at 1254°C. to the cubic polymorph carnegieite, the melting point of which is 1526°C. Carnegieite can exist metastably below

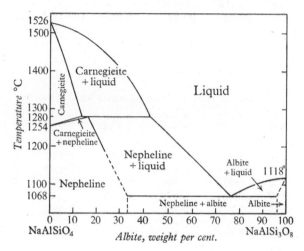

Fig. 78. Phase diagram of the system NaAlSiO₄ (nepheline, carnegieite)–NaAlSi₃O₈ (albite) (after Greig and Barth, 1938).

1254°C. and undergoes a rapid reversible metastable transformation at 692·1°C. on heating, and at 687°C. on cooling, to a twinned, low-temperature, low symmetry form (Schairer and Bowen, 1956): neither of the two forms of carnegieite have been found in nature. The transformation of high-carnegieite to high-nepheline is sluggish, and by quenching, high-carnegieite may be obtained in the stability field of nepheline. Carnegieite is not stable at elevated water pressures, and Yoder (1958) has reported that in the system NaAlSiO₄–H₂O a form of nepheline melts directly to a water-saturated liquid and that the liquidus is lowered by some 700°C. at a water pressure of 10,000 bars.

The system NaAlSiO₄ (nepheline, carnegieite)–NaAlSi₃O₈ (albite) was studied by Greig and Barth (1938) who concluded that about 33 wt. per cent. (equivalent to Ne₈₅Q₁₅ in the system NaAlSiO₄–SiO₂) and 14·5 per cent. NaAlSi₃O₈ can be accommodated in solid solution in nepheline and carnegieite respectively (Fig. 78). They found the nepheline–albite eutectic temperature to be 1068°C. at the composition Ne₂₄Ab₇₆ by weight. From a preliminary study of the

Table 29.   NEPHELINE ANALYSES

	1.	2.	3.	4.	5.	6.	7.
SiO_2	44·65	43·42	44·40	43·24	42·28	45·02	43·61
TiO_2	0·00	0·00	0·00	0·00	0·07	0·04	0·00
Al_2O_3	32·03	33·92	33·14	33·56	33·71	32·72	33·05
Fe_2O_3	0·59	0·14	0·18	0·47	0·80	0·52	0·85
MgO	0·00	0·08	0·05	0·05	0·03	0·06	0·05
CaO	0·71	1·37	0·36	0·77	0·56	0·60	0·53
Na_2O	17·25	17·05	17·17	16·88	16·61	16·36	16·09
K_2O	3·66	3·85	3·72	4·71	5·75	4·70	4·92
H_2O^+	0·96	0·11	0·94	0·07	0·34	0·44	0·70
H_2O^-	0·21	—	0·02	—	0·03	0·00	0·01
Total	100·06	99·94	99·98	99·86	100·18	100·46	99·82
ϵ	1·531	1·532	—	1·534	—	—	—
ω	1·535	1·536	—	1·538	—	—	—

NUMBERS OF IONS ON THE BASIS OF 32 OXYGENS

	1.	2.	3.	4.	5.	6.	7.
Si	8·585	8·292	8·503	8·305	8·170	8·567	8·406
Al	7·361	7·637	7·483	7·599	7·680	7·342	7·511
Ti	—	—	—	—	0·010	0·006	—
Fe^{+3}	0·085	0·020	0·025	0·067	0·116	0·076	0·123
Mg	—	0·023	0·014	0·014	0·008	0·017	0·014
Na	6·428	6·312	6·376	6·285	6·224	6·036	6·012
Ca	0·147	0·281	0·074	0·158	0·116	0·112	0·109
K	0·897	0·936	0·909	1·154	1·417	1·142	1·212
$\sum R$	7·61	7·81	7·43	7·76	7·87	7·40	7·44
Ne	81·9	81·8	81·3	80·4	78·4	77·5	77·5
Ks	12·9	15·5	12·9	16·4	20·0	16·3	17·2
Q	5·2	2·7	5·8	3·2	1·6	6·2	5·3

1. Nepheline, phonolite, Abbot's Hill, Dunedin, New Zealand (Tilley, 1954). Anal. J. H. Scoon.
2. Nepheline, jacupirangite, Chaunggyi, Mogok district, Burma (Tilley, 1954). Anal. J. H. Scoon.
3. Nepheline, theralitic canadite, Trooper Lake, Glamorgan Township, Haliburton County, Ontario (Tilley & Gittins, 1961).   Anal. J. H. Scoon (H_2O determined as loss on ignition).
4. Nepheline, ijolitic nepheline-syenite, Sinkwa, Mogok district, Burma (Tilley, 1954).   Anal. J. H. Scoon (Includes CO_2 0·11).
5. Nepheline, leucite–nepheline dolerite, Meiches, Hessen (Tilley, 1958b).   Anal. J. H. Scoon (H_2O determined as loss on ignition).
6. Nepheline, ditroite, Bratholmen, Langesundsfjord, Norway (Tilley & Gittins, 1961).   Anal. J. H. Scoon (H_2O determined as loss on ignition).
7. Nepheline, nepheline-syenite, Monmouth Township, Haliburton County Ontario (Tilley & Gittins, 1961).   Anal. J. H. Scoon (Includes 0·01 MnO).

Table 29. NEPHELINE ANALYSES—*continued*

	8.	9.	10.	11.	12.	13.
SiO_2	41·94	41·88	41·48	42·41	42·89	46·41
TiO_2	—	0·03	—	0·05	0·00	0·00
Al_2O_3	34·26	32·99	34·12	33·16	33·99	31·07
Fe_2O_3	0·55	0·74	1·26	1·36	0·36	0·78
MgO	0·30	0·00	0·00	0·07	0·00	0·11
CaO	0·28	0·78	0·12	0·48	0·23	0·87
Na_2O	15·82	16·11	16·20	16·08	16·27	15·67
K_2O	6·02	6·82	6·06	6·83	6·57	3·81
H_2O^+	1·32	0·71	0·17	—	—	0·97
H_2O^-	0·25	0·03	0·00	0·07	—	0·17
Total	100·83	100·16	99·70	100·51	100·31	99·86
ϵ	1·537	—	1·541	—	—	—
ω	1·541	—	1·545	—	—	—

NUMBERS OF IONS ON THE BASIS OF 32 OXYGENS

	8.	9.	10.	11.	12.	13.
Si	8·132	8·179	8·061	8·194	8·243	8·873
Al	7·833	7·595	7·818	7·554	7·701	7·004
Ti	—	0·005	—	0·007	—	—
Fe^{+3}	0·079	0·109	0·231‡	0·197	0·052	0·112
Mg	0·086	0·012†	—	0·020	—	0·032
Na	5·948	6·098	6·103	6·024	6·061	5·806
Ca	0·058	0·163	0·025	0·099	0·047	0·178
K	1·489	1·699	1·504	1·683	1·610	0·927
$\sum R$	7·55	8·12	7·66	7·91	7·76	7·08
Ne	75·7	76·1	75·5	75·3	75·2	74·8
Ks	21·1	23·6	21·8	23·2	22·2	13·2
Q	3·2	0·3	2·7	1·5	2·6	12·0

8. Nepheline, nepheline-syenite pegmatite, Shinjozan, Fukushinzan district, Korea (Miyashiro & Miyashiro, 1955). Anal. N. Saito (Includes Cl 0·09).
9. Nepheline, foyaite, Pilansberg, Transvaal (Tilley, 1956). Anal. J. H. Scoon (Includes MnO 0·07).
10. Nepheline, cancrinite ijolite, Iivaara, Finland (Lehijärvi, 1956). Anal. M. Lehijärvi (Includes FeO 0·29).
11. Nepheline, nephelinite, Etinde, Cameroons (Tilley, 1953). Anal. J. H. Scoon.
12. Nepheline, biotite nepheline-syenite, Blue Mountain, Methuen Township, Ontario (Tilley, 1952a). Anal J. H. Scoon (Includes MnO < 0·01).
13. Nepheline, phonolite, Nairobi, Kenya (Bowen & Ellestad, 1936). Anal R. B. Ellestad.

† Includes Mn 0·012.
‡ Includes Fe^{+2} 0·047.

Table 29.   NEPHELINE ANALYSES—*continued*

	14.	15.	16.	17.	18.	19.	20.
SiO_2	41·06	42·23	41·52	43·55	43·97	40·74	40·20
TiO_2	0·00	0·00	—	—	—	0·11	0·05
Al_2O_3	33·93	34·08	34·09	34·66	32·89	33·39	32·51
Fe_2O_3	0·83	0·12	0·79	—	—	0·83	1·82
MgO	0·00	0·00	—	0·05	—	0·25	0·10
CaO	0·19	0·15	0·06	4·44	0·43	0·91	1·44
Na_2O	15·92	16·21	15·76	12·09	15·73	12·53	10·86
K_2O	7·14	7·12	6·85	4·87	5·45	11·13	12·22
H_2O^+	0·74	—	0·55	0·25	—	0·23	0·00
H_2O^-	0·00	0·03	—	0·25	—	0·06	0·00
Total	99·81	99·94	99·65	100·16	98·47	100·18	99·77
ϵ	—	—	1·539	1·5266	—	—	1·539
ω	—	—	1·543	1·5299	—	—	1·543

NUMBERS OF IONS ON THE BASIS OF 32 OXYGENS

Si	8·049	8·176	8·105	8·293	8·513	8·036	8·014
Al	7·840	7·779	7·846	7·781	7·506	7·764	7·641
Ti	—	—	—	—	—	0·016	0·007
Fe^{+3}	0·122	0·016	0·116	—	—	0·123	0·369†
Mg	—	—	—	0·014	—	0·074	0·030
Na	6·050	6·085	5·966	4·463	5·903	4·796	4·198
Ca	0·040	0·031	0·013	0·906	0·090	0·192	0·308
K	1·786	1·759	1·706	1·183	1·348	2·802	3·108
$\sum R$	8·12	7·91	7·70	7·46	7·43	7·98	7·92
Ne	74·8	74·4	73·5	72·7	75·1	60·2	54·7
Ks	24·5	24·1	23·5	21·5	19·1	39·2	45·3
Q	0·7	1·5	3·0	5·8	5·8	0·6	—

14. Nepheline, nepheline-syenite, Assynt, Sutherland, Scotland (Tilley, 1956). Anal. J. H. Scoon.
15. Nepheline, nepheline-syenite (mariupolite) dyke, Vaal River, Transvaal (Tilley, 1953).   Anal. J. H. Scoon.
16. Nepheline, complex pegmatite, Bearpaw Mountains, Montana (Pecora, 1942). Anal. F. A. Gonyer (Includes BaO 0·03).
17. Nepheline, on block containing augite, biotite, hornblende, sanidine and vesuvianite, Monte Somma, Italy (Bannister & Hey, 1931).   Anal. M. H. Hey.
18. Nepheline, average of 16 nephelines from nepheline-syenites (Chirvinsky, 1953).
19. Nepheline, nephelinite, Lake Kivu, Congo (Bowen & Ellestad, 1936).   Anal. R. B. Ellestad.
20. Nepheline, potash ankaratrite, Mt. Nyiragongo, Congo (Sahama, 1952).   Anal. Th. G. Sahama (Includes FeO 0·57).

† Includes Fe^{+2} 0·096.

system $NaAlSiO_4$–$NaAlSi_3O_8$–H_2O, MacKenzie (1954) gave the minimum melting temperature as 870°C.[1] at 1000 bars at the composition $Ne_{28}Ab_{72}$; the limit of nepheline–albite solid solution at 750°C. and a water pressure of 1000 bars is $Ne_{75}Ab_{25}$.

Saha (1961) has determined the P,T curve of the transition nepheline hydrate I + water = nepheline + water. Below the P,T-curve nepheline hydrate I crystallizes readily from runs made with glass of $NaAlSiO_4$ composition. Attempts to synthesize nepheline hydrate I by the reaction of nepheline crystals with water below the curve, however, resulted in the formation of analcite; in runs made in the lower stability range of nepheline hydrate I grains of paragonite appeared, and Saha concluded that nepheline is not stable below 400° to 500°C. at moderate to high pressure in the presence of excess water. The phase equilibrium relations in the system nepheline–water have been discussed by Morey (1957).

From a study of the nepheline–kalsilite system Tuttle and Smith (1958) have shown that, whereas compositions between Ne_{100} and $Ne_{37.5}$ at temperatures above 1070°C. consist of a single-phase solid solution which can be quenched to room temperature without unmixing, compositions between $Ne_{37.5}$ and $Ne_{0.0}$ do not consist of a single-phase solid solution (Fig. 79). The complete

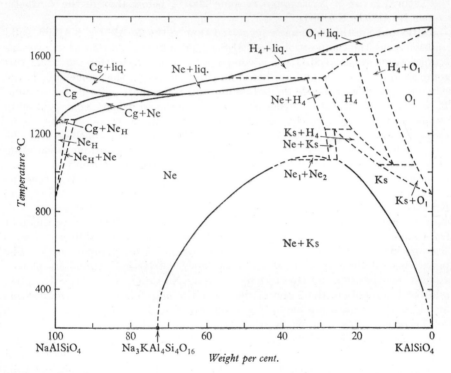

Fig. 79. Phase diagram of the system $NaAlSiO_4$–$KAlSiO_4$. Inferred phase boundaries are shown by broken lines. Cg carnegieite, Ne_H high-temperature nepheline, Ne low-temperature nepheline, Ks kalsilite, H_4 tetrakalsilite, O_1 orthorhombic kalsilite (after Tuttle and Smith, 1958).

[1] More recent work indicates that this temperature should be 835°C.

solid solution at high temperature, originally described by Bowen (1917), is thus replaced by a miscibility gap (solvus) at lower temperatures. The maximum temperature of the solvus is 1070°C. at a composition close to Ne_{30}; thus 1070°C. is the minimum temperature at which Ne_{30} can exist as a stable phase. Compositions between $Ne_{73\cdot0}$ and $Ne_{0\cdot0}$ have a different minimum temperature of stable existence as given by the solvus, and under equilibrium conditions intergrowths of nepheline and kalsilite will form at the appropriate temperature on cooling. The unmixing of nepheline solid solutions is thus comparable with the formation of alkali felspar intergrowths, and in the same manner that the felspar intergrowths can be homogenized by heating, so also can nepheline-kalsilite solid solutions. The discontinuity at higher temperatures between the nepheline and kalsilite solid solutions in the composition range Ne_{30} to Ne_{20} is indicated by a structural change and is marked by a hiatus at the top of the solvus.

In contrast with the data for the synthetic system $NaAlSiO_4$–$KAlSiO_4$, Sahama (1957) has shown from heating experiments on complex phenocrysts (average composition approximately 70 weight per cent. $KAlSiO_4$) of the Nyiragongo lava (see p. 265) that the temperature of the reaction tetrakalsilite ⇌nepheline–kalsilite "perthite" is about 800°C.; thus the effective solvus in the natural lavas of Nyiragongo is some 200°C. below that in the synthetic system $NaAlSiO_4$–$KAlSiO_4$.

Tuttle and Smith (1958) have suggested that in the $NaAlSiO_4$–$KAlSiO_4$ solid solution series the composition $Na_3KAl_4Si_4O_{16}$ is unique, and that at sub-solidus temperatures $Na_3KAl_4Si_4O_{16}$ is a compound. The reasons for regarding this composition as a compound are based on the assumption that some sites in the structure are more suitable for potassium and some more suitable for sodium. Thus the $Na_3KAl_4Si_4O_{16}$ structure may be modified when some potassium atoms occupy sites normally occupied only by sodium atoms, or when some sodium atoms occupy potassium sites. Tuttle and Smith consider that the uniqueness of this composition is also manifested by the discontinuous variation in the lattice parameters of the series, the common approximation to this composition shown by nephelines from plutonic rocks, and the observation that the sodium-rich side of the sub-solidus immiscibility gap between $NaAlSiO_4$ and $KAlSiO_4$ approaches this composition at low temperatures but does not cross it. Thus the solid solution of $NaAlSiO_4$ in $Na_3KAl_4Si_4O_{16}$ is believed to be different from the solid solution of $KAlSiO_4$ in $Na_3KAl_4Si_4O_{16}$ because different atomic sites are involved; i.e. there are two binary systems at low temperatures. The persistence of the change in slope of the curve of lattice parameters plotted against composition in the ternary system $NaAlSiO_4$–$KAlSiO_4$–SiO_2 gives additional support to these arguments, since the uniqueness of the composition at which all six sites suitable for Na atoms are filled is retained in the omission solid solution series from $Na_6K_2Al_8Si_8O_{32}$ to $Na_6\square_2Al_6Si_{10}O_{32}$.

In the system $NaAlSiO_4$–$KAlSiO_4$–SiO_2 (Fig. 80) a large field of nepheline solid solution crystallization is present in the area between the alkali felspar join and that of $NaAlSiO_4$–$KAlSiO_4$ (Schairer, 1950). The nepheline solid solutions are separated from the field of orthorhombic $(K,Na)AlSiO_4$ solid solution at about 65 per cent. $NaAlSiO_4$ for compositions without excess SiO_2, and at 80 per cent. $NaAlSiO_4$ for compositions containing approximately 15 per cent. excess SiO_2.

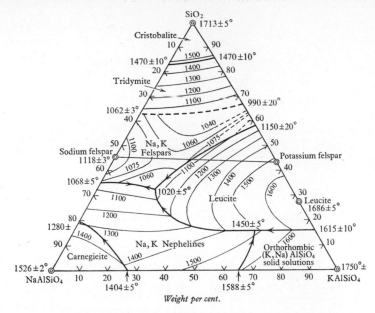

FIG. 80. Phase diagram for the system NaAlSiO₄–KAlSiO₄–SiO₂ (after Schairer, 1950).

Tuttle and Smith (1958) have illustrated the probable stability relations in the nepheline–kalsilite–quartz system at different temperatures in four iso-thermal, isobaric diagrams. The relations at temperatures above the nepheline–kalsilite solvus (Fig. 81a) show an extensive range of nepheline solid solution compositions, a three-phase region in which potassium felspar solid solution, leucite, and nepheline solid solution coexist, and three two-phase regions: one with felspar solid solution in equilibrium with nepheline solid solution, a second in which felspar solid solution and leucite are in equilibrium, and a third in which leucite is in equilibrium with nepheline–kalsilite solid solution. The probable relationship at a temperature below the maximum of the nepheline–kalsilite solvus but above the albite–potassium felspar solvus is shown in Fig. 81b. The field of nepheline solid solution is smaller in this temperature range, and there is a second compositional field in which three solid phases, leucite, kalsilite solid solution and nepheline solid solution, coexist. At temperatures below the alkali felspar solvus a third three-phase region appears, in which potassium felspar solid solution, albite solid solution, and nepheline solid solution coexist, and the range of nepheline solid solution is further reduced (Fig. 81c). Tuttle and Smith suggested that the low temperatures at which the latter three-phase relations occur may be comparable with those of the final crystallization of nepheline-syenites. An alternative diagram (Fig. 81d) of the possible phase relations at low temperatures shows $Na_3KAl_4Si_4O_{16}$ as a unique composition in the nepheline–kalsilite solid solutions, and an immiscibility gap between $Na_3KAl_4Si_4O_{16}$ and $NaAlSiO_4$. In volcanic rocks nepheline solid solutions have a wide range of composition, and the phase relationships illustrated in Fig. 81 indicate that the following phases may possibly develop from the unmixing of

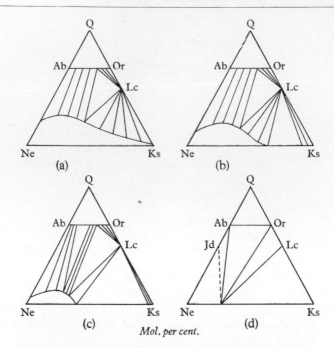

Mol. per cent.

Fig. 81. Schematic isothermal, isobaric, diagram for the
nepheline–kalsilite–quartz system showing the probable
phases at different temperatures.   a. Temperature above
the nepheline–kalsilite solvus.   b. Temperature below
the top of the nepheline–kalsilite solvus but above the
albite–orthoclase miscibility gap.   c. Temperature below
the top of the felspar miscibility gap.   d. Section at
low temperature in which a miscibility gap between
$Na_3KAl_4Si_4O_{16}$ and $NaAlSiO_4$ is postulated.   Jadeite will
appear at high pressures and, if nepheline is stable at this
pressure, the join jadeite–nepheline will be present (after
Tuttle and Smith, 1958).

nepheline solid solutions; nepheline + kalsilite, nepheline + kalsilite + leucite,
nepheline + leucite, nepheline + leucite + potassium felspar, nepheline + potassium felspar, nepheline + potassium felspar + albite, nepheline + albite.

Hamilton and MacKenzie (1960) investigated the limits of nepheline solid
solutions in the system $NaAlSiO_4$–$KAlSiO_4$–SiO_2–H_2O at 700 °C. and a water
pressure of 15,000 lb./in.², and suggested that an approximate temperature for
the establishment of equilibrium in a nepheline–alkali felspar assemblage is
provided by this field boundary.   Hamilton (1961) later determined the limits
of nepheline solid solutions at 500° and 775 °C. (Fig. 82) and thus provided a
more precise temperature scale for the varying amounts of excess SiO_2 in natural
nephelines.   The approximate limit of nepheline solid solution at 1068 °C. is
also shown in the figure, its position being determined from the limit of nepheline
solid solution in the system $NaAlSiO_4$–$NaAlSi_3O_8$ (Greig and Barth, 1938), and
the limit of nepheline solid solution at 1008 °C. in the system $NaAlSiO_4$–$KAlSiO_4$
(Tuttle and Smith, 1958).

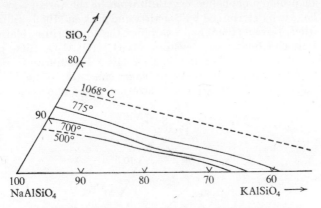

FIG. 82. Part of the triangular diagram NaAlSiO₄–KAlSiO₄–SiO₂ showing the limits of nepheline solid solution at 500°, 700° and 775°C. The upper broken line represents the approximate limit of nepheline solid solution at 1068°C. (after Hamilton, 1961).

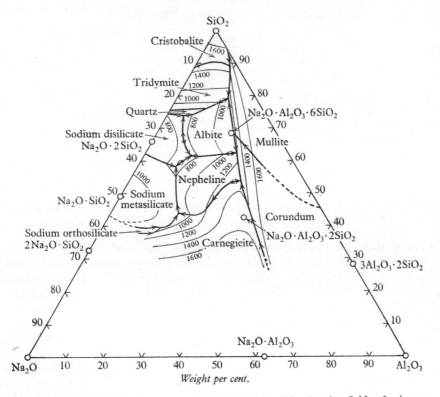

FIG. 83. Phase diagram for the system Na₂O–Al₂O₃–SiO₂ showing fields of primary crystalline phases and isotherms (after Schairer and Bowen, 1956).

The field of primary nepheline crystallization in the ternary system Na_2O–Al_2O_3–SiO_2 has been determined by Schairer and Bowen (1956) and is shown in Fig. 83. Earlier, Bowen (1945) had examined the equilibrium relations of those compositions in the quaternary system Na_2O–CaO–Al_2O_3–SiO_2 pertinent to the formation of nepheline-bearing basic rocks. Equilibrium crystallization for such compositions gives rise to assemblages consisting of nepheline, melilite and wollastonite, and fractional crystallization gives nepheline, wollastonite

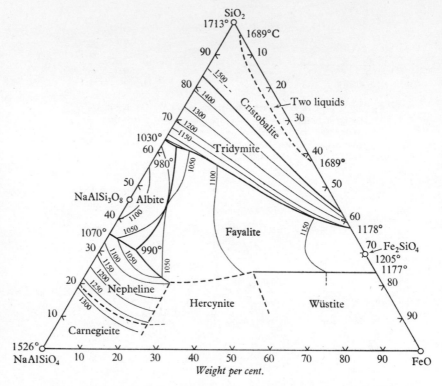

Fig. 84. Phase diagram for the system $NaAlSiO_4$–FeO–SiO_2 (after Bowen and Schairer, 1938).

and plagioclase of increasing albite content, these two assemblages approximating in mineral content to melilite nephelinite, and tephrite or phonolite respectively. The results of a series of phase equilibrium studies of the linear and triangular joins $NaAlSiO_4$–$CaSiO_3$–$NaAlSi_3O_8$, $NaAlSiO_4$–$CaSiO_3$–$CaAl_2Si_2O_8$, $NaAlSiO_4$–$CaSiO_3$–Na_2SiO_3, $NaAlSiO_4$–$Ca_2Al_2SiO_7$, $NaAlSiO_4$–$CaAl_2Si_2O_8$–$Ca_2Al_2SiO_7$, $NaAlSiO_4$–$CaSiO_3$–$Ca_2Al_2SiO_7$ and $NaAlSiO_4$–$CaO\cdot Al_2O_3$ in the quaternary system Na_2O–CaO–Al_2O_3–SiO_2 have been summarized by Schairer and Bowen (1956).

In the system $NaAlSiO_4$–FeO–SiO_2 (Fig. 84), nepheline, albite and fayalite form a ternary eutectic at 990 °C.; the eutectic proportions of the three phases are comparable with the content of these minerals in fayalite phonolites (Bowen and Schairer, 1938). The phase relations in mixtures of nepheline and diopside have been investigated by Bowen (1922) who showed that compositions consisting of less than 80 per cent. of either component behave as a two-component mixture at high temperatures. Intermediate compositions, however, have a more complex cooling history, *e.g.* crystallization of composition 30 per cent. nepheline and 70 per cent. diopside begins with the separation of forsterite at 1260°C., followed at 1240°C. by the crystallization of diopside and the resorption of forsterite. The latter process continues with cooling to 1180°C. at which

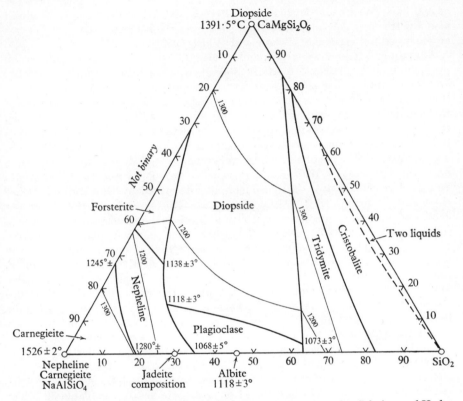

Fig. 85. Phase diagram for the system nepheline–diopside–silica (after Schairer and Yoder, 1960).

temperature melilite, $Ca_2MgSi_2O_7$, crystallizes; the reaction which takes place when $NaAlSiO_4$ is added to diopside may thus be illustrated by the equation:

$$8CaMgSi_2O_6 + 3NaAlSiO_4 = 4Ca_2MgSi_2O_7 + 2Mg_2SiO_4 + 3NaAlSi_3O_8$$
$$\text{diopside} \qquad \text{nepheline} \qquad \text{melilite} \qquad \text{forsterite} \qquad \text{albite}$$

Similarly, for some compositions in the system nepheline–diopside–silica (Fig. 85), forsterite occurs as a primary phase and is resorbed at lower temperatures by reaction with the liquid; melilite, however, was not detected at any temperatures in mixtures in the ternary system.

In the system nepheline–calcite, the intermediate compound, cancrinite, melts incongruently under a carbon dioxide pressure of 110 bars to nepheline and liquid (Eitel, 1923).

In addition to the crystallization of nepheline in the various synthetic systems, the mineral has been synthesized in relatively large crystals (up to 7 mm. in diameter and 1 to 2 mm. in thickness) by mixing the stoichiometric proportions of oxides with LiF and sodium silico-fluorides at temperatures above 1200°C. (Winkler, 1947). Nephelines of compositions $K_{0.19}Na_{0.84}Al_{1.05}Si_{0.99}O_4 \cdot \frac{1}{3}H_2O$ (a 9·88, c 8·26 Å) and $K_{0.31}Na_{0.75}Al_{1.02}Si_{0.96}O_4 \cdot 0.15H_2O$ (a 10·3, c 8·35 Å) have been synthesized hydrothermally, from mixtures having the composition $Na_xK_{1-x}AlSiO_4$ (where $x=0.6$ to 0·8), at 415°C. and water vapour pressure of 400 bars (Wyart and Michel Lévy, 1949). Nepheline has been crystallized also by treating gels of composition $Na_2O \cdot Al_2O_3 \cdot 1{-}12SiO_2 + aq$. with excess aqueous sodium carbonate (Barrer and White 1952).

Alteration. Nepheline is frequently altered, and the common alteration products include analcite, cancrinite, sodalite and the fibrous zeolites, natrolite and thomsonite. Nepheline also alters to a colourless mica, possibly paragonite, the basal plane of which is frequently oriented parallel to the {0001} cleavage of the nepheline. The terms gieseckite and hydronepheline are commonly used to describe the green and pink alteration products of nepheline; both consist of fine-grained micaceous aggregates containing two or more individual minerals. The alteration of nepheline to white, very fine-grained, fibrous hydronepheline has been described by Walker and Parsons (1926), Tilley and Harwood (1931) and by Jérémine (1948). A hydronepheline described by Dunham (1933) has the composition SiO_2 43·31, Al_2O_3 29·92, CaO 3·27, Na_2O 11·66, H_2O 12·38 per cent. and probably consists of natrolite and an unidentified pseudo-hexagonal mineral (Oftedahl, 1952). A light blue-green microscopically opaque alteration product of nepheline in a melanite melteigite (Eckermann, 1948) has been identified as a mixture of haüyne and nosean. The partial alteration of nepheline to cancrinite, sodalite and hackmanite occurs locally in the nepheline gneisses of southeastern Ontario (Moyd, 1949). In these rocks nepheline is also altered by low temperature hydrothermal activity to natrolite, muscovite, hydronepheline and gieseckite; in this area the latter alteration products are associated with joints and other openings of comparatively late origin. The alteration of nepheline is discussed by Saha (1961) with particular reference to hydrothermal studies in the system $NaAlSiO_4{-}NaAlSi_3O_8{-}H_2O$.

Kalsilite Analyses of five kalsilite and kalsilite solid solutions, together with the numbers of ions of the basis of 32 oxygens, are detailed in Table 30. The general chemistry of the kalsilite solid solutions is similar to that of the nepheline solid solutions except that, from the evidence of the small number of available analyses, the content of Si is more restricted, and the range of $Al \rightleftharpoons Fe^{+3}$ substitution is more extensive in the kalsilite solid solutions; the kalsilite analyses all show some cation deficiency.

Roedder (1951) has synthesized a compound, $K_2O \cdot MgO \cdot 3SiO_2$, which is structurally similar to kalsilite. Although in the latter mineral magnesium is usually present only in small quantities, it is possible that MgSi may substitute for 2Al.

Wyart (1947), and Wyart and Michel-Lévy (1949), synthesized kalsilite from the theoretical proportions of SiO_2, Al_2O_3 and KOH in the absence of sodium, from mixtures of SiO_2, Al_2O_3, KOH and NaOH, and by interaction of muscovite, silica and KOH in aqueous solution at pressures above 300 bars at temperatures below 500°C. Earlier Rigby and Richardson (1947) had stated that they could

Table 30. KALSILITE ANALYSES

	1.	2.	3.	4.	5.
SiO_2	37·89	38·48	37·98	38·47	38·50
TiO_2	0·19	0·05	0·05	0·00	0·09
Al_2O_3	32·60	31·01	31·73	30·81	26·27
Fe_2O_3	1·26	1·12	0·98	1·63	5·07
FeO	0·00	—	—	0·26	0·53
MnO	0·01	0·01	0·01	0·00	0·02
MgO	0·29	0·00	0·00	0·63	0·87
CaO	0·21	0·03	0·00	0·20	0·44
Na_2O	0·00	0·30	0·87	2·09	2·07
K_2O	27·88	28·33	27·99	25·65	24·85
H_2O^+	0·00	0·67	0·40	0·20	1·04
H_2O^-	0·00	—	—	0·00	0·05
Total	100·33	100·00	100·01	99·94	99·80
ϵ	1·532	1·533	1·534	1·537	1·550
ω	1·538	1·539	1·539	1·543	1·554
D	—	—	—	2·625	2·663

NUMBERS OF IONS ON THE BASIS OF 32 OXYGENS

	1.	2.	3.	4.	5.
Si	7·898	8·125	7·997	8·044	8·212
Al	8·009	7·720	7·879	7·596	6·607
Ti	0·030	0·008	0·008	—	0·014
Fe^{+3}	0·197	0·178	0·077	0·256	0·814
Mg	0·090	—	—	0·196	0·276
Fe^{+2}	—	—	—	0·045	0·094
Mn	0·002	0·002	0·002	—	0·004
Na	—	0·123	0·355	0·847	0·856
Ca	0·047	0·006	—	0·045	0·100
K	7·413	7·635	7·523	6·846	6·766
$\sum R$	7·51	7·77	7·88	7·78	7·820
Ks	98·1	96·8	95·3	88·9	88·1
Ne	—	1·4	4·1	9·9	10·0
Q	1·9	1·8	0·6	1·2	1·9

1. Kalsilite, synthetic, blast furnace lining (Sahama *et al.*, 1956). Anal. H. B. Wiik.
2. Kalsilite, complex phenocryst of kalsilite and nepheline, lava of Baruta crater, Nyiragongo area, Congo (Sahama *et al.*, 1956). Anal. P. Ojanperä (Analysis recalculated after correcting for 10 per cent. nepheline, 31·1 atomic per cent. K : (K + Na + Ca) in sample ; total iron as Fe_2O_3).
3. Kalsilite, kalsilite fraction of kalsilitic perthite, fallen block, Baruta crater, Nyiragongo area, Congo (Sahama *et al*, 1956). Anal. P. Ojanperä (Analysis recalculated after correcting for 22·7 per cent. nepheline, 30·2 atomic per cent. K : (K + Na + Ca) ; total iron as Fe_2O_3).
4. Kalsilite, venanzite, San Venanzo, Umbria, Italy (Bannister *et al.*, 1953). Anal. H. B. Wiik.
5. Kalsilite, mafurite, Kyambogo crater, Bunyaruguru field, southwestern Uganda (Sahama, 1954). Anal. H. B. Wiik.

obtain kalsilite by dry synthesis only in the presence of sodium. They found, however, that from the correct proportions of SiO_2, Al_2O_3 and K_2O, to which 1·5 per cent. Na_2O was added, some kalsilite formed at 1100° and 1200°C., and that with the addition of 2 and 5 per cent. Na_2O to the mixture kalsilite formed readily at temperatures above 650°C. Tuttle and Smith (1958) have prepared kalsilite hydrothermally from mixtures of potassium disilicate and alumina at temperatures below 840°C. as well as from the high-temperature orthorhombic polymorph of $KAlSiO_4$. During their investigation of the nepheline–kalsilite system, Tuttle and Smith showed that kalsilite can take approximately 25 per cent. $NaAlSiO_4$ in solid solution.

Table 31. KALIOPHILITE ANALYSES

	1.	2.	3.
SiO_2	39·04	38·0	39·2
Al_2O_3	31·96	28·8	33·36
Fe_2O_3	0·98	—	—
MgO	0·15	—	—
CaO	0·33	0·5	0·47
Na_2O	3·89	tr.	2·88
K_2O	22·84	32·2	24·13
H_2O^+	0·60	—	—
Total	99·79	99·5	100·04
ϵ	1·5273	1·527	1·5258
ω	1·5316	1·531	1·5296
D	2·61	2·598	2·606

NUMBERS OF IONS ON THE BASIS OF 32 OXYGENS

	1.	2.	3.
Si	8·079	8·21	8·040
Al	7·798	7·35	8·060
Fe^{+3}	0·152	—	—
Mg	0·046	—	—
Na	1·560	—	1·142
Ca	0·073	0·12	0·103
K	6·034	8·88	6·311

1. Kaliophilite, in ejected blocks, Monte Somma, Vesuvius, Italy (Mügge, 1927). Anal. N. Sahlbom.
2. & 3. Kaliophilite, in cavities in augite and biotite block, Monte Somma, Vesuvius Italy (Bannister & Hey, 1931). Anal. M. H. Hey.

Orthorhombic $KAlSiO_4$ is the stable form at high temperature; some replacement of K by Na occurs, and it is probable that between 10 and 20 per cent. $NaAlSiO_4$ can be taken into solid solution. The inversion kalsilite ⇌ orthorhombic $KAlSiO_4$ (O_1) is sluggish, and the high-temperature form (orthorhombic $KAlSiO_4$) can be preserved at normal temperatures by quenching. Tuttle and Smith (1958) have also described a second orthorhombic $KAlSiO_4$ (O_2) phase (b 10·5 Å). This phase, associated with glass, was obtained from charges of Ne_{20} composition heated above 1520°C. and quenched. The composition of the crystals is not known but they are probably close to Ne_{15}. A new sodium kalsilite phase, tetrakalsilite, has been described by Tuttle and Smith. This phase was obtained by heating a glass, Ne_{30} in composition, at 1520°C. for six hours, and the provisional composition is given by Tuttle and Smith as $K_3NaAl_4Si_4O_{16}$ (23 weight per cent. $NaAlSiO_4$). It is probable, however, that the composition of this phase varies a little on either side of the 3:1 K:Na ratio. The field of tetrakalsilite in the system $NaAlSiO_4$–$KAlSiO_4$ is shown in Fig. 79, but the precise extent of the stability field is uncertain.

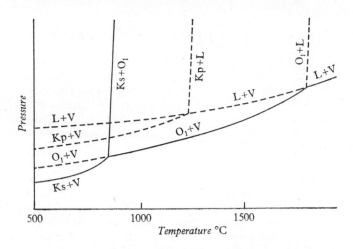

FIG. 86. Schematic *PT* diagram for $KAlSiO_4$ showing the probable interrelations of the various polymorphic modifications. Broken lines represent metastable equilibria. Ks, kalsilite; O_1, orthorhombic kalsilite; Kp, kaliophilite; L, liquid; V, vapour (after Tuttle and Smith, 1958).

The replacement of K by Na in kalsilite is accompanied by an increase in the inversion temperature of both kalsilite $\rightleftharpoons$ orthorhombic (K,Na)$AlSiO_4$ and kalsilite$\rightleftharpoons$tetrakalsilite. Synthetic preparations in the compositional range Ne_{30} to Ne_0 are inhomogeneous, and leucite is usually present in small quantities; the experimental results show some inconsistencies and the phase relations at the top of the solvus illustrated in Fig. 79 are approximate only, and are designed to represent the probable stability field for tetrakalsilite and to show the break in the nepheline–kalsilite solid solutions.

A further (K,Na)$AlSiO_4$ mineral, trikalsilite (a 15·4 Å), from a lava, has been reported by Sahama and Smith (1957). Its composition is unknown but is probably similar in range to that of tetrakalsilite. A schematic pressure–temperature diagram showing the probable relationship of some of the polymorphic modifications of $KAlSiO_4$ is given in Fig. 86.

Kaliophilite. The chemistry of kaliophilite (Table 31) does not differ significantly from that of kalsilite. Some replacement of K by Na is shown by the analyses, and as with kalsilite some cation deficiency occurs. The dry synthesis of kaliophilite (at 1075°C.) was reported by Bowen (1917), and Rigby and Richardson (1947) have prepared crystals of kaliophilite by heating china clay and potassium carbonate at temperatures between 900° and 1300°C. Kaliophilite was synthesized by Tuttle and Smith (1958) during their investigation of the nepheline–kalsilite system, the kaliophilite crystallizing from mixtures of $Ne_{10}Ks_{90}$ composition heated at 1000° to 1100°C. and a water vapour pressure of 500 bars. The synthetic material is not identical with natural kaliophilite, and Tuttle and Smith suggested that it is probably a disordered form of kaliophilite. The same authors are of the opinion that kaliophilite is a metastable phase at all temperatures at atmospheric pressure.

OPTICAL AND PHYSICAL PROPERTIES

A detailed study of the relationship between the optical properties and chemical composition of nephelines by Bannister and Hey (1931) showed that, although the substitution of sodium by potassium tends to increase the refractive indices, the effect is small. The correlation, moreover, is not precise, and some nephelines with a relatively high content of potassium do not have higher indices than others with smaller amounts; the refractive indices are also affected by omission solid solution. Solid solution of $CaO \cdot Al_2O_3$ in synthetic nephelines is accompanied by an increase in refractive indices (Goldsmith, 1949). The ϵ index increases at a greater rate than ω, and at approximately 20 weight per cent. $CaO \cdot Al_2O_3$ the crystals are isotropic. Solid solutions with higher contents of $CaO \cdot Al_2O_3$ are optically positive, and the refractive indices of the solid solution containing 60 weight per cent. $CaO \cdot Al_2O_3$ are ϵ 1·600, ω 1·593. The dispersive power, $P = (n_F - n_C)/(n_{Na} - 1)$, of four nephelines has been measured by Bannister and Hey (1931), and is approximately 0·016 for both P_ω and P_ϵ.

The change in birefringence, on heating, of the nepheline margin, and of the kalsilite or of the homogenized phase of the core, of nepheline–kalsilite phenocrysts of the Kabfumu lava, Nyiragongo, Congo, has been reported by Sahama (1957). More detailed measurements of birefringence at different temperatures indicate the existence, in the medio- and perpotassic nephelines, of two structural types and a continuous gradation between them (Sahama, 1962). The two types probably represent different degrees of Si,Al ordering. For type I (the ordered form) birefringence is high at room temperature and decreases on heating, and for type II (disordered) it is low at room temperature and increases on heating. Birefringence is, however, also influenced by the Na:K ratio.

The replacement of sodium by potassium increases the density of nepheline solid solutions, but due to variation in the number of silicon and aluminium atoms and in the value of $\sum R (= Na + K + 2Ca)$, the measurement of density is not a useful method for estimating compositions.

Details of a number of occurences of zoned nepheline in phonolites have been summarized by Shand (1939), who concluded that the zoning is due to the rhythmic deposition of nepheline layers containing alternately more and less silicon, and is not related to variable contents of either potassium or sodium. Nepheline crystals in the Wolf Rock phonolite show a narrow peripheral zone of lower refraction and birefringence, considered by Tilley (1959) probably to indicate a more siliceous composition. A method of measuring very small differences in birefringence between successive zones in nepheline is discussed by Sahama (1959).

A petrofabric study of the orientation of nepheline in a litchfieldite from Blue Mountain, Ontario (Fairbairn, 1941), showed that the *z*-axes are concentrated in the S-surface, and in particular are parallel with the lineation. In this rock the S-surface is marked by a dimensional orientation of the associated albite, the (010) plane of which is parallel with the foliation. Preferred orientation of nepheline in nepheline-syenite gneisses has been described by Sturt (1961).

The optical properties of carnegieite are $2V_\alpha$ 12° to 15°, α 1·509, β 1·514, γ 1·514; the density is 2·513 gm./cm.^{3} (Bowen, 1917).

The refractive indices of kalsilite overlap those of the more potassium-rich nepheline solid solutions, and kalsilite cannot be distinguished from them by optical measurements.

The refractive indices of kaliophilite also fall within the range of the indices of potassium-rich nepheline solid solutions but are a little lower than those of kalsilite. The indices of synthetic kaliophilite are ϵ 1·527, ω 1·532. The dispersion of the Monte Somma kaliophilite (Table 31, anal. 3) has been measured by Bannister and Hey (1931): the dispersive power $P = (n_F - n_C)/(n_{Na} - 1)$ is 0·016.

DISTINGUISHING FEATURES

The main diagnostic features of nepheline are its low birefringence and poor cleavage, which, together with its uniaxial character, distinguish it from the alkali felspars; also nepheline is readily soluble in HCl. Apatite and melilite have a similar range of birefringence, but both have higher refringence. Scapolites rich in the marialitic component have higher refractive indices, and, with increasing meionitic content, higher birefringence. Analcite and sodalite are isotropic, and leucite characteristically displays complex twinning. A staining technique by which nepheline may be distinguished from leucite, sodalite and analcite using phosphoric acid and methylene blue has been described by Shand (1939).

In complex nepheline–kalsilite phenocrysts the optical properties of the two phases are not greatly different, but, provided the two phases are in parallel orientation, they can usually be distinguished from each other by the slightly lower refractive indices, and by the somewhat higher birefringence of the kalsilite phase. When the boundaries between the two phases are irregular they may be more easily identified by increasing the contrast in interference colour by using a rotating (elliptical) mica compensator (Sahama, 1959). The distinction between the two phases in complex phenocrysts is also facilitated by the usually clear appearance of the kalsilite phase, which is in contrast to the common occurrence of minute inclusions in the nepheline phase. When nepheline and kalsilite occur as individual grains the difference in refraction and birefringence is too small to distinguish the two minerals in thin section. Nepheline and kalsilite may be distinguished by their X-ray powder patterns.

17.—R.F.M. IV.

PARAGENESIS

Nepheline

Nepheline is the characteristic mineral of the alkaline rocks, and is the most common of the felspathoid minerals. It is associated with alkali felspars in the nepheline-syenites and nepheline gneisses and with plagioclase in rocks of the alkali gabbro clan. In the basic alkaline and ultra-alkaline rocks nepheline occurs together with the common ferromagnesian minerals, olivine, augite and diopside, as well as with sodium-rich pyroxenes and amphiboles, but is not found in association with orthopyroxene or pigeonite. It occurs with melilite, monticellite and wollastonite in some calcium-rich basic rocks, and with leucite in some potassium-rich hypabyssal and volcanic rocks. There are three common nepheline parageneses; it forms as a primary phase of magmatic crystallization, as a product of metasomatism (nephelinization), and as a result of reaction (contamination) of both basic and acid magmas with calcium-rich sediments. Of those specimens studied by Sahama (1962), plutonic nephelines are of type I (ordered) and volcanic nephelines range between type I and type II (disordered), see p. 256.

Igneous rocks. Nephelines occur in many alkaline rocks, especially in the European plateau, *e.g.* Oslo (Brøgger, 1933), Alnö (Högbom, 1895, Eckermann, 1948), Almunge (Quensel, 1914), Särna (Magnusson, 1925), Norra Kärr (Adamson, 1944), Kuusamo and Kuolajärvi (Hackman, 1900, 1925), Kola peninsula (Ramsay, 1899; Fersman, 1937; Kupletsky, 1937) and the Mariupol Massif (Morozewicz, 1929, Luchitzky and Lebedev, 1934). A comparative study of these nepheline-bearing rocks has been presented by Polański (1949).

The compositions of nephelines of nepheline-syenites and nepheline gneisses range approximately between $Ne_{73}Ks_{27}$ weight per cent., the Buerger ideal nepheline composition, and $Ne_{75}Ks_{21}Q_4$, the composition originally suggested for rock-forming nephelines by Morozewicz (1928); this compositional range Tilley (1954) has named the Morozewicz-Buerger convergence field. In nepheline-syenites and nepheline gneisses, nepheline is associated with low-temperature felspars of the albite–microcline series. In volcanic rocks the composition of the nepheline varies more widely in response to the different composition of the host rock, and compared with nephelines of plutonic paragenesis includes more sodium- and more potassium-rich varieties (see Table 29); in these rocks the associated felspars belong to the high-temperature anorthoclase–sanidine series. This contrast in nephelines which crystallized in chemically similar but physically different environments is related to the nepheline structure, nephelines approaching the ideal composition $Na_3KAl_4Si_4O_{16}$ being characteristically associated with lower temperatures of crystallization; at higher temperatures the tolerance of both alkali sites of the structure for greater departures from the $Na_3KAl_4Si_4O_{16}$ composition is increased.

The relationships between the compositions of the nepheline and the co-existing alkali felspar phases, and the normative salic composition of the host rock, have been investigated by Tilley (1952a, 1954, 1956): see also Miyashiro (1951). Recrystallization, due either to slow cooling of plutonic rocks or to metamorphism, may be expected to lead to an adjustment of the nepheline composition attained at higher temperatures, towards the convergence field. Thus in nephelines of phonolite parentage such a change would involve the formation of a less silicon-rich nepheline and a decrease in the Na:K ratio; the accompanying change in the associated felspar involves the formation of albite–microcline from the single high-temperature felspar. These changes, expressed in terms of phase equilibria, are equivalent to the removal of albite and adjustment to a more potassium-rich nepheline:

sodium-rich nepheline + anorthoclase→Na,K nepheline + albite + microcline

(volcanic association)   (plutonic and metamorphic association)

Compositional changes in nephelines crystallizing under plutonic conditions have also been discussed by Hamilton (1961). The course of crystallization of liquids in the system $NaAlSiO_4$–$KAlSiO_4$–SiO_2–H_2O, comparable in composition with nepheline-syenite magmas, shows that with falling temperature the composition of the nepheline may change in two ways, by adjustment of the Na:K ratio, and by the replacement of Si by Al. If equilibrium is maintained the nepheline continuously reacts with the magma, and material passes between the solid and liquid phases so long as magmatic liquid is present. That ionic exchange also occurs between nepheline and felspar at sub-solidus temperatures is clearly demonstrated by the different slope of the nepheline–felspar tie lines in heteromorphic nepheline-syenites; as Tilley (1954, 1956) has shown, these changes lead to a convergence of the nepheline composition towards the Morozewicz-Buerger field. Hamilton, however, has suggested, that in contrast to the chemical exchanges between nepheline and silicate liquid, those between nepheline and felspar at sub-solidus temperatures may involve only the intraframework atoms, and that the Al:Si ratios in both phases remain constant. Hamilton's theory of the permanence of the (Si, Al) framework in nepheline at subsolidus temperatures is based on the absence of exsolved felspar in nephelines of plutonic and metamorphic rocks, and on the absence of felspar developed from nepheline at a lower temperature of equilibrium in the experimental system.

In many sodium-rich hypabyssal and volcanic rocks nepheline is a mineral of early crystallization, and an example of the felspathoid–felspar crystallization sequence in a leucite–nepheline dolerite (Meiches, Hessen) has been described by Tilley (1958b). The composition of the salic fraction of this rock lies in the nepheline field of the system $NaAlSiO_4$–$KAlSiO_4$–SiO_2. The crystallization of such a composition begins with nepheline, and is followed by nepheline and leucite to the reaction point when crystallization is completed by a reaction involving the partial resorption of leucite and the precipitation of sanidine and nepheline (Fig. 87). This crystallization sequence, nepheline (Table 29, anal. 5), leucite, sanidine, is demonstrated by the textural relationships of these minerals in the Meiches leucite–nepheline dolerite.

Potassium-rich nephelines, containing as much as 45 mol. per cent. $KAlSiO_4$, are common constituents of the Nyiragongo, Congo, lavas (Sahama, 1957, 1960). Both mediopotassic and perpotassic nephelines occur as phenocrysts and in the groundmass of these lavas, and the nepheline composition appears to depend largely on the amount of leucite present in the rock, the most potassium-rich nephelines occurring in those lavas containing the least amount of leucite. In some "nepheline aggregate" flows the nepheline phenocrysts have a very high content of potassium and may contain up to 45 mol. per cent. $KAlSiO_4$. For these lavas the normative rock and modal nepheline tie lines deviate from the usual trend shown by volcanic associations. From this evidence, and from the common zoning of more potassium-rich cores surrounded by more sodium-rich margins, Sahama concluded that the crystallization of these nephelines occurred at high temperature.

Metasomatic rocks. Following the pioneer study by Adams and Barlow (1910), the nepheline-syenites and nepheline gneisses of the Blue Mountain, Haliburton–Bancroft, and French River areas of southern Ontario, have been examined by many investigators, including Osborne (1930), Keith (1939), Chayes (1945), Gummer and Burr (1946), Moyd (1949), Derry (1951), Friedlaender (1952), Carlson (1957), Tilley (1958a), Hewitt (1960), Tilley and Gittins

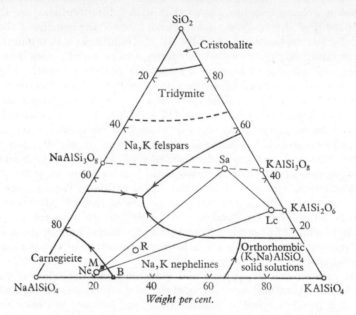

FIG. 87. Plot of the compositions of the Vogelsberg leucite–nepheline dolerite and its salic minerals in the system NaAlSiO$_4$–KAlSiO$_4$–SiO$_2$. R, rock; Ne, nepheline; Sa, sanidine; Lc, leucite; M and B, nepheline formulae of Morozewicz and Buerger respectively (after Tilley, 1958b).

(1961) and Gittins (1961). Many of the nepheline-bearing rocks of this region display a general metamorphic character. They are located in a region of high grade metamorphism, and commonly occur as relicts surrounded by later syenitic and granitic gneisses. The primary structures and textures of the nepheline-bearing rocks have in general been greatly modified by the regional metamorphism. The rocks are mostly gneissose in structure and show considerable variation in the relative proportions of the major constituents, nepheline, plagioclase (albite to andesine), and the ferromagnesian minerals, hastingsite, aegirine-augite and biotite.

It is generally accepted that many of these nepheline-bearing rocks are metasomatic in origin and are derived from a variety of earlier rocks, including limestones and amphibolites, that have subsequently been modified by nephelinization. This term is used to describe a series of related processes which result in the formation of nepheline-bearing rocks, the varied mineralogy of which is dependent on the composition both of the pre-existing rocks and of the fluids involved in the metasomatic process. Striking examples of metasomatic textures, *e.g.* nepheline enclosing rounded and embayed grains of felspar, and vermicular nepheline–albite intergrowths, have been observed in the gneisses of the nepheline belt of the York River area (Tilley, 1958a). In some nephelinized limestones, plagioclase encloses relicts of an altered and presumed more calcium-rich plagioclase, and Gittins (1961) has suggested that the limestone was first converted to a plagioclase rock which subsequently was converted to a nepheline–plagioclase (albite to andesine composition) assemblage.

Gummer and Burr (1946) and Moyd (1949) considered that the metasomatic fluids had a granitic parentage, but Tilley (1958a) and Gittins (1961) have presented evidence that fluids derived from nepheline-bearing magmas were the source of the widespread nephelinization. The latter conclusion is based on their recognition of magmatic textures in some of the nepheline-bearing rocks of Monmouth and Glamorgan townships, and on the nepheline–felspar tie lines (Tilley and Gittins, 1961), as well as on the evidence, presented by Hewitt (1960), of intrusive relationships in other parts of the Haliburton–Bancroft area. Further evidence that the nephelinization fluids were derived from a nepheline-bearing and not a granitic source is contained in the account, by Hewitt, of the conversion of nepheline gneisses to syenite. This metasomatic transformation took place in two stages, firstly by hydration and silication during which process nepheline was converted to albite, and secondly by the introduction of potassium which gave rise to microcline or microcline perthite at the expense of the plagioclase felspar.

Nephelinization has been reported from other areas; thus at Alnö, Sweden, nepheline-syenite intruded into granitic gneiss is surrounded by a zone of metasomatic nepheline-bearing rocks (Eckermann, 1948, 1950). In these so-called fenites the nepheline formed during the modification of the wall rocks consequent on the intrusion of carbonatitic liquids, and the nepheline has replaced felspar which, at an earlier phase of the fenitization, was pseudomorphed by natrolite and sericitic mica. In the fenites the cores of the nephelines are more sodium-rich than the margins, in contrast to the more potassium-rich cores and more sodium-rich margins of the nepheline of the magmatic rocks of the complex. Fenitized zones around alkaline rocks in the Fen region, Norway, and at Iivaara, Finland, have been described by Saether (1957) and Lehijärvi (1960).

Eckermann restricted the term fenite to rocks which have been metasomatically altered in situ to alkaline types, but its use has been extended by Strauss and Truter (1950) to include similar rocks, considered to represent the ultimate stages of fenitization, and which show intrusive relationships towards adjacent rocks. Thus these authors regard the melteigite and jacupirangite of the central mass of the alkali complex, Spitskop, eastern Transvaal, as fenitized fayalite diorite and theralite respectively. In the Messum complex, South-West Africa, the intrusion of a central core of foyaite was accompanied by the intense nephelinization of the adjacent tuffs and agglomerates which gave rise to an outer zone of syenite and an inner zone of foyaite. The latter rock differs

from the magmatic foyaite by its heterogeneity and by the presence of partially
nephelinized xenoliths of variable composition (Korn and Martin, 1954).
Melteigite derived from the nephelinization of pyroxenite at Tuva, southern
Siberia, has been described by Kononova (1958).   In the urtite–ijolite–melteigite
complex of Homa Bay, Kenya, many of the mineralogical variations displayed
are considered by Pulfrey (1949) to have arisen from the metasomatic alteration
of an early nepheline accumulate which formed at the top of the intrusion
chamber where the nepheline is partially replaced by aegirine-augite, wollastonite, cancrinite and zeolites.

Contaminated rocks.   Localized occurrences of nepheline-bearing basic rocks
may form by reaction of basic magmas with carbonate-rich sediments, and such
contamination processes have been discussed by Tilley (1952b) with particular
reference to the olivine gabbro–limestone contact at Camas Mòr, Muck (Tilley
1947), and to the dolerite–chalk junction at Scawt Hill, Northern Ireland
(Tilley and Harwood, 1931).   The syntectic assemblages of Camas Mòr and
Scawt Hill include nepheline dolerite, melilite–nepheline dolerite, theralite
and melilite theralite, rocks mineralogically comparable with nephelinite,
melilite nephelinite and nepheline tephrite lavas.

Pyroxenite and a coarse nepheline–pyroxene–melanite rock (ijolite) form
part of the Iron Hill stock, Colorado.   The ijolite, in common with other
nepheline-bearing rocks of this complex, is considered by Larsen (1941) to have
formed by reaction between a basaltic liquid and marble, and the subsequent
fractional crystallization of the contaminated magma.

Nepheline-bearing rocks may also develop by limestone contamination of
magmas of intermediate composition.   Thus Knopf (1957) considers that the
nepheline shonkinite dykes in the pyrometasomatized carbonate xenoliths of
the Boulder batholith, Montana, are a reaction product of limestone with a
granodiorite magma.   Limestone assimilation in both basic and intermediate
magmas has been considered by many petrologists to be the primary cause of
the formation of nepheline-bearing rocks.   This process, of which Shand (1930)
and Daly (1933) were the chief proponents, has subsequently been shown to be
untenable in many instances, and is no longer generally accepted as leading to
the large scale formation of nepheline-bearing rock.

Miscellaneous parageneses.   An interesting occurrence of nepheline in some
of the dyke rocks, located along shear zones in an aplite mass in central Wisconsin, has been described by Emmons (1953).   The dykes show a wide variation in
mineralogy, texture and colour; nepheline is present in about a quarter of the
dykes and varies in amount from a minor constituent to some 50 per cent. of
the syenite.   The formation of the nepheline is considered by Emmons to result
from the concentration of sodic plagioclase material along the shear zones under
the influence of pressure differentials, the sodium-rich solutions being derived
from the unmixing of the perthitic felspar of the wall rock aplite.

A unique association of nepheline and jadeite, originally described by Bauer
(1896) and later by Lacroix (1930), has been re-examined by Tilley (1956).
The nepheline occurs in thin veins traversing the jadeite, and has been derived
from the breakdown of the pyroxene.   The composition of the nepheline is
approximately $Ne_{80}Ks_{20}$, a composition typical of low temperature assemblages
in alkali felspar rocks, and there is little doubt that the breakdown of the jadeite
was associated with the metasomatic introduction of potassium.

Nepheline is also known from the brick-scab layers of blast furnace linings, and its occurrence, as phenocrysts and skeletal crystals, in recuperator tubes of a glass furnace has been reported by Lambert (1947).

Kalsilite

In the lavas of Bunyaruguru (Holmes, 1942; Bannister and Hey, 1942) and Katunga, Uganda (Combe and Holmes, 1945), and San Venanzo, Italy (Bannister *et al.*, 1953), kalsilite occurs in rocks exceptionally poor in sodium. Here the kalsilite, which is an anhedral interstitial constituent of the fine-grained groundmass, crystallized late in the consolidation of the lava, and its formation instead of nepheline was directly related to the relative concentrations of potassium and sodium in the magma. Kalsilite is the characteristic constituent of the potassic ultrabasic alkaline lava, mafurite, and in this rock occurs as an interstitial mineral poikilitically enclosing the ferromagnesian constituents, olivine and clinopyroxene, as well as in segregations larger in grain size than the enclosing lava (Sahama, 1954). Kalsilite-bearing and kalsilite-free katungites occur in the volcanic rocks of the Bunyaruguru area; in these lavas the absence of kalsilite, and the development of leucite in its place, can frequently be demonstrated to be associated with the incorporation of sialic material (Holmes, 1950).

Kalsilite both in complex phenocrysts and in the groundmass, accompanied by either nepheline or nepheline and leucite, occurs in some of the lavas of Mt. Nyiragongo, Congo (Sahama, 1953a, b, 1957, 1960). In these rocks the most striking mode of occurrence of the kalsilite is in complex nepheline–kalsilite phenocrysts, formed during the early, high-temperature stage of crystallization. These phenocrysts commonly display a "perthitic" core of nepheline and kalsilite surrounded by a homogeneous nepheline margin. In some phenocrysts the nepheline lamellae of the "perthite" are coarse (kalsilite "perthite"), in some they are finer and visible only in thin section (kalsilite "microperthite"), while in others the exsolution texture may be detected only from X-ray powder photographs (kalsilite "cryptoperthite"); all gradations from kalsilite "perthite" to kalsilite "cryptoperthite" occur. The following co-axial oriented phases have been identified in the cores of the phenocrysts:—two nepheline phases containing 59 and 35 mol. per cent. $KAlSiO_4$ respectively, disordered kalsilite ($a \simeq 5 \cdot 15$ Å) and orthorhombic kalsilite ($a \simeq 8 \cdot 9$ Å) of average compostion $90 \cdot 7$ mol. per cent. $KAlSiO_4$, and trikalsilite ($a \simeq 15 \cdot 3$ Å). The nepheline margins surrounding the core are variable in thickness and, where a number of phenocrysts are aggregated together, a homogeneous nepheline rim is present only around those parts of the crystals which are in contact with the groundmass; at this early stage of exsolution in the core the marginal nepheline phase commonly exhibits a "drop-like" arrangement (Fig. 88b). In other crystals containing a coarser perthitic-textured core the latter is separated from the nepheline margin by a narrow zone of kalsilite (Fig. 88c), the formation of which is considered by Sahama (1960) to be due to the transfer, by diffusion, of sodium atoms into the margin. The next stage in the progressive exsolution of the core is marked by the development of nepheline ($27 \cdot 5$ mol. per cent. $KAlSiO_4$) as thick lamellae, or as separate patches of rectangular outline, within the kalsilite base ($96 \cdot 4$ mol. per cent. $KAlSiO_4$). The final stage in the exsolution process is characterized by a nepheline-free kalsilite core, of more or less rectangular outline, surrounded by a wide nepheline margin (Fig. 88e).

It is not known whether the crystal structure of the early precipitated $(K,Na)AlSiO_4$ solid solution of the Nyiragongo lavas was originally that of nepheline, tetrakalsilite, or an orthorhombic (O_2) phase, nor is it possible to determine whether these first precipitates crystallized as stable or unstable constituents. Nevertheless the formation of a nepheline margin to the complex nepheline–kalsilite phenocrysts, at an early stage in the exsolution, indicates

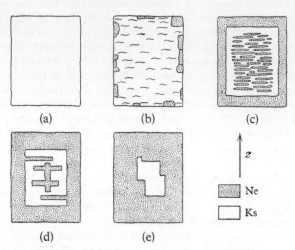

Fig. 88. Schematic representation of the exsolution phenomena in the complex nepheline–kalsilite phenocrysts of the Nyiragongo lavas. (a) Homogeneous crystal of a potassium-rich high-temperature phase (70 per cent. $KAlSiO_4$) as originally crystallized from the lava. (b) Beginning of exsolution, "cryptoperthitic" to finely "microperthitic" core, nepheline drops at the margin. (c) Coarsely "microperthitic" kalsilite core surrounded by a narrow zone of nepheline-free kalsilite and a continuous margin of homogeneous nepheline. (d) Core of a homogeneous kalsilite phase containing a few thick nepheline lamellae perpendicular to the z-axis, and sometimes connected by a nepheline plug parallel to the z-axis; fairly thick homogeneous nepheline margin. (e) Homogeneous kalsilite core containing more than 90 per cent. $KAlSiO_4$ surrounded by a thick nepheline margin (after Sahama, 1960).

that instability between phenocrysts and the magma occurred shortly after their formation, and it is probable that under conditions of slower cooling the complex phenocrysts would have been completely converted into a homogeneous nepheline. The development of the nepheline margin is believed by Sahama to result both from the exsolution of the potassium-rich core, and from a chemical readjustment with the surrounding liquid or solid groundmass. The preservation of the complex nepheline–kalsilite phenocrysts in the Nyiragongo lavas up to the time of their extrusion was possible because of their mechanical accumulation into aggregates, and later, after extrusion, because of the rapid cooling of the lava to temperatures at which the phenocrysts could no longer react with the crystallizing groundmass.

In addition to its occurrence in the complex phenocrysts, kalsilite is one of the main constituents of the groundmass in some of the Nyiragongo lavas. It occurs, as also does the nepheline, in individual homogeneous grains. Although the temperature of the final consolidation of the kalsilite-bearing lavas is not known, it is evident from the coexistence of kalsilite and nepheline in the groundmass that crystallization occurred at temperatures below the solvus in the nepheline–kalsilite system. The kalsilite of the groundmass contains more than 90 mol. per cent. $KAlSiO_4$, and the coexisting nepheline between 30 and 35 mol. per cent. $KAlSiO_4$. Sahama (1957) has shown that the temperature of the reaction

tetrakalsilite ⇌ nepheline–kalsilite "perthite"

is some 200°C. below the solvus maximum in the nepheline–kalsilite system (see p. 246). It is thus probable that the entire solvus effective in the natural lavas of Nyiragongo was below the solvus of the artificial system; for this reason the temperature of crystallization of the coexisting nepheline and kalsilite of the groundmass cannot be estimated with certainty.

The occurrence of kalsilite in blast-furnace linings has been reported by Rigby and Richardson (1947).

Kaliophilite is a very rare mineral but is known from ejected blocks of biotite pyroxenite and augite–melilite–calcite rock at Monte Somma, and also in ejected blocks, associated with clinopyroxene, garnet, leucite, haüyne and latiumite at Albano, Latium, Italy (Tilley and Henry, 1953).

REFERENCES

Adams, F. D. and Barlow, A. E., 1910. Geology of the Haliburton and Bancroft Areas, Province of Ontario. *Geol. Surv. Canada, Memoir* No. 6.

Adamson, O. J., 1944. The petrology of the Norra Kärr district. *Geol. För. Förh.* Stockholm, vol. 66, p. 113.

Bannister, F. A. and Hey, M. H., 1931. A chemical, optical and X-ray study of nepheline and kaliophilite. *Min. Mag.*, vol. 22, p. 569.

—— —— 1942. Kalsilite, a polymorph of $KAlSiO_4$ from Uganda. *Min. Mag.*, vol. 26, p. 218.

—— Sahama, Th. G. and Wiik, H. B., 1953. Kalsilite in venanzite from San Venanzo, Umbria, Italy. *Min. Mag.*, vol. 30, p. 46.

Barrer, R. M. and White, E. A. D., 1952. The hydrothermal chemistry of silicates. Part II. Synthetic crystalline sodium aluminosilicates. *Journ. Chem. Soc.*, p. 1561.

Barth, T. F. W. and Posnjak, E., 1932. Silicate structures of the cristobalite type. I. The crystal structure of carnegieite (NaAlSiO4). *Zeit. Krist.*, vol. 81, p. 135.

Bauer, M., 1896. Jadeit von "Tibet". *Neues Jahrb. Min.*, vol. 1, p. 89.

Bowen, N. L., 1912. The binary system $Na_2Al_2Si_2O_8$ (nepheline, carnegieite)–$CaAl_2Si_2O_8$ (anorthite). *Amer. Journ. Sci.*, 4th ser., vol. 33, p. 551.

—— 1917. The sodium–potassium nephelines. *Amer. Journ. Sci.*, 4th ser., vol. 43, p. 115.

—— 1922. Genetic features of alnoitic rocks at Isle Cadieux, Quebec. *Amer. Journ. Sci.*, 5th ser., vol. 3, p. 1.

Bowen, N. L., 1945. Phase equilibria bearing on the origin and differentiation of alkaline rocks. *Amer. Journ. Sci.*, Daly vol., p. 75.

—— and **Ellestad, R. B.**, 1936. Nepheline contrasts. *Amer. Min.*, vol. 21, p. 363.

—— and **Schairer, J. F.**, 1938. Crystallization equilibrium in nepheline–albite–silica mixtures with fayalite. *Journ. Geol.*, vol. 46, p. 397.

Brøgger, W. C., 1933. Die Eruptivgesteine des Oslogebietes. VII. Die chemische Zusammensetzung der Eruptivgesteine des Oslogebietes. *Vid. Akad. Skr.*, *Mat. Nat.*, Oslo.

Buerger, M. J., 1954. The stuffed derivatives of the silica structures. *Amer. Min.*, vol. 39, p. 600.

—— **Klein, G. E.** and **Donnay, G.**, 1954. Determination of the crystal structure of nepheline. *Amer. Min.*, vol. 39, p. 805.

Carlson, H. D., 1957. Origin of the corundum deposits of Renfrew County, Ontario, Canada. *Bull. Geol. Soc. Amer.*, vol. 68, p. 1605.

Chayes, F., 1945. Recent studies of Haliburton–Bancroft alkaline rocks. A discussion. *Journ. Geol.*, vol. 83, p. 405.

Chirvinsky, P. N., 1953. *The average chemical composition of the principal minerals of eruptive, metamorphic and sedimentary rocks.* Lvov. Geol. Soc.

Claringbull, G. F. and **Bannister, F. A.**, 1948. The crystal structure of kalsilite. *Acta. Cryst.*, vol. 1, p. 42.

Combe, A. D. and **Holmes, A.**, 1945. The kalsilite-bearing lavas of Kabirenge and Lyakanli, south-west Uganda. *Trans. Roy. Soc. Edin.*, vol. 61, p. 359.

Daly, R. A., 1933. *Igneous rocks and the depths of the earth.* McGraw-Hill, New York.

Derry, D. R., 1951. The Lakefield nepheline-syenite; evidence of a non-intrusive origin. *Trans. Roy. Soc. Canada*, Sect. IV, 3rd ser., vol. 46, p. 31.

Donnay, G., 1957. Synthetic nephelines. *Carnegie Institution of Washington, Ann. Rept. Dir. Geophys. Lab.*, 1956–7, p. 237.

—— **Schairer, J. F.** and **Donnay, J. D. H.**, 1959. Nepheline solid solution. *Min. Mag.*, vol. 32, p. 93.

Dunham, K. C., 1933. Crystal cavities in lavas from the Hawaiian Islands. *Amer. Min.*, vol. 18, p. 369.

Eckermann, H. von., 1948. The alkaline district of Alnö Island. *Sveriges Geol. Undersök.*, Ser. Ca., No. 136.

—— 1950. The process of nephelinization. *XVIII Intern. Geol. Congr. (London)*, Pt. 3, p. 90.

Eitel, W., 1923. Über das System $CaCO_3$–$NaAlSiO_4$ (Calcit–Nephelin) und den Cancrinit. *Neues Jahrb. Min.*, vol. 2, p. 45.

Emmons, R. C., 1953. Petrogeny of the syenites and nepheline syenites of central Wisconsin. *Mem. Geol. Soc. Amer.*, No. 52, p. 71.

Fairbairn, H. W., 1941. Petrofabric relations of nepheline and albite in litchfieldite from Blue Mountain, Ontario. *Amer. Min.*, vol. 26, p. 316.

Fersman, A., 1937. Mineralogy and geochemistry of the Khibine and Lovozero Tundras. *XVII Intern. Geol. Congr.* U.S.S.R., North Excursion, Kola Peninsula.

Friedlaender, C., 1952. Alkaligesteine von Blue Mountains, Ontario. *Schweiz. Min. Petr. Mitt.*, vol. 32, p. 213.

Gittins, J., 1961. Nephelinization in the Haliburton–Bancroft District, Ontario, Canada. *Journ. Geol.*, vol. 69, p. 291.

Goldsmith, J. R., 1949. Some aspects of the system $NaAlSiO_4$–$CaO\cdot Al_2O_3$. *Amer. Min.*, Vol. 34, p. 471.

Gossner, B. and **Mussgnug, F.**, 1930. Beitrag zur Kenntnis des Kaliophilites. *Zeit. Krist.*, vol. 73, p. 187.

Greig, J. W. and **Barth, T. F. W.**, 1938. The system $Na_2O \cdot Al_2O_3 \cdot 2SiO_2$ (nepheline, carnegieite)–$Na_2O \cdot Al_2O_3 \cdot 6SiO_2$ (albite). *Amer. Journ. Sci.*, 5th ser., vol. 35A, p. 93.

Gummer, W. K. and **Burr, S. V.**, 1946. Nephelinized paragneisses in the Bancroft area, Ontario. *Journ. Geol.*, vol. 54, p. 137.

Hackman, V., 1900. Neue Mitteilungen über das Ijolitmassiv von Kuusamo. *Bull. Comm. géol. Finlande*, No. 11.

—— 1925. Das Gebiet der Alkaligesteine von Kuolajärvi in Nordfinland. *Bull. Comm. géol. Finlande*, No. 72.

Hahn, T. and **Buerger, M. J.**, 1955. The detailed structure of nepheline $KNa_3Al_4Si_4O_{16}$. *Zeit Krist.*, vol. 106, p. 308.

Hamilton, D. L., 1961. Nephelines as crystallization temperature indicators. *Journ. Geol.*, vol. 69, p. 321.

—— and **MacKenzie, W. S.**, 1960. Nepheline solid solution in the system $NaAlSiO_4$–$KAlSiO_4$–SiO_2. *Journ. Petr.*, vol. 1, p. 56.

Hewitt, D. F., 1960. Nepheline syenite deposits of southern Ontario. *Ontario Dept. Mines*, vol. 69, Pt. 8.

Högbom, A. G., 1895. Über das Nephelinsyenitgebiet auf der Insel Alnö. *Geol. För. Förh.*, Stockholm, vol. 17.

Holmes, A., 1942. A suite of volcanic rocks from south-west Uganda containing kalsilite, a polymorph of $KAlSiO_4$. *Min. Mag.*, vol. 26, p. 197.

—— 1950. Petrogenesis of katungite and its associates. *Amer. Min.*, vol. 35. p. 772.

—— 1952. The potash ankaratrite-metaleucitite lavas of Nabungando and Mbuga craters, south-west Uganda. *Trans. Edin. Geol. Soc.*, vol. 15, p. 187.

Jérémine, E., 1948. Sur quelques roches provenant du Maroc oriental. Aïounite et mestigmérite. *Notes et Mém. Serv. Géol. Maroc.*, No. 71, p. 67 (M.A. 11–40).

Keith, M. L., 1939. Petrology of the alkaline intrusive at Blue Mountain. *Bull. Geol. Soc. Amer.*, vol. 50, p. 1795.

Knopf, A., 1957. The Boulder bathylith of Montana. *Amer. Journ. Sci.*, vol. 255, p. 81.

Kononova, V. A., 1958. On the nephelinization of pyroxenites and marbles. *Bull. Acad. Sci. U.R.S.S., Sér. Géol.*, vol. 6, p. 58.

Korn, H. and **Martin, H.**, 1954. The Messum igneous complex in South-West Africa. *Trans. Geol. Soc. South Africa*, vol. 57, p. 83.

Kunze, G., 1954. Über die rhombische Modifikation von $KAlSiO_4$ in Anlehnung an den Kalsilit. *Heidelberger Beitr. zur Min. Petr.*, vol. 4, p. 99.

Kupletsky, B., 1937. *Petrographical description of the Khibina Tundras* (Minerals of the Khibina and Lovozero Tundras, Lomonossov Inst. Acad. Sci. U.S.S.R., Moscow).

Lacroix, M. A., 1930. La jadéite de Birmanie; les roches qu'elle consititue ou qui l'accompagnent. Composition et origine. *Bull. Soc. franç. Min.*, vol. 53, p. 216.

Lambert, A. J., 1947. An occurrence of synthetic nepheline. *Journ. Roy. Soc. New South Wales*, vol. 80, p. 143.

Larsen, E. S., 1941. Alkalic rocks of Iron Hill, Gunnison County, Colorado. *U.S. Geol. Surv. Prof. Paper* 197–A.

Lehijärvi, M., 1956. Cancrinite-ijolite from Iivaara, Kuusamo, Finland. *Bull. Comm. géol. Finlande*, No. 172.

—— 1960. The alkaline district of Iivaara, Kuusamo, Finland. *Bull. Comm. géol. Finlande*, No. 185.

Luchitzky, V. I. and **Lebedev, P. I.**, 1934. *The petrography of the Ukraine.* Petrogr. Inst. Acad. Sci. U.S.S.R. (M.A. 6–315).

Lukesh, J. S. and Buerger, M. J., 1942. The unit cell and space group of kaliophilite. *Amer. Min.*, vol. 27, p. 226.

MacKenzie, W. S., 1954. The system NaAlSiO₄–NaAlSi₃O₈–H₂O. *Carnegie Inst. Washington, Ann. Rept. Dir. Geophys. Lab.*, 1953–54, p. 119.

Magnusson, N., 1925. The alkaline rocks of Siksjörberget and Skorrasen. *Geol. För. Förh., Stockholm*, vol. 45, p. 295.

McConnell, J. D. C., 1962. Electron-diffraction study of subsidiary maxima of scattered intensity in nepheline. *Min. Mag.*, vol. 33, p. 114.

Miyashiro, A., 1951. The ranges of chemical composition in nepheline and their petrogenetic significance. *Geochim. et Cosmochim. Acta.*, vol. 1, p. 278.

— and **Miyashiro, T.,** 1954. Unit cell dimensions of synthetic nepheline. *Journ. Fac. Sci. Univ. Tokyo*, Sect. 2, vol. 9, p. 267.

—— —— 1955. Nepheline syenites and associated alkalic rocks of the Fukushin-zan District, Korea. *Journ. Fac. Sci. Univ. Tokyo*, vol. 10, p. 1.

Morey, G. W., 1957. The system water–nepheline–albite; a theoretical discussion. *Amer. Journ. Sci.*, vol. 255, p. 461.

Morozewicz, J., 1928. Ueber die chemische Zusammensetzung des Gesteinsbilden-den Nephelins. *Fennia*, vol. 22, p. 1.

—— 1929. La mariopolite et ses parentes. *Trav. Serv. Géol. Pologne*, vol. 2, p. 217 (M.A. 4–395).

Moyd, L., 1949. Petrology of the nepheline and corundum rocks of south-eastern Ontario. *Amer. Min.*, vol. 34, p. 736.

Mügge, O., 1927. Zur Kenntnis des Kaliophilit. *Zeit. Krist.*, vol. 65, p. 380.

Oftedahl, C., 1952. On "apoanalcite" and hydronephelite. *Norsk Geol. Tidskr.*, vol. 30, 1952, p. 1.

Osborne, F. F., 1930. Non-metallic mineral resources of Hastings County. *Ontario Dept. Mines*, vol. 39, pt. 6, p. 22.

Pecora, W. T., 1942. Nepheline syenite pegmatites, Rocky Boy stock, Bearpaw Mountains, Montana. *Amer. Min.*, vol. 27, p. 397.

Polański, A., 1949. The alkaline rocks of the east European Plateau. *Bull. Soc. Sci., Poznań*, Ser. B., p. 119.

Pulfrey, W., 1949. Ijolitic rocks near Homa Bay, western Kenya. *Quart. Journ. Geol. Soc.*, vol. 105, p. 425.

Quensel, P., 1914. The alkaline rocks of Almunge. *Bull. Geol. Inst. Upsala*, vol. 12, p. 129.

Ramsay, W., 1899. Das Nephelinsyenitgebiet auf der Halbinsel Kola. *Fennia*, vol. 15.

Rigby, G. R., and Richardson, H. M., 1947. The occurrence of artificial kalsilite and allied potassium aluminium silicates in blast furnace linings. *Min. Mag.*, vol. 28, p. 75.

Roedder, E. W., 1951. The system K₂O–MgO–SiO₂. *Amer. Journ. Sci.*, vol. 249, pp. 81 and 224.

Saether, E., 1957. The alkaline rock province of the Fen area in Southern Norway. *Det. Kgl. Norske Vidensk. Selsk. Skrift.*, No. 1.

Saha, P., 1961. The system NaAlSiO₄ (nepheline)–NaAlSi₃O₈(albite)–H₂O. *Amer Min.*, vol. 46, p. 859.

Sahama, Th. G., 1952. Leucite, potash nepheline and clinopyroxene from S.W Uganda and Belgian Congo. *Amer. Journ. Sci.*, Bowen vol., p. 460.

—— 1953a. Mineralogy and petrology of a lava flow from Mt. Nyiragongo, North Kivu, Belgian Congo. *Ann. Acad. Sci. Fennicae*, ser A–III, No. 35, p. 1.

—— 1953b. Parallel growths of nepheline and microperthitic kalsilite from North Kivu, Belgian Congo. *Ann. Acad. Sci. Fennicae*, ser. A–III, No. 36, p. 1.

—— 1954. Mineralogy of mafurite. *Bull. Comm. géol. Finlande*, No. 166, p. 21.

Sahama, Th. G., 1957.   Complex nepheline–kalsilite phenocrysts in Kabfumu lava, Nyiragongo area, North Kivu in Belgian Congo.   *Journ. Geol.*, vol. 65, p. 515.

—— 1958.   A complex form of natural nepheline from Iivaara, Finland.   *Amer. Min.*, vol. 43, p. 165.

—— 1959.   Detection of zoning in orthorhombic and uniaxial colourless minerals.   *Amer. Min.*, vol. 44, p. 1303.

—— 1960.   Kalsilite in the lavas of Mt. Nyiragongo (Belgian Congo).   *Journ. Petr.*, vol. 1, p. 146.

—— 1962.   Order–disorder in natural nepheline solid solutions.   *Journ. Petr.*, vol. 3, p. 65.

—— **Neuvonen, K. J.** and **Hytönen, K.**, 1956.   Determination of the composition of kalsilites by an X-ray method.   *Min. Mag.*, vol. 31, p. 200.

—— and **Smith, J. V.**, 1957.   Tri-kalsilite, a new mineral.   *Amer. Min.*, vol. 42, p. 286.

Schairer, J. F., 1950.   The alkali-feldspar join in the system $NaAlSiO_4$–$KAlSiO_4$–SiO_2.   *Journ. Geol.*, vol. 58, p. 512.

—— and **Bowen, N. L.**, 1956.   The system Na_2O–Al_2O_3–SiO_2.   *Amer. Journ. Sci.*, vol. 254, p. 129.

—— and **Yoder, H. S.**, 1958.   The quaternary system Na_2O–MgO–Al_2O_3–SiO_2.   *Carnegie Inst. Washington, Ann. Rept. Dir. Geophys. Lab.*, 1957–58, p. 211.

—— —— 1960.   The nature of residual liquids from crystallization, with data on the system nepheline–diopside–silica.   *Amer. Journ. Sci.*, vol. 258–A, p. 273.

Schiebold, E., 1930.   On the structure of nepheline and analcite.   *Naturwiss.*, vol. 18, p. 705.

Shand, S. J., 1921.   The nepheline rocks of Sekukuniland.   *Trans. Geol. Soc. South Africa*, vol. 24, p. 111.

—— 1930.   Limestone and the origin of feldspathoidal rocks.   *Geol. Mag.*, vol. 67, p. 415.

—— 1939.   On the staining of feldspathoids and on the zoned structure in nepheline.   *Amer. Min.*, vol. 24, p. 508.

—— 1946.   The origin of nepheline rocks in Ontario.   *Journ. Geol.*, vol. 54, p. 398.

Smith, J. V. and **Sahama, Th. G.**, 1954.   Determination of the composition of natural nephelines by an X-ray method.   *Min. Mag.*, vol. 30, p. 439.

—— —— 1957.   Order-disorder in kalsilite.   *Amer. Min.*, vol. 42, p. 287.

—— and **Tuttle, O. F.**, 1957.   The nepheline–kalsilite system.   I: X-ray data for the crystalline phases.   *Amer. Journ. Sci.*, vol. 255, p. 282.

Strauss, C. A. and **Truter, F. C.**, 1950.   The alkali complex at Spitskop, Sekukuniland, eastern Transvaal.   *Journ. Geol. Soc., South Africa*, vol. 53, p. 81.

Streckeisen, A., 1952.   Das Nephelinsyenit–massiv von Ditro (Siebenbürgen). I Teil. *Schwiez. Min. Petr. Mitt.*, vol. 32, p. 251.

—— 1954.   II Teil.   *Schweiz. Min. Petr. Mitt.*, vol. 34, p. 336.

Sturt, B. A., 1961.   Preferred orientation of nepheline in deformed nepheline syenite gneisses from Sørøy, northern Norway.   *Geol. Mag.*, vol. 98, p. 464.

Tilley, C. E., 1947.   The gabbro–limestone contact zone of Camas Mòr, Muck, Inverness-shire.   *Bull. Comm. géol. Finlande*, No. 140, p. 97.

—— 1952a.   Nepheline parageneses.   *Sir Douglas Mawson Anniv. vol., Univ. of Adelaide*, p. 167.

—— 1952b.   Some trends of basaltic magma in limestone syntexis.   *Amer. Journ. Sci.*, Bowen vol., p. 529.

—— 1953.   The nephelinite from Etinde, Cameroons, W. Africa.   *Geol. Mag.*, vol. 90, p. 145.

—— 1954.   Nepheline–alkali feldspar paragenesis.   *Amer. Journ. Sci.*, vol. 252, p. 65.

Tilley, C. E., 1956. Nepheline associations. *Kon. Ned. Geol. Mijnb., Geol. Ser.,* Brouwer vol., p. 403.

—— 1958a. Problems of alkali rock genesis. *Quart. Journ. Geol. Soc.,* vol. 113, p. 323.

—— 1958b. The leucite nepheline dolerite of Meiches, Vogelsberg, Hessen. *Amer. Min.,* vol. 43, p. 759.

—— 1959. A note on the nosean phonolite of the Wolf Rock, Cornwall. *Geol. Mag.,* vol. 96, p. 503.

—— and **Harwood, H. F.,** 1931. The dolerite–chalk contact of Scawt Hill, Co. Antrim. *Min. Mag.,* vol. 22, p. 439.

—— and **Gittins, J.,** 1961. Igneous nepheline-bearing rocks of the Haliburton–Bancroft Province of Ontario. *Journ. Petr.,* vol. 2, p. 38.

—— and **Henry, N. F. M.,** 1953. Latiumite (sulphatic potassium–calcium–aluminium silicate), a new mineral from Albano, Latium, Italy. *Min. Mag.,* vol. 30, p. 39.

Tuttle, O. F. and **Smith, J. V.,** 1958. The nepheline–kalsilite system II: Phase relations. *Amer. Journ. Sci.,* vol. 256, p. 571.

Walker, T. L. and **Parsons, A. L.,** 1926. Minerals from the new nepheline syenite area, French River, Ontario. *Univ. Toronto Studs., Geol. Ser.,* No. 22, p. 5.

Winchell, A. N., 1941. Nepheline. *Amer. Min.,* vol. 26, p. 536.

Winkler, H. G. F., 1947. On the synthesis of nepheline. *Amer. Min.,* vol. 32, p. 131.

Wyart, J., 1947. Synthèse de la kalsilite et de l'orthose. *Compt. Rend. Acad. Sci. Paris,* vol. 225, p. 944.

—— and **Michel-Lévy, M.,** 1949. Cristallisation des mélanges $Na_xK_{1-x}AlSiO_4$ en présence d'eau sous pression. *Compt. Rend. Acad. Sci. Paris.,* vol. 229, p. 131.

Yoder, H. S., 1958. Effect of water on the melting of silicates. *Carnegie Inst. Washington, Ann. Rept. Dir. Geophys. Lab.,* 1957–58, p. 189.

Petalite

$Li[AlSi_4O_{10}]$

MONOCLINIC $(+)$

α 1·504–1·507
β 1·510–1·513
γ 1·516–1·523
δ 0·011–0·017
$2V_\gamma$ 82°–84°
$\alpha : x$ 2°–8°, $\beta : z$ 24°–30°
$\gamma = y$, O.A.P. $\perp$ (010).

Dispersion : $r > v$
     D   2·412–2·422
     H $6\frac{1}{2}$
Cleavage :   {001} perfect, {201} good ;
     (001) : (201) = $38\frac{1}{2}$°.
Twinning :   Lamellar twins with twin plane (001), common.
Colour :   Greyish white to white, more rarely pink or green ; colourless in thin section.
Unit cell : a 11·76, b 5·14, c 7·62 Å, β 112·4°.
     $Z = 2$. Space group Pa.
   Unattacked by acids, except HF.

Petalite is a mineral of granite pegmatites, often occurring associated with spodumene, tourmaline, lepidolite, etc. The name is from the Greek *petalon*, a leaf, in allusion to its leaf-like cleavage; castor or castorite are synonyms.

STRUCTURE

The unit cell of petalite was first determined by Gossner and Mussgnug (1930) who reported a cell containing $4(3SiO_2 \cdot SiO_4 \cdot AlLi)$, with a' 11·79, b' 5·14, c' 15·20 Å, β 112°44'. A similar cell, with space group $P2_1/n$, was reported by Tavora (1952), but according to Zemann-Hedlik and Zemann (1954, 1955), the true unit cell has $c \simeq \frac{1}{2}c'$ and space group $P2/a$. The latter authors have shown that the structure consists of a framework of SiO_4 and AlO_4 tetrahedra linked by sharing apices ; the coordination polyhedron of Li is a distorted tetrahedron. The structure can alternatively be regarded as composed of SiO_4 tetrahedra arranged in sheets parallel to (001) which are joined to one another through AlO_4 tetrahedra : this sheet-like feature of the structure is consistent with the presence of perfect (001) cleavage. In a further refinement of the structure (Liebau, 1961), oxygen atoms previously placed in special positions of $P2/a$ were found to be slightly displaced, and the true space group is given as Pa.

CHEMISTRY

Although the formula $LiAlSi_4O_{10}$ is the one usually accepted, others which have been suggested are $Li_2O \cdot 2Al_2O_3 \cdot 14SiO_2$ by Comucci (1915) and $4Li_2O \cdot 5Al_2O_3 \cdot 40SiO_2$ by Mikkola and Wiik (1947). The total number of analyses of petalite is still rather small, however, and more work on strictly pure material is required before a formula other than $LiAlSi_4O_{10}$ can be justified.

Table 32.   PETALITE ANALYSES

	1.	2.	3.	4.	5.	6.
SiO_2	78·00	77·18	78·68	77·18	78·15	77·47
Al_2O_3	17·03	16·04	16·62	17·05	15·88	17·12
Fe_2O_3	0·01	0·64	0·09	0·20	1·42	0·24
FeO	0·03	—	—	—	—	—
MnO	0·00	—	tr.	0·00	—	tr.
MgO	0·00	0·26	0·00	0·00	0·23	tr.
CaO	0·00	0·22	0·00	0·14	0·20	0·13
Li_2O	4·74	4·36	4·13	4·11	4·10	3·95
Na_2O	0·07	1·14	0·08	0·61	}0·44	0·78
K_2O	0·05	—	0·00	0·17		0·30
H_2O^+	0·04	0·40	0·01	0·44	}0·19	0·25
H_2O^-	0·00	0·02	0·00	0·10		0·03
Total	99·99	100·26	99·61	100·03	100·61	100·27
α	1·506	1·507	—	—	1·504	1·504
β	1·513	1·512	—	—	1·511	1·510
γ	1·523	1·518	—	—	1·515	1·516
$2V_\gamma$	84°	82°	—	—	82°20′	83°
D	2·366	2·422	2·42	2·418	2·327–8	2·412

NUMBERS OF IONS ON THE BASIS OF 20 OXYGENS

	1.	2.	3.	4.	5.	6.
Si	7·968 }8·00	7·958 }8·00	8·056	7·963 }8·00	8·009	7·966 }8·00
Al	0·032	0·042	—	0·037	—	0·034
Al	2·018 }2·02	1·950 }2·00	2·006 }2·01	2·036 }2·04	1·919 }2·03	2·042 }2·06
Fe^{+3}	0·001	0·050	0·007	0·008	0·110	0·019
Mg	—	0·040	—	—	0·035	—
Fe^{+2}	0·002	—	—	—		—
Li	1·948 }1·97	1·807 }2·10	1·701 }1·72	1·705 }1·87	1·690 }1·82†	1·634 }1·84
Na	0·014	0·227	0·016	0·122	—	0·156
Ca	—	0·024	—	0·016	0·022	0·014
K	0·006	—	—	0·022		0·040

1. Greyish white petalite, pegmatite vein, Hirvikallio, Tammela, S.W. Finland (Vesasalo, 1959). Anal. A. Heikkinen (Includes P_2O_5 0·02).
2. Petalite, in pegmatite with lepidolite and amblygonite, Karibib, South-West Africa (Nel, 1946). Anal. C. J. Liebenberg.
3. Colourless petalite, veins in pegmatite, Londonderry, Central Div., Western Australia (Simpson, 1938). Anal. H. P. Rowledge.
4. Greyish white petalite, in pegmatite with cleavelandite and quartz, Varuträsk, Sweden (Quensel, 1937). Anal. T. Berggren (Includes F 0·03).
5. Colourless transparent petalite, pegmatite, eastern Transbaikal, Siberia (Ginzburg & Gushchina, 1954).
6. Platy petalite, pegmatite, Somero parish, S.W. Finland (Mikkola & Wiik, 1947). Anal. H. B. Wiik.

† Includes (Na + K) 0·074.

In Table 32 the petalite analyses have been recalculated on the basis of 20(O), and although the Li group in the material of analyses 3 to 6 is low, in the Karibib petalite (anal. 2) it is high, though possibly this represents felspar contamination. Iron is present to a limited extent, but other elements, apart from the alkalis, are not found in significant amount. The element lithium was first discovered, in petalite, by Arfvedson in 1817.

The system $Li_2O-Al_2O_3 \cdot 2SiO_2-SiO_2$ was studied experimentally by Roy *et al.* (1950) who investigated the subsolidus phase relations of the anhydrous ternary compounds and obtained petalite at temperatures between 380° and 680°C. It has also been obtained synthetically by Barrer and White (1951) using $LiOH$, $Al(OH)_3$ and silicic acid, when it appeared at temperatures of 330° to 400°C. In an investigation of the $\alpha-\beta$ spodumene ($LiAlSi_2O_6$) inversion, Isaacs and Roy (1958) found that in no case could the low-temperature spodumene be synthesized from material of the appropriate composition, but that the assemblage petalite + eucryptite ($LiAlSiO_4$) consistently appeared instead. Natural petalite crystals, after heating to 1200°C., gave crystallites of probable composition $Li_2O \cdot Al_2O_3 \cdot 6SiO_2$ (Saalfeld, 1961).

Petalite commonly alters to montmorillonite, which may occur as a fibrous pale to deep pink coating on the petalite (McLintock, 1923; Quensel, 1937): on further decomposition of the petalite the montmorillonite becomes more massive. Petalite from Elba develops an alteration product which has been called hydrocastorite, but which may be a mixture of heulandite and stilbite: cookeite, $LiAl_4(Si,Al)_4O_{10}(OH)_8$, may also occur as an alteration product of petalite (Ginzburg and Gushchina, 1954). In the laboratory, petalite has been converted to kaolinite by the action of CO_2-charged water at temperatures around 300°C. (Norton, 1939).

OPTICAL AND PHYSICAL PROPERTIES

The refractive indices, birefringence and optic axial angle all show but little variation with the reported Li content. In addition to optic axial dispersion, weak crossed dispersion may also occur. The Elba petalite is reported to become uniaxial on heating to between 1000° and 1100°C., becoming isotropic at 1200°C. and at 1370°C. forming a glass with n 1·495, D 2·29. Multiple lamellar twinning is relatively common in petalite; the twin plane is (001).

DISTINGUISHING FEATURES

The felspars have higher refractive indices than petalite and also have a slightly lower birefringence; quartz also has a higher relief. The cleavage of petalite may be distinctive, the angle between the perfect (001) cleavage and the fairly good cleavage on (201) being $38\frac{1}{2}°$: the small extinction angle ($\alpha : x = 2°-8°$) on to the best cleavage, the large positive optic axial angle and the length-fast nature of most of the crystals are also characteristic. Petalite will give a bright carmine red Li coloration to a flame: details of flame tests for identifying petalite in composite samples and for an approximate determination of the amount of petalite present are given by Hosking (1957).

18.—R.F.M. IV.

PARAGENESIS

Petalite occurs chiefly in granitic pegmatites and related rocks, where it is found typically associated with spodumene, tourmaline, lepidolite, topaz, microcline, amblygonite, apatite, pollucite, columbite, etc. In the pegmatites of the eastern Transbaikal region three varieties of petalite are distinguishable (Ginzburg and Gushchina, 1954) : irregular massive petalite which formed later than the associated spodumene which it often completely replaces, prismatic well crystallized petalite (Table 32, anal. 5) formed during the albitization process in the pegmatite, and acicular petalite formed during the latest hydrothermal stages and during hypergenesis. In the Hirvikallio pegmatite, Finland, the petalite (Table 32, anal. 1) is often surrounded by a net-like formation of spodumene (Vesasalo, 1959). Such an association of petalite and spodumene, which is often accompanied by relatively fine-grained quartz, may be the result of the reaction :

$$\underset{\text{petalite}}{\text{LiAlSi}_4\text{O}_{10}} \rightleftharpoons \underset{\text{spodumene}}{\text{LiAlSi}_2\text{O}_6} + \underset{\text{quartz}}{2\text{SiO}_2}$$

The relative specific volumes of these minerals suggest that petalite is possibly the lower pressure phase.

In the Varuträsk pegmatite, petalite (Table 32, anal. 4) is relatively abundant, and several thousand tons have been mined. Here it occurs in the lithium replacement unit of the pneumatogenic stage (Quensel, 1957), which is considered to have crystallized in the 600°–400°C. temperature range. The Karibib petalite (anal. 2) is also present in commercially important amounts, over 60,000 tons having been proved. In Japan, petalite occurs in the Nagatare granite pegmatite (Shibata, 1952).

REFERENCES

Barrer, R. M. and **White E. A. D.**, 1951. The hydrothermal chemistry of silicates. Part I. Synthetic lithium aluminosilicates. *Journ. Chem. Soc.*, p. 1267.

Comucci, P., 1915. Sopra la petalite elbana. *Rend. R. Accad. Lincei, Roma*, Ser. 5, vol. 24, p. 1141 (M.A. 1–352).

Ginzburg, A. I. and **Gushchina, N. S.**, 1954. Petalite from pegmatites of the eastern Transbaikal region. *Trans. Miner. Mus. Acad. Sci. USSR*, vol. 6, p. 71 (M.A. 13–182).

Gossner, B. and **Mussgnug, F.**, 1930. Über die strukturelle und molekulare Einheit von Petalit. *Zeit. Krist.*, vol. 74, p. 62.

Hosking, K. F. G., 1957. Identification of lithium minerals. *Mining Mag.*, vol. 96, p. 271.

Isaacs, T. and **Roy, R.**, 1958. The α–β inversions in eucryptite and spodumene. *Geochim. et Cosmochim. Acta*, vol. 15, p. 213.

Liebau, F., 1961. Untersuchungen an Schichtsilikaten des Formeltyps $A_m(\text{Si}_2\text{O}_5)_n$. III. Zur Kristallstruktur von Petalit, $\text{LiAlSi}_4\text{O}_{10}$. *Acta Cryst.*, vol. 14, p. 399.

McLintock, W. F. P., 1923. On the occurrence of petalite and pneumatolytic apatite in the Meldon aplite, Okehampton, Devonshire. *Min. Mag.*, vol. 20, p. 140.

Mikkola, T. and **Wiik, H. B.**, 1947. Petalite a mineral new to Finland. *Bull. Comm. géol. Finlande*, No. 140, p. 281.

Nel. H. J., 1946.   Petalite and amblygonite from Karibib, South West Africa.
Amer. Min., vol. 31, p. 51.
Norton, F. H., 1939.   Hydrothermal formation of clay minerals in the laboratory.
Amer. Min., vol. 24, p. 1.
Quensel, P., 1937.   Minerals of the Varuträsk pegmatite.   IV. Petalite and its
alteration product montmorillonite.   *Geol. För. Förh. Stockholm*, vol. 59,
p. 150.
—— 1957.   The paragenesis of the Varuträsk pegmatite.   *Arkiv. Min. Geol.*,
vol. 2, p. 9.
Roy, R., Roy, D. M. and Osborn, E. F., 1950.   Compositional and stability relation-
ships among the lithium alumino-silicates, eucryptite, spodumene and petalite.
Journ. Amer. Ceram. Soc., vol. 33, p. 152.
Saalfeld, H., 1961.   Zur thermischen Umwandlung und Kristallographie von
Petalit und Spodumen.   *Zeit. Krist.*, vol. 115, p. 420.
Shibata, H., 1952.   Mineralizations in granite-pegmatites in Japan and Korea,
Parts I and II.   *Sci. Repts., Tokyo Univ. of Education, sect. C.*, vol. 2, p. 63 &
p. 107 (M.A. 15–288).
Simpson, E. S., 1938.   Contributions to the mineralogy of Western Australia.
Series XI.   *Journ. Roy. Soc. W. Australia*, vol. 24, p. 107 (M.A. 7–340).
Tavora, E., 1952.   The redetermination of the space group of petalite.   *Anais Acad.
Brasil. Cienc.*, vol. 24, p. 175 (M.A. 12–98).
Vesasalo, A., 1959.   On the petalite occurrences of Tammela, S.W. Finland.   *Bull.
Comm. géol. Finlande*, vol. 29, No. 184, p. 59.
Zemann-Hedlik, A. and Zemann, J., 1954.   Zur Kenntnis der Kristallstruktur von
petalite.   *Naturwiss.*, vol. 41, p. 476.
—— —— 1955.   The structure of petalite, $LiAlSi_4O_{10}$.   *Acta Cryst.*, vol. 8, p. 781.

Leucite   K[AlSi₂O₆]

TETRAGONAL (PSEUDOCUBIC) (+)

n 1·508–1·511 δ 0·001

Dispersion : Moderate. D 2·47–2·50. H $5\frac{1}{2}$–6.

Cleavage : {110} very poor.

Twinning : {110} repeated.

Colour : White or grey, colourless in thin section.

Unit cell : $a \simeq 13\cdot0$, $c \simeq 13\cdot8$ Å.

$\qquad$ Z=16. Space group $I4_1/a$.

Decomposed by HCl.

Leucite is a highly characteristic mineral of the potassium-rich, silica-poor lavas of Tertiary and recent age. It occurs in some hypabyssal rocks, *e.g.* nepheline dolerite, but has not been described in rocks that have crystallized in a plutonic environment, and is unknown in metamorphic rocks. Aggregates showing the crystal habit of leucite but mainly consisting of potassium felspar and nepheline, sometimes together with smaller amounts of sodalite, cancrinite or a zeolite, occur in both plutonic and volcanic rocks. These so-called pseudo-leucites are generally considered to have crystallized initially as leucite, which either reacted with the magma, or subsequently unmixed, to form potassium felspar and nepheline. Leucite crystals are often euhedral showing the form {211}, sometimes combined with {100} and {110}. The name is derived from the Greek *leukos*, white.

STRUCTURE

The structure of leucite has been investigated by Wyart (1938, 1940, 1941) and by Náray-Szabó (1942). At ordinary temperatures leucite is tetragonal (pseudo-cubic) with $a \simeq 13\cdot0$, $c \simeq 13\cdot8$ Å and space group $I4_1/a$, but it gradually changes on heating until at about 625°C. it is cubic with a 13·4 Å and space group $Ia3d$. Both cubic and tetragonal leucite have 16(KAlSi₂O₆) in the unit cell but, whereas in the cubic cell oxygens occupy a set of 96-fold equivalent positions, in the tetragonal cell they are distributed among six sets of 16-fold positions. The structure is based on an (Si,Al)–O framework similar to that of analcite NaAlSi₂O₆·H₂O (Taylor, 1930), and pollucite CsAlSi₂O₆·xH₂O (Strunz, 1936; Náray-Szabó, 1938).[1] In all three minerals (Si,Al)O₄ tetrahedra are linked by sharing corners to form rings of six tetrahedra (similar to those in beryl) and rings of four tetrahedra, as illustrated in Fig. 89. In analcite and in cubic leucite and pollucite, the six- and four-membered rings are respectively

---

[1] Wairakite, CaAl₂Si₄O₁₂·2H₂O, has a similar aluminosilicate framework (Coombs 1955). For further discussion of analcite and related minerals see p. 340.

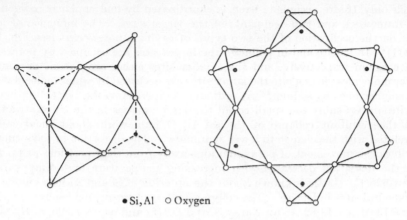

●Si, Al   ○ Oxygen

Fɪɢ. 89.   Rings of four and six tetrahedra of the type which occur in the leucite structure.

normal to triad and tetrad axes.   The content of the lower half of the cubic cell is illustrated in Fig. 90, where large circles show the positions of K ions in leucite but also represent the positions of Cs in pollucite and of water molecules in analcite.   These 16 positions (at $\frac{1}{8}$, $\frac{1}{8}$, $\frac{1}{8}$, etc.) are co-ordinated by 12 oxygens and are in line with the centres of large channels (formed by the six-membered rings) which run along four non-intersecting triad directions.   In addition the structure contains a set of 24 smaller cavities (at $\frac{1}{8}$, 0, $\frac{1}{4}$, etc.) of

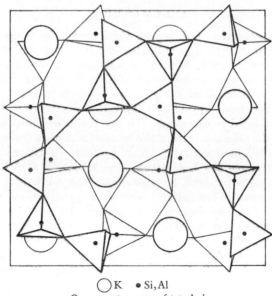

◯ K   ● Si, Al
Oxygens at corners of tetrahedra

Fɪɢ. 90.   Lower half of the unit cell of leucite (after Náray-Szabó, 1938).

which only 16 are occupied; each is coordinated by four coplanar oxygens of the framework and two occupants of the larger sites. The influence of ionic sizes on the occupation of the two types of cavity is noteworthy (see Fig. 104, p. 341). In leucite and in pollucite the larger sites are occupied by potassium and caesium respectively, and the smaller sites either are vacant or contain water molecules; in analcite the larger sites are occupied by water molecules and the smaller ones by sodium. At ordinary temperatures the potassium ions in leucite are probably too small to fill the large cavities in the cubic structure, and the resultant collapse of the (Si,Al)–O framework about them can be correlated with the change to lower symmetry. The distortion of the structure involves the movement of potassium ions away from their positions at $(\frac{1}{3}, \frac{1}{3}, \frac{1}{3})$ but the deviation decreases with increasing temperature and disappears at about 625°C. Little is known about the ordering of Si and Al ions among the tetrahedral sites in leucite. The cell parameters of tetragonal leucite are given as $a = 13 \cdot 01$, $c = 13 \cdot 82$ Å, by Náray-Szabó (1942) and as $a = 12 \cdot 95$, $c = 13 \cdot 65$ Å, by Wyart (1941). The pseudo-cubic cell has also been described as orthorhombic (Bannister, 1931) and as monoclinic (Onorato, 1938).

Water molecules and cations can easily leave and enter the aluminosilicate framework of the analcite-type structure, and exchange of cations can be effected using appropriate solutions to transform leucite into analcite and vice-versa (Barrer, 1950). The correlation between structure and the substitution of various cations in leucite has been investigated (Barrer and Hinds, 1953), and the synthesis of a hydrated leucite (*i.e.* a true potassium analcite) has been reported (Barrer *et al.*, 1953). The latter substance is cubic with a 13·79 Å.

CHEMISTRY

Leucite compositions do not depart significantly from the ideal formula, $KAlSi_2O_6$. The Si : Al ratio approximates closely to 2 : 1, and the main replacement, the substitution of K by Na, occurs only to a limited extent; thus approximately 13 per cent. replacement of K by Na is the maximum shown by the recent analyses detailed in Table 33, while the K : Na ratio for the average of fourteen leucites from Vesuvius is 84·6 : 15·4 (Chirvinsky, 1953). Further evidence of the limited replacement of K by Na in leucite is provided by the compositions of the salic minerals in the leucite–nepheline dolerite from Vogelsberg (Tilley, 1958), in which the alkali contents of the associated leucite, nepheline and sanidine are K_2O 19·42, Na_2O 1·12; K_2O 5·75, Na_2O 16·61; K_2O 12·09, Na_2O 2·66 per cent. respectively. The contrasting distribution of potassium and sodium in coexisting leucite and nepheline is also illustrated by two leucite–nepheline associations from central African lavas, in which the leucites contain K_2O 18·50, Na_2O 0·60, and K_2O 19·44, Na_2O 0·98 per cent. and the associated nephelines contain K_2O 8·78, Na_2O 13·23, and K_2O 12·22, Na_2O 10·66 per cent. respectively (Sahama, 1952). The role of the small amounts of calcium in leucite is not apparent and its position in the structure is uncertain.

Pure leucite melts congruently at 1686° ± 5°C. (Bowen and Schairer, 1929). Potassium felspar melts incongruently at 1150° ± 20°C. to leucite and liquid the composition of which is leucite 57·8, silica 42·2 per cent. (Schairer and Bowen,

1955). There is a large compositional field of primary leucite crystallization in the system $K_2O–Al_2O_3–SiO_2$ (Fig. 91), and crystallization temperatures vary from the congruent melting point to the lowest temperature in the leucite field, $810° \pm 5°C$. Small crystals of leucite quenched from temperatures below 900°C. remain completely isotropic. In the sub-system $KAlSiO_4–Al_2O_3–SiO_2$, leucite is in equilibrium at temperatures from the liquidus to just below those of complete consolidation with corundum, mullite, potassium felspar,

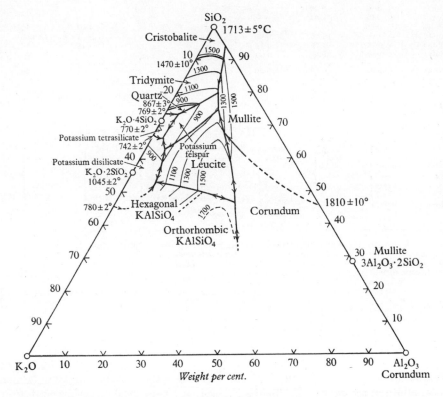

Fig. 91. Phase diagram of the system $K_2O–Al_2O_3–SiO_2$ (after Schairer and Bowen, 1955).

tridymite and cristobalite. Leucite is not compatible, in the same temperature range, with quartz, tridymite or cristobalite in the sub-system $KAlSiO_4–K_2O \cdot 2SiO_2–SiO_2$.

In the system $NaAlSi_3O_8–KAlSi_3O_8–H_2O$ the leucite field diminishes in size with increasing water pressure. Thus in the dry system the leucite field extends to 51 per cent. $NaAlSi_3O_8$, at a P_{H_2O} of 1000 bars to 29 per cent., and at 2000 bars to 5 per cent. $NaAlSi_3O_8$ (see Fig. 20, p. 50). The range of crystallization temperatures at 1000 and 2000 bars water pressure is from 1135° to 1000°C. and 1000° to 960°C. respectively. In the system $KAlSi_3O_8–H_2O$ (Goranson, 1938) leucite is not stable above approximately 2500 bars water pressure at 950°C.; above this pressure potassium felspar melts to a liquid of

Table 33.　Leucite analyses

	1.	2.	3.	4.	5.	6.	7.
SiO$_2$	54·62	54·30	53·69	55·4	54·66	54·12	56·39
TiO$_2$	0·00	0·26	0·15	0·2	0·17	1·39	—
Al$_2$O$_3$	22·93	20·08	22·72	23·3	23·15	22·19	23·10
Fe$_2$O$_3$	0·26	1·44	1·01	}0·5	0·36	}0·68	—
FeO	0·26	0·22	0·14		0·11		—
MnO	—	—	0·00	—	0·01	0·23	—
MgO	0·00	0·00	0·21	0·0	0·04	0·17	—
CaO	0·08	1·84	0·46	1·1	0·11	1·19	0·27
Na$_2$O	0·66	1·88	0·30	1·8	0·63	1·02	2·17
K$_2$O	21·02	19·02	20·69	18·3	20·04	18·41	18·05
H$_2$O +	0·12	0·75	0·19	}0·2	0·36	0·43	—
H$_2$O −	0·00	0·00	0·00		0·05	0·23	—
Total	99·95	99·79	99·56	100·8	99·77	100·44	99·98
n	1·509	1·511	1·511	—	—	1·505	—
D	—	—	—	—	2·477	—	—

NUMBERS OF IONS ON THE BASIS OF 6 OXYGENS

	1.	2.	3.	4.	5.	6.	7.
Si	1·994	2·008	1·972	1·99	1·992	1·970	2·019
Al	0·986	0·876	0·984	0·98	0·995	0·953	0·975
Ti	—	0·007	0·004	0·01	0·005	0·038	—
Fe^{+3}	0·007	0·040	0·028	0·01	0·010	0·019	—
Mg	— ⎬1·00	— ⎬1·00	0·011 ⎬1·05	0·011 ⎬1·04	0·002 ⎬1·02	0·009 ⎬1·07†	— ⎬0·99
Fe^{+2}	0·008	0·007	0·004	—	0·003	—	—
Ca	0·002	0·073	0·018	0·04	0·004	0·046	0·010
Na	0·047 ⎬1·03	0·135 ⎬1·03	0·021 ⎬0·99	0·13 ⎬0·97	0·045 ⎬0·98	0·072 ⎬0·93	0·151 ⎬0·98
K	0·978	0·897	0·970	0·84	0·932	0·856	0·825

1. Leucite, leucitite (mikenite), Mt. Mikeno, Lake Kivu, Congo (Sahama, 1952).　Anal. Th. G. Sahama.
2. Leucite, potash–ankaratrite, Nyamunuka crater, Uganda (Sahama, 1952).
3. Leucite, venanzite, San Venanzo, Italy (Bannister *et al.*, 1953).　Anal. H. B. Wiik.
4. Leucite, leucite theralite, Nyamlagira volcano, Congo (Bowen & Ellestad, 1937).　Anal. R. B. Ellestad (Includes some felspar impurity).
5. Leucite, giant leucite aggregate, Nyiragongo, Congo (Sahama, 1960).　Anal. P. Ojanperä (Includes P$_2$O$_2$ 0·08).
6. Isotropic material, rim surrounding core of granite xenolith in hybrid olivine-rich ugandite, Lake Kariya crater, Uganda (Holmes, 1945).　Anal. E. Kroupa (Includes CO$_2$ 0·25, P$_2$O$_5$ 0·13).
7. Leucite, average of 14 leucites from Vesuvius (Chirvinsky 1953).

† Includes Mn 0·007.

hydrated felspar composition (Fig. 92).　Whereas the presence of some 50 per cent. albite in the system $KAlSi_3O_8$–$NaAlSi_3O_8$ ensures the direct precipitation of an alkali felspar instead of leucite from the melt (Schairer, 1950), the addition of anorthite (*i.e.* in the system $KAlSi_3O_8$–$CaAl_2Si_2O_8$) does not prohibit the separation of leucite; the pair leucite and anorthite form a eutectic at $1413 \pm 2°C$. at the composition 45 per cent. anorthite (Schairer and Bowen, 1947).　In the system anorthite–leucite–silica the ternary reaction point is at $1040 \pm 20°C$., the composition containing rather less than 5 per cent. anorthite.　Leucite forms a eutectic with diopside at $1300°C$. at the composition 61·5 per cent. diopside, and in the system leucite–diopside–silica (Schairer and Bowen, 1938) the composition and temperature of the ternary reaction point are not very different from those of the reaction point (42·2 per cent. SiO_2, $1150°C$.) in the binary system leucite–silica.　In both the systems leucite–corundum–spinel and leucite–forsterite–spinel the leucite field is small, and the relationships are of only general petrological interest (Schairer, 1954, 1955).　For the majority of potassium-rich magmas, there is no evidence that leucite has crystallized, and

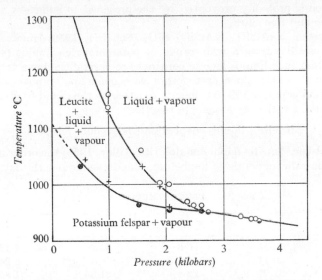

FIG. 92. Projection on the PT plane of the system $KAlSi_3O_8$–
H_2O. ●, Potassium felspar + vapour; ○, liquid +
vapour; +, leucite + liquid + vapour (after Goranson,
1938).

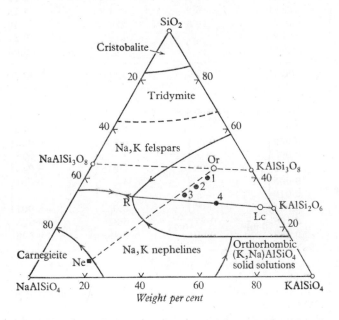

FIG. 93. Plot of pseudoleucite compositions (numbers 1 to 4
refer to analyses of Table 34) in the $NaAlSiO_4$–$KAlSiO_4$–
SiO_2 system. Ne, Morozewicz's nepheline composition;
Lc, average composition of leucite; Or, average composition of potassium felspar; R, reaction point leucite +
liquid→nepheline + potassium felspar.

its separation is probably prevented by the presence, in sufficient amounts, of water, albite and free silica.

In the system $NaAlSiO_4$–$KAlSiO_4$–SiO_2 (Schairer, 1950) leucite is the first phase to crystallize from a wide range of potassium-rich liquids (see Fig. 80, p. 247). From such liquids leucite continues to crystallize down to a temperature of 1020°C., either alone or together with nepheline or potassium felspar. At the reaction point, at 1020°C., leucite reacts with the liquid to give nepheline and orthoclase, *i.e.* the pseudoleucite reaction:

$$\text{leucite} + \text{liquid} \rightarrow \text{nepheline} + \text{potassium felspar}$$

In the Vogelsberg leucite–nepheline dolerite (Tilley, 1958) the order of crystallization of the salic minerals is nepheline, leucite, sanidine, the latter in part

Table 34. PSEUDOLEUCITE ANALYSES

	1.	2.	3.	4.
SiO_2	55·55	56·9	56·26	57·42
TiO_2	0·11	0·1	—	0·24
Al_2O_3	22·27	22·6	21·93	21·85
Fe_2O_3	1·66	0·6	0·67	1·70
FeO	0·33	—	—	0·00
MgO	0·09	0·0	—	0·07
CaO	2·16	1·3	1·46	0·19
Na_2O	2·80	3·9	4·95	4·78
K_2O	10·37	10·8	10·63	13·40
H_2O^+	4·09	}3·5	}4·16	0·27
H_2O^-	0·99			0·03
Total	100·42	99·7	100·06	100·26

NUMBERS OF IONS ON THE BASIS OF 6 OXYGENS

	1.	2.	3.	4.
Si	2·025	2·05	2·043	2·034
Al	0·959⎫	0·96⎫	0·939⎫	0·912⎫
Ti	0·003⎪	—⎪	—⎪	0·006⎪
Fe^{+3}	0·046⎬1·11	0·02⎬1·03	0·018⎬1·01	0·045⎬0·98†
Mg	0·005⎪	—⎪	—⎪	0·004⎪
Fe^{+2}	0·010⎪	—	—	—
Ca	0·084⎭	0·05⎭	0·057⎭	0·007⎭
Na	0·198⎫0·68	0·27⎫0·77	0·348⎫0·84	0·328⎫0·93
K	0·482⎭	0·50⎭	0·493⎭	0·606⎭

1. Pseudoleucite, tinguaite, Tzu Chin Shan, Shansi, North China (Yagi, 1954). Anal. K. Yagi.
2. Pseudoleucite, basalt, Highwood Mountains, Montana (Larsen & Buie, 1938). Anal. F. A. Gonyer.
3. Pseudoleucite, borolanite, Cnoc-na Sroine, Scotland (Shand, 1910). Anal. J. Shand.
4. Pseudoleucite, tinguaite, Bearpaw Mountains, Montana (Zies & Chayes, 1960) Anal. E. G. Zies (Includes MnO 0·03, BaO 0·28).

† Includes Mn 0·001 ,Ba 0·004.

enveloping the leucite. From the normative salic composition of the rock (see Fig. 87) plotted in the $NaAlSiO_4$–$KAlSiO_4$–SiO_2 system it is clear that nepheline would be the first phase to crystallize, and would be joined subsequently by leucite, the two crystallizing together to the reaction point R, where crystallization would be completed by a reaction involving the partial resorption of leucite and the precipitation of sanidine.

Leucite has been prepared from analcite by heating the latter in a concentrated solution of potassium chloride at 200 °C.; analcite and leucite are readily interconvertible by ion exchange (Barrer, 1950; Barrer *et al.*, 1953):

$$NaAlSi_2O_6 \cdot H_2O + K^+aq. \rightleftharpoons KAlSi_2O_6 + Na^+aq. + H_2O$$
analcite   leucite

The extent to which the exchange of Na by K has occurred can be measured by determining the loss of water from hydrothermally synthesized analcite, which contains 8·46 per cent. H_2O, the derived leucite having 0·75 per cent. (Barrer and Hinds, 1953). Leucite has also been obtained, together with kalsilite and kaliophilite, from gels of composition $K_2O \cdot Al_2O_3 \cdot nSiO_2$ where $1 \leqslant n \leqslant 12$, the maximum yield being obtained at 300 °C. from a gel of composition $K_2O \cdot Al_2O_3 \cdot 3SiO_2$ plus 135 per cent. molar excess of KOH in aqueous solution (Barrer and Baynham, 1956). The crystallization of leucite from muscovite ground for 24 hours and heated to 1000 °C. has been reported by Mackenzie and Milne (1953). In addition to the pseudoleucite reaction, leucite may show alteration to analcite, sericite or kaolinite. Kotlyar (1945) has described a number of leucite-bearing intrusive and extrusive rocks in which the replacement products of leucite include alkali felspar, muscovite, biotite, analcite, nepheline and carbonates. The composition of the decomposition layer on leucite in relation to the pH of the solution, as well as the amounts of K_2O, Al_2O_3 and SiO_2 leached from leucite with a solvent of pH 3, have been estimated by Correns and Engelhardt (Eitel, 1954).

OPTICAL AND PHYSICAL PROPERTIES

The small range of ionic replacements shown by leucite is accompanied by correspondingly minor variations in the optical and physical properties; the refractive index is generally $1·510 \pm 0·001$ and the density $2·485 \pm 0·015$ gm./cm.^{3} Though normally uniaxial, leucite may show a very small optic axial angle. Leucite, except in very small crystals, shows complex repeated twinning on {110} and weak anisotropy; it is usually developed in equant and often euhedral crystals with icositetrahedral {211}, or more rarely the dodecahedral {110}, habit, and exhibits octagonal outlines in thin section. Skeletal growths and inclusions, the latter arranged in regular, either radial or concentric, patterns, are not uncommon. On heating low-temperature leucite the *c* parameter contracts from 13·65 Å at 20 °C. to 13·40 Å at 625 °C., the *a* parameter over the same temperature range expands from 12·95 to 13·40 Å. Equal values of the *a* and *c* cell dimensions, 13·45 Å, are also obtained at 750 °C. (Wyart 1938). The inversion of low- to high-temperature leucite, determined by Grossman (Eitel, 1954) from thermogoniometric measurements, occurs at 620 °C. For synthetic leucite Bowen and Schairer (1929) gave the inversion temperature as 603 °C.

DISTINGUISHING FEATURES

Leucite is distinguished from analcite by the common presence of complex twinning, and by having a higher refractive index. These characteristics also serve to distinguish leucite from the sodalite group of minerals which in addition are sometimes pale blue in thin section. Microcline has a higher birefringence and higher refringence.

PARAGENESIS

Leucite is a particularly characteristic mineral of potassium-rich basic lavas, and is especially abundant in the Leucite Hills, Wyoming, and central Montana areas, the Roman region, in West Kimberley (Australia), and in south-western Uganda and the Congo. Wade and Prider (1940) and Prider (1960) have described a suite of leucite-bearing volcanic and hypabyssal rocks from West Kimberley which, with the exception of the almost pure leucite rock italite (Washington, 1920) from the Roman region, are the rocks richest in leucite yet described. The leucite, associated with olivine (nontronite pseudomorphs), titaniferous phlogopite, diopside, magnophorite, and wadeite, $K_2(Ca, Na)Zr(Si, Al)_4O_{12}$, occurs in the siliceous groundmass of the lamproites. In bulk composition the rocks are saturated, and they contain sufficient silica to form sanidine. Thus the leucite, which may show alteration to a turbid material, crystallized at a temperature above that of the pseudoleucite reaction, and the enclosing liquid was chilled sufficiently rapidly to prevent its reaction with leucite to form potassium felspar.

Leucite occurs in a variety of potassium-rich lavas, *e.g.* leucite basanite, leucite tephrite, leucite–melilite basalt, leucite ankaratrite (Table 33, anal. 2) and the leucitite (Table 33, anal. 1) of the lava fields east and south-east of Ruwenzori (Holmes and Harwood, 1932). Elsewhere in Uganda it is a constituent of the potassium-rich ultrabasic volcanic rocks ugandite (olivine + augite + leucite) and katungite (melilite + leucite glass with or without leucite) and is associated with kalsilite in leucite mafurite and leucite–melilite mafurite (Combe and Holmes, 1945; Holmes, 1950). The leucitization of granite xenoliths enclosed in the olivine-rich ugandite bombs of the katungite tuffs of Kariya, Uganda, has been described by Holmes (1945). The xenoliths are surrounded by a zone in which the orthoclase, oligoclase and quartz of the granite are replaced by a buff-coloured isotropic material which passes marginally into leucite crystals. Some of the xenoliths are completely replaced by isotropic material (Table 33, anal. 6) with a refractive index of 1·505 and the composition of leucite. A series of leucite-bearing basic lavas, including leucite shonkinite and leucite tephrite from the Muriah volcano, central Java, have been described by Bemmelen (1947) and are considered to have been derived from a basaltic magma by desilication consequent on limestone assimilation. Jérémine *et al.* (1958) have described leucite occurring in veins in the analcite basanite of Causses, Auvergne, France.

Giant leucites in blocks in the talus of the Nyiragongo volcano, Congo, have been described by Sahama and Meyer (1958) and Sahama (1960). The blocks, which may be widely separated or so closely spaced as to be in contact with the adjacent aggregates, are typically some 7 cm. in diameter and consist of a core of relatively fine-grained leucites with pyroxene, olivine, magnetite and glass between the leucite crystals, and a wide rim of radially oriented coarse-grained leucite. Those parts of the lava containing large numbers of the giant leucite aggregates have an extremely high content of potassium; a magma of such composition is not possible and Sahama (1960) suggests that the aggregates gradually crystallized as they rose in the magma and accumulated at the top of the lava mass.

In some rocks leucite is completely replaced by an intergrowth of potassium-rich alkali felspar and nepheline, or is surrounded by a rim consisting mainly of potassium felspar and nepheline. These intergrowths, some of which show a zonal arrangement, are described as pseudoleucite. Thus in the Tzu Chin Shan pseudoleucite (Table 34, anal. 1) the narrow outer zone consists of ortho-clase and nepheline in random orientation, the inner zone of orthoclase, nepheline and analcite with their longer dimensions normal to the crystal margins (the characteristic "palisade" structure), and the central part of equant grains of orthoclase, nepheline and analcite. Smaller amounts of sericite and kaolinite are also present. The pseudoleucite from the Highwood Mountains (Table 34, anal. 2) consists of a mixture of orthoclase, containing approximately K_2O 10·8, Na_2O 3·9, CaO 1·3 weight per cent., and amorphous material the composition of which is close to nepheline plus water. In some of the more altered rocks of this area natrolite and analcite take the place of the amorphous fraction of the pseudoleucite.

In a pseudoleucite tinguaite dyke, Bearpaw Mountains, Montana, nepheline, sanidine, perthite-like intergrowths of nepheline in sanidine, and aegirine are the essential constituents of the pseudoleucite (Zies and Chayes, 1960). The average mode of the pseudoleucite is sanidine 66·2, nepheline 29·8, and aegirine 3 per cent.; the nepheline contains K_2O 7·9, Na_2O 15·7 per cent., and the sanidine K_2O 16·5, Na_2O 0·3 per cent. The calculated mode of the groundmass is nepheline 26·8, sanidine 46·5, aegirine 26·7 per cent. and the compositions of the nepheline (K_2O 7·6, Na_2O 15·3 per cent.) and sanidine (K_2O 15·94, Na_2O 0·28 per cent.) are similar to those of the nepheline and sanidine in the pseudoleucite.

Pseudoleucite occurs mainly in volcanic rocks, and pseudoleucites with well defined crystal boundaries are confined to quickly chilled rocks. Pseudoleucite is found also in some plutonic rocks (Shand, 1910) but here the intergrowths are less well defined and have rounded margins which merge into the other rock constituents. In the Highwood Mountains pseudoleucite occurs in shonkinite; in the quickly cooled rocks the pseudoleucite has sharply defined outlines, but in the more slowly cooled rocks of the laccoliths it occurs in rounded patches which merge into the surrounding groundmass.

The genesis of pseudoleucite has been ascribed to a number of different processes, *e.g.* the breakdown of sodium-leucite to an intergrowth of orthoclase and nepheline (Yagi, 1954), the product of sodium pneumatolysis (Rittman, 1933), the decomposition of potassium-rich analcite (Larsen and Buie, 1938) and the reaction of early formed leucite with magmatic liquids, the so-called pseudoleucite reaction (Bowen and Ellestad, 1937). The view that pseudoleucite results from the breakdown of leucite in which a notable amount of potassium has been replaced by sodium is difficult to sustain for all pseudoleucites. The replacement of K by Na in leucites (see Table 33) is small, and Bowen and Ellestad have demonstrated that the Nyamlagira leucite (Na_2O content

1–1·5 per cent.) which is surrounded by a rim of pseudoleucite (Na_2O content 6–7 per cent.) does not contain sufficient sodium to give pseudoleucite by a simple transformation. Moreover the rock contains leucite in the groundmass which is considered to have crystallized at approximately the temperature at which the pseudoleucite formed. In the system $NaAlSiO_4$–$KAlSiO_4$–SiO_2, the fields of leucite, alkali felspar and nepheline meet in a reaction point at 1042°C., the pseudoleucite reaction point, at which leucite reacts with the liquid to give alkali felspar and nepheline. In this system the reaction of early formed leucite with the liquid at R (Fig. 93) gives rise to the solid products nepheline and potassium felspar, the composite composition of which will be close to the line LcR; some pseudoleucite analyses plot close to this line. If, however, a comparable reaction occurs in natural magmas the composition of the liquid should be close to that of the pseudoleucite reaction point, but Zies and Chayes (1960) have shown that the composition of the groundmass in which the Bearpaw Mountains pseudoleucite occurs is remote from the pseudoleucite reaction point. Bowen's discussion of the reaction was essentially related to liquids approximating to low-temperature compositions in the system $KAlSiO_4$–$NaAlSiO_4$–SiO_2. Most pseudoleucite-bearing rocks are not of such a composition and the hypothesis cannot be applied indiscriminately to the genesis of all pseudoleucites. Moreover the sodium content of some pseudoleucites (*e.g.* the Tzu Chin Shan material) is less than that required by Bowen's hypothesis, and Yagi (1954) has suggested that this pseudoleucite is not the product of reaction of leucite with a sodium enriched residual magma, but may have been derived from the unmixing of a leucite only a little richer in sodium than many unaltered varieties. The pseudoleucite from the Highwood Mountains basalts, although containing more sodium than the Tzu Chin Shan material, is also relatively poor in sodium. These basalts carry leucite, analcite and pseudoleucite phenocrysts, the analcite is a potassium-rich variety (see analcite, p. 343) some of which is surrounded by a reaction rim or is completely replaced by potassium felspar, and it has been suggested (Larsen and Buie, 1938) that the primary phase of the Highwood Mountains pseudoleucite may have been a potassium-rich analcite (see also Fudali, 1957). An unusual development of pseudoleucite in a metamorphosed sandstone, 10 cm. from the contact of a leucite-bearing dyke, has also been reported from this locality by Larsen and Buie; such a paragenesis is difficult to reconcile with the pseudoleucite reaction hypothesis.

REFERENCES

Bannister, F. A., 1931. The distinction of analcime from leucite in rocks by X-ray methods. *Min. Mag.*, vol. 22, p. 469.
—— Sahama, Th. G. and Wiik, H. B., 1953. Kalsilite in venanzite from San Venanzo, Umbria, Italy. *Min. Mag.*, vol. 30, p. 46.
Barrer, R. M., 1950. Ion-exchange and ion-sieve processes in crystalline zeolites. *Journ. Chem. Soc.*, p. 2342.
—— and Baynham, J. W., 1956. The hydrothermal chemistry of the silicates. Part VII. Synthetic potassium aluminosilicates. *Journ. Chem. Soc.*, p. 2882.
—— —— and McCallum, N., 1953. Hydrothermal chemistry of silicates. V. Compounds structurally related to analcite. *Journ. Chem. Soc.*, p. 4035.
—— and Hinds, L., 1953. Ion-exchange in crystals of analcite and leucite. *Journ. Chem. Soc.*, p. 1879.

Barrer, R. M., Hinds, L. and **White, E. A.**, 1953. The hydrothermal chemistry of silicates. Part III. Reactions of analcite and leucite. *Journ. Chem. Soc.*, p. 1466.

Bemmelen, R. W. van, 1947. The Muriah volcano (central Java) and the origin of its leucite-bearing rocks. *Proc. K. Nederl. Akad. Wetens.*, vol. 50, p. 653.

Bennet, J. A. E., 1945. Some occurrences of leucite in East Lothian. *Trans. Edin. Geol. Soc.*, vol. 14, p. 34.

Bowen, N. L. and **Ellestad, R. B.**, 1937. Leucite and pseudoleucite. *Amer. Min.*, vol. 22, p. 409.

—— and **Schairer, J. F.**, 1929. The system leucite–diopside. *Amer. Journ. Sci.*, 5th ser., vol. 18, p. 301.

—— and **Tuttle, O. F.**, 1950. The system $NaAlSi_3O_8$–$KAlSi_3O_8$–H_2O. *Journ. Geol.*, vol. 58, p. 489.

Chirvinsky, P. N., 1953. *The average chemical composition of the principal minerals of eruptive, metamorphic, and sedimentary rocks.* Lvov. Geol. Soc.

Combe, A. D. and **Holmes, A.**, 1945. The kalsilite-bearing lavas of Kabirenge and Lyakaute, south-west Uganda. *Trans. Roy. Soc. Edin.*, vol. 61, p. 359.

Coombs, D. S., 1955. X-ray observations on wairakite and non-cubic analcime. *Min. Mag.*, vol. 30, p. 699.

Eitel, W., 1954. *The physical chemistry of the silicates.* Univ. Chicago Press, p. 953.

Fudali, R. F., 1957. On the origin of pseudoleucite. *Trans. Amer. Geophys. Union*, vol. 38, p. 391.

Goranson, R. W., 1938. Silicate–water systems phase equilibria in the $NaAlSi_3O_8$–H_2O and $KAlSi_3O_8$–H_2O systems at high temperatures and pressures. *Amer. Journ. Sci.*, 5th ser., vol. 35A, p. 71.

Holmes, A., 1945. Leucitized granite xenoliths from the potash-rich lavas of Bunyaruguru, south-west Uganda. *Amer. Journ. Sci.*, Daly vol., p. 313.

—— 1950. Petrogenesis of katungite and its associates. *Amer. Min.*, vol. 35, p. 772.

—— 1952. The potash ankaratrite–metaleucite lavas of Nabungando and Mbuga craters, south-west Uganda. *Trans. Edin. Geol. Soc.*, vol. 15, p. 187.

—— and **Harwood, H. F.**, 1932. Petrology of the volcanic fields east and south-east of Ruwenzori, Uganda. *Quart. Journ. Geol. Soc.*, vol. 88, p. 370.

Jérémine, E., Gèze, B. and **Christophe-Michel-Lévy, M.**, 1958. Sur la présence de leucite dans les basanites des Causses. *Compt. Rend. Acad. Sci., Paris*, vol. 246, p. 798.

Kotlyar, V. N., 1945. The Pamback complex of alkaline rocks. *Bull. Acad. Sci. URSS, Sér. Géol.*, no. 2, p. 97 (M.A. 11–29).

Larsen, E. S. and **Buie, B. F.**, 1938. Potash analcime and pseudoleucite from the Highwood Mountains of Montana. *Amer. Min.*, vol. 23, p. 837.

Mackenzie, R. C. and **Milne, A. A.**, 1953. The effect of grinding on micas. I. Muscovite. *Min. Mag.*, vol. 30, p. 178.

Náray-Szabó, St. v., 1938. Die Struktur des Pollucits $CsAlSi_2O_6 \cdot xH_2O$. *Zeit. Krist.*, vol. 99, p. 277.

—— 1942. Die Struktur des Leucits $KAlSi_2O_6$. *Zeit. Krist.*, vol. 104, p. 39.

Onorato, E., 1938. Richerche röntgenographiche sulla leucite. *Period. Min. Roma*, vol. 9, p. 85.

Prider, R. T., 1939. Some minerals from the leucite-rich rocks of the West Kimberley area, Western Australia. *Min. Mag.*, vol. 25, p. 373.

—— 1960. The leucite lamproites of the Fitzroy Basin, Western Australia. *Journ. Geol. Soc. Australia*, vol. 6, p. 71.

Rittman, A., 1933. Evolution und Differentiation des Somma-Vesuvmagmas. *Zeit. Volkanologie*, vol. 15, p. 8.

Sahama, Th. G., 1952.   Leucite, potash nepheline and clinopyroxene from volcanic lavas from south western Uganda and adjoining Belgian Congo. *Amer. Journ. Sci.,* Bowen vol., p. 457.

—— 1960.   Kalsilite in the lavas of Mt. Nyiragongo (Belgian Congo). *Journ Petr.,* vol. 1, p. 146.

—— and **Meyer, A.,** 1958.   Study of the volcano of Nyirayongo.   A progress report.   *Inst. des Parcs Nationaux du Congo Belge, Mission d'Études Vulcanologiques,* Fasc. 2.

Schairer, J. F., 1950.   The system NaAlSiO$_4$–KAlSiO$_4$–SiO$_2$.   *Journ. Geol.,* vol. 58, p. 512.

—— 1954.   The system K$_2$O–MgO–Al$_2$O$_3$–SiO$_2$.   I. Results of quenching experiments on four joins in the tetrahedron cordierite–forsterite–leucite–silica and on the join cordierite–mullite–potash feldspar.   *Journ. Amer. Ceram. Soc.,* vol. 37, p. 501.

—— 1955.   The ternary systems leucite–corundum–spinel and leucite–forsterite–spinel.   *Journ. Amer. Ceram. Soc.,* vol. 38, p. 153.

—— and **Bowen, N. L.,** 1938.   The system leucite–diopside–silica.   *Amer. Journ. Sci.,* 5th ser., vol. 35A, p. 289.

—— —— 1947.   The system anorthite–leucite–silica.   *Bull. Comm. géol. Finlande,* no. 140, p. 67.

—— —— 1955.   The system K$_2$O–Al$_2$O$_3$–SiO$_2$.   *Amer. Journ. Sci.,* vol. 253, p. 681.

Shand, S. J., 1910.   On borolanite and its associates in Assynt.   *Trans. Edin. Geol. Soc.,* vol. 9, p. 376.

Strunz, H., 1936.   Die chemische Zusammensetzung von Pollucit.   *Zeit. Krist.,* vol. 95, p. 1.

Taylor, W. H., 1930.   The structure of analcite (NaAlSi$_2$O$_6$·H$_2$O).   *Zeit. Krist.,* vol. 74, p. 1.

Tilley, C. E., 1958.   The leucite nepheline dolerite of Meiches, Vogelsberg, Hessen.   *Amer. Min.,* vol. 43, p. 759.

Wade, A. and **Prider, R. T.,** 1940.   The leucite-bearing rocks of the West Kimberley area, Western Australia.   *Quart. Journ. Geol. Soc.,* vol. 96, p. 39.

Washington, H. S., 1920.   Italite, a new leucite rock.   *Amer. Journ. Sci.,* ser. 5, vol. 1, p. 33.

Wyart, J., 1938.   Étude sur la leucite.   *Bull. Soc. franç. Min.,* vol. 61, p. 228.

—— 1940.   Étude cristallographique, d'une leucite artificielle.   Structure atomique et symmétrie du minéral.   *Bull. Soc. franç. Min.,* vol. 63, p. 5.

—— 1941.   Structure atomique de la leucite.   *Compt. Rend. Acad. Sci. Paris,* vol. 282, p. 356.

Yagi, K., 1954.   Pseudoleucite from Tzu Chin Shan, Shansi, North China.   *Jap. Journ. Geol. Geogr.,* vol. 24, p. 93.

Zies, E. G. and **Chayes, F.,** 1960.   Pseudoleucite in a tinguaite from the Bearpaw Mountains, Montana.   *Journ. Petr.,* vol. 1, p. 86.

SODALITE GROUP

Sodalite $Na_8[Al_6Si_6O_{24}]Cl_2$
Nosean $Na_8[Al_6Si_6O_{24}]SO_4$
Haüyne $(Na,Ca)_{4-8}[Al_6Si_6O_{24}](SO_4,S)_{1-2}$

CUBIC

	Sodalite	Nosean	Haüyne
n	1·483–1·487	1·495	1·496–1·505
D	2·27–2·33	2·30–2·40	2·44–2·50
H	$5\frac{1}{2}$–6	$5\frac{1}{2}$	$5\frac{1}{2}$–6
Cleavage:	{110} poor.	{110} poor.	{110}
Twinning:	{111}	{111}	{111}
Colour:	Pale pink, grey, yellow, blue, green; colourless or very pale pink or blue in thin section.	Grey, brown, or blue; colourless or blue in thin section.	White, grey, green or blue; colourless or pale blue in thin section.
Unit cell: a (Å)	8·91	9·05	9·13
Z	1	1	1
Space group:	$P\bar{4}3m$	$P\bar{4}3m$	$P\bar{4}3m$

Readily gelatinized by acids.

The members of the sodalite group mainly occur, generally in association with nepheline or leucite, in nepheline-syenites, phonolites and related under-saturated igneous rocks. Lazurite, however, and occasionally sodalite, are found in contact metamorphosed limestones. Sodalite is named in allusion to its composition, nosean after the German mineralogist K. W. Nose of Brunswick, and haüyne after the noted crystallographer Abbé Haüy (1734–1822). Hack-manite is a fluorescent variety of sodalite showing on freshly fractured surfaces a pink colour which fades on exposure to light, and lazurite may be regarded as a sulphur-rich variety of haüyne. Lapis-lazuli is the name given to the typical lazurite-rich rock, usually containing also calcite, pyrite, colourless pyroxene, etc. Ultramarine is a synonym of lazurite but is a name generally applied specifically to synthetic materials.

STRUCTURE

Sodalite is cubic with $a \simeq 8·9$ Å, space group $P\bar{4}3m$ and one formula unit $Na_8Cl_2[AlSiO_4]_6$ per unit cell. Its structure can be described as an alumino-silicate framework the cavities of which are occupied by sodium and chlorine ions.   The configuration of the $AlSiO_4$ framework was first determined in the study of the ultramarines by Jaeger (1929a, b).   It is formed by the linkage of SiO_4 and AlO_4 tetrahedra in approximately equal numbers, each corner oxygen being shared by two tetrahedra.   In sodalite, cage-like cubo-octahedral units are formed (Fig. 94) bounded by six rings of four tetrahedra parallel to {100} and eight rings of six tetrahedra parallel to {111}; these cages are stacked in eightfold coordination so that each six-membered ring is shared by two cages. The six-membered rings define a set of channels (Fig. 103b, p. 339) which intersect at the corners and centres of the unit cells to form large cavities.

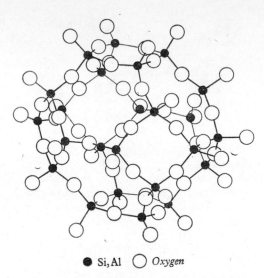

● Si,Al   ○ *Oxygen*

Fig. 94.   Part of the aluminosilicate framework in the structure of sodalite (after Bragg, 1937).

The sodalite structure was described by Barth (1926, 1927, 1932a) and by Pauling (1930).   The large cavities in the framework are occupied by chlorine ions and these are tetrahedrally co-ordinated by sodium ions which lie on cube diagonals, four near the chlorine at the centre and four near the chlorines at the cube corners.   The eight sodium ions are structurally equivalent; each lies close to one chlorine and three framework oxygens.

In the ideal structure, if the Al,Si distribution were random, the cell would be body-centred.   Little is known, however, about the ordering of the Al,Si atoms.   The framework is in any case somewhat distorted since the sodium and chlorine ions are smaller than the cavities in the ideal structure; the tetrahedra are twisted about cube triad axes, and the framework is slightly collapsed.

A synthetic "basic" sodalite, *i.e.* one in which (OH) has been substituted for Cl, is cubic with a 8·95 Å.   Lithium basic sodalite, silver basic sodalite and a potassium-rich basic sodalite have also been prepared and these have cube edges 8·72, 8·99 and 9·15 Å respectively (Barrer and Falconer, 1956).

The minerals nosean, haüyne, danalite, helvite and genthelvite all have structures similar to that of sodalite, and their cell parameters are listed in Table 35. Nosean contains the larger ion $(SO_4)^{-2}$ in place of the Cl of sodalite so that the framework is less collapsed, and in haüyne, which contains more $(SO_4)^{-2}$ ions and has some Ca replacing Na, the collapse is still less marked (compare cell parameters). The structures of nosean and haüyne have been investigated by Barth (1932a), by Machatschki (1933, 1934), and by Saalfeld (1959, 1961). For nosean Saalfeld confirmed Machatschki's suggestion that the $(SO_4)^{-2}$ ions (one per cell) are distributed randomly among the two sites, $(0,0,0)$ and $(\frac{1}{2},\frac{1}{2},\frac{1}{2})$, which are occupied by chlorine in sodalite. As shown by Barth (1932a) the eight sodium ions per cell are not all structurally equivalent and the space group is $P\bar{4}3m$, not $P\bar{4}3n$. Saalfeld has also shown that the structure of a synthetic nosean which contains tungstate in place of sulphate ions is similar to that of natural nosean but has a larger unit cell with a 9·19 Å.

The mineral haüyne is similar to nosean but involves the additional substitution of calcium for sodium. A possible formula for haüyne would thus be $Ca_4(SO_4)[AlSiO_4]_6$, but in this case the structure would be an extremely open one since in terms of the sodalite structure only half of the Cl sites and half of the Na sites would be occupied. If additional Ca and SO_4^{-2} ions were present so that all available anion sites were filled the limiting formula would be $Ca_5(SO_4)_2[AlSiO_4]_6$. Analyses of haüyne show in fact compositions intermediate between those of nosean and the two given above, and therefore can be expressed as $(Na,Ca)_{8-4}(SO_4)_{1-2}[AlSiO_4]_6$. The structure of haüyne is similar to that of nosean, but Saalfeld (1961) reports evidence of a superstructure which involves the distribution of the SO_4 groups and the (Ca,Na) ions. The distribution of Si and Al atoms among tetrahedral sites is unknown in nosean and haüyne.

Table 35.   UNIT CELLS OF SODALITE AND RELATED MINERALS

Mineral	Formula (per unit cell)			a Å	Space group	Reference
Sodalite	Na_8	Cl_2	$[AlSiO_4]_6$	8·91	$P\bar{4}3m$	Barth (1932a)
Nosean	Na_8	SO_4	,,	9·05	,,	,, ,,
Haüyne	$(Na,Ca)_{8-4}$	$(SO_4)_{1-2}$	,,	9·13	,,	,, ,,
Lazurite	$(Na,Ca)_8$	$(SO_4,S,Cl)_2$	,,	9·08	,,	Strunz (1957)
Danalite	Fe_8	S_2	$[BeSiO_4]_6$	8·20	,,	Glass *et al.* (1944)
Helvite	$(Mn,Fe,Zn)_8$	S_2	,,	8·21–8·29	,,	,, ,,
Genthelvite	Zn_8	S_2	,,	8·12	,,	,, ,,

CHEMISTRY

Sodalite is not only the most sodium-rich member of the sodalite group but also differs from the other minerals of the group in containing chlorine as an essential constituent. Seven analyses are given in Table 36, where they have been recalculated on the basis of the 21 oxygens in the $3Al_2O_3 \cdot 6SiO_2$ of the formula unit. There is little variation in the Na content beyond that related to a slight substitution of Na by both K and Ca. The latter, however, rarely rise above 1 per cent. K_2O or CaO: similarly, the replacement of Al by Fe^{+3} takes place only to a limited extent. Some analyses report appreciable amounts of sulphur, and it is present in small amounts in the fluorescent variety hackmanite.　It seems probable, from analogy with experimental work, that small amounts of water may be replacing chlorine though it will be seen from Table 36 that not all the water reported as H_2O^+ can be accepted in the structural formulae.　Natural sodalite containing 0·9 mg. of iodine per kg. was reported by Fellenberg and Lunde (1926), and artificial analogues containing bromine and other anions have been prepared.　A molybdenum-bearing sodalite, containing 2·87 per cent. MoO_3 has been recorded (Zambonini, 1910), and a mineral provisionally termed beryllium sodalite has been reported from a vein in nepheline-syenite in southwest Greenland (Sørensen, 1960).

Table 36.　SODALITE ANALYSES (including hackmanite)

	1.	2.	3.	4.	5.	6.	7.
SiO_2	36·69	36·99	36·70	38·06	36·36	36·72	37·60
Al_2O_3	31·40	31·77	32·01	31·30	32·09	31·17	31·63
Fe_2O_3	0·85	0·17	0·07	tr.	0·07	0·70	0·55
CaO	0·19	—	—	tr.	—	—	0·28
Na_2O	25·96	25·84	24·79	24·77	24·73	24·53	24·02
K_2O	0·23	0·16	0·17	—	0·12	1·13	0·46
Cl	5·64	6·44	7·00	7·18	6·79	7·22	5·56
S	0·38	0·39	tr.	—	0·00	—	1·10
H_2O^+	0·30	—	0·36	} 0·82	0·86	—	0·28
H_2O^-	0·04	—	0·00		0·12	0·23	—
	101·71	'101·81'	101·39	102·13	101·70	101·70	101·62
$O \equiv Cl,S$	1·39	1·64	1·58	1·62	1·53	1·63	1·80
Total	100·32	100·17	99·81	100·51	100·17	100·07	99·82
n	1·487	—	1·487	—	1·483	1·484	—
D	2·285	2·33	2·286	2·27	2·278	2·290	—

NUMBERS OF IONS ON THE BASIS OF THE 21(O) ASSOCIATED WITH $3Al_2O_3·6SiO_2$

	1.	2.	3.	4.	5.	6.	7.
Si	5·933 ⎫	5·959 ⎫	5·925 ⎫	6·079 ⎫	5·894 ⎫	5·961 ⎫	5·993 ⎫
Al	5·986 ⎬12·02	6·034 ⎬12·01	6·091 ⎬12·02	5·894 ⎬11·97	6·132 ⎬12·03	5·965 ⎬12·01	5·942 ⎬12·00
Fe^{+3}	0·102 ⎭	0·020 ⎭	0·008 ⎭	— ⎭	0·008 ⎭	0·086 ⎭	0·065 ⎭
Na	8·138 ⎫	8·070 ⎫	7·760 ⎫	7·672 ⎫	7·772 ⎫	7·721 ⎫	7·423 ⎫
Ca	0·033 ⎬8·22†	— ⎬8·10	— ⎬7·80	— ⎬7·67	— ⎬7·81‡	— ⎬7·96	0·048 ⎬7·60 ‖
K	0·047 ⎭	0·033 ⎭	0·035 ⎭	— ⎭	0·025 ⎭	0·234 ⎭	0·094 ⎭
Cl	1·546	1·756	1·915	1·944	1·866	1·986	1·502
S	0·115	0·118	—	—	—	—	0·329
OH	0·324	—	0·380	0·872	0·928	—	0·296

1. Light grey sodalite, pegmatite cutting sodalite nepheline-syenite, Khibina tundra, Kola peninsula (Fersman and Bonshtedt, 1937).　Anal. M. Vladimirova (Includes MgO 0·03).
2. Hackmanite, sodalite–aegirine rock, Kola peninsula (Borgström, 1901).　Anal. L. H. Borgström.
3. White or colourless hackmanite, tinguaite, Magnet Cove, Arkansas (Miser and Glass, 1941).　Anal. J. J. Fahey (Includes $CaCO_3$ 0·29).
4. Blue sodalite, associated with colourless hackmanite, nepheline-syenite, Kishengarh, Rajputana, India (Vredenburg, 1904).　Anal. E. Vredenburg.
5. Blue sodalite, associated with colourless hackmanite (anal. 3), tinguaite, Magnet Cove, Arkansas (Miser and Glass, 1941).　Anal. J. J. Fahey (Includes MnO 0·06, $CaCO_3$ 0·50).
6. Dark blue sodalite, dyke associated with nepheline-syenite, Cerro Sapo, dept. Cochabamba, Bolivia (Brendler, 1932).
7. Hackmanite, Luyavrurt, Kola peninsula (Vorobieva, 1946).　Anal. V. A. Moleva (Includes MnO 0·02, MgO 0·12).

† Includes Mg 0·007.
‡ Includes Mn 0·008.
‖ Includes Mn 0·003, Mg 0·029.

Sodalite may be produced synthetically relatively easily by hydrothermal treatment of the component oxides together with NaCl, or by heating muscovite or kaolinite with NaCl at about 500°C. (*e.g.* Friedel and Friedel, 1890). By heating a mixture $3Na_2CO_3 + 3Al_2O_3 + 6SiO_2 + 2NaCl$ in nitrogen at 900°C. Prener and Ward (1950) obtained sodalite with *a* 8·89 Å. By heating kaolinite in a concentrated solution of NaOH in the proportion kaolinite : NaOH = 3 : 8, at 100° and then at up to 500°C. for 30 hours, Borchert and Keidel (1947) produced "β-hydroxyl sodalite", $4Na_2O \cdot 3Al_2O_3 \cdot 6SiO_2aq.$, with *a* 8·860 Å : likewise, Wyart and Michel-Lévy (1949) synthesized "hydrosodalite" with chlorine replaced by water and CO_2, by heating a mixture of NaOH, Al_2O_3, SiO_2 and water in an autoclave. "Basic" sodalite has been obtained also by the hydrothermal treatment of Na–Al silicate gels over the temperature range 150° to 450°C. (Barrer and White, 1952) giving up to 100 per cent. yields (*a* 8·87 Å, *n* 1·488), and by the hydrothermal treatment of artificial analcite (Barrer *et al.*, 1953). A synthetic product whose properties resemble those of hackmanite was prepared by Medved (1954) : it is essentially pure sodalite which has been heated in a reducing atmosphere with no sulphur present. A stoichiometric mixture of Al_2O_3, SiO_2, NaOH and NaCl was heated slowly to 1060°C. and kept at that temperature for 1 to 3 days : crystal growth occurred pyrolytically, *i.e.* below the melting point of sodalite ($\simeq 1100$°C.), and sodalite was formed through the medium of solid state reactions :

$$6NaOH + 3Al_2O_3 + 6SiO_2 + 2NaCl \rightarrow Na_6Al_6Si_6O_{24} \cdot 2NaCl + 3H_2O.$$

Kirk (1955), however, considered that traces of sulphur may have been present in the starting reagents of such material, and that synthetic sodalites containing S only in the form of Na_2SO_4 or Na_2S, or containing no S, are non-luminescent. He obtained synthetic sodalite with emission peaks identical with those of hackmanite by preparing the sodalite with sulphur partially reduced from sulphate, by heating in hydrogen a mixture of composition $6NaAlSiO_4 \cdot 1 \cdot 8NaCl \cdot 0 \cdot 1Na_2SO_4$ at 900°C., and firing the resulting monosulphide-containing material in air at 900°C. for 15 minutes causing a partial oxidation of the sulphur. The preparation of a Br- and Li-bearing sodalite was reported by Weiberg (1905) and the replacement of NaCl by other salts has been demonstrated also by Barrer (1954). The production of sodalite in boiler scales has been reported by Alcock *et al.* (1944) and by Clark (1948), the latter noting that when sodalite and analcite occur in the same scale the sodalite is found in the hottest part of the system, and the analcite on the water side of the scale.

The alteration of sodalite to thomsonite, natrolite, gismondine, cancrinite, kaolin and diaspore has been recorded : the chemical relationship between sodalite and its alteration products was discussed by Thugutt (1946). The probable alteration of hackmanite to ussingite ($Na_2Al_2Si_6O_{16} \cdot 2NaOH$) has been reported by Gerasimovsky (1937).

Nosean has the composition $Na_8Al_6Si_6O_{24} \cdot SO_4$, with a limited amount of substitution of calcium for sodium permitting an increase in the sulphate ions over the ideal value of one per unit cell. Barth (1932b) has shown that in a Ca-bearing variety the upper limit will be two sulphate ions, for varieties grading towards haüyne in composition. Three analyses of nosean are given in Table 37 (anals. 1–3), where they have been recalculated on the basis of 21 oxygens, as for sodalite. Small but appreciable amounts of Fe^{+3} are consistently reported, even in the water-clear nosean of anal. 2, and this is presumably substituting for Al, though in other samples it may be present as iron ore impurities. Ca varies but may amount to over 4 per cent. CaO; small amounts of K are also present, replacing Na. Sulphate is the dominant anion but it may be partially replaced by appreciable amounts of chlorine. For a nosean from the Laacher See, Brauns (1916) recorded 1·27 per cent. CO_2 (with Cl 1·08, SO_3 7·97) and suggested the presence of a carbonate-sodalite molecule.

Nosean has been synthesized (Barrer, 1954) by hydrothermal treatment of a gel of composition $Na_2O \cdot Al_2O_3 \cdot 2SiO_2 + Na_2SO_4$, nosean being produced in the presence of an excess of alkali. In nosean the Na_2SO_4 component can be replaced by others such as Na_2CO_3, NaOH or H_2O; such replacements are, however, made by direct synthesis rather than by ion-exchange. A crystalline product with nosean structure was obtained by heating aluminous chabazite with fused $AgNO_3$ at 250°C. (Barrer and Baynham, 1956), and nosean has been prepared by treating analcite with a saturated solution of Na_2SO_4 at approximately 360°C. (Barrer, 1954). The production of nosean together with cancrinite has been reported from boiler deposits (Clark, 1948): the cancrinite appears to be deposited in contact with the hot metal whilst nosean is formed in a layer farther away from the hottest zone. The preparation of a synthetic tungstate nosean, with WO_4 in place of SO_4, has been reported by Saalfeld (1959).

Haüyne differs chemically from nosean in having a much higher proportion of Ca and in being richer in the sulphate radicle: two haüyne analyses are given in Table 37 (anals. 4 and 5). The chemistry of haüyne was reviewed, in the light of the determination of its crystal structure, by Barth (1932b) who showed its formula to be $(Na,Ca)_{8-4}Al_6Si_6O_{24} \cdot (SO_4)_{1-2}$, *i.e.* intermediate between that of nosean $(Na_8Al_6Si_6O_{24} \cdot SO_4)$ and a hypothetical end-member $Ca_4Al_6Si_6O_{24} \cdot SO_4$, but with the addition of extra SO_4^{-2} groups to a total limit of two per unit cell, the electrostatic balance being maintained by the replacement $2Na^+ \rightleftharpoons Ca^{+2}$. Some haüyne analyses show minor replacement of Al by Fe^{+3} and the substitution of K for Na appears to be more important in haüyne (*e.g.* anal. 5) than in other members of the sodalite group, no doubt due to its relatively open structure. Appreciable amounts of chlorine may occur, substituting for the sulphate ion. *Roeblingite*, previously believed to be a sulphite and silicate of Pb and Ca, was reported by Blix (1931) to have a composition approximating to $R_7H_{10}Si_6O_{24} \cdot 2PbSO_4$, analogous to haüyne (which at that time was believed to have the formula $Na_6Al_6Si_6O_{24} \cdot 2CaSO_4$).

The variety *lazurite* was not specifically distinguished from lapis-lazuli, the lazurite-rich rock, until described as a discrete mineral by Fischer (1869). Brögger and Bäckström (1891) first separated a lazurite for analysis (Table 37, anal. 6) and further analyses are given by Voskoboinikova (1938) for lazurite from Slyudyanka, Siberia. Synthetic ultramarine was prepared by Gmelin (1828) and both normal and substituted (Ag, AgNa, Se, Tl, Sr, Ba, Zn, Mn and Pb) ultramarines have been studied by Jaeger (1929a, b; 1930). Prener and Ward (1950) reported that on heating synthetic sodalite in H_2S and igniting in air ultramarine was obtained: they also prepared a deep blue ultramarine by heating a mixture of $3Na_2CO_3 + 3Al_2O_3 + 6SiO_2 + Na_2S$ in nitrogen at 900°C. followed by heating in H_2S and then in air. The general formula of the ultramarines is usually taken to be $M_8Al_6Si_6O_{24}S_x$, where M = alkalies, or alkali

Table 37. NOSEAN AND HAÜYNE ANALYSES

	1.	2.	3.	4.	5.	6.
SiO_2	36·69	36·87	34·95	32·18	34·04	32·52
Al_2O_3	28·45	26·60	29·41	27·11	28·27	27·61
Fe_2O_3	0·47	0·28	1·38	—	—	—
CaO	0·63	4·05	4·40	10·26	9·51	6·47
Na_2O	23·90	20·75	19·01	16·34	10·39	19·45
K_2O	—	—	0·33	0·08	5·44	0·28
SO_3	7·30	10·00	8·11	14·10	10·02	10·46
Cl	1·05	1·08	0·86	0·31	0·76	0·47
H_2O	2·15	0·37	1·83	—	0·34	—
	100·64	100·00	100·28	100·38	100·34	99·97
$O \equiv Cl$	0·23	0·24	0·19	0·07	0·17	0·55
Total	100·41	99·76	100·09	100·31	100·17	99·42
D	2·299	2·399	—	—	—	—

NUMBERS OF IONS ON THE BASIS OF THE 21(O) ASSOCIATED WITH $3Al_2O_3 \cdot 6SiO_2$

	1.	2.	3.	4.	5.	6.
Si	6·203 ⎫	6·394 ⎫	5·945 ⎫	6·0 8 ⎫	6·055 ⎫	5·998 ⎫
Al	5·670 ⎬11·93	5·438 ⎬11·87	5·897 ⎬12·02	5·976 ⎬11·99	5·927 ⎬11·98	6·000 ⎬12·00
Fe^{+3}	0·060 ⎭	0·036 ⎭	0·177 ⎭	—	—	—
Na	7·834 ⎫	6·978 ⎫	6·269 ⎫	5·924 ⎫	3·583 ⎫	6·954 ⎫
Ca	0·114 ⎬7·95	0·752 ⎬7·73	0·802 ⎬7·14	2·056 ⎬8·00	1·813 ⎬6·86†	1·279 ⎬8·30
K	—	—	0·072 ⎭	0·019 ⎭	1·233 ⎭	0·066 ⎭
Cl	0·301 ⎫	0·317 ⎫	0·248 ⎫	0·098 ⎫	0·229 ⎫	0·146 ⎫
SO_4	0·926 ⎬1·23	1·302 ⎬1·62	1·035 ⎬1·28	1·979 ⎬2·08	1·336 ⎬1·57	1·448 ⎬2·53‡
OH	2·415	0·428	2·077		0·403	

1. Light blue-grey nosean, with sanidine, mica and magnetite, ejected block, Laacher See, Lower Rhine (Rath, 1864).
2. Water-clear nosean, with sanidine, mica, sphene and zircon, ejected block, Laacher See, Lower Rhine (Rath, 1864).
3. Nosean, phonolite, Covão, Cape Verde Islands (Doelter, 1882).   Anal. C. Doelter.
4. Haüyne, Alban Hills, Italy (Parravano, 1913).
5. Haüyne, haüyne riedenite, Monte Vulture, Italy (Rittmann, 1931).   Anal. A. Rittmann (Includes FeO 0·69, MgO 0·48, CO_2 0·4).
6. "Lazurite", lapis-lazuli, central Asia (Brögger and Bäckström, 1891).   Anal. H. Bäckström (Includes S 2·71).

† Includes Fe^{+2} 0·103, Mg 0·127.
‡ Includes S 0·936.

metals and x has a value between 1 and 4.   Rogers (1938) investigated a natural lazurite from California and demonstrated that it contains both sulphide and sulphate sulphur in addition to calcium and sodium: he considered that it is a sulphide-bearing haüyne and suggested that if the name lazurite were retained it could be used for the pure sulphide molecule $Na_8Al_6Si_6O_{24}S_2$.

OPTICAL AND PHYSICAL PROPERTIES

The minerals of the sodalite group are isotropic or rarely weakly anisotropic: nosean and haüyne may show weak birefringence in samples containing inclusions.   The refractive index is lowest for sodalite and increases with the introduction of sulphate in nosean and rises slightly higher for haüyne, but for all the minerals of the group the refractive index is comparatively low and well below that of Canada Balsam. Brendler (1934) reported a Bolivian sodalite to have a moderate dispersion with n_{Li} 1·4806, n_{Na} 1·4837, n_{Tl} 1·4868. Voskoboinikova (1938) reported a possibly orthorhombic variety of lazurite with α 1·504, β 1·510, γ 1·514, $2V_\gamma$ 60°. The specific gravities of minerals of the group rise from sodalite (2·27 to 2·33) to haüyne (2·44 to 2·50): for nosean the lighter varieties (2·30) are those poor in Ca while those with around 4 per cent. CaO have a higher specific gravity. The infra-red spectrum of sodalite is given by Matossi and Krüger (1936).

The colour of the minerals of the sodalite group is extremely variable, ranging from colourless or white, to grey, yellow, green, brown, pink, or very typically blue. Blue, green, red, and violet ultramarines have been synthesized, and for these the depth of colour is considered to be related mainly to the sulphur content. In sodalite itself, however, the blue colour does not appear to be directly related to the chemistry of its major constituents: thus in Table 36, anals. 4, 5 and 6 of blue sodalites do not show any marked variation from anal. 1 of a light grey sodalite or from anal. 3 of a white or colourless hackmanite.

Many sodalites show appreciable fluorescence in ultra-violet light: *e.g.* the sodalite of the sodalite syenite of Ruma, French Guinea, has an orange-red fluorescence (Lacroix, 1931), as has that from the nepheline-syenite of Red Hill, New Hampshire (Quinn, 1935). Kirk (1955) has shown that the luminescence emission spectrum of sodalite is almost identical with that of a sodium polysulphide-sulphate mixture, and has tentatively suggested that the orange luminescence of sodalite may be due to the presence of sodium polysulphide. Specimens of haüyne from several localities were noted by Haberlandt (1935) to have a similar orange luminescence.

It has long been known that some varieties of sodalite have a distinct pink tinge when freshly fractured and that the colour fades on exposure to light but returns when the mineral is kept in the dark for a few weeks, or is bombarded by X-rays. Indeed the original sodalite from Greenland (Thomson, 1810) was later described as having this property (Allan, 1834), and sodalite from Kola showing this colour change was given the name hackmanite (Borgström, 1901). This variety of sodalite is known also from India (Vredenburg, 1904), Korea (Iwase, 1938), and Magnet Cove, Arkansas (Miser and Glass, 1941), but the material from near Bancroft, Ontario, has been particularly thoroughly investigated (Walker and Parsons, 1925; Lee, 1936). Hackmanite from Kola, on heating, changes first to green (700°–900°C.) and then to blue (950°–1150°C.) and the colour does not disappear on cooling or on exposure to light: Vorobieva (1946) suggested that the colour might be due mainly to the polarized ions of sulphur present in the ultramarine component of the mineral (Table 36, anal. 7). Many analyses of hackmanite, however, report only trace amounts of sulphur (*e.g.* anal. 3), see also Medved (1954). The reversible bleaching, or tenebrescence, of the Bancroft hackmanite was explained by Medved in terms of the band theory of solids, electron donor levels arising from a substitutional or interstitial impurity in the crystal. Kirk (1955), however, concluded that the colour centres of hackmanite are related to the combined presence of sodium chloride and sodium (mono) sulphide in the structure. The loss of tenebrescence of a synthetic hydrogen-fired S-containing sodalite on extended heating in air at 900°C. is attributed to the oxidation of all the monosulphide sulphur to a polysulphide or higher oxidation state. Thus the hackmanite variety of sodalite is thought to contain small amounts of both sodium mono- and poly-sulphide (no analysis of hackmanite reports a complete absence of S, and the tenebrescence shown by the occasional supposedly pure synthetic sodalites is attributed by Kirk to traces of S in the starting reagents). The Bancroft hackmanite has also been reported to exhibit a tenebrescent blue colour on exposure to 1850 Å ultra-violet excitation (Kirk, 1955), in addition to the usual red-purple colour.

DISTINGUISHING FEATURES

The minerals of the sodalite group may be distinguished by their isotropic character and by their refractive index being considerably less than that of Canada Balsam. Fluorite has an even lower refractive index and a much better cleavage, leucite generally has weakly birefringent twins, and analcite poor {001} cleavage. Within the sodalite group chemical tests may differentiate the minerals. When the mineral on a glass slide is treated with nitric acid and the solution is allowed to evaporate slowly, the formation of cubic crystals of NaCl indicates sodalite, while monoclinic needles of gypsum indicate haüyne. If neither product is formed before the addition of $CaCl_2$, and both appear after it is added, nosean is indicated. The lazurite variety may evolve H_2S on treatment with nitric acid.

Ultra-violet light may be helpful in causing the sodalite in nepheline-syenites, etc., to fluoresce with an orange-red colour, thus distinguishing it from nepheline and felspar.

PARAGENESIS

Sodalite commonly occurs in nepheline-syenites and associated rock types (Table 36, anals. 4 and 6). In the nepheline-syenite of Fukushinzan, Korea, it is associated with cancrinite, melanite, fluorite, etc., and has been considered to be of pneumatolytic origin (Haraguchi, 1928). Nepheline-syenites rich in blue sodalite have been described from Northern Rhodesia (Adams and Osborne, 1932; 1934), and in the greyish nepheline-syenite of Red Hill, New Hampshire, sodalite may be recognized in hand specimen by its orange fluorescence in ultra-violet light (Quinn, 1935). Sodalite can be similarly recognized in the poikilitic sodalite syenite from Pilansberg, Transvaal (Partridge, 1938), and in the nepheline-syenite of Beemerville, New Jersey (Wilkerson, 1946). Blue sodalite is common in the ditroite (nepheline-syenite) of the Ditró complex in the eastern Carpathians (*e.g.* Streckeisen, 1960). Pegmatitic veins in nepheline-syenite may contain sodalite, *e.g.* the deep lilac sodalite occurring with greenish yellow nepheline in the Mogok district of Burma (Adams and Graham, 1926), large crystals of sodalite between plates of microcline in pegmatites on an island off French Guinea (Lacroix, 1931), and the sodalite in pegmatites associated with the sodalite syenites and nepheline-syenites of the Kola peninsula (Table 36, anal. 1; see also Gerasimovsky, 1937). A rather similar occurrence of sodalite, but with sanidine and nepheline, is found in the nepheline-syenite pegmatites of the Rocky Boy stock, in the Bearpaw Mountains, Montana (Pecora, 1942).

The hackmanite variety of sodalite is also found in nepheline-syenites and related rocks. It was first described from the nepheline-syenite complex of the Kola peninsula (Table 36, anal. 2), see also Gerasimovsky (1936) and Vorobieva (1946). The original sodalite from Greenland (Thomson, 1810) was later described as having the pink tinge which faded on exposure to light (Allan, 1834) and occurs associated with felspar, arfvedsonite, eudialyte, etc. Iwase (1938) has recorded hackmanite associated with nepheline from near Kisshu, Korea, which he considered to be derived from the decomposition of sodalite. An association of hackmanite and sodalite has also been described by Vredenburg (1904) from India (Table 36, anal. 4), and from Magnet Cove, Arkansas (Miser and Glass, 1941). At the Magnet Cove locality the hackmanite (anal. 3) occurs as a white centre patch, surrounded by a mottled zone of blue sodalite (anal. 5), in lenses of irregular masses in a tinguaite dyke rock. Hackmanite is also well known from nepheline-syenites of the Bancroft district, Ontario (Walker and Parsons, 1925; see also Lee, 1936; Medved, 1954; Kirk, 1955).

Sodalite is found also in some dyke rocks, as in a dyke associated with nepheline-syenite in the Bolivian Andes (Table 36, anal. 6) and in the sodalite tinguaite of the Messum igneous complex, South-West Africa (Mathias, 1956). It is of frequent occurrence in phonolites and related under-saturated volcanic rocks. It occurs, for example, in the Traprain Law phonolite, Scotland (MacGregor, 1922), and in the sodalite phonolites of Portugese East Africa (Teale and Smith, 1923) and the phonolites of Ahaggar, central Sahara (Bourcart and Denaeyer, 1925). Sodalite trachytes are found in the neighbourhood of Naples and sodalite is also known from the trachytes and sanidinites of the Laacher See. The occurrence of sodalite in the drusy cavities of ejected volcanic blocks has been recorded (Kalb, 1939) from Rhineland and it is similarly known in volcanic bombs at Monte Somma, Vesuvius.

Sodalite may also occur in metasomatized calcareous rocks, in contact with alkaline igneous assemblages. A band of contorted calcareous quartzofelspathic rock occurring within the massive anorthosite of southern Angola has been converted to a calcite–albite–cancrinite–sodalite assemblage, the deep sky-blue sodalite occasionally forming large aggregates of crystals up to 20 cm. in size (Simpson and Otto, 1960).

Nosean occurs chiefly in phonolites and related under-saturated volcanic rocks and in volcanic bombs. It is a relatively common constituent of ejected blocks in the Laacher See, Lower Rhine (Table 37, anals. 1 and 2), where it is associated with sanidine, mica, sphene, etc. (Rath, 1864; Brauns and Uhlig, 1913). From ejectamenta from the same area, Schuster (1919) has described a possible carbonate-nosean. Doelter (1882) has reported the occurrence of nosean in phonolites of the Cape Verde Islands (*e.g.* anal. 3), and the nosean phonolite of the Wolf Rock, Cornwall, is well known for its abundant phenocrysts of nosean, which typically have a clear rim and a centre turbid with iron ore inclusions. Nosean is not common in other than volcanic rocks but a series of nosean-bearing aegirine-augite syenites and porphyries have been reported from northern China (Nyström, 1927).

Haüyne is typically found in phonolites and related rock types. It occurs in the lavas of Vesuvius, and in those of the Campagna, Rome, and of the Alban Hills (*e.g.* anal. 4, Table 37), and in the riedenite (nosean melteigite) of Monte Vulture, Naples (anal. 5). The ejected blocks in the "peperino" of the Alban

Hills provide fine examples of white octahedral haüyne: here the haüyne is associated with leucite, garnet, melilite, and rare latiumite (Tilley and Henry, 1953). It is also known in ejected blocks of hornblende–haüyne–scapolite rock from the Laacher See (Brauns, 1917). In addition to its occurrence in haüyne basalt, where it is found with leucite, nepheline and augite, haüyne is also known from nepheline-free alkaline extrusives, such as haüyne trachyte containing sanidine, haüyne and a ferromagnesian mineral. The mineral also occurs in ankaratrites, as in the haüyne ankaratrite of Jebel Tourguejid, Morocco (Jérémine, 1955) and it has been reported from an andesitic sill in the Auvergne (Michel, 1954). A plug of okaite, a monticellite alnöite, containing haüyne, melilite and biotite, occurs in the Monteregian area of Quebec (Stansfield, 1923) and a nepheline–haüyne alnöite, with melilite, phlogopite and apatite, has been described from Winnett, Montana (Ross, 1926). Roeblingite, the supposed Pb analogue of haüyne, occurs intimately associated with axinite and garnet in the skarns of Franklin, New Jersey (Palache, 1937).

The lapis-lazuli of Badakshan, Afghanistan, containing fine crystals of lazurite, occurs in metamorphosed limestone associated with phlogopite, humite and forsterite (Barthoux, 1933): likewise the Slyudyanka, Siberia, lazurite is found along the borders and cross joints of pegmatite veins in marble (Voskoboinikova, 1938). The lapis-lazuli of Cascade Canyon, San Bernardino County, California, has been described by Rogers (1938) as a haüyne-bearing diopside–muscovite gneiss, with sporadic pyrite, grading into a gneissoid limestone. Lapis-lazuli is also known from Chile and from near Mogok in Burma.

REFERENCES

Adams, F. D. and Graham, R. P. D., 1926. On some minerals from the ruby mining district of Mogok, Upper Burma. *Trans. Roy. Soc. Canada*, ser. 3, vol. 20, sect. 4, p. 113.

—— and Osborne, F. F., 1932. On two nepheline-sodalite-syenites from new localities in Northern Rhodesia. *Canad. Journ. Res.*, vol. 6, p. 571.

—— 1934. Nepheline syenite from Solwezi, Northern Rhodesia. *Amer. Journ. Sci.*, ser. 5, vol. 27, p. 135.

Alcock, T. C., Clark, L. M. and Thurston, E. F., 1944. The scaling of boilers. Part V. Identification of the combinations of silica and magnesia in boiler scales. *Journ. Soc. Chem. Ind.*, vol. 63, p. 292.

Allan, R., 1834. *A manual of mineralogy.* Edinburgh.

Barrer, R. M., 1954. Contributions to synthetic mineral chemistry. *Proc. Internat. Symp. Reactivity of Solids, Gothenburg*, Pt. 1, p. 373.

—— and Baynham, J. W., 1956. Synthetic chabazites: correlation between isomorphous replacements, stability, and sorption capacity. *Journ. Chem. Soc.*, p. 2892.

—— and Falconer, J. D., 1956. Ion exchange in felspathoids as a solid state reaction. *Proc. Roy. Soc.*, A, vol. 236, p. 227.

—— Hinds, L. and White, E. A., 1953. The hydrothermal chemistry of silicates. Part III. Reactions of analcite and leucite. *Journ. Chem. Soc.*, p. 1466.

—— and White, E. A., 1952. The hydrothermal chemistry of silicates. Part II. Synthetic crystalline sodium aluminosilicates. *Journ. Chem. Soc.*, p. 1561.

Barth, T. F. W., 1926. Die kristallographische Beziehung zwischen Helvin und Sodalit. *Norsk Geol. Tidssk.*, vol. 9, p. 40.

Barth, T. F. W., 1927. *Vidensk. Akad. Skr., I. Mat.-Nat. Kl., Oslo,* No. 8.
—— 1932a. The structures of the minerals of the sodalite family. *Zeit. Krist.,* vol. 83, p. 405.
—— 1932b. The chemical composition of noselite and haüyne. *Amer. Min.,* vol. 17, p. 466.

Barthoux, J., 1933. Lapis-lazuli et rubis balais des cipolins afghans. *Compt. Rend. Acad. Sci. Paris,* vol. 196, p. 1131.

Blix, R., 1931. The chemical composition of roeblingite. *Amer. Min.,* vol. 16, p. 455.

Borchert, W. and **Keidel, J.,** 1947. Beiträge zur Reaktionsfähigkeit der Silikate bei niedrigen Temperaturen. I. Mitteilung Reaktionen zwischen Kaolin und NaOH. *Heidelberger Beiträge zur Min. Petr.,* vol. 1, p. 2 (M.A. 10–364).

Borgström, L. H., 1901. Hackmanit ett nytt mineral i sodalitgruppen. *Geol. För., Stockholm,* vol. 23, p. 563.

Bourcart, J. and **Denaeyer, M. E.,** 1925. Sur les caractères lithologiques des laves de l'Ahaggar, Sahara central (Mission Jacques Bourcart, 1922–1923). *Compt. Rend. Acad. Sci. Paris,* vol. 181, p. 1073.

Bragg, W. L., 1937. *Atomic structure of minerals.* Cornell Univ. Press.

Brauns, R., 1916. Über den Apatit aus dem Laacher Seegebiet. Sulfatapatit und Carbonatapatit. *Neues Jahrb. Min.,* vol. 41, p. 60.
—— 1917. Neue Skapolithführende. Auswürflinge aus dem Laacher Seegebiet. Die Brechungsexponenten des Sulfatskapoliths. *Neues Jahrb. Min.,* vol. 42, p. 9.
—— and **Uhlig, J.,** 1913. Cancrinit- und nephelinführende Auswürflinge aus dem Laacher Seegebiet. *Neues Jahrb. Min.,* vol. 35, p. 119.

Brendler, W., 1932. Über sodalith vom Cerro Sapo, Bolivien. *Centr. Min.,* Abt. A, p. 42.
—— 1934. Sodalite from Bolivia. *Amer. Min.,* vol. 19, p. 28.

Brögger, W. C. and **Bäckström, H.,** 1891. Die Mineralien der Granatgruppe. *Zeit. Kryst.,* vol. 18, p. 209.

Clark, L. M., 1948. The identification of minerals in boiler deposits. Examples of hydrothermal synthesis in boilers. *Min. Mag.,* vol. 28, p. 359.

Doelter, C., 1882. *Min. Petr. Mitt. (Tschermak).,* vol. 4, p. 565.

Fellenberg, Th. de and **Lunde, G.,** 1926. Contribution à la géochemie de l'iode. *Norsk Geol. Tidssk.,* vol. 9, p. 48.

Fersman, A. E. and **Bonshtedt, E. M.,** 1937. *Minerals of the Khibina and Lovozero tundras.* Lomonossov Inst. Acad. Sci. U.S.S.R.

Fischer, H., 1869. *Kritische mikroskopisch-mineralogische Studien.* Freiburg.

Friedel, C. and **Friedel, G.,** 1890. Action des alcalis et des silicates alcalins sur le mica (deuxième note); production de l'amphigène et de la sodalithe. *Bull. Soc. Franç. Min.,* vol. 13, p. 182.

Gerasimovsky, V. I., 1936. On the mineralogy of the south-eastern part of Lujavr-Urt. *Trans. Lomonossov Inst. Geochem. Cryst. Min., Acad. Sci. USSR,* no. 7, p. 5 (M.A. 7–209).
—— 1937. Ussingite of Lovozersky tundras. *Trans. Lomonossov Inst. Acad. Sci. USSR, Sér. Min.,* no. 10, p. 5 (M.A. 8–222).

Glass, J. J., Jahns, R. H. and **Stevens, R. E.,** 1944. Helvite and danalite from New Mexico and the helvite group. *Amer. Min.,* vol. 29, p. 163.

Gmelin, C. G., 1828. *Schweigger's Polyt. Journ.,* vol. 54, p. 360.

Haberlandt, H., 1935. Lumineszenzuntersuchungen an Fluoriten und anderen Mineralien, II. *Sitz.-Ber. Akad. Wiss. Wien,* Abt. IIa, vol. 144, p. 663.

Haraguchi, K., 1928. Sodalite in nepheline-syenite of Fukushinzan, Korea. *Chikyu,* vol. 10, p. 262 (M.A. 4–218).

Iwase, E., 1938. Über die photochemischen Eigenschaften des Sodaliths von Kisshu, Korea. *Zeit. Krist.*, vol. 99, p. 314.

Jaeger, F. M., 1929a. Investigations about the structure of ultramarines, IV. On ultramarines of thallium and on the analogous derivatives of the bivalent metals calcium, strontium, barium, zinc, manganese and lead. *Proc. Sect. Sci., Akad. Wiss. Amsterdam*, vol. 30, pt. 1, p. 249.

—— 1929b. On the constitution and structure of ultramarine. *Trans. Faraday Soc.*, vol. 25, p. 320.

—— 1930. Sur les outremers naturels et artificiels. *Bull. Soc. Franç. Min.*, vol. 53, p. 183.

Jérémine, E., 1955. L'ankaratrite à haüyne du jebel Tourguejid (Haut Atlas de Midelt). Quelques considérations sur les ankaratrites du Maroc et sur les ankaratrites en général. *Notes et Mém. Serv. géol. Maroc*, vol. 12, p. 61 (M.A. 13–671).

Kalb, G., 1939. Über Mineralien und Gesteine der niederrheinischen Vulkangebiete. *Decheniana, Verh. Nat. Ver. Rheinlande v. Westfalens*, vol. 98A, p. 173 (M.A. 10–408).

Kirk, R. D., 1955. The luminescence and tenebrescence of natural and synthetic sodalite. *Amer. Min.*, vol. 40, p. 22.

Lacroix, A., 1931. Les pegmatites de la syénite sodalitique de l'île Rouma (archipel de Los, Guinée française). Description d'un nouveau minéral (serandite) qu'elles renferment. *Compt. Rend. Acad. Sci. Paris*, vol. 192, p. 189.

Lee, O. I., 1936. A new property of matter: reversible photosensitivity in hackmanite from Bancroft, Ontario. *Amer. Min.*, vol. 21, p. 764.

MacGregor, A. G., 1922. The Traprain Law phonolite. Part I: Nepheline, analcite, sodaite, and olivine in the Traprain Law phonolite. *Geol. Mag.*, vol. 59, p. 514.

Machatschki, F., 1933. Zur Hauynformel. *Centr. Min.*, A, p. 145.

—— 1934. Kristallstruktur von Hauyn und Nosean. *Centr. Min.*, A, p. 136.

Mathias, M., 1956. The petrology of the Messum igneous complex, South-West Africa. *Trans. Geol. Soc. South Africa*, vol. 59, p. 23.

Matossi, F. and Krüger, H., 1936. Das ultrarote Reflexionsspektrum von Silikaten. II. *Zeits. Physik.* vol. 99, p. 1.

Medved, D. B., 1954. Hackmanite and its tenebrescent properties. *Amer. Min.*, vol. 39, p. 615.

Michel, R., 1954. Étude géologique et pétrographique du sill de Mirefleurs (Comté d'Auvergne). *Bull. Soc. Geol. France*, IV, p. 139 (M.A. 13–131).

Miser, H. D. and Glass, J. J., 1941. Fluorescent sodalite and hackmanite from Magnet Cove. *Amer. Min.*, vol. 26, p. 437.

Nyström, E. T., 1927. Some alkaline rocks of Shansi province, N. China. *Bull. Geol. Inst. Upsala*, vol. 22, p. 59.

Palache, C., 1937. The minerals of Franklin and Sterling Hill, Sussex County, New Jersey. *U.S. Geol. Surv., Prof. Paper* 180.

Parravano, N., 1913. Sulla composizione chimica della hauynite du Colli Albani. *Rend. R. Accad. Linc., Cl. Sci. fis. mat. nat.*, vol. 21, p. 631.

Partridge, F. C., 1938. A poikilitic sodalite syenite from Pilansberg. *Trans. Geol. Soc. South Africa*, vol. 41, p. 173.

Pauling, L., 1930. The structure of sodalite and helvite. *Zeit. Krist.*, vol. 74, p. 213.

Pecora, W. T., 1942. Nepheline syenite pegmatites, Rocky Boy stock, Bearpaw Mountains, Montana. *Amer. Min.*, vol. 27, p. 397.

Prener, J. S. and Ward, R., 1950. The preparation of ultramarines. *Journ. Amer. Chem. Soc.*, vol. 72, p. 2780.

Quinn, A., 1935. A petrographic use of fluorescence. *Amer. Min.*, vol. 20, p. 466.

Rath, G. vom, 1864.   Skizzen aus dem vulkanischen Gebiete des Nieder-rheins.   2. Fortsetzung.   _Zeits. deutsch. geol. Ges._, vol. 16, p. 82.

Rittmann, A., 1931.   Gesteine und Mineralien von Monte Vulture in der Basilicata (Hier der Hauyn aus Hauyn-Riedenit).   _Schweiz. Min. Petr. Mitt._, vol. 11, p. 250.

Rogers, A. F., 1938.   Lapis lazuli from San Bernardino County, California.   _Amer. Min._, vol. 23, p. 111.

Ross, C. S., 1926.   Nephelite-hauynite alnoite from Winnett, Montana.   _Amer. Journ. Sci._, ser. 5, vol. 11, p. 218.

Saalfeld, H., 1959.   Untersuchungen über die Nosean-Struktur.   _Neues Jahrb. Min., Monatshefte_, p. 38.

—— 1961.   Strukturbesonderheiten des Hauyngitters.   _Zeit. Krist._, vol. 115, p. 132.

Schuster, E., 1919.   Calcitführende Auswürflinge aus dem Laacher Seegebiet.   _Neues Jahrb. Min._, vol. 43, p. 295.

Simpson, E. S. W. and Otto, J. D. T., 1960.   On the Pre-Cambrian anorthosite mass of southern Angola.   _Rept. 21st Intern. Geol. Congr., Norden_, Part 13, p. 216.

Sørensen, H., 1960.   Beryllium minerals in a pegmatite in the nepheline syenites of Ilimaussaq, southwest Greenland.   _Rept. 21st Intern. Geol. Congr., Norden_, Part 17, p. 31.

Stansfield, J., 1923.   Extensions of the Monteregian petrographical province to the west and northwest.   _Geol. Mag._, vol. 60, p. 433.

Streckeisen, A., 1960.   On the structure and origin of the nepheline-syenite of Ditro (Transylvania, Roumania).   _Rept. 21st. Intern. Geol. Congr., Norden_, Part. 13, p. 228.

Strunz, H., 1957.   _Mineralogische Tabellen._   Leipzig, Akad. Verlag.

Teale, E. O. and Smith, W. C., 1923.   Nepheline-bearing lavas and intrusive rocks from south of the Zambesi River, with a note on an outcrop of Karroo lavas in the Buzi Valley, Portuguese East Africa.   _Geol. Mag._, vol. 60, p. 226.

Thomson, T., 1810.   Chemical analyses of sodalite, a new mineral from Greenland.   _Trans. Roy. Soc. Edin._, vol. 5, p. 387.

Thugutt, St. J., 1946.   Sur la sodalite et ses dérivés.   _Arch. Min. Soc. Sci. Lett. Varsovie_, vol. 16, p. 14 (M.A. 10–293).

Tilley, C. E. and Henry, N. F. M., 1953.   Latiumite (sulphatic potassium-calcium-aluminium silicate), a new mineral from Albana, Latium, Italy.   _Min. Mag._, vol. 30, p. 39.

Vorobieva, O. A., 1946.   Thermocoloration of hackmanite from Luyavrurt.   _D.S Belyankin jubilee vol._ (_Acad. Sci. USSR_), p. 122.

Voskoboinikova, N. V., 1938.   Mineralogy of the Sludianka lazurite deposit.   _Mém. Soc. Russe Min._, ser. 2, vol. 67, p. 601 (M.A. 7–524).

Vredenburg, E., 1904.   Elaeolite and soda syenites in Kishengarh State, Rajputana, India.   _Rec. Geol. Surv. India_, vol. 31, p. 43.

Walker, T. L. and Parsons, A. L., 1925.   Evanescent pink sodalite and associated minerals from Dungannon township, Ontario.   _Univ. Toronto Studs., Geol. Ser._, no. 20, p. 5.

Weiberg, S., 1905.   Über den Bromlithium-Sodalith.   _Ann. Univ. Varsovie_, vol. 3, p. 1.

Wilkerson, A. S., 1946.   Nepheline syenite from Beemerville, Sussex County, New Jersey.   _Amer. Min._, vol. 31, p. 284.

Wyart, J. and Michel-Lévy, M., 1949.   Cristallisation des mélanges $Na_xK_{1-x}AlSiO_4$ en présence d'eau sous pression (formation de néphéline, kalsilite, hydro-cancrinite, hydrosodalite, mica).   _Compt. Rend. Acad. Sci. Paris_, vol. 229, p. 131.

Zambonini, F., 1910.   Mineralogia Vesuviana.   _Mem. R. Accad. Sci. Fis. Mat., Napoli_, ser. 2, vol. 24, p. 214.

Helvite
Danalite
Genthelvite

$Mn_4[Be_3Si_3O_{12}]S$
$Fe_4[Be_3Si_3O_{12}]S$
$Zn_4[Be_3Si_3O_{12}]S$

CUBIC

	Helvite	Danalite	Genthelvite
n	1·728–1·749	1·749–1·770	1·740–1·746
D	3·20–3·44	3·28–3·44	3·44–3·70
H	6	6	$6\frac{1}{2}$
Cleavage:	{111}, poor.	{111}, poor.	{111}, poor.
Twinning:	{111}	—	—
Colour:	Honey-yellow, brown, reddish brown; pale yellow or pale brown to colourless in thin section.	Yellow, pink, reddish brown, red; pink to colourless in thin section.	Purplish pink, reddish brown; pale pink or colourless in thin section.
Unit cell:	a (Å) $\simeq$ 8·29	8·20	8·12

$Z = 2.$　　Space group $P\bar{4}3m$.

Decomposed by HCl, with evolution of H_2S.

The minerals of the helvite group occur typically in contact zones and skarns and in granites or granite pegmatites. They represent an important source of beryllium. The name helvite is from the Greek *helios*, sun, in allusion to the yellow colour; danalite was named in honour of J. D. Dana, mineralogist, and genthelvite in honour of F. A. Genth, who first described the species (as a Zn-rich danalite).

STRUCTURE

The structure of minerals of the helvite group was first shown to be similar to that of sodalite by Barth (1926) and was later described in more detail by Pauling (1930). The Al atoms of the sodalite structure (Fig. 94, p. 290) may be considered to be replaced by Be, the Na by Mn, Fe^{+2} or Zn, and the Cl by S. The silicon tetrahedra probably have the same dimensions as in sodalite while the beryllium tetrahedra are probably only slightly larger. Pauling (1930) considered only the two species helvite and danalite: the cell size of genthelvite was determined by Glass *et al.* (1944) and the powder diffraction data for an analysed sample are given by Knorring and Dyson (1959). Powder data for an analysed helvite are given by Yoshinaga (1959).

CHEMISTRY

The helvite group consists of three isomorphous minerals whose chemical composition may be expressed as $R_4Be_3Si_3O_{12}S$, with R representing Mn in helvite, Fe in danalite and Zn in genthelvite, with complete substitution between these three end-members.

Seven analyses of minerals of the group are given in Table 38, where they have also been recalculated on the basis of 26(O,S), the unit cell contents. Further analyses were tabulated by Glass *et al.* (1944) who quoted all the analyses of the helvite group then available. None of these minerals corresponds to an end-member composition; all contain both Mn and Fe and the majority also contain Zn. The helvite of Table 38, anal. 1, is low in Fe and Zn and contains 45·46

Table 38.　Helvite, danalite and genthelvite analyses

	1.	2.	3.	4.	5.	6.	7.
SiO_2	33·62	32·35	31·54	34·08	29·48	30·70	30·26
BeO	12·88	13·75	13·60	16·32	14·17	12·39	12·70
Al_2O_3	1·21	0·33	0·37	—	—	0·18	0·51
FeO	2·24	16·35	18·02	30·66	37·53	11·73	6·1
MnO	45·46	28·99	26·51	13·28	11·53	1·72	1·5
ZnO	1·20	4·88	5·61	2·97	4·87	40·56	46·0
MgO	tr.	0·00	0·00	—	—	tr.	—
CaO	0·30	0·23	1·62	—	—	tr.	—
S	5·64	5·50	5·34	5·61	5·04	5·50	5·49
H_2O	0·02	0·17	0·06	—	—	—	—
	102·83	102·55	102·68	102·92	102·62	102·78	102·56
$O \equiv S$	2·81	2·75	2·67	2·80	2·52	2·74	2·74
Total	100·02	99·80	100·01	100·12	100·10	100·04	99·82
n	1·732	1·737	1·746	1·752	1·758‖	1·745	1·744
D	3·22	3·32	3·334	3·32	3·350	3·62	3·66
$a(Å)$	—	—	8·23	—	—	—	8·131‖

NUMBERS OF IONS ON THE BASIS OF 26(O,S)

	1.	2.	3.	4.	5.	6.	7.
Be	5·654 ⎫	6·117 ⎫	6·075 ⎫	6·961 ⎫	6·425 ⎫	5·832 ⎫	5·997 ⎫
Si	6·143 ⎬12·06	5·990 ⎬12·18	5·864 ⎬12·02‡	6·050 ⎬13·01	5·564 ⎬11·99	6·015 ⎬11·93	5·948 ⎬12·05
Al	0·261 ⎭	0·072 ⎭	0·082 ⎭	—	—	0·084 ⎭	0·108 ⎭
Fe^{+2}	0·343 ⎫	2·532 ⎫	2·802 ⎫	4·552 ⎫	5·924 ⎫	1·922 ⎫	1·003 ⎫
Zn	0·161 ⎬7·74†	0·667 ⎬7·79	0·770 ⎬8·07	0·389 ⎬6·94	0·678 ⎬8·45	5·863 ⎬8·07	6·677 ⎬7·93
Mn	7·037 ⎬	4·548 ⎬	4·176 ⎬	1·997 ⎭	1·844 ⎭	0·286 ⎭	0·250 ⎭
Ca	0·058 ⎭	0·046 ⎭	0·323 ⎭				
S	1·932	1·909	1·860	1·866	1·783	2·028	2·022

1. Sulphur-yellow helvite, associated with microcline-perthite, petalite, spodumene, muscovite and spessartine, Casa Ventura pegmatite, near Salisbury, Southern Rhodesia (Knorring, 1959). Anal. O. von Knorring (Includes Na_2O 0·03, K_2O 0·08, Li_2O 0·15).
2. Helvite, Iron Mountain, Socorro and Sierra Counties, New Mexico (Gruner, 1944).
3. Brownish helvite, tactite, Discovery Gulch, Socorro and Sierra Counties, Iron Mountain, New Mexico (Glass *et al.*, 1944). Anal. R. E. Stevens (Includes TiO_2 0·01).
4. Reddish brown danalite, associated with garnet and cassiterite, pegmatite in diorite, Imalka, Transbaikal, Siberia (Grigoriev, 1944).
5. Red danalite, Redruth, Cornwall (Miers and Prior, 1892).
6. Purplish pink genthelvite, associated with albite–biotite granite, Jos, Northern Nigeria (Knorring and Dyson, 1959). Anal. O. von Knorring.
7. Genthelvite, West Cheyenne Cañon, El Paso County, Colorado (Genth, 1892; Glass *et al.*, 1944). Anal. F. A. Genth (MnO, FeO, ZnO by R. E. Stevens, 1944).

† Includes Na 0·011, K 0·018, Li 0·108.
‡ Includes Ti 0·001.
‖ Determined by Glass *et al.* (1944).

per cent. MnO: helvite containing 40·56 per cent. MnO together with 8·59 per cent. Mn was, however, reported from Amelia, Virginia (Sloan, 1882), and other old analyses are recorded with an equivalent of about 50 per cent. MnO. Danalites poorer in Fe and considerably richer in Zn than those of anals. 4 and 5 were reported by Cooke (1866). Helvite with MnO 47·36, FeO 4·19, ZnO nil has been recorded by Yoshinaga (1959); genthelvite rich in iron (FeO 19·8 per cent.), and danalite with 39·5 per cent. FeO have been reported from Cornwall (Kingsbury, 1961).

The alteration of helvite to an earthy ochre-yellow product considerably poorer in beryllium has been reported from Argentina by Fischer (1926): a black surface alteration product of manganese oxides and hydroxides may also occur. A chemical test for the identification of any helvite group mineral is described in the section on distinguishing features (below): in addition, micro-chemical tests may be made for Be, Mn and Zn.

OPTICAL AND PHYSICAL PROPERTIES

In general the properties and appearance of the minerals of the helvite group resemble those of garnet. The helvites are isotropic and have relatively high refractive indices and medium specific gravities. The relationships between the composition, in terms of end-member components, and the properties of the helvite minerals, assuming that the values of such properties are additive functions of the molecular proportions of the end-members, are shown in Fig. 95. The colour of the helvite minerals in hand specimen is very variable, ranging from sulphur-yellow for some helvite and danalite, to mahogany-red (helvite) or dark reddish brown or purplish pink (genthelvite), though a black Mn-rich surface weathering product may sometimes obscure the colour. In thin section they are typically pale shades of yellow, brown or pink, or colourless.

DISTINGUISHING FEATURES

The helvite group minerals may be distinguished from most of the commonly associated species by their isotropic character. They strongly resemble garnet, however, but may be distinguished from it by their lower specific gravity and lesser hardness, and frequently by their tetrahedral habit. The associated andradite (and vesuvianite) may show appreciable double refraction: helvite dissolves slowly in boiling HCl, giving H_2S and a silica gel, whereas garnet is only soluble with great difficulty and does not yield H_2S. Minerals of the helvite group may be detected easily, and their amounts estimated, by a method devised by Gruner (1944). A small amount of the mineral powder is covered with dilute H_2SO_4, a pinch of As_2O_3 added and the solution boiled for one or two minutes: the acid is then decanted, the powder washed with water by further decantation and the wet powder examined under a binocular microscope. Any helvite present will be stained a brilliant canary yellow (As_2S_3). The test is claimed to be sufficiently sensitive to distinguish one grain of helvite among thousands of gangue mineral grains, including yellow garnet. If any doubt arises metallic antimony may be substituted for As_2O_3 and will give a brilliant red stain (Sb_2S_3).

Danalite and grossular may have a very similar appearance and may occur together: this association has been recorded from New Mexico where both the minerals show optical anomalies (Glass *et al.*, 1944). In the latter occurrence it was possible to distinguish the two minerals by immersing the grains in a liquid of refractive index 1·760, the grains of lower index being danalite, and those of higher index being grossular.

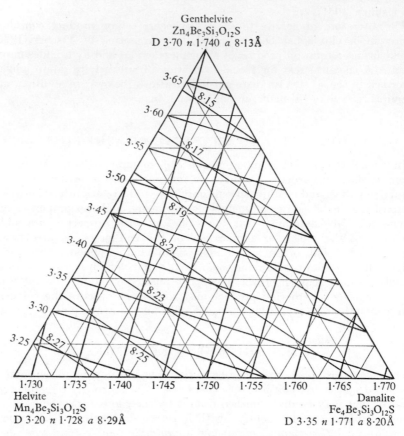

FIG. 95. The variation in specific gravity, refractive index and cell size of minerals of the helvite group with composition, in terms of the molecular proportions of the end-members (after Glass *et al.*, 1944).

PARAGENESIS

Helvite is found both in granites and granite pegmatites and in contact metasomatic rocks. In granitic pegmatites it is typically associated with lithium minerals such as petalite and spodumene (*e.g.* Table 38, anal. 1), and spessartine is also often present (Holser, 1953; Knorring, 1959). Helvite in association with corundum has been described from a syenitic pegmatite in the Urals (Kityaev, 1928), and in Argentina it has been recorded with fluorite, albite and garnet in a pegmatite vein, separated by a contact zone of vesuvianite rock from the enclosing gneiss and marble (Fischer, 1926). In many other similar granitic pegmatites the Be-bearing mineral is beryl, and Holser (1953) has postulated that beryl is formed in aluminium-rich rocks whereas helvite is deposited in rocks relatively poor in aluminium, the criterion being whether there is enough Al to form felspars or similar minerals. A tetrahedron of helvite in a cavity in nordmarkite has been reported from Norway by Neumann (1950), who also lists 8 other Norwegian occurrences of the mineral.

Helvite is most frequently found, often in relatively large amounts, in contact metasomatic deposits and skarns. In the Butte district, Montana, it occurs in veinlets associated with sulphides in massive rhodonite and rhodochrosite (Hewett, 1937), and minute crystals occur enclosed in fluorite with sphalerite at Grandview mine, Swartz, New Mexico (Weissenborn, 1948). In a metamorphic contact zone between limestone and rhyolites and granites at Iron Mountain, southwestern New Mexico, both helvite (Table 38, anals. 2, 3) and danalite occur (Glass *et al.*, 1944), the host rock being a banded "tactite" of magnetite, fluorite, chlorite and diopside. In some parts of the Iron Mountain a conspicuously banded "ribbon rock" is developed, with white veinlets of fluorite in which are embedded small crystals of helvite and Be-bearing grossular, in a grey groundmass of magnetite, fluorite and silicates (Glass *et al.*, 1944; Jahns, 1944). At Lupikko, on the north shore of Lake Ladoga, Finno-Karelia, helvite occurs with fluorite, vesuvianite and chondrodite in iron ore (Eskola, 1951), and well developed crystals of helvite are known from the contact metamorphic zone at Hörtekollen, near Oslo (Goldschmidt, 1911). In the Victorio Mountains, New Mexico, helvite occurs in yellow tetrahedral crystals in a coarse-grained calcsilicate rock composed of about 30 per cent. calcite, 20 per cent. grossular, a maximum of 10 per cent. helvite and about 40 per cent. tremolite (Holser, 1953). In thin section this helvite shows dark peripheral zones of very fine-grained inclusions: these are also found in some pegmatite helvites. In this area beryl occurs in adjacent quartz–tungsten veins, and the same Be- and Al-rich solutions may have given rise to the helvite, the composition of the solution having been changed by permeation into the limestone, and the excess Al removed to form grossular and vesuvianite. Helvite has also been recorded from the metasomatic manganese ore bodies of Yagisawa mine, Nagano Prefecture, Japan (Yoshinaga, 1959).

Danalite occurs mainly in granites or granitic pegmatites but is also found in contact metamorphosed rocks. It has been reported from granite at Rockport and Gloucester, Massachusetts (Cooke, 1866), and from the pneumatolytic stage of tin-bearing pegmatites in diorite, Imalka, Transbaikal (Grigoriev, 1944), where the danalite (*e.g.* Table 38, anal. 4) is associated with albite, cassiterite, pyrite and muscovite. At Iron Mountain, New Mexico, danalite occurs in the "ribbon rock", the latter consisting essentially of magnetite, fluorite, biotite and chlorite with whitish veins of fluorite containing scattered crystals of yellow danalite (Glass *et al.*, 1944), and having been produced at the contact of limestone and acid igneous rocks. At Yxsjöberg, Sweden, danalite occurs with garnet, hedenbergite, etc., in a skarn (Ramdohr and Ramdohr, 1954). Mahogany-red danalite has been recorded from various localities in Cornwall (Kingsbury, 1961), where it occurs in hydrothermal deposits or in metamorphosed greenstone.

Genthelvite was discovered by Genth (1892) in West Cheyenne Cañon,

Colorado (Table 38, anal. 7), and re-examined and named by Glass *et al.* (1944). Crystals of genthelvite have been found in miarolitic pegmatites in the Pikes Peak granite, El Paso County, Colorado (Glass and Adams, 1953; Scott, 1957), where they are associated with quartz, microcline perthite, topaz, phenakite, zircon and siderite.　The first report of genthelvite occurring elsewhere than in Colorado is that by Knorring and Dyson (1959), who found a notable amount of the mineral both in an albite-rich vein cutting albite–biotite granite and in a nearby coarse pegmatite containing green amazonite microcline, in the Jos-Bukuru complex, Northern Nigeria.　Iron-rich genthelvite has since been recorded from Treburland, Cornwall, where it occurs associated with garnet in calc-silicate rock near the Bodmin Moor granite (Kingsbury, 1961).

REFERENCES

Barth, T., 1926.　Die kristallographische Beziehung zwischen Helvin und Sodalit. *Norsk Geol. Tidssk.*, vol. 9, p. 40.
Cooke, J. P., 1866.　On danalite, a new mineral species from the granite of Rockport, Mass.　*Amer. Journ. Sci.*, ser. 2, vol. 42, p. 73.
Eskola, P., 1951.　Around Pitkäranta.　*Suom. Tied. Toimit*, ser. AIII, no. 27.
Fischer, W., 1926.　Die Helvinlagerstätte von Casa La Plata (Sierra de Córdoba, Argentinien).　*Centralbl. Min.*, Abt. A, p. 33.
Genth, F. A., 1892.　Contributions to mineralogy, No. 54, with crystallographic notes by S. L. Penfield : (6) Danalite.　*Amer. Journ. Sci.*, ser. 3, vol. 44, p. 385.
Glass, J. J. and Adams, J. W., 1953.　Genthelvite crystal from El Paso County, Colorado.　*Amer. Min.*, vol. 38, p. 858.
—— Jahns, R. H. and Stevens, R. E., 1944.　Helvite and danalite from New Mexico and the helvite group.　*Amer. Min.*, vol. 29, p. 163.
Goldschmidt, V. M., 1911.　Die Kontaktmetamorphose im Kristianiagebiet : Mineralogischer Teil, Helvin.　*Vidensk. Skrift.*, No. 1, p. 394.
Grigoriev, I. F., 1944.　Danalite in the pegmatites of the Imalka deposit, eastern Transbaikal.　*Doklady Acad. Sci. URSS*, vol. 44, p. 114.
Gruner, J. W., 1944.　Simple tests for the detection of the beryllium mineral helvite. *Econ. Geol.*, vol. 39, p. 444.
Hewett, D. F., 1937.　Helvite from the Butte district, Montana.　*Amer. Min.*, vol. 22, p. 803.
Holser, W. T., 1953.　Beryllium minerals in the Victorio Mountains, Luna County, New Mexico.　*Amer. Min.*, vol. 38, p. 599.
Jahns, R. H., 1944.　"Ribbon rock", an unusual beryllium-bearing tactite.　*Econ. Geol.*, vol. 39, p. 173.
Kingsbury, A. W. G., 1961.　Beryllium minerals in Cornwall and Devon : helvine, genthelvite, and danalite.　*Min. Mag.*, vol. 32, p. 921.
Kityaev, A. G., 1928.　Deposit of corundum, helvite, and rare earth minerals in southern Urals.　*Mineral'noe Syr'e, Geol.*, vol. 3, p. 76.
Knorring, O. von, 1959.　Helvine from a lithium pegmatite near Salisbury, Southern Rhodesia.　*Min. Mag.*, vol. 32, p. 87.
—— and Dyson, P., 1959.　An occurrence of genthelvite in the Younger Granite province of Northern Nigeria.　*Amer. Min.*, vol. 44, p. 1294.
Miers, H. A. and Prior, G. T., 1892.　Danalite from Cornwall.　*Min. Mag.*, vol. 10, p. 10.
Neumann, H., 1950.　A new find of helvite in the Oslo area.　*Norsk. Geol. Tiddsk.*, vol. 28, p. 234.

Pauling, L., 1930.   The structure of sodalite and helvite.   *Zeit. Krist.*, vol. 74, p. 213.

Ramdohr, P. and **Ramdohr, H.**, 1954.   Helvin ("danalith") von Yxsjöberg in Västmanland, Schweden.   *Geol. För. Förh., Stockholm*, vol. 76, p. 381.

Scott, G. R., 1957.   Genthelvite from Cookstove Mountain, El Paso County, Colorado. *Amer. Min.*, vol. 42, p. 425.

Sloan, B. E., 1882.   Helvite from near Amelia Courthouse, Virginia.   *Chem. News*, vol. 46, p. 195.

Weissenborn, A. E., 1948.   A new occurrence of helvite.   *Amer. Min.*, vol. 33, p. 648.

Yoshinaga, M., 1959.   Helvite from Yagisawa mine, Nagano Prefecture, Japan. *Mem. Fac. Sci. Kyushu Univ.*, Ser. D, vol. 9, p. 47.

Cancrinite
Vishnevite

$(Na,Ca)_{7-8}[Al_6Si_6O_{24}](CO_3,SO_4,Cl)_{1.5-2.0} \cdot 1-5H_2O$

$(Na,Ca,K)_{6-7}[Al_6Si_6O_{24}](SO_4,CO_3,Cl)_{1.0-1.5} \cdot 1-5H_2O$

HEXAGONAL $(-)$

	Cancrinite	Vishnevite
ϵ	1·503–1·495	1·495–1·488
ω	1·528–1·507	1·507–1·490
δ	0·025–0·012	0·012–0·002
Dispersion:	very weak	very weak
D	2·51–2·42	2·42–2·32
H	5–6	5–6

Cleavage: $\{10\bar{1}0\}$ perfect, $\{0001\}$ poor.

Twinning: lamellar, rare.

Colour: Colourless, white, light blue to light greyish blue, honey-yellow, reddish; colourless in thin section.

Unit cell: a 12·58–12·76, c 5·11–5·20 Å.

Z=1.   Space group $P6_32$.

Gelatinizes in acids; carbonate-rich varieties effervesce in HCl.

The cancrinite–vishnevite minerals form a solid solution series in which the main substitution is $CO_3 \rightleftharpoons SO_4$. The carbonate-rich members of the series contain appreciably more calcium ions per formula unit than the sulphatic varieties; there is, however, no corresponding increase in the number of sodium ions in the vishnevite minerals and the number of both $(Na+Ca+K)$ and (CO_3+SO_4) ions in the latter are less than in cancrinite. The naming of the cancrinite–vishnevite minerals has not previously been precisely defined and it is now proposed to restrict the name cancrinite to minerals containing between 100 and 80 per cent. of the cancrinite end-member, sulphatic cancrinite to between 80 and 50, carbonate vishnevite to between 50 and 20, and vishnevite to between 20 and 0 per cent. of the cancrinite end-member. The names microsommite and davyne have been used to describe cancrinites rich in potassium and chlorine and here the term microsommite is retained to describe this rare variety. The cancrinite–vishnevite minerals are characteristically found in nepheline-syenites and ultra-alkaline plutonic rocks in which they occur both as minerals of primary crystallization and as a pneumatolytic alteration or reaction product of nepheline. Cancrinite is named after Count Cancrin, a former Russian Minister of Finance, and vishnevite is named from the type locality, Vishnevy Gory, Urals.

STRUCTURE

The structure of cancrinite has not been precisely determined; it is thought, however, to consist of a framework (composition $Al_6Si_6O_{24}$) in which $(Si,Al)-O$ tetrahedra are linked to form four-, six- and twelve-membered rings. These rings define cavities and channels within which the Na and Ca ions, and also the larger CO_3^{-2} and SO_4^{-2} ions, and water molecules, are accommodated. The low density of cancrinite and its cation exchange properties are related to the open-ness of its structure. Cell dimensions have been measured by Gossner and Mussgnug (1930), Zambonini and Ferrari (1930), Kôzu and Takané (1933) and by Phoenix and Nuffield (1949). The range of cell size (a 12·47–12·71, c 5·07–5·20 Å) for a number of synthetic cancrinites has been given by Barrer and White (1952).

CHEMISTRY

Cancrinite–vishnevite analyses calculated either on the basis of $12(Si+Al)$ or on 24 oxygens (Berman, 1937; Stewart, 1941; Phoenix and Nuffield, 1949) show that the composition can be expressed:

$$(Na,Ca,K)_{6-8}Al_6Si_6O_{24}(CO_3,SO_4,Cl)_{1-2} \cdot 1-5H_2O$$

Nine analyses of members of the cancrinite–vishnevite series, calculated on the basis of $12(Si,Al)$, are given in Table 39; six of these analyses calculated on the basis of 24 oxygens are shown in Table 40. In general high contents of Ca are associated with high values of CO_2, whereas the more sulphatic varieties are relatively rich in sodium.

The sulphate-rich minerals contain a significantly lower number of $(Na+Ca+K)$ ions and a correspondingly smaller number of (CO_3+SO_4) anions per formula unit than the carbonate-rich members of the series. Thus in vishnevites more of the intraframework positions are vacant and it is mainly on this account that their densities are lower. Vishnevite contains more K than cancrinite and in this respect microsommite is more closely related chemically to vishnevite than to cancrinite. Chlorine is the dominant anion in microsommite (Table 41) and in consequence the number of anions per formula unit is considerably higher in this variety than in either cancrinite or vishnevite.

Zambonini and Ferrari (1930) considered that the water present in all cancrinite analyses is not an essential constituent: Beliankin (1944), however, has shown that vishnevite (Table 39, anal. 9) loses water continuously on heating and has suggested that the water is probably zeolitic in character. Kôzu (1931) observed that the loss of weight curve of a cancrinite (Table 39, anal. 2) shows breaks at 300° and 460°C., and interpreted these breaks as most probably due to loss of carbon dioxide.

Cancrinite occurs as a binary compound in the system calcite–nepheline (Fig. 96) and melts incongruently under a carbon dioxide pressure of 110 bars to nepheline and liquid (Eitel, 1954). Hexagonal prisms of cancrinite, $Na_8Al_6Si_6O_{24}CO_3$, have been synthesized by the hydrothermal treatment of $Na_2O \cdot Al_2O_3 \cdot nSiO_2$ ($n=1-2$) gels with excess $Na_2CO_3aq.$ in the temperature range 300° to 420°C. (Barrer and White, 1952). With excess NaOH and in the absence of CO_3 ions a basic cancrinite with composition $Na_6Al_6Si_6O_{24} \cdot xNaOH \cdot yH_2O$

Table 39.   CANCRINITE AND

	1.	2.	3.	4.
SiO_2	33·64	35·22	35·38	33·98
TiO_2	0·07	—	—	—
Al_2O_3	29·82	29·79	28·42	29·11
Fe_2O_3	—	tr.	—	—
FeO	—	—	—	—
MnO	—	—	—	—
MgO	0·39	0·05	—	—
CaO	8·64	8·17	11·66	4·80
Na_2O	15·41	18·16	9·82	18·69
K_2O	0·50	0·17	1·23	0·64
H_2O^+	}4·61	2·73	6·39	4·34
H_2O^-		—	0·60	0·23
CO_2	6·79	5·88	6·18	7·00
SO_3	0·03	0·08	0·19	1·37
Cl	tr.	0·03	0·08	0·42
	99·90	100·28	99·95	100·58
$O \equiv Cl$	—	—	0·02	0·10
Total	99·90	100·28	99·93	100·48
ϵ	1·501	1·5015	1·503	1·496
ω	1·524	1·5238	1·528	1·515
δ	0·023	0·022	0·025	0·019
D	2·51	2·44	2·476	2·422

NUMBERS OF IONS ON

	1.		2.		3.		4.	
Si	5·867	}12·00	6·007	}12·00	6·164	}12·00	5·971	}12·00
Al	6·130		5·990		5·838		6·032	
Ti	0·009		—		—		—	
Fe^{+3}	—		0·000		—		—	
Mg	0·102		0·012		—		—	
Fe^{+2}	—	}7·05	—	}7·55	—	}5·77	—	}7·42
Mn	—		—		—		—	
Na	5·210		6·004		3·316		6·368	
Ca	1·614		1·493		2·177		0·904	
K	0·111		0·036		0·274		0·144	
H_2O	2·682		1·553		3·714		2·544	
C	1·617	}1·62	1·369	}1·39	1·470	}1·52	1·679	}1·98
S	0·004		0·010		0·025		0·180	
Cl	0·000		0·008		0·023		0·125	
100C:(C + S)	99·7		99·3		98·3		90·7	

1. Cancrinite, associated with monticellite and melanite in vein, Iron Hill, Gunnison County, Colorado (Larsen and Foshag, 1926).   Anal. W. F. Foshag.
2. Cancrinite, sodalite–nepheline-syenite, Dôdô, Kôgendô, Korea (Kôzu, 1931).   (Average of analyses by K. Seto and S. Turumi.)
3. Cancrinite, veins in nepheline, Bancroft, Ontario (Meen, 1938).   Anal. V. B. Meen.
4. Cancrinite, Blue Mountain, Methuen township, Ontario (Phoenix and Nuffield, 1949). Anal. R. Phoenix.

VISHNEVITE ANALYSES

5.	6.	7.	8.	9.	
33·70	35·40	34·76	35·29	34·53	SiO_2
—	0·00	—	—	0·10	TiO_2
29·40	29·78	30·81	28·79	29·06	Al_2O_3
—	0·05	—	0·19	0·56	Fe_2O_3
—	0·42	—	—	0·11	FeO
—	0·00	—	—	0·09	MnO
—	0·13	—	0·10	0·09	MgO
4·18	1·12	3·87	1·49	1·48	CaO
18·52	20·77	18·90	15·65	16·51	Na_2O
1·45	0·96	1·29	4·15	5·11	K_2O
4·24	4·17	2·30	7·62	5·35	H_2O^+
0·72	0·00	0·20	—	1·36	H_2O^-
3·18	2·16	1·90	1·01	0·26	CO_2
4·65	4·70	5·93	5·76	5·02	SO_3
—	0·35	—	—	0·09	Cl
100·12	100·01	100·28	100·05	100·02	
—	0·08	—	—	0·02	$O \equiv Cl$
100·12	99·93	100·28	100·05	100·00	Total
1·500	1·493	1·497	n1·492–1·493	—	ϵ
1·509	1·499	1·502	—	1·489	ω
0·009	0·009	0·005	—	$\simeq$0·004	δ
2·443	2·402	2·42	2·35	2·328	D

THE BASIS OF $12(Si+Al)$

5.	6.	7.	8.	9.	
5·916 ⎫ 12·00	6·025 ⎫ 12·00	5·866 ⎫ 12·00	6·118 ⎫ 12·00	6·022 ⎫ 12·00	Si
6·086 ⎭	5·976 ⎭	6·129 ⎭	5·886 ⎭	5·976 ⎭	Al
—	0·000	—	—	0·012	Ti
—	0·006	—	0·025	0·074	Fe^{+3}
—	0·033	—	0·026	0·023	Mg
—	0·059	—	—	0·016	Fe^{+2}
— 7·42†	0·000 7·37	— 7·19‡	— 6·51	0·014 6·57	Mn
6·302	6·854	6·182	5·260	5·582	Na
0·786	0·205	0·700	0·277	0·277	Ca
0·325	0·208	0·278	0·919	0·569	K
2·483	2·368	1·295	4·408	3·112	H_2O
0·762 ⎫	0·502 ⎫	0·438 ⎫	0·239 ⎫	0·062 ⎫	C
0·613 ⎬1·38	0·600 ⎬1·20	0·751 ⎬1·19	0·749 ⎬0·99	0·764 ⎬0·85	S
—	0·101 ⎭	—	—	0·026 ⎭	Cl
55·4	45·6	36·8	24·2	7·5	$100C:(C+S)$

5. Sulphatic cancrinite, Iron Hill, Gunnison County, Colorado (Larsen and Steiger, 1916). Anal. G. Steiger (Includes SrO 0·08).
6. Carbonate vishnevite (sulphatic cancrinite), cancrinite ijolite, Iivaara, Kuusamo, Finland (Lehijärvi, 1960). Anal. M. Lehijärvi.
7. Carbonate vishnevite (sulphatic cancrinite), Loch Borolan, Assynt, Scotland (Stewart, 1941). Anal. F. H. Stewart (Includes SrO 0·32).
8. Carbonate vishnevite (sulphatic cancrinite), small nests and veinlets in nepheline in pegmatite in nepheline-syenite, Ilmen mountains, U.S.S.R. (Zavaritsky, 1929). Anal. Y. V. Morachevsky.
9. Vishnevite, Vishnevy Gory, Urals (Beliankin, 1944) (Includes S 0·30).

† Includes Sr 0·008.   ‡ Includes Sr 0·031.

was formed at 390°C.; replacement of Na_2CO_3 by Na_2SO_4 in cancrinite has also been reported by Barrer (1954). The synthesis of a hydrocancrinite from mixtures of NaOH, KOH, Al_2O_3 and SiO_2 in proportions corresponding to the formula $Na_xK_{1-x}AlSiO_4$ ($x=0.5–1.0$) at 415°C. and 400 kg./cm.² pressure has been described by Wyart and Michel Lévy (1949). The formation of cancrinite at temperatures between 164° and 336°C. and pressures of between 100 and 200 lb./in.² has been observed on boiler walls, and here it is considered

Table 40.   CANCRINITE AND VISHNEVITE, NUMBERS OF IONS ON THE BASIS OF 24 OXYGENS (Phoenix and Nuffield, 1949).

	1.	2.	3.	4.	5.	7.
Si	5·94	5·97	6·28	6·17	5·99	5·94
Al	6·21	5·96	5·94	6·23	6·16	6·21
Na	5·27	5·97	3·38	6·59	6·38	6·26
Ca	1·63	1·48	2·22	0·93	0·80	0·71
K	0·11	0·04	0·28	0·15	0·33	0·28
CO_3	1·64	1·36	1·50	1·74	0·77	0·44
SO_4	0·01	0·01	0·03	0·19	0·62	0·76
Cl	—	0·01	0·02	0·13	—	—
H_2O	2·71	2·71	3·78	2·63	2·51	1·31
(Si,Al)	12·00	11·93	12·00	12·00	12·00	12·00
(Na,K,Ca,Al)	7·16	7·49	6·10	8·07	7·66	7·40
(CO_3,SO_4,Cl)	1·65	1·38	1·55	2·06	1·39	1·20

Mineral numbers are the same as for Table 39.

Table 41.   MICROSOMMITE ANALYSES

	1.	2.	Numbers of ions on basis of 12(Si + Al)		
				1.	2.
SiO_2	32·21	32·23			
Al_2O_3	29·22	28·98	Si	5·799 ⎤ 12·0	5·824 ⎤ 12·0
CaO	12·60	10·36	Al	6·202 ⎦	6·174 ⎦
Na_2O	10·14	11·01	Na	3·538 ⎫	3·858 ⎫
K_2O	6·79	7·11	Ca	2·430 ⎬ 7·53	2·006 ⎬ 7·50
CO_2	—	1·26	K	1·560 ⎭	1·640 ⎭
SO_3	4·43	4·11	C	— ⎫	0·310 ⎫
Cl	6·71	6·25	S	0·598 ⎬ 2·65	0·557 ⎬ 2·78
			Cl	2·047 ⎭	1·913 ⎭
	102·10	101·31			
$O \equiv Cl$	1·51	1·56			
Total	100·59	99·75			
D	2·42–2·53	2·444			

1. Microsommite, Monte Somma, Vesuvius (Scacchi, 1876).
2. Microsommite, Monte Somma, Vesuvius (Rauff, 1878).

to be a secondary product after earlier formed minerals such as nosean (Clark, 1948). Ion-exchange in synthetic cancrinite has been reported by Barrer and White (1952). Later Barrer and Falconer (1956) made a quantitative study of ion-exchange diffusion and equilibria in "basic" cancrinites ($M_2O \cdot Al_2O_3 \cdot 2 \cdot 4SiO_2 \cdot 0 \cdot 6MOH \cdot xH_2O$ where M is Na, Ag or Li and $x = 0 \cdot 9$ for Na and Ag "basic" cancrinite and $x = 0 \cdot 14$ for Li "basic" cancrinite). It was found that

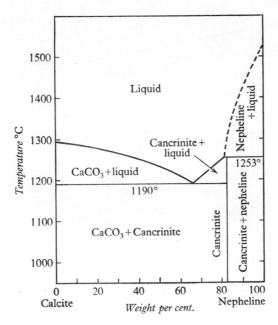

FIG. 96. The system calcite–nepheline at 110 bars pressure of CO_2 (after Eitel, 1954).

100 per cent. exchange could be effected with Li, Na and Ag, that partial exchange occurred with K, Tl and Rb, but that Cs, as for analcite, was not exchanged.

OPTICAL AND PHYSICAL PROPERTIES

The optical properties of the cancrinite–vishnevite series show a fair correlation with the varying contents of CO_3 and SO_4, and both the ω and ϵ indices are lower in the more sulphatic varieties (Fig. 97). The rate of decrease of the ω index with increasing content of the vishnevite component is greater than that of the ϵ index, and the birefringence varies from about 0·025 for cancrinite to between 0·002 to 0·004 for vishnevite. In addition to the smaller rate of decrease, the ϵ index shows a more irregular variation; thus in estimating compositions from refractive indices ω is a more reliable guide than ϵ. Anomalous biaxial optical characters have been reported for some cancrinites (Stewart, 1941), and the chlorine-rich cancrinite, microsommite, is distinguished from the normal members of the cancrinite–vishnevite series by its optically positive character. The specific gravity of the cancrinite end-member is approximately

2·50; there is a progressive decrease in density with increasing content of the vishnevite component and the specific gravity of the vishnevite end-member is approximately 2·30. Beliankin (1944) reported that the dehydration of vishnevite is accompanied by a decrease in the ω refractive index and in density

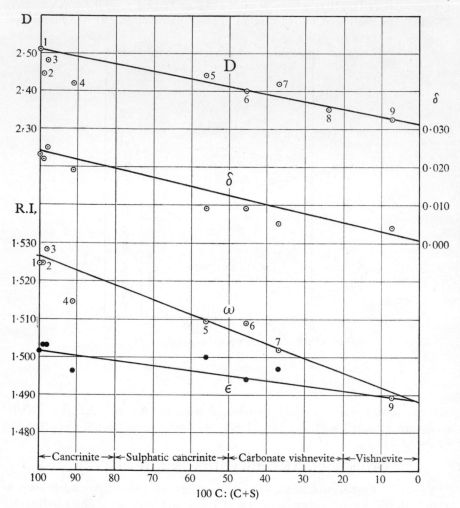

FIG. 97. Relationship between chemical composition (mol. per cent.) and optical properties and density of the cancrinite–vishnevite series. Numbers refer to analyses in Table 39.

(Table 42), but for cancrinite Zambonini and Ferrari (1930) found that water is lost without affecting the optical properties.

DISTINGUISHING FEATURES

The carbonate-rich varieties of the cancrinite–vishnevite series are distinguished from nepheline by their stronger birefringence, from scapolite by their different cleavage and lower refractive indices, and from calcite by their

Table 42. DEHYDRATION, REFRACTIVE INDEX AND DENSITY RELATIONSHIPS
FOR VISHNEVITE (Beliankin, 1944).

Temperature °C.	Loss of H_2O wt. per cent.	Refractive index ω	Density (g./cm.^{3})
15	—	1·489	2·328
150	3·51	—	—
200	4·99	—	—
250	5·53	—	—
300	6·01	1·474	2·310
350	6·41	—	—
400	6·61	1·472	2·308
450	6·71	—	—
500	6·71	1·463	2·306

much weaker birefringence. Cancrinite may be confused with muscovite, and particularly with near basal sections of the latter mineral, but is distinguished by its uniaxial optical character, as it is also from thomsonite and other biaxial zeolites. Vishnevite has lower refractive indices and better cleavage than nepheline. The rare potassium- and chlorine-rich cancrinite, microsommite, is optically positive.

PARAGENESIS

Cancrinite is an important constituent of the juvite, melanite juvite (cancrinite $\simeq 9$ per cent.) and cancrinite juvite ($\simeq 20$ per cent.) in the Alnö Island alkaline complex (Eckermann, 1948). In these rocks it occurs as a primary mineral and was formed at the end of the crystallization sequence after melanite aegirine-augite, nepheline and a sodium-bearing orthoclase. Cancrinite, together with potassium felspar, also occurs in the central portion of the juvite pegmatite, the margins of which consist of calcite, nepheline and orthoclase. The chemical composition is similar in both parts of the pegmatite except for a lower content of SO_3 and H_2O in the marginal rock, and the two different assemblages are probably due to a higher CO_2 pressure during the formation of the inner portion of the pegmatite according to the reaction:

$$\text{nepheline} + \text{calcite} \rightarrow \text{cancrinite}$$

No examples of the reverse reaction, namely the formation of nepheline and calcite from cancrinite, have been noted in the Alnö rocks.

Cancrinite is present in the juvite, urtite, ijolite and melteigite of the Fen area, southern Norway, and in some of these rocks it forms reaction rims between nepheline and calcite (Brøgger, 1921). The sequence nepheline→ cancrinite→calcite is interpreted by Saether (1957) as a normal magmatic reaction series in which the cancrinite was formed by reaction between the earlier nepheline with CO_2-rich residual fluids. Comparable occurrences of cancrinite in urtite and jacupirangite in the Kovdor-Ozero region, Kola Peninsula, have been reported by Ivensen (1941).

In the ijolitic mass at Homa Bay, western Kenya, cancrinite in small amounts is present in both urtite and ijolite. It is a more abundant constituent of the wollastonite ijolites, biotite ijolites and calcite ijolites of the complex; much of the cancrinite is secondary and has replaced nepheline but some is of primary origin. In the urtites cancrinite occurs both as interstitial grains and as "fibrous" crystals enclosed in interstitial calcite, and is in part a reaction product between nepheline and calcite (Pulfrey, 1949).

Cancrinite is present in the urtite, ijolite and melteigites of the alkaline district of Iivaara, Kuusamo, Finland (Lehijärvi, 1960). Here the formation of cancrinite is a characteristic feature of the fenitization of the surrounding granodiorite and quartz diorite, advanced stages of which are represented by cancrinite fenite. Cancrinite makes up approximately 30 per cent. of the cancrinite–nepheline–wollastonite rock of this area where it also occurs in cancrinite ijolite fissure veins in the country rock. CO_2-rich and SO_3-rich varieties (*e.g.* Table 39, anal. 6) are both known from the ijolites and melteigites. Cancrinite (anal. 2) is present as a primary constituent in the sodalite–nepheline-syenite at Dôdô, Kôgendô, Korea (Kôzu, 1931), and in the cancrinite syenite at Budeda, south-east Uganda (Davies, 1956).

Cancrinite is a common mineral in the alkali rocks of Iron Hill, Gunnison County, Colorado. Here it occurs mainly as an alteration product of nepheline, but also as a reaction product between nepheline and calcite in contact metamorphosed limestones, and as a hydrothermal replacement of melilite (Larsen, 1942). In a vein cutting uncompahgrite, cancrinite (Table 39, anal. 1) occurs in large cleavage plates 10 cms. in width and encloses monticellite and melanite. Sulphatic cancrinite (Table 39, anal. 5), derived from either nepheline or melilite, has also been described from this area (Larsen and Steiger, 1916). Carbonate vishnevite (Table 39, anal. 7), associated with orthoclase and melanite, occurs in pegmatitic patches and veins in borolanite at Allt a' Mhuillin, Assynt (Stewart, 1941), and has been reported in nests and veinlets in the nepheline of a nepheline-syenite pegmatite from the Ilmen Mountains, U.S.S.R. (Zavaritsky, 1929). The type locality of vishnevite (Table 39, anal. 9) is the Vishnevy Mountains, southern Urals (Beliankin, 1944).

Primary cancrinite is an important constituent of the central core of busorite in the carbonatite at Lueshe, Kivu, Congo (Meyer and Béthune, 1960). Cancrinite–sodalite–calcite–albite assemblages, in which the cancrinite and sodalite occasionally form large aggregates of crystals, up to 20 cm. in size, in contorted bands in the Pre-Cambrian anorthosite of southern Angola have been reported by Simpson and Otto (1960). Cancrinite–corundum rocks at granite–limestone contacts occur in association with the tin deposits at Hsianghualing, Lingwa, Hunan (Meng and Chang, 1935). A cancrinite–natrolite–hastingsite–albite–andesine assemblage is developed in some xenoliths in the peridotite–serpentine massif of Verblyuzhaya Mountains, southern Urals, and is considered to result from the metasomatism of amphibolite by granitic fluids (Sokolov, 1934). A cancrinite–calcite contact rock containing tremolite and possibly thulite has been described from the nepheline-syenites of Kishengarh, Rajputana (Biswas, 1922; Heron, 1924).

REFERENCES

Barrer, R. M., 1954. Contributions to synthetic mineral chemistry. *Proc. Internat. Symposium on Reactivity of Solids, Gothenburg,* pt. 1, p. 373.

Barrer, R. M. and **Falconer, J. D.,** 1956. Ion exchange in felspathoids as a solid-state reaction. *Proc. Roy. Soc., A.,* vol. 236, p. 227.

—— and **White, E. A. D.,** 1952. The hydrothermal chemistry of silicates, Part II. Synthetic crystalline sodium aluminosilicates. *Journ. Chem. Soc.,* p. 1561.

Beliankin, D. S., 1944. Vishnevite, and not sulphatic cancrinite. *Doklady Acad. Sci. USSR,* vol. 42, p. 304.

Berman, H., 1937. Constitution and classification of the natural silicates. *Amer. Min.,* vol. 22, p. 342.

Biswas, S. L., 1922. On the cancrinite from Kishengarh, Rajputana. *Journ. Dept. Sci. Univ. Calcutta,* vol. 4, p. 127 (M.A. 5–37).

Brauns, R. and **Uhlig, J.,** 1913. Cancrinit- und nephelinführende Auswürflinge aus dem Laacher Seegebiet. *Neues Jahrb. Min.,* vol. 35, p. 119.

Brøgger, W. C., 1921. Das Fengebiet in Telemarken. *Vidensk. Skrifter* 1, No. 9.

Clark, L. M., 1948. The identification of minerals in boiler deposits. Examples of hydrothermal synthesis in boilers. *Min. Mag.,* vol. 28, p. 359.

Davies, K. A., 1956. The geology of south-east Uganda. *Geol. Surv. Uganda, Mem.* No. 8.

Eckermann, H. von, 1948. The alkaline district of Alnö Island. *Sveriges Geol. Undersök., ser. Ca.,* No. 36.

Eitel, W., 1954. *The physical chemistry of the silicates.* Chicago Univ. Press.

Gossner, B. and **Mussgnug, F.,** 1930. Über Davyn und seine Beziehungen zu Hauyn und Cancrinit. *Zeit. Krist.,* vol. 73, p. 52.

Heron, A. M., 1924. The soda-bearing rocks of Kishengarh, Rajputana. *Rec. Geol. Surv. India,* vol. 56, p. 179.

Ivensen, J. P., 1941. On the alkaline rocks of the Kovdor-Ozero region of the Kola peninsula. *Doklady Acad. Sci. URSS,* vol. 30, p. 337.

Kôzu, S., 1931. Preliminary note on studies of cancrinite from Korea. *Japan. Journ. Geol. Geogr.,* vol. 9, Abstract, pp. (1)–(2).

—— and **Takané, K.,** 1933. Crystal structure of cancrinite. *Proc. Imp. Acad. Tokyo,* vol. 9, p. 56 (M.A. 5–325).

Larsen, E. S., 1942. Alkalic rocks of Iron Hill, Gunnison County, Colorado. *U.S. Geol. Surv., Prof. Paper* 197-A.

—— and **Foshag, W. F.,** 1926. Cancrinite as a high temperature hydrothermal mineral from Colorado. *Amer. Min.,* vol. 11, p. 300.

—— and **Steiger, G.,** 1916. Sulphatic cancrinite from Colorado. *Amer. Jour. Sci.,* 4th ser., vol. 42, p. 332.

Lehijärvi, M., 1956. Cancrinite–ijolite from Iivaara, Kuusamo, Finland. *Bull. Comm. géol. Finlande,* No. 172.

—— 1960. The alkaline district of Iivaara, Kuusamo, Finland. *Bull. Comm. géol. Finlande,* No. 185.

Meen, V. B., 1938. An unusual cancrinite. *Univ. Toronto Studs., Geol. Ser.,* vol. 41, p. 35.

Meng, H. M. and **Chang, K.,** 1935. Geology of the Hsianghualing tin deposits, Lingwa, Hunan. *Mem. Nat. Res. Inst. Geol. Acad. Sinica, Nanking,* No. 15, p. 15.

Meyer, A. and **Béthune, P. de,** 1960. The Lueshe carbonatite (Kivu, Belgian Congo). *Rept. 21st Intern. Geol. Congr., Norden,* Part 13, p. 304.

Phoenix, R. and **Nuffield, E. W.,** 1949. Cancrinite from Blue Mountain, Ontario. *Amer. Min.,* vol. 34, p. 452.

Pulfrey, W., 1949. Ijolitic rocks near Homa Bay, western Kenya. *Quart. Journ. Geol. Soc.,* vol. 105, p. 428.

Rauff, H., 1878. Ueber die chemische Zusammensetzung des Nephelins, Cancrinits und Microsommits. *Zeit. Krist.,* vol. 2, p. 445.

Saether, E., 1957.   The alkaline rock province of the Fen area in southern Norway. *Det. Kgl. Norske Videnskabers Selskabs Skrifter,* Nr. 1, p. 1.

Scacchi, A., 1876.   Microsommite del Monte Somma.   *Rend. Accad. Sci. fis. mat., Napoli.*

Simpson, E. S. W. and **Otto, J. D. T.,** 1960.   On the Pre-Cambrian anorthosite mass of southern Angola.   *Rept. 21st Intern. Geol. Congr., Norden,* Part 13, p. 216.

Sokolov, G. A., 1934.   Alkaline metasomatism in amphibolites of Verbliugjia Mt. *Trav. Inst. Petrogr. Acad. Sci. USSR,* vol. 6, p. 179 (M.A. 6–426).

Stewart, F. H., 1941.   On sulphatic cancrinite and analcite (eudnophite) from Loch Borolan, Assynt.   *Min. Mag.,* vol. 26, p. 1.

Wyart, J. and **Michel Lévy, M.,** 1949.   Cristallisation des mélanges $Na_xK_{1-x}AlSiO_4$ en présence d'eau sous pression (formation de néphéline, kalsilite, hydrocancrinite, hydrosodalite, mica).   *Compt. Rend. Acad. Sci. Paris,* vol. 229, p. 131.

Zambonini, F. and **Ferrari, A.,** 1930.   Sulla identitá di struttura cristallina della cancrinite del Monte Somma con quella di Mias.   *Atti Rend. Accad. Lincei, Cl. Sci. fis. mat. nat.,* vol. 2, p. 182 (M.A. 4–355).

Zavaritzky, A. N., 1929.   Sulphatic cancrinite from the Ilmen Mountains (south Urals).   *Mém. Soc. Russe. Min.,* vol. 38, p. 201 (M.A. 4–379).

Scapolite $(Na,Ca,K)_4[Al_3(Al,Si)_3Si_6O_{24}](Cl,F,OH,CO_3,SO_4)$

TETRAGONAL $(-)$

	Marialite[1]	Meionite[1]
	$Na_4[Al_3Si_9O_{24}]Cl$	$Ca_4[Al_6Si_6O_{24}]CO_3$
ϵ	1·540–1·541	1·556–1·562
ω	1·546–1·550	1·590–1·600
$(\epsilon+\omega)/2$	1·535†	1·585†
δ	0·004–0·008	0·024–0·037
Dispersion:	Moderate.	Moderate.
D	2·50–2·62	2·78
H	5–6	5–6
Cleavage:	{100}, {110} good.	{100}, {110} good.
Colour:	Colourless, white, bluish grey, pale greenish yellow, yellow, pink, violet, brown or orange-brown; colourless in thin section.	

Unit cell: a Å 12·075‡   (12·01–12·29)§   12·13‡
c Å 7·516   (7·54–7·76)   7·69
$Z=2$.   Space group $P4/m$.

Sodium-rich scapolites are almost insoluble, calcium-rich scapolites decompose in HCl.

Although the compositions of natural scapolites do not cover the whole range between the two theoretical end-members marialite and meionite they can be considered as members of the solid solution series $3NaAlSi_3O_8 \cdot NaCl$–$3CaAl_2$ $Si_2O_8 \cdot CaCO_3$. Replacement of the cations does not occur to any appreciable extent but substantial replacement of Cl and CO_3 by F and SO_4 is common. Pure marialite has not been found, pure meionite likewise is unknown in natural rocks, and scapolites containing more than 80 per cent. of either the marialite or meionite components are rare. Scapolites are relatively common constituents of calcium-rich metamorphic rocks, and the development of scapolite-bearing rocks on a regional scale has been described from the Kiruna district, Sweden (Sundius, 1915), the Cloncurry district, north-west Queensland (Edwards and Baker, 1953), and from the Mount Lofty Ranges, South Australia (White, 1959). Scapolite is not known to form in sedimentary environments and, except for some pegmatites, does not occur as a primary constituent of igneous rocks.

[1] Values of ϵ, ω, δ and D of intermediate members of the series lie between those quoted for the end-members.
† Extrapolated values for pure marialite and meionite (see Fig. 101).
‡ Values for synthetic marialite and meionite.
§ Range for natural scapolites.

Following Shaw (1960) the nomenclature of the scapolite series adopted here is marialite Me_0–Me_{20}, dipyre Me_{20}–Me_{50}, mizzonite Me_{50}–Me_{80}, and meionite Me_{80}–Me_{100}. Other names which have been used to describe members of the scapolite series are listed by Shaw; like wernerite, the old group name, they are no longer used. Scapolite is named from the Greek *skapos*, shaft, in allusion to its common stumpy prismatic habit; marialite is named after Maria Rosa, wife of G. vom Rath; the name dipyre refers to the effects of heating, *i.e.* fusion and

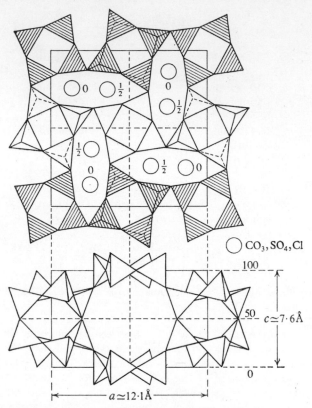

Fɪɢ. 98. The structure of scapolite projected on (001) and (100) (after Schiebold and Seumel, 1932).

phosphorescence; mizzonite is from the Greek *meizon*, greater, in allusion to its larger c/a ratio in comparison with meionite. The latter name is derived from the Greek *meion*, less, in reference to its less acute pyramid form compared with vesuvianite, a mineral with which it sometimes is associated at Vesuvius.

STRUCTURE

The structure of scapolite has not been investigated in detail but it probably consists of ring-like groups of four (Si,Al)–O tetrahedra, the vertices of which are directed alternately towards the opposite ends of the z-axis. The tetrahedral groups are linked as shown in Fig. 98 to form chains parallel to the vertical axis and the individual chains are joined by other rings of four (Si,Al)–O tetrahedra, the edges of which are parallel to the *z*-axis.   Within this framework are cavities of smaller and larger dimensions; the former are occupied by Na and Ca ions and the latter by CO_3, SO_4 and Cl ions (Gossner and Brückl, 1928; Pauling, 1930; Schiebold and Seumel, 1932; Scherillo, 1935).   The cell dimensions of synthetic marialite, *a* 12·075, *c* 7·516 Å, and of synthetic meionite, *a* 12·13, *c* 7·69 Å, have been measured by Eugster and Prostka (1960).   The cell

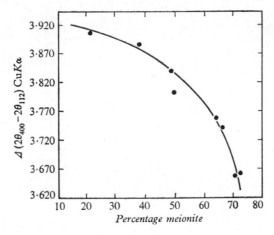

FIG. 99. Variation in parameter $2\theta_{400} - 2\theta_{112}$ (CuK_α) with composition (after Burley *et al.*, 1961).

dimensions of some scapolites are outside the range shown by the two pure end-members and such differences may be due to high contents of sulphate or potassium ions.   The space group of scapolite was considered by Pauling (1930) and Scherillo (1935) to be *I*4/*m*.   Recent work by Burley *et al.* (1961), however, has shown that the X-ray powder data are compatible with a primitive rather than a body-centred lattice, and these authors conclude that the most probable space group is *P*4/*m*.   Correlation of the angular separation between the 400 and 112 peaks with the meionite content of scapolites (Fig. 99) has been demonstrated.   X-ray powder diffraction data for scapolite (Me 37·8 per cent.) are also given by Kaitaro (1955).

CHEMISTRY

Twenty-one analyses of scapolites are detailed in Table 43; with the exception of anal. 18 all are included by Shaw (1960) who has listed 135 analyses of minerals belonging to this series.   Because of the lack of full details of the scapolite structure the formulae and variable anion content have been calculated on the basis of half the unit cell content of silicon and aluminium, *i.e.* 12(Si + Al). Scapolites form a solid solution series the principal end-members of which can be expressed empirically as $3NaAlSi_3O_8 \cdot NaCl$, chloride marialite, and $3CaAl_2Si_2O_8 \cdot CaCO_3$, carbonate meionite.   Chlorine-rich scapolites are rich in sodium

Table 43.　Scapolite analyses

	1.	2.	3.	4.	5.	6.	7.
SiO_2	59·60	57·89	56·77	55·22	54·73	52·42	51·63
TiO_2	—	0·01	—	—	0·01	—	—
Al_2O_3	19·87	21·62	22·27	23·18	22·85	25·05	24·21
Fe_2O_3	1·01	0·07	0·24	—	0·08	0·58	0·20
FeO	—	—	—	—	—	—	—
MnO	—	0·01	—	—	0·00	—	—
MgO	0·21	0·03	0·09	0·21	0·03	0·37	0·08
CaO	3·42	4·81	6·64	7·97	8·29	9·10	11·13
Na_2O	10·66	10·50	9·40	9·04	8·55	7·07	7·02
K_2O	1·47	1·16	0·83	0·88	1·08	2·52	0·90
H_2O^+	0·66	0·44	}0·25	}0·17	0·13	0·67	0·60
H_2O^-	—	0·06			0·00	—	—
CO_2	—	1·11	0·51	1·20	1·69	1·66	1·59
SO_3	—	0·03	0·07	—	0·39	—	0·98
F	—	0·00	—	—	0·00	—	—
Cl	3·23	2·96	3·30	2·76	2·19	1·30	2·32
	100·13	100·70	100·37	100·63	100·02	100·74	100·66
$O \equiv Cl,F$	0·74	0·67	0·74	0·63	0·49	0·29	0·52
Total	99·39	100·03	99·63	100·00	99·53	100·45	100·14
ϵ	—	1·541	1·541	1·541	1·547	1·5454	1·550
ω	—	1·549	1·552	1·555	1·560	1·5653	1·5694
D	—	2·619	2·572	—	2·660	2·612	—

Numbers of ions on the basis of 12(Si,Al)

	1.	2.	3.	4.	5.	6.	7.
Si	8·614 }12·00	8·331 }12·00	8·204 }12·00	8·026 }12·00	8·042 }12·00	7·675 }12·00	7·728 }12·00
Al	3·386	3·668	3·796	3·972	3·958	4·324	4·272
Ti	—	0·001	—	—	0·001	—	—
Fe^{+3}	0·110	0·007	0·026	—	0·008	0·064	0·022
Mg	0·045	0·006	0·019	0·045	0·006	0·081	0·018
Fe^{+2}	— }3·94	— }3·90	— }3·86	— }3·99	— }3·96	— }4·05	— }4·03
Mn	—	0·001	—	—	0·000	—	—
Na	2·986	2·930	2·634	2·546	2·436	2·006	2·036
Ca	0·580	0·742	1·028	1·241	1·305	1·427	1·785
K	0·270	0·212	0·152	0·162	0·202	0·472	0·170
H	0·636	0·422	0·242	0·164	0·126	0·654	0·600
C	—	0·218	0·101	0·238	0·339	0·332	0·325
S	— }0·79	0·003 }0·94	0·008 }0·92	— }0·92	0·043 }0·93	— }0·66	0·110 }1·02
F	—	0·000			0·000		
Cl	0·791	0·722	0·808	0·679	0·545	0·323	0·588

$$\frac{100 \times (Ca + Mg + Fe + Mn + Ti)}{(Na + K + Ca + Mg + Fe + Mn + Ti)}$$

| | 17·4 | 19·3 | 27·8 | 32·1 | 33·3 | 38·8 | 45·2 |

1. Marialite, Pezh Island, north Karelia (Solodovnikova, 1957).
2. Marialite, syenitic pegmatite, Gooderham, Glamorgan Township, Ontario (Shaw, 1960). Anal. C. O, Ingamells (total Fe as Fe_2O_3).
3. Dipyre, scapolite–hornblende rock (ødegårdite), Ødegården, southern Norway (Brøgger, 1935).
4. Dipyre, scapolite dyke in hyperite, Langå Sound, southern Norway (Brøgger, 1935). Anal. E. Klüver (Analysis recalculated after correcting for Fe_2O_3 0·32).
5. Dipyre, pegmatitic skarn, Monmouth Township, Ontario (Shaw, 1960). Anal. C. O. Ingamells (total Fe as Fe_2O_3).
6. Dipyre, Zdár Mountain, Ruda, Moravia (Konečný and Rosický, 1926). Anal. B. Konečný.
7. Dipyre, Haliburton, Ontario (Borgström, 1915). Anal. L. M. Borgström.

Table 43. SCAPOLITE ANALYSES—*continued*

	8.	9.	10.	11.	12.	13.	14.
SiO_2	52·10	51·83	50·80	51·10	50·47	47·52	47·17
TiO_2	0·02	0·03	—	0·05	—	—	0·03
Al_2O_3	23·79	24·29	24·14	25·10	25·20	25·21	26·29
Fe_2O_3	0·23	0·07	0·11	0·33	0·10	—	0·15
FeO	—	—	0·90	0·12	—	0·30	—
MnO	tr.	tr.	—	0·01	0·06	0·02	0·01
MgO	0·18	0·02	0·09	0·00	0·04	0·14	1·00
CaO	11·13	11·66	12·06	12·54	14·07	15·48	14·31
Na_2O	6·86	6·40	5·43	5·38	4·95	4·52	3·82
K_2O	0·87	1·16	1·87	1·03	0·73	0·10	1·01
H_2O^+	0·07	0·22	0·12	0·49	0·20	0·22	0·93
H_2O^-	0·10	0·04	—	0·13	0·02	0·08	0·50
CO_2	2·14	2·28	2·71	2·88	2·81	2·16	2·66
SO_3	0·80	0·72	—	0·11	0·79	4·17	1·42
F	0·11	0·02	0·37	—	—	0·00	0·04
Cl	1·85	1·66	1·59	1·42	1·15	0·06	0·56
	100·25	100·40	100·28	100·69	100·59	100·01	99·90
$O \equiv Cl,F$	0·46	0·38	0·36	0·31	0·26	0·01	0·14
Total	99·79	100·02	99·92	100·38	100·33	100·00	99·76
ϵ	1·550	1·551	1·5490	1·549	1·552	1·564	1·557
ω	1·568	1·569	1·5698	1·574	1·575	1·587	1·581
D	2·689	2·686	2·67	2·68	2·698	2·72	2·705

NUMBERS OF IONS ON THE BASIS OF 12(Si,Al)

	8.	9.	10.	11.	12.	13.	14.
Si	7·799 ⎫12·00	7·729 ⎫12·00	7·690 ⎫12·00	7·599 ⎫12·00	7·553 ⎫12·00	7·382 ⎫12·00	7·241 ⎫12·00
Al	4·200 ⎭	4·271 ⎭	4·308 ⎭	4·400 ⎭	4·446 ⎭	4·618 ⎭	4·758 ⎭
Ti	0·002	0·003	—	0·005	—	0·000	0·004
Fe^{+3}	0·024	0·007	0·012	0·037	0·010	—	0·016
Mg	0·040	0·004	—	0·000	0·009	0·033	0·229
Fe^{+2}	— ⎫4·01	— ⎫3·95	0·114 ⎫4·04†	0·015 ⎫3·80	— ⎫3·86	0·039 ⎫4·03	— ⎫3·94
Mn	—	0·000		0·001	0·007	0·003	0·001
Na	1·990	1·849	1·594	1·552	1·436	1·360	1·136
Ca	1·785	1·863	1·956	1·998	2·256	2·577	2·353
K	0·166 ⎭	0·220 ⎭	0·360 ⎭	0·195 ⎭	0·138 ⎭	0·020 ⎭	0·198 ⎭
H	0·070	0·218	0·122	0·486	0·200	0·228	0·952
C	0·437 ⎫	0·464 ⎫	0·560 ⎫	0·584 ⎫	0·574 ⎫	0·458 ⎫	0·557 ⎫
S	0·090 ⎬1·05	0·081 ⎬0·97		0·012 ⎬0·95	0·089 ⎬0·95	0·486 ⎬0·96	0·163 ⎬0·89
F	0·052	0·009	0·177 ⎬1·14				0·019
Cl	0·470 ⎭	0·419 ⎭	0·407 ⎭	0·357 ⎭	0·291 ⎭	0·016 ⎭	0·146 ⎭

$$\frac{100 \times (Ca + Mg + Fe + Mn + Ti)}{(Na + K + Ca + Mg + Fe + Mn + Ti)}$$

46·1	47·5	51·8	54·1	59·1	65·7	66·1

8. Dipyre, pegmatitic skarn, Huddersfield Township, Quebec (Shaw, 1960). Anal. C. O. Ingamells (total Fe as Fe_2O_3).
9. Dipyre, pegmatitic skarn, Huddersfield Township, Quebec (Shaw, 1960). Anal. C. O. Ingamells (total Fe as Fe_2O_3).
10. Mizzonite, Tsarasaotra, Madagascar (Lacroix, 1922). Anal. M. Raoult (Includes SrO 0·09).
11. Mizzonite, calc-silicate rock, Milendella area, Mount Lofty Ranges, South Australia (White, 1959). Anal. A. J. R. White.
12. Mizzonite, Nautanen, Sweden (Geijer, 1917).
13. Mizzonite, garnet–hornblende–pyroxene–scapolite gneiss, Shai Hills, Ghana (Knorring and Kennedy, 1958). Anal. O. von Knorring (Includes P_2O_5 0·03).
14. Mizzonite, pegmatitic skarn, Huddersfield Township, Quebec (Shaw, 1960). Anal. C. O. Ingamells (total Fe as Fe_2O_3).

† Includes Sr 0·008.

Table 43. SCAPOLITE ANALYSES—*continued*

	15.	16.	17.	18.	19.	20.	21.
SiO$_2$	45·91	45·14	44·45	45·18	43·44	41·32	41·38
TiO$_2$	0·07	—	—	0·03	0·00	—	—
Al$_2$O$_3$	28·19	27·83	28·06	26·23	28·72	30·07	31·59
Fe$_2$O$_3$	0·11	0·31	0·44	0·30	0·26	—	tr.
FeO	—	—	—	0·72	0·22	0·23	—
MnO	0·01	0·00	—	0·01	0·03	—	—
MgO	0·46	0·29	0·31	0·38	0·05	0·30	0·29
CaO	15·76	17·34	17·72	18·12	19·93	20·09	20·72
Na$_2$O	2·44	3·72	2·71	2·74	1·97	0·50	1·38
K$_2$O	2·21	0·20	0·29	0·43	0·51	2·33	0·48
H$_2$O$^+$	1·12	0·64	}0·85	1·20	0·40	0·61	0·29
H$_2$O$^-$	0·03	—		0·08	0·09	—	—
CO$_2$	2·86	3·78	4·74	4·64	4·51	4·10	4·35
SO$_3$	0·94	0·08	0·00	—	0·08	0·60	0·35
F	0·01	—	—	—	—	—	—
Cl	0·05	0·66	0·03	0·06	0·12	—	0·18
	100·17	99·99	99·60	100·12	100·33	100·15	101·01
O≡Cl,F	0·02	0·20	0·01	0·02	0·03	—	0·04
Total	100·15	99·79	99·59	100·10	100·30	100·15	100·97
ε		1·555	1·553	1·5569	1·556	—	1·556	1·5612
ω		1·587	1·584	1·5924	1·593	—	1·590	1·5992
D		2·703	—	2·722	—	2·757	—	2·740

NUMBERS OF IONS ON THE BASIS OF 12(Si,Al)

	15.	16.	17.	18.	19.	20.	21.
Si	6·960 }12·00	6·948 }12·00	6·879 }12·00	7·124 }12·00	6·744 }12·00	6·459 }12·00	6·315 }12·00
Al	5·038	5·052	5·120	4·876	5·256	5·542	5·684
Ti	0·008	—	—	0·004	—	—	—
Fe^{+3}	0·012	0·034	0·050	0·036	0·030	—	0·000
Mg	0·104	0·067	0·072	0·089	0·011	0·069	0·066
Fe^{+2}	—	—	—	0·095	0·029	0·030	—
Mn	0·001 }3·83	0·000 }4·11	— }3·93	0·001 }4·21	0·004 }4·08	— }4·08	— }3·96
Na	0·716	1·110	0·812	0·838	0·594	0·152	0·407
Ca	2·560	2·860	2·938	3·062	3·315	3·364	3·388
K	0·428	0·038	0·058	0·086	0·100	0·464	0·094
H	1·133	0·656	0·878	1·262	0·414	0·636	0·296
C	0·592	0·795	1·002	0·999	0·956	0·874	0·906
S	0·107 }0·72	0·023 }0·99	0·000 }1·01	— }1·02	0·009 }1·00	0·070 }0·94	0·040 }0·99
F	0·004	—	—	—	—	—	—
Cl	0·013	0·172	0·007	0·016	0·032	—	0·048
$\dfrac{100 \times (Ca + Mg + Fe + Mn + Ti)}{(Na + K + Ca + Mg + Fe + Mn + Ti)}$	70·1	72·0	77·8	78·1	83·0	84·8	87·3

15. Mizzonite, pegmatitic skarn, Grenville, Quebec (Shaw, 1960). Anal. C. O. Ingamells (total Fe as Fe$_2$O$_3$).
16. Mizzonite, Glamorgan Township, Ontario (Gittins, unpublished, quoted by Shaw (1960)). (Optics by Shaw; SO$_3$ value is for S.)
17. Mizzonite, Pargas, Finland (Borgström, 1915). Anal. L. M. Borgström.
18. Mizzonite, meionite–diopside gneiss, western Uusimaa, south-western Finland (Parras, 1958).
19. Meionite, limestone contact, Helsinki (Lokka, 1943). Anal. L. Lökka.
20. Meionite, limestone xenolith in granodiorite, Gnivan, Vinnitza district, U.S.S.R. (Bobrovnik, 1948).
21. Meionite, geode in limestone, Vesuvius (Scherillo, 1935).

and the CO$_3$(SO$_4$)-scapolites have a high Ca content (Fig. 100); thus the average numbers of Cl anions per formula unit for the marialites, dipyres, mizzonites and meionites in Table 43 are respectively 0·76, 0·53, 0·17 and 0·03 and the corresponding numbers of CO$_3$ ions are 0·22, 0·34, 0·68 and 0·91. The SO$_4$ ion is a relatively important constituent in some scapolites, and sulphate-marialite and sulphate-meionite are regarded by some workers as additional end-member compositions of the scapolite solid solution series. Small amounts of F may proxy for Cl. The significance of H_2O, reported in varying quantity in all scapolite analyses, is not known but it is probably an integral part of the scapolite composition (Shaw, 1960).

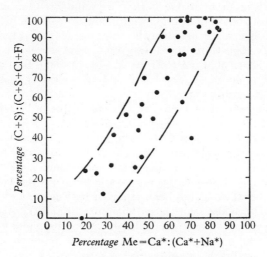

Fig. 100. Relationship between percentage meionite and percentage $(C+S):(C+S+Cl+F)$ for a number of scapolites. $Ca^* = (Ca+Mg+Fe+Mn+Ti)$, $Na^* = (Na+K)$ (after Shaw, 1960).

The main substitution is $NaSi \rightleftharpoons CaAl$ as in the plagioclase felspars; the charge on the (Si,Al)–O framework for the ideal marialite and meionite compositions varies between 3 and 6 and the valency balance is maintained as shown below:

$$(Na,Ca)_4[Al_3(Al,Si)_3Si_6O_{24}](Cl,OH,CO_3,SO_4)$$

$$\begin{array}{ccc} 4 \rightarrow 8 & 3 \rightarrow 6 & 1 \rightarrow 2 \\ (+) & (-) & (-) \end{array}$$

$$\underbrace{\qquad\qquad\qquad\qquad}$$

$$4 \rightarrow 8$$
$$(-)$$

Shaw (1960) has presented a scheme for calculating the proportions of the following scapolite end-members:

$$Na_4Al_3Si_9O_{24}Cl, \qquad Na_4Al_3Si_9O_{24}F, \qquad Na_4Al_3Si_9O_{24}HSO_4,$$
$$Na_4Al_3Si_9O_{24}OH, \qquad Ca_4Al_6Si_6O_{24}CO_3, \qquad Ca_4Al_6Si_6O_{24}SO_4.$$

The ideal formula can be expressed

$$(Na_xCa_y)Al_{0.75x+1.5y}Si_{2.25x+1.5y}O_{24}R_{1-2}$$

where $x+y=4$; or more generally as

$$W_4Z_{12}O_{24} \cdot R$$

where W is principally Ca, Na and K but may include small amounts of Mg, Fe,

Mn and Ti, Z is Si and Al, and R is Cl, F, HCO_3, HSO_4 or OH for marialite and CO_3, SO_4, $(OH)_2$, Cl_2 or F_2 for meionite. The majority of analyses show a deficiency of aluminium and an excess of silicon, *i.e.* the substitution of Al for Si is not sufficient to satisfy the stoichiometric requirements.

Shaw determined the trace element content of some 50 scapolites, the majority of which occur in rocks of the Grenville Pre-Cambrian province of Quebec and Ontario, but did not find a significant correlation between either the trace elements themselves or between the trace elements and the major element contents. The average concentrations (p.p.m.) in these minerals are B 25, Be 9·3, Ga 33, Ti 82, Li 56, Cu 4·4, Zr 59, Mn 57, Sr 1800, Ba 120, Rb 20. The elements Cr, Ni, Co, Mo, Sn, V, Sc, Ag, Y and La are rarely present in amounts above the limits of sensitivity.

Eitel (1925) synthesized meionite at CO_2 pressures of 112 bars during his investigation of the system Na_2CO_3–$CaCO_3$–$NaAlSiO_4$–$NaAlSi_3O_8$. Fyfe *et al.* (1958) failed to synthesize scapolite from anorthite–calcite–calcium chloride mixtures at temperatures between 400° and 700°C. at water pressures of 500 bars. The dry synthesis of marialite from seeded mixtures of $Na_2O \cdot 6SiO_2$, Al_2O_3 and NaCl at one atmosphere pressure and temperatures between 700° and 850°C. in runs of 1 to 2 weeks has been reported by Eugster and Prostka (1960). The same authors have also synthesized meionite from SiO_2, Al_2O_3 and $CaCO_3$, at 850°C. and a pressure of one atmosphere. Marialite melts incongruently to albite + liquid at $860° \pm 10°C.$, the liquid containing more than 90 weight per cent. NaCl; the marialite–halite eutectic lies near 800°C. and very close to the composition of halite.

The alteration of scapolite first to an undertermined turbid material and subsequently to a mixture of calcite, plagioclase and sericite, or to aggregates consisting of epidote, plagioclase and vesuvianite surrounded by a narrow rim of grossular has been reported by Parras (1958). In pegmatites of the Ultevis district, north Sweden (Byström, 1956), scapolite has been altered by barium-bearing hydrothermal solutions to harmotome, montmorillonite and kaolinite. Landes (1938) has reported the alteration of scapolite to lilac-coloured wilsonite in the Wallingford phlogopite–apatite deposit, Quebec.

OPTICAL AND PHYSICAL PROPERTIES

Shaw's (1960) investigation of the relationship between the optical properties and chemical composition of the scapolite minerals confirmed the conclusions of earlier workers that there is an approximately linear variation between the mean refractive index, $(\epsilon + \omega)/2$, and composition (plots of ϵ and ω refractive indices do not show as good a correlation with composition). There is a linear relationship also between birefringence and composition for the normal scapolite, $Na_4Al_3Si_9O_{24}Cl$ – $Ca_4Al_6Si_6O_{24}CO_3$, solid solution series. The relation between the mean refractive index and proportion of the meionite end-member shown in Fig. 101 is constructed by a linear regression method treating the meionite mol. per cent. as the independent variable; the equation is:

$$(\epsilon + \omega)/2 = 1 \cdot 5346 + 0 \cdot 000507 \text{ (Me. per cent.)}$$

The uncertainty in estimating the content of meionite from the mean refractive index is ± 6.5 per cent. for most scapolites but is probably greater for those minerals containing relatively large amounts of S, F or K. Scapolites showing a small, less than $10°$, negative optic axial angle have been reported (Parras, 1958; Iiyama, 1959).

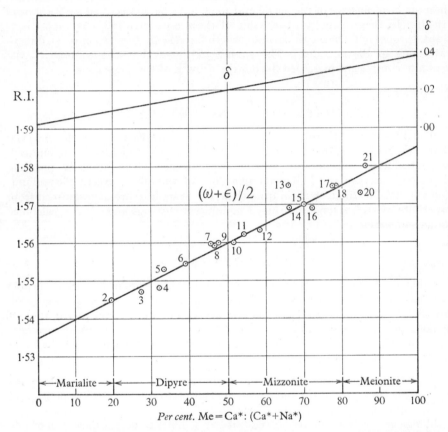

FIG. 101. Relationship between chemical composition of scapolites expressed as mol. per cent. meionite $[=Ca^*:(Ca^*+Na^*)=(Ca+Mg+Fe+Mn+Ti):(Na+K+Ca+Mg+Fe+Mn+Ti)]$ and mean refractive index, $(\epsilon+\omega)/2$, and birefringence. (Numbers refer to analyses in Table 43. Variation of birefringence with composition after Shaw, 1960).

The density of scapolite increases with the content of the meionite component; the relationship, however, is not precise and density is of little value as a determinative parameter. The dispersion (λ 6878 to λ 4308 Å) of a gem variety of scapolite (ϵ 1.5556, ω 1.5769) from Rio Pardo, Brazil, is ϵ 0.015 and ω 0.0166 (Payne, 1939). Some scapolites fluoresce in ultra-violet light (Haberlandt and Köhler, 1934; Meixner, 1939; Iwase, 1937, 1940, 1944). The fluorescence, originally believed to be due to the presence of small amounts of uranium in such minerals, is now considered to result from the presence in the structure of a polysulphide ion (Haberlandt, 1949; Kirk, 1955). The luminescence emission spectrum at 20°C. with 3650 Å excitation of a scapolite from Argenteuil, Quebec, has been determined by Kirk. The effects of thermoluminescence and tribo-luminescence of scapolite and of its fluorescence and phosphorescence in ultra-violet light are described by Northup and Lee (1940).

Zoned scapolites, in which the birefringence of the cores is about 0·003 less than the birefringence of the peripheral zone, have been described by Tomlinson (1943). In these scapolites the value of the ε refractive index is almost constant throughout the crystals and the difference in birefringence is due to variations in the ω index. The zoning indicates that the content of the meionite component increased during the growth of the scapolites.

DISTINGUISHING FEATURES

Scapolites are distinguished from the felspars by cleavage angle, uniaxial character, straight extinction and absence of twinning; in addition calcium-rich scapolites have considerably greater birefringence. The optically negative character, cleavage and higher birefringence of scapolites, except the sodium-rich varieties, distinguish them from quartz. Scapolites are distinguished from cancrinite by their stronger refringence, different cleavage and greater resistance to decomposition in HCl.

PARAGENESIS

Although the paragenesis of scapolite is essentially confined to metamorphic and metasomatic environments a wide variety of occurrences have been described. Lacroix (1889) gave the first detailed account of the distribution of scapolite-bearing rocks and Eitel (1925) reviewed the various occurrences reported prior to that date. More recently Shaw (1960) has listed the main parageneses of scapolite as:

(a) Metamorphic rocks of regional distribution, especially marbles, calcareous gneisses, granulites and greenschists and, to a lesser extent, pelitic and psammitic metamorphic rocks.

(b) Skarns at the contacts of calcareous sediments and adjacent plutonic intrusions.

(c) Pneumatolytically or hydrothermally altered basic igneous rocks.

(d) Veins in regionally metamorphosed rocks.

(e) Blocks ejected from volcanoes, and contact volcanic action.

(f) Metamorphosed salt deposits.

Although in many rocks there is an antipathetic relationship between scapolite and plagioclase, in other rocks both minerals occur together in apparent equilibrium, but in these there is generally no consistent relationship between the compositions of the coexisting scapolite and plagioclase as some authors have suggested. Scapolite occurs in association with a wide range of minerals but is most characteristically found in assemblages formed in the P,T environment of the upper amphibolite facies, a typical example of which is scapolite–pyroxene–sphene. The formation of scapolite is not, however, confined to this relatively restricted range of P,T conditions and its occurrence has been reported in rocks of the greenschist facies (Flett, 1907), granulite–eclogite facies (Knorring and Kennedy, 1958), sanidinite facies (Brauns, 1914) and pyroxene hornfels facies (Goldschmidt, 1911).   In veins cutting a dolerite sill at Falls of French Creek, Pennsylvania, scapolite, capped by and intergrown with prehnite, is associated also with heulandite, chlorite, sphene, apatite and epidote (Tomlinson, 1943), an assemblage which may have formed under zeolite facies conditions (Shaw, 1960).

Regional metamorphism.   The formation of scapolite in regionally metamorphosed rocks has commonly been regarded as a result of metasomatic processes associated with the introduction particularly of such fugitive constituents as Cl, CO_2 and SO_3.   Sundius (1915), however, while recognizing that many of the scapolite-bearing rocks of the Kiruna region, northern Sweden, were metasomatic in origin, noted that rocks containing scapolite, especially of the more calcium-rich type, may arise by isochemical recrystallization during regional or contact metamorphism.   A number of recent studies have shown that the formation of non-metasomatic scapolite, often on a regional scale, is not uncommon.

Thus Knorring and Kennedy (1958) have described a sulphate-rich mizzonite (Table 43, anal. 13) from the garnet–hornblende–pyroxene–scapolite gneiss of the Mampong inselberg, Shai Hills, Ghana.   Here the scapolite occurs throughout the gneiss as well as in veinlets and bands; the scapolite is not an alteration product of plagioclase but is a stable constituent in equilibrium with the other minerals, and appears to be a primary product of the regional metamorphism, the P,T conditions of which were transitional between the amphibolite and eclogite facies.   Knorring and Kennedy consider that the scapolite resulted from the interaction of sulphide and other minerals present in an originally basic igneous rock.   At this locality the scapolite-bearing gneisses are associated with eclogite and related rocks and the scapolite assemblage is considered to have formed under the influence of intense stress and high temperature.   The presence of scapolite in banded gneisses associated with eclogites in the Glenelg district, Inverness-shire, has been reported by Alderman (1936).

Scapolite–diopside gneisses derived from the regional metamorphism of impure calcareous sedimentary rocks, and scapolite–diopside amphibolites, possibly representing originally volcanic material, have been described by Parras (1958) from the West Uusimaa complex, southwestern Finland.   The scapolite, a calcium-rich mizzonite (Table 43, anal. 18) occurs in individual crystals and with quartz in symplectic intergrowths.   The mizzonite is present in those gneisses in which Ca:(Ca+Al+Na+K) is > 0.39; in such rocks the mizzonite takes the place of plagioclase which is the dominant calcium aluminium silicate in those gneisses in which Ca:(Ca+Al+Na+K) is < 0.39.   Thus in addition to the temperature required for the formation of diopside (quartz+ calcite+biotite$\rightleftharpoons$microcline+diopside+CO_2+H_2O)   the   crystallization   of scapolite was dependent not only on the presence of a high CO_2 pressure but also on a deficiency of (Al+Na+K) with respect to Ca.   Under such conditions calcium-rich scapolite and not plagioclase is the stable aluminosilicate:

$$3CaAl_2Si_2O_8 + CaCO_3 \rightarrow Ca_4Al_6Si_6O_{24}CO_3$$
$$\text{anorthite} \qquad \text{calcite} \qquad \text{meionite}$$

The widespread occurrence of mizzonite-rich marbles and calc-silicate rocks in high grade metamorphosed limestones and shales of the Mount Lofty Range of South Australia has been reported by White (1959). In this area the development of diopsidic pyroxene and plagioclase ($> An_{30}$), together with almandine and some sillimanite, in adjacent quartz-felspathic schist, indicates that amphibolite facies conditions prevailed during the main metamorphism which is considered by White to have been essentially isochemical in character. In the Tungkillo area the characteristic calc-silicate assemblage is a pyroxene–scapolite–sphene rock but hornblende–scapolite and scapolite–pyroxene rocks containing plagioclase are also present. In the Milendella area, scapolite is associated with calcite, potassium felspar and pyroxene. The scapolite is a sodium-rich mizzonite (Table 43, anal. 11), the chlorine of which is considered to have been derived from the original sediments.

Metasomatism and scapolitization. Scapolite in many metamorphic rocks is clearly metasomatic in origin, especially where it is associated with contact phenomena and skarn formation. The formation of metasomatic scapolite on a regional scale is less common but the widespread development of scapolite-bearing granulites and marbles in the Pre-Cambrian rocks of the Cloncurry district, Queensland, has been described by Edwards and Baker (1953). Here the formation of scapolite is associated with the albitization of calcareous shales and was associated with metasomatic introduction of sodium and chlorine contemporaneously with the regional metamorphism of the original sediments. The scapolite is a chlorine-bearing dipyre and Edwards and Baker have calculated that its formation in these Queensland rocks required the addition of 500×10^6 tons of chlorine; the source of the chlorine is unknown. Scapolite is developed in a variety of rocks, including metagabbros, amphibolites, gneisses and marbles in the Pre-Cambrian Grenville province and here is generally regarded as due to the introduction of chlorine from granite magma at the time of the regional metamorphism (*e.g.* Buddington, 1939). Scapolite (Me_{60}), in spongy intergrowths with diopside and less commonly with pargasitic hornblende, is found in the calc-silicate paragneisses of Lewisian age in the Rodil district, South Harris. Mizzonite is also present in the orthogneisses of the same area; in these rocks it replaces labradorite and its formation is ascribed by Davidson (1943) to volatile activity during a phase of migmatization.

Scapolite-bearing rocks of pneumatolytic metasomatic origin in the Kiruna area, northern Sweden, have been described by Sundius (1915). Scapolite associated with skarn iron ores in the Urals have been reported by Sumin (1954), and the development of scapolite skarns in Siberia has been reviewed by Marakushev (1958). Marialite scapolite (Ma_{81}), associated with the Cl-rich amphibole dashkesanite, and with Ni–Co–As ores, occurs in skarns at Tuva, U.S.S.R. (Ontoev, 1958). It is also present in the endocontact zone of the granite, the felspar of which is entirely replaced by scapolite. Scapolite occurs in the scapolitized pegmatite dykes and at the contact between the dykes and limestone in the rocks of the Mansjö mountain, Loos, Sweden (Eckermann, 1922). At this locality it is associated with, among other minerals, albite, plagioclase, diopside, wollastonite, pargasite, grossular and fluorite, and is commonly found in symplectite intergrowths with either diopside or quartz; similar scapolite-bearing rocks occur at Pargas, Finland (Laitakari, 1920). The latter author has also described lenses of scapolite rock, containing crystals

50 cm. long and 20–30 cm. wide, which occur in layers of dolomitic limestone in granite gneiss and hornblende schist at Pusunsaari, Finland (Laitakari, 1947). At this locality the scapolite formed by replacement of the felspar and quartz as the parent gas-rich pegmatite magma penetrated the limestone; similar scapolite pegmatites are also known at Korpo and Pargas (Laitakari, 1916, 1920). Scapolite–quartz symplectites in which the quartz occurs in worm-shaped individuals in scapolite have been described from inclusions in calcite in the Pre-Cambrian rocks of the Holsteinborg district, west Greenland (Pauly, 1948).

Scapolite-bearing rocks occur in the nepheline gneiss complex at Renfrew County, Ontario (Carlson, 1957), and scapolite is present in some of the marbles, and nepheline and corundum syenites of the Haliburton–Bancroft district (Adams and Barlow, 1910). At Craigmont, Renfrew County, scapolite is associated with nepheline, corundum and plagioclase but there is no positive evidence to suggest that these rocks have formed by the metasomatic alteration of calcareous and aluminous metasediments, or as a result of the intrusion of sill-like masses of anorthositic magma into the metasediments. Scapolite rocks grade into plagioclase rocks and there is a textural gradation between the two end-member rock types from the sugary granular texture of the scapolite rock to the interlocking mosaic of the plagioclase rock, but no evidence as to whether the scapolite replaces plagioclase or vice versa has been found.

Scapolite is one of the commoner minerals in the phlogopite–apatite deposits of Quebec and Ontario, and is present chiefly in contact zones between microline pegmatites and pyroxenites, and in narrow veins cutting the pyroxenite (Landes, 1938). The scapolite occurs in dense intergrowths with microcline in the relatively fine-grained parts of the pegmatite, and its formation is believed to be due to reaction between the pyroxenite and the pegmatite magma.

A widespread regional scapolitization of norite in the Mavuzi-Tete district, Mozambique, has been described by Davidson and Bennett (1950). The norite was first sheared during a period of dynamic metamorphism to a strongly foliated epidiorite, later hypogene mineralizing solutions penetrated along the shear zones and the epidiorite was progressively altered to scapolite–hornblende rock. Local intense alteration along some shear zones have given rise to pure scapolite and scapolite–calcite rocks.

Interbanded scapolite-bearing and scapolite-free metagabbros in Bucks County, Pennsylvania, have been described by Weiss (1947). In the scapolite-bearing bands, mizzonite (Me_{63}) and diopside take the place of the plagioclase and hornblende of the metagabbros. Both rocks are similar in composition, and Weiss has suggested that the scapolite formed as a result of the recrystallization of the metagabbro during a period of dynamic metamorphism and the introduction of hydrothermal solutions. Cross-cutting bands and isolated masses of scapolite and diopside are also present in the adjacent limestones. The formation of a sodium-rich dipyre from both plagioclase and amphibole in metadiabase at Dorodaevki, Dniepr River, U.S.S.R., has been described by Verbitskiĭ (1952). The conversion of plagioclase to scapolite is observed in all stages of transition, and the scapolite and amphibole commonly occur in parallel intergrowths of the two minerals. Here the scapolitization took place during a period of hydrothermal and tectonic activity subsequent to the consolidation of the diabase. The widespread formation of scapolite–hornblende rocks (ødegårdites) in the Kragerø region, southern Norway, has been described by Brøgger (1935). In these rocks scapolite (Table 43, anal. 3) has been derived mainly from plagioclase during a post-consolidation pneumatolytic metamorphism of the original basic igneous rocks (hyperites) by gases and solutions rich in Cl, CO_2 and water.

Miscellaneous parageneses. Serdyuchenko (1955) has described potassium-rich scapolite (K_2O 5·88 per cent., $\simeq 1·1$ K ions per formula unit) in some Pre-Cambrian rocks of south Yakutia, U.S.S.R. The scapolite is associated with diopside, hornblende, garnet and tourmaline, and in some of the schists occurs as monomineralic lenses. These rocks, many of which are skarn-like in appearance, are believed to represent a suite of regionally metamorphosed sediments which included salt deposits containing sulphate.

Emmons and Calkins (1913) have described scapolite-bearing calcium-rich pyroxene aplites in the Phillipsburg quadrangle, Montana. These rocks occur in calcareous sediments and the scapolite is believed to have crystallized as a primary mineral from an aplitic magma contaminated by incorporation of limestone.

Scapolite has been reported in blocks of hornblende–scapolite rock, hornblende–haüyne–scapolite rock, augite–scapolite rock, and anorthite–hornblende–scapolite rock from the volcanoes of Laacher See (Brauns, 1914), and from scoriaceous trachybasalt at Chuquet-Genestoux, Puy de Dôme (Iiyama, 1959). It is an important constituent in a pegmatite dyke at Långö, Åland Island, Finland (Kaitaro, 1955), in which it is associated with biotite, allanite, quartz, fluorite, calcite and apatite.

In some metamorphic rocks formed under amphibolite facies conditions scapolite has been replaced by garnet during subsequent retrograde conditions. Thus in some of the calc-silicate rocks of the Mount Lofty Ranges (White, 1959) scapolite is partially replaced by garnet in which it occurs as relict cores. In those rocks containing abundant garnet, the scapolite and pyroxene are usually separated by a rim of garnet, and the formation of the latter, and of the associated epidote, may be illustrated by the equations:

$$\underset{\text{meionite}}{Ca_4Al_6Si_6O_{24}CO_3} + H_2O \rightarrow \underset{\text{epidote}}{2Ca_2Al_3Si_3O_{12}(OH)} + CO_2$$

$$\underset{\text{meionite}}{Ca_4Al_6Si_6O_{24}CO_3} + \underset{\text{calcite}}{5CaCO_3} + \underset{\text{quartz}}{3SiO_2} \rightarrow \underset{\text{grossular}}{3Ca_3Al_2Si_3O_{12}} + 6CO_2$$

$$\underset{\text{meionite}}{Ca_4Al_6Si_6O_{24}CO_3} + \underset{\text{pyroxene}}{3Ca(Mg,Fe^{+2})Si_2O_6} \rightarrow \underset{\text{grossular}}{3Ca_2(Mg,Fe^{+2})Al_2Si_3O_{12}} + \underset{\text{calcite}}{CaCO_3}$$
$$+ \underset{\text{quartz}}{3SiO_2}$$

In many of the anorthositic rocks of the Sittampundi complex, Salem district, Madras, scapolite occurs as an alteration product of the calcium-rich plagioclase (Subramaniam, 1956). In these rocks the meionite component of the scapolite is related to the anorthite content of the associated plagioclase (*e.g.* Me_{65} with An_{86}, Me_{65} with An_{91}, Me_{70} with An_{98}):

$$\underset{\text{anorthite}}{4CaAl_2Si_2O_8} + CO_2 \rightarrow \underset{\text{meionite}}{Ca_4Al_6Si_6O_{24}CO_3} + \underset{\text{corundum}}{Al_2O_3} + 2SiO_2$$

Scapolite is widely distributed in the calc-silicate hornfelses and metamorphosed limestone of Moinian age at Ardgour, Argyllshire (Drever, 1939, 1940). In some of these rocks it is surrounded by rims of garnet which formed after the scapolite due probably to the activity of later solutions. The partial replacement of scapolite by analcite in pegmatites in the Deeside area has been reported by Hutchison (1933).

REFERENCES

Adams, F. D. and **Barlow, A. E.**, 1910. Geology of the Haliburton and Bancroft areas. *Mem. Geol. Surv. Canada*, No. 6.

Alderman, A. R., 1936. Eclogites from the neighbourhood of Glenelg, Inverness-shire. *Quart. Journ. Geol. Soc.*, vol. 92, p. 488.

Bobrovnik, D. P., 1948. Scapolite in crystalline limestone (xenolith) from a granodiorite quarry near Gnivan station, Vinnitza district. *Doklady Acad. Sci. USSR*, vol. 59, p. 311.

Borgström, L. M., 1914. Die Skapolithelagerstätte von Laurinkari. *Bull. Comm. géol. Finlande*, No. 41.

—— 1915. Die chemische Zusammensetzung der Skapolithe. *Zeit. Krist.*, vol. 54, p. 238.

Brauns, R., 1914. Neue skapolithführende Auswürflung aus dem Laacher Seegebiet. Die Brechungsexponenten des Sulfatskapoliths. *Neues Jahrb. Min. Geol.*, vol. 39, p. 79.

Brøgger, W. C., 1935. On several archean rocks from the south coast of Norway. II. The south Norwegian hyperites and their metamorphism. *Norsk. Skr. Vidensk. Acad., I. Mat.-nat. Kl.*, No. 1, p. 1.

Buddington, A. F., 1939. Adirondack igneous rocks and their metamorphism. *Geol. Soc. Amer., Mem.* No. 7.

Burley, B. J., Freeman, E. B. and **Shaw, D. M.**, 1961. Studies on scapolite. *Canadian Min.*, vol. 6, p. 670.

Byström, A. M., 1956. Harmotome penetration of a scapolite partly altered to argillic material in Ultevis, north Sweden. *Geol. För. Förh. Stockholm*, vol. 78, p. 645.

Carlson, H. D., 1957. Origin of the corundum deposits of Renfrew County, Ontario, Canada. *Bull. Geol. Soc. Amer.*, vol. 68, p. 1605.

Davidson, C. F., 1943. The Archean rocks of the Rodil district, South Harris, Outer Hebrides. *Trans. Roy. Soc. Edin.*, vol. 61, p. 71.

—— and **Bennett, J. A. E.**, 1950. The uranium deposits of the Tete district, Mozambique. *Min. Mag.*, vol. 29, p. 291.

Drever, H. I., 1939. A petrological study of the limestone in the Moine Series of Ardgour, Argyllshire. *Geol. Mag.*, vol. 76, p. 501.

—— 1940. The geology of Ardgour, Argyllshire. *Trans. Roy. Soc. Edin.*, vol. 60, p. 141.

Eckermann, H. von, 1922. The rocks and contact minerals of the Mansjö Mountain. *Geol. För. Förh. Stockholm*, vol. 44, p. 203.

Edwards, A. B. and **Baker, G.**, 1953. Scapolitization in the Cloncurry district, north-western Queensland. *Journ. Geol. Soc. Australia*, vol. 1, p. 1.

Eitel, W., 1925. Die Synthese der Skapolithe auf Grund der Beobachtungen über ihre Vorkommnisse. *Min. Petr. Mitt. (Tschermak)*, vol. 38, p. 1.

Emmons, W. H. and **Calkins, F. C.**, 1913. Geology and ore deposits of the Philipsburg quadrangle, Montana. *U.S. Geol. Surv., Prof. Paper* No. 78.

Eugster, H. P. and **Prostka, H. J.**, 1960. Synthetic scapolites. *Bull. Geol. Soc. Amer.*, vol. 71, p. 1859 (abstract).

Flett, J. S., 1907. The scapolite-bearing rocks of Scotland. *Geol. Surv. G.B., Summ. Progr.*, p. 116.

Fyfe, W. S., Turner, F. J. and **Verhoogen, J.,** 1958.　Metamorphic reactions and metamorphic facies.　*Geol. Soc. Amer., Mem.* 73.

Geijer, P., 1917.　Nautanen omradet, en malmgeologisk undersökning.　*Sverig. Geol. Vidensk. Selsk. Christ., I. Mat.-nat. Kl.,* No. 1.

Goldschmidt, V. M., 1911.　Die Kontaktmetamorphose im Kristianiagebiet.　*Skr. Vidensk. Selsk. Christ., Mat.-nat. Kl.,* No. 1.

Gossner, B. and **Brückl, K.,** 1928.　Untersuchungen über die Scapolithgruppe.　*Neues Jahrb. Min., Abt. A.,* vol. 58, p. 349.

Haberlandt, H., 1949.　Neue Lumineszenzuntersuchungen an Fluoriten und anderen Mineralien IV.　*Sitz. Ber. Österr. Akad. Wiss. Wien,* vol. 158, p. 609.

—— and **Köhler, A.,** 1934.　Fluoreszenanalyse von Skapolithen.　*Chem. Erde,* vol. 9, p. 139 (M.A. 6–72).

Hutchison, A. G., 1933.　The metamorphism of the Deeside limestone, Aberdeenshire.　*Trans. Roy. Soc. Edinburgh,* vol. 57, p. 557.

Iiyama, J. T., 1959.　Présence de scapolite dans les projections volcaniques de la carrière du Chuquet Genestoux (Puy-de-Dôme).　*Bull. Soc. franç. Min. Crist.,* vol. 82, p. 95.

Iwase, E., 1937.　Luminescence of scapolite from North Burgess, Canada.　*Sci. Papers Inst. Phys. Chem. Res. Tokyo,* vol. 33, p. 299 (M.A. 7–252).

—— 1940.　On the fluorescence spectrum and composition of scapolite.　*Sci. Papers Inst. Phys. Chem. Res. Tokyo,* vol. 37, p. 58 (M.A. 8–127).

—— 1944.　Study of fluorescent uranium scapolite found in Korea.　*Bull. Inst. Phys. Chem. Res. Tokyo, Chem. Ed.,* vol. 23, p. 328 (Chem. Abst. 42–6707).

Kaitaro, S., 1955.　Scapolite from Långö, Åva area, Åland Islands.　*Bull. Comm. géol. Finlande,* No. 168, p. 131.

Kirk, R. D., 1955.　The luminescence and tenebrescence of natural and synthetic sodalite.　*Amer. Min.,* vol. 40, p. 22.

Knorring, O. von and **Kennedy, W. Q.,** 1958.　The mineral paragenesis and metamorphic status of garnet–hornblende–pyroxene–scapolite gneiss from Ghana (Gold Coast).　*Min. Mag.,* vol. 31, p. 846.

Konečný, B. and **Rosický, V.,** 1926.　On some Moravian scapolites.　*Publ. Fac. Sci. Univ. Masaryk,* No. 77, 23 pp. (M.A. 3–348).

Lacroix, A., 1889.　Contributions à l'étude des gneiss à pyroxene et des roches à wernerite.　*Bull. Soc. franç. Min.,* vol. 12, p. 83.

—— 1922.　*Minéralogie de Madagascar, vol.* 1, Paris.

Laitakari, A., 1916.　Le gisement de calcaire cristallin de Kirmoniemi à Korpo en Finlande.　*Bull. Comm. géol. Finlande,* No. 46, p. 1.

—— 1920.　Über die Petrographie und Mineralogie der Kalksteinlagerstätten von Parainen.　*Bull. Comm. géol. Finlande,* No. 54, p. 7.

—— 1929.　Über Mineralbildung längs schmalen Spalten.　*Bull. Comm. géol. Finlande,* No. 87, p. 64.

—— 1947.　The scapolite occurrence of Pusunsaari.　*Bull. Comm. géol. Finlande,* No. 140, p. 115.

Landes, K. K., 1938.　Origin of the Quebec phlogopite–apatite deposits.　*Amer. Min.,* vol. 23, p. 360.

Lokka, L., 1943.　Beiträge zur Kenntnis des Chemismus der finnischen Minerale.　*Bull. Comm. géol. Finlande,* No. 129.

Marakushev, A. A., 1958.　Parageneses of calcareous skarns in a Siberian forest magnesium-skarn iron-ore deposit in the Archean of the Aldan Shield.　*Geokhimiya,* 155–162.

Meixner, H., 1939.　Eine Karbonatskapolithparagenese von Typus Pargas aus dem Sulmtal bei Schwanberg, Koralpe, Steiermark.　*Ann. Natur-hist. Mus. Wien,* vol. 50, p. 672 (M.A. 10–271).

Northup, M. A. and **Lee, O. I.**, 1940. Experiments on the thermoluminescence of some common and unusual minerals. *Journ. Opt. Soc. Amer.*, vol. 30, p. 206 (M.A. 8–265).

Ontoev, D. O., 1958. Chlorine-containing minerals (scapolite and dashkesanite) from the Khavuaksinky deposit (Tuva). *Mem. All-Union Min. Soc.*, vol. 87, p. 48 (M.A. 14–138).

Parras, K., 1958. On the charnockites in the light of a highly metamorphic rock complex in southwestern Finland. *Bull. Comm. géol. Finlande*, No. 181.

Pauling, L., 1930. The structure of some sodium and calcium aluminosilicates. *Proc. Acad. Sci. Washington*, vol. 16, p. 453.

Pauly, H., 1948. Calcite and skarn minerals in the gneisses of the Holsteinborg District, west Greenland. *Medd. Dansk. Geol. För.*, vol. 11, p. 328.

Payne, C. J., 1939. Dispersions of some rarer gemstones. *Gemmologist*, vol. 9, p. 33.

Scherillo, A., 1935. La meionite del Somma-Vesuvio. *Periodico Min. Roma*, vol. 6, p. 227.

Schiebold, E. and **Seumel, G.**, 1932. Über die Kristallstruktur von Skapolith. *Zeit. Krist.*, vol. 81, p. 110.

Serdyuchenko, D. F., 1955. Potash scapolites from south Yakutia. *Problems of geology of Asia*, Acad. Sci. USSR, vol. 2, p. 742 (M.A. 13–186).

Shaw, D. M., 1960. The geochemistry of scapolite. Part I. Previous work and general mineralogy. Part II. Trace elements, petrology and general geochemistry. *Journ. Petr.*, vol. 1, p. 218, p. 261.

Solodovnikova, L. L., 1957. Genesis of scapolites. *Utchen. Zap. Leningrad*, vol. 215, p. 3 (Chem. Abstr., 52, 11665).

Stewart, G. W., 1941. Idocrase and scapolite from Manchester, New Hampshire. *Amer. Min.*, vol. 26, p. 509.

Subramaniam, A. P., 1956. Mineralogy and petrology of the Sittampundi complex, Salem District, Madras State, India. *Bull. Geol. Soc. Amer.*, vol. 67, p. 317.

Sumin, N. G., 1954. On certain features of the skarn minerals of the iron-ore deposits. *Trans. Miner. Mus. Acad. Sci. USSR*, vol. 6, p. 131 (M.A. 13–161).

Sundius, N., 1915. Beiträge zur Geologie des südlichen Teils der Kirunagebiets. *Vetensk. och. prakt. Unders. i Lapland, Upsala.*

—— 1918. Beiträge zur Kenntnis der Skapolithe. *Bull. Geol. Inst. Univ. Upsala*, vol. 16, p. 96.

Tomlinson, W. A., 1943. Occurrence of sodic scapolite at Falls of French Creek, Pennsylvania. *Amer. Min.*, vol. 28, p. 110.

Verbitskiĭ, P. G., 1952. Scapolitization of amphiboles. *Doklady Acad. Sci. URSS*, vol. 86, p. 165.

Weiss, J., 1947. Origin of a scapolite metagabbro in Bucks County, Pennsylvania. *Bull. Geol. Soc. Amer.*, vol. 58, p. 821.

White, A. J. R., 1959. Scapolite-bearing marbles and calc-silicate rocks from Tungkillo and Milendella, South Australia. *Geol. Mag.*, vol. 96, p. 285.

Analcite

Na[AlSi$_2$O$_6$]·H$_2$O

n 1·479–1·493

D 2·24–2·29   H 5½

Cleavage: {001} very poor.
Twinning: {001}, {110} lamellar.
Colour: White, pink or grey; colourless in thin section.
Unit cell: $a \simeq 13·7$ Å.
                   $Z = 16$.   Space group $Ia3d$.

Gelatinizes with HCl.

Analcite occurs as a primary constituent of some igneous rocks; it is relatively common as a late-stage or secondary mineral, often in cavities in association with prehnite or zeolites. The mineral is named from the Greek *analkis*, weak, in allusion to the weak electrostatic charge developed when it is heated or rubbed. Analcite is in all respects a valid member of the zeolite group of minerals, but in structure, chemistry and paragenesis it has close affinities with the felspathoids.

STRUCTURE

Analcite is cubic (space group $Ia3d$) with $a \simeq 13·7$ Å and 16(NaAlSi$_2$O$_6$·H$_2$O) per unit cell. Its structure was determined by Taylor (1930), and is illustrated in Fig. 102 by a projection on (001) of the lower half of the unit cell. This shows only the aluminosilicate framework, which is built of linked (Si,Al)O$_4$ tetrahedra in such a way that each corner oxygen is shared by two tetrahedra. The framework contains rings of six tetrahedra and of four tetrahedra (respectively normal to triad and tetrad axes). The framework contains a set of sixteen large cavities (at $\frac{1}{8}$, $\frac{1}{8}$, $\frac{1}{8}$, etc.), which form continuous channels parallel to four non-intersecting triad axes of the cubic lattice (Fig. 103a) and which are occupied by water molecules. Adjacent to these cavities are a set of twenty-four smaller ones (at 0, $\frac{1}{4}$, $\frac{1}{8}$, etc.), sixteen of which are occupied by sodium.[1] The sodium ions are octahedrally coordinated by four coplanar oxygens of the aluminosilicate framework and two water molecules. These water and sodium sites are referred to as W and S in the following paragraphs. Since eight out of twenty-four S equivalent positions are vacant it is surprising that the numbers of

---

[1] According to Náray-Szabó (1938a, 1938b) the sodium ions in analcite probably occupy the sixteen-fold positions at ($\frac{1}{8}$, $\frac{1}{8}$, $\frac{1}{8}$, etc.), and the sixteen water molecules are in the sites at (0, $\frac{1}{4}$, $\frac{1}{8}$, etc.). Taylor (1938), however, on the basis of dehydration and substitution experiments, affirmed that his original description of the structure was correct.

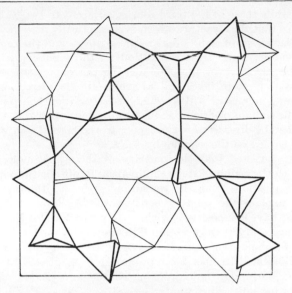

Fig. 102. Projection on (001) of the aluminosilicate framework of analcite, showing six- and four-membered rings of tetrahedra. Only the lower half of the unit cell content is shown.

sodium ions and the Si : Al ratio in naturally occurring analcites vary only slightly from those in the ideal formula. An explanation of this was offered by Taylor (1930), who suggested that if the true symmetry of analcite were not cubic but tetragonal, then instead of 48 equivalent sites being occupied randomly by silicon and aluminium, 16 Al and 32 Si would occupy different sets of sixteen-fold sites. The restriction on the ratio of Si and Al atoms would imply also a restriction to 16 Na atoms. Furthermore the twenty-four equivalent sites for Na atoms in cubic analcite become three distinct sets of eight in the tetragonal cell. The sites of two of these sets are adjacent to one Si tetrahedron and one Al

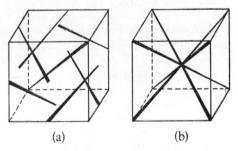

(a)   (b)

Fig. 103. Arrangement of channels parallel to triad axes in aluminosilicate frameworks, (a) non-intersecting as in analcite, (b) intersecting as in sodalite (after Barrer and Falconer, 1956).

tetrahedron, while those of the third set are adjacent to two Si tetrahedra. It seems probable that the structure which is energetically most favourable is that in which the latter set of eight sites are unoccupied, and the remaining sixteen contain the sodium ions. This restriction on the numbers of Si, Al and Na atoms may be carried over in some way to the cubic structure of analcite (Beattie, 1954). Even if the Si and Al atoms are disordered, only sixteen out of every twenty-four sites will be energetically favourable for sodium ions. In this case the sodium positions, though dependent upon the (Si,Al) positions, will nevertheless be disordered with respect to the crystal as a whole, and each site will be occupied on the average by $\frac{2}{3}$ Na.

Taylor has suggested that the polarity of the water molecules and their interaction with the sodium ions are influential in differentiating sixteen of the twenty-four S positions from the remaining eight. Although it had seemed necessary to explain the relative constancy of sodium content in natural analcites (most have compositions within the range Na_{14} to Na_{17} per unit cell), Saha (1959) in a study of the system albite–nepheline–water has shown that a wide range of compositions can be represented while retaining the analcite structure. Thus analcite has been produced from glasses of (a) albite, (b) anhydrous analcite, and (c) anhydrous natrolite compositions. These analcites have the following unit cell contents:

$$\text{(a) } Na_{12}Al_{12}Si_{36}O_{96} \cdot 18H_2O$$
$$\text{(b) } Na_{16}Al_{16}Si_{32}O_{96} \cdot 16H_2O$$
$$\text{(c) } Na_{19\cdot2}Al_{19\cdot2}Si_{28\cdot8}O_{96} \cdot 14\cdot4H_2O$$

Their cell dimensions increase linearly with decreasing silicon content. Although the presence of more than 16 Na ions per unit cell in some "analcites" favours the correctness of the structure described by Taylor, in the analcite of albite composition there are more water molecules than there are W sites, and the excess may be occupying some of the S sites only half of which contain sodium, or they may lie in some intermediate position between the S and W sites.

Water molecules are easily removeable and replaceable in the analcite structure without significant change in the aluminosilicate framework. Sodium can be exchanged for certain other cations with little change in the cell size and no other change in structure; thus Li-, Na-, and Ag-analcite are all hydrated and have a 13·5, 13·66 and 13·7 Å respectively (Barrer, 1957). Cs, however, is too large an ion to be exchanged for Na in analcite. A mineral with a formula similar to that of analcite, but with caesium instead of sodium, is pollucite, the structure of which was described by Strunz (1936) and by Náray-Szabó (1938a). In pollucite ($CsAlSi_2O_6$) the Cs ions are too large for the S sites and instead occupy the sixteen W positions. Nel (1944) has shown that substitution of a given number of Cs ions for Na results in the loss of an equal number of water molecules, so that analcite and pollucite are the end-members (with $x = 16$ and zero respectively) of a series with general formula:

$$Cs_{16-x}Na_xAl_{16}Si_{32}O_{96}(H_2O)_x$$

Nel argues that the analcite–pollucite series favours the Náray-Szabó structure of analcite, $(Na + H_2O)$ substituting directly for Cs. As was shown in the previous paragraph, however, the series can be regarded as one where Cs in pollucite substitutes for H_2O in analcite and this is accompanied by loss of Na ions to maintain the charge balance. When ions of intermediate size (*e.g.* potassium) are substituted, it seems that they may enter the analcite structure in either of two ways. In the first, potassium may take up the *S* positions and the water molecules remain unchanged. This replacement, yielding a true potassium analcite $KAlSi_2O_6 \cdot H_2O$, with *a* 13·79 Å, has been reported only for a synthetic specimen (Barrer *et al.*, 1953). Alternatively potassium may enter the *W* sites in the same way as caesium does in pollucite, and the resulting mineral,

W sites	S sites	W sites	S sites	W sites	Name	System	*a*Å	*c*Å
16 H2O	16 K	16 H2O	16 K	16 H2O	Potassium analcite $KAlSi_2O_6 \cdot H_2O$	Cubic	13·8	
16 H2O	16 Na	16 H2O	16 Na	16 H2O	Sodium analcite $NaAlSi_2O_6 \cdot H_2O$	Cubic	13·7	
8H2O 8Cs	8 Na	8H2O 8Cs	8 Na	8H2O 8Cs	A sodium-caesium analcite $Na_\frac{1}{2}Cs_\frac{1}{2}AlSi_2O_6 \cdot \frac{1}{2}H_2O$			
16 Cs		16 Cs		16 Cs	Pollucite $CsAlSi_2O_6$	Cubic	13·6	
16 K		16 K		16 K	Leucite (above 625°C) $KAlSi_2O_6$	Cubic	13·4	
16 K		16 K		16 K	Leucite (below 625°C) $KAlSi_2O_6$	Tetragonal	13·0	13·8

FIG. 104. Schematic illustration of the contents of sites W ($\frac{1}{8}$, $\frac{1}{8}$, $\frac{1}{8}$) and $S(0, \frac{1}{4}, \frac{1}{4})$ in substances with the "analcite type" aluminosilicate framework. The diagram does not represent spatial relationships.

leucite, is anhydrous. The form of leucite which has precisely this structure is that stable above 625°C.; it is cubic with *a* 13·4 Å. Below 625°C. leucite is tetragonal, the potassium ions lie near *W* between the *W* and *S* sites, and again no water is present.

A comparison of the probable cation site occupation in several substances which have similar aluminosilicate frameworks is shown schematically in Fig. 104.

Although the ideal structure of analcite is cubic, with Si and Al atoms distributed randomly among the available sites, many specimens are optically biaxial, probably through the ordering of these atoms. In some cases ordering may occur without appreciable change from cubic lattice dimensions, but in others distortion of the structure occurs, leading to rhombohedral symmetry (*e.g.* Låven analcite, Coombs, 1955). It seems likely that analcites, when formed at high temperatures, have strictly cubic symmetry, but on cooling they invert to a tetragonal or trigonal (pseudo-cubic) modification.

The calcium analcite, *wairakite*, is monoclinic, Ia or $I2/a$, with a 13·69, b 13·68, c 13·56 Å, β 90·5° and $8(CaAl_2Si_4O_{12} \cdot 2H_2O)$ per cell. The structure has not been fully determined, but it is pseudo-cubic and is closely related to that of analcite (Coombs, 1955). Viséite, a zeolite in which phosphorus replaces some of the (Si,Al) atoms in the aluminosilicate framework, is cubic, with a 13·65 Å, and its structure is thought to be similar to that of analcite (McConnell, 1952).

CHEMISTRY

The chemical composition of the majority of natural analcites is remarkably constant, the only appreciable variation being in the partial replacement of sodium by minor amounts of potassium or calcium, and in the substitution of Al for Si, which necessitates an increase in the $(2Ca+Na+K)$ ions to maintain the charge balance. Analyses of ten natural analcites are given in Table 44, where the analyses have also been recalculated on the basis of the seven oxygen atoms of the ideal formula $NaAlSi_2O_6 \cdot H_2O$. A compilation of 93 analcite analyses from the literature has been given by Saha (1959), 59 of which were considered to be analyses of reasonable accuracy, based on the equivalence of the numbers of atoms of Al and $(2Ca+Na+K)$ to within approximately 1 in 15 : a plot of the latter analyses was considered to indicate an increase in the water content of analcite with the increase in silica content. An excess of silica over the ratio $Al_2O_3 : 4SiO_2$ has been noted in some analyses of analcite, and Thugutt (1951) suggested that such analcite has been derived from leucite with replacement of K by Na (see also Wherry, 1923, who considered that the small amount of water in analcite merely fills the gaps left by the replacement of K by Na). The structure of pollucite $(CsAlSi_2O_6)$ is rather similar to that of analcite and an analcite–pollucite series with the general formula $Cs_{16-x}Na_{x-y}Al_{16-y}Si_{32+y}O_{96} \cdot xH_2O$ has been postulated (Nel, 1944): intermediate members of the series appear to be unknown, however, and no values are available for Cs in analcites, though for wairakite (Table 44, anal. 11) Steiner reported 0·017 per cent. Cs_2O. Clear analcite phenocrysts (Table 44, anal. 10), associated with pseudoleucite, occur in the basaltic rocks of the Highwood Mountains area of Montana and contain 4·48 per cent. K_2O (Larsen and Buie, 1938): other potassium-rich analcites have been recorded by Lyons (1944) from trachybasalt, while that of anal. 9 contains 1·62 per cent. K_2O.

The naturally occurring calcium analogue of analcite, wairakite (Table 44, anal. 11) has been described (Steiner, 1955; Coombs, 1955). In this mineral sodium is replaced by calcium on a valency basis, *i.e.* Ca for 2Na.

The dehydration of analcite has been investigated by Stoklossa (1918), and also by Milligan and Weiser (1937) who found that the dehydration was not wholly reversible. The d.t.a. curve of analcite is given by Koizumi (1953).

The synthetic production of analcite from precipitated $Al(OH)_3$ and silica gel in the ratio 1:4, heated with an excess of NaOH at 300°C. and 87 atmospheres pressure, was reported by Noll (1936). More recently Barrer and White (1952) and Barrer *et al.* (1959) have reported the hydrothermal synthesis of analcite from aluminosilicate gels in the presence of excess NaOH, and Guyer *et al.* (1957)

Table 44. ANALCITE ANALYSES

	1.	2.	3.	4.	5.	6.	7.	8.	9.	10.	11.
SiO_2	52·89	56·42	55·11	54·23	54·4	54·10	54·58	56·05	54·19	51·41	55·9
Al_2O_3	24·63	22·21	22·86	23·67	23·6	23·68	23·05	22·36	23·12	23·03	23·0
MgO	—	—	0·00	—	—	tr.	0·10	0·02	0·10	0·43	—
CaO	0·19	tr.	0·12	0·00	tr.	0·45	0·45	tr.	1·54	1·19	11·7
Na_2O	13·31	13·02	13·79	13·81	13·5	13·40	13·50	13·44	11·08	8·48	1·06
K_2O	0·73	tr.	0·18	tr.	0·2	0·34	0·00	0·10	1·62	4·48	0·16
H_2O^+	7·66	8·67	8·20	8·34	8·2	8·22	8·70	8·13	8·20	9·32	8·35
H_2O^-	0·29	—	—	—	—	—	—	0·01	—	0·28	0·15
Total	99·70	100·32	100·26	100·05	99·9	100·19	100·38	100·15	99·85	99·97	100·39
n	1·486–1·488	—	1·4848	—	—	—	—	1·485	—	1·493	α 1·498 γ 1·502
δ	0·002	0·0003	—	—	0·0027	—	—	—	—	—	0·004
D	2·268	—	2·26	2·286	2·7(?)	2·249	—	2·252	—	—	2·26

NUMBERS OF IONS ON THE BASIS OF 7(O)

	1.	2.	3.	4.	5.	6.	7.	8.	9.	10.	11.
Si	1·964	2·039	2·013	1·982	1·99	1·981	1·983	2·004	1·995	1·904	2·017
Al	1·078	0·946	0·984	1·020	1·02	1·022	0·987	0·962	1·030	1·006	0·978
Mg	—	—	—	—	—	—	0·006	0·001	0·006	0·024	—
Na	0·958	0·992	0·977	0·979	0·96	0·951	0·951	0·950	0·791	0·609	0·074
Ca	0·008	—	0·005	—	—	0·018	0·018	—	0·061	0·047	0·452
K	0·035	—	0·008	—	0·01	0·016	—	0·005	0·076	0·212	0·007
OH	1·898	2·090	1·999	2·033	2·00	2·008	2·108	1·978	2·014	2·303	2·010
R†	1·001	0·992	0·990	0·979	0·97	0·985	0·975	—	0·934	—	—

1. Analcite, associated with orthoclase, melanite, sphene and orthite, in pegmatitic patch in borolanite, Allt a' Mhuillin. Loch Borolan, Assynt, Scotland (Stewart, 1941). Anal. F. H. Stewart.
2. Analcite, basalt?, Faeroe Islands (Tiselius, 1935).
3. Analcite, basaltic lava, Diredaua, Eritrea (Morgante, 1945).
4. Analcite, Tertiary basalt, Kyogle, Rous Co., N.E. New South Wales (Hodge-Smith, 1929).
5. Analcite masses, nepheline-syenite pegmatite, Kassa Island, Los Islands, French Guinea (Roques, 1947). Anal. M. Roques.
6. Analcite, basalt, Cyclopean Islands, Sicily (Di Franco, 1926).
7. Analcite, Mazé, Echigo Province, Japan (Shimizu, 1915).
8. Colourless analcite, on natrolite in cavities in basalt, Table Mountain, Golden, Colorado (King, 1955; Yoder and Weir, 1960). Anal. E. H. Oslund (Includes TiO₂ 0·01, Fe₂O₃ 0·03).
9. Analcite, Cyclopean Islands, Sicily (Grassi-Cristaldi and Scafile, 1929).
10. Potassium-bearing analcite, phenocrysts in basalt, Highwood Mts., Montana (Larsen and Buie, 1938). Anal. F. A. Gonyer (Includes Fe₂O₃+FeO 1·35).
11. Wairakite, hydrothermally altered tuffaceous sandstones, etc., Wairakei, central North Island, New Zealand (Steiner, 1955). Anal. J. A. Ritchie (Includes SrO 0·05, Cs₂O 0·017, Rb₂O 0·0003, Sr 0·001).

† $R = Ca + Mg + Na + K$.

have prepared a series of analcites with the formula $Na_2O \cdot Al_2O_3 \cdot xSiO_2 \cdot yH_2O$, with x 2, 4, 6, 8 or 10. Saha (1959) prepared analcites hydrothermally from glasses of composition $Na_2Al_2Si_3O_{10}$, $NaAlSi_2O_6$ and $NaAlSi_3O_8$ and showed that these analcites can be represented by the formulae $Na_4Al_4Si_6O_{20} \cdot 3H_2O$ (partially dehydrated natrolite composition), $NaAlSi_2O_6 \cdot H_2O$ (ideal analcite composition) and $Na_2Al_2Si_6O_{16} \cdot 3H_2O$ (hydrous albite composition) respectively. The water contents of these synthetic analcites vary linearly with the variation in silica, as had been suggested for natural analcites: the range of NaAl:Si ratios is, however, very much greater in the synthetic analcites than that found in natural material. Analcite has also been produced in the attempted synthesis of jadeite (*e.g.* Adams, 1953), the latter having the composition of anhydrous analcite. A preliminary phase boundary for the reaction

$$\text{NaAlSi}_2\text{O}_6 + \text{H}_2\text{O} \rightleftharpoons \text{NaAlSi}_2\text{O}_6 \cdot \text{H}_2\text{O}$$
$$\text{jadeite} \qquad\qquad\qquad \text{analcite}$$

in the pressure and temperature range 12,000 to 19,000 bars and 250° to 650°C. has been given by Griggs and Kennedy (1956). The *P–T* curve for the dehydration of analcite to nepheline + water + vapour was obtained by Yoder (Roy and Tuttle, 1956). A potassium analcite has been prepared hydrothermally by Barrer and Baynham (1956). A natural analcite from Golden, Colorado (Table 44, anal. 8), shows a reversible transition in its compressibility at about 8400 atmospheres. Yoder and Weir (1960) report that the high-pressure phase thus formed is distinctly birefringent and that the crystals exhibit a large and variable optic axial angle : its symmetry has not been determined but it is evidently lower than that of the low-pressure analcite. The hydrothermal crystallization of wairakite, the calcium analogue of analcite, has been reported by Coombs (1960) from kaolin–calcite–quartz mixes.

The ion-exchange properties of synthetic analcite have been investigated by Barrer (1950) who found that Na was freely exchanged with K, NH_4, Ag, Tl and Rb but only slightly exchanged with Li, Cs, Mg, Ca and Ba. Ag-analcite had 8·6 per cent. H_2O, while the other analcite derivatives were nearly anhydrous. The hydronium form of analcite was also prepared by ion-exchange (Beattie and Dyer, 1957). The introduction of foreign ions has been shown not to affect the potential energy barrier for the ionic migration of the original cation (Beattie, 1955).

The sorption and diffusion of ammonia gas in analcite (Table 44, anal. 2) after dehydration was studied by Tiselius (1935) who reported a sorption of 124 ml. NH_3 per gm., equivalent to nearly 1 mol. per cent. H_2O. In addition to ammonia, Barrer (1938) also studied the sorption of hydrogen, nitrogen, argon and helium by dehydrated analcite.

OPTICAL AND PHYSICAL PROPERTIES

Analcite may occur in clear or opaque, well formed crystals (often icositetrahedra), in radiating aggregates, or in irregular granular masses. The structure of analcite ideally is cubic and accordingly many specimens are isotropic (refractive index about 1·487). Synthetic analcites prepared by Saha (1959) are isotropic, and their refractive indices decrease with increasing SiO_2 content, from 1·493 for analcite with natrolite composition to 1·488 for the ideal analcite composition and to 1·482 for albite composition. Many specimens of analcite, however, exhibit slight birefringence (usually $\leqslant 0\cdot001$) which has been variously attributed to loss of water (Náray-Szabó, 1938a), or to strain (*e.g.* Bannister, 1931), or to ordering of the (Si,Al) atoms in the structure. Factors such as these cause variations in refractive index in different crystallographic directions, and the precise effects may vary from one crystal to another. Thus analcites are often anomalously biaxial with negative sign, and $2V_\alpha$ may vary from 85° to near zero (see, for example, Stewart, 1941 ; Roques, 1947 ; Walker, 1951 ; Kiriyama and Azumi, 1958). When birefringence is so low, small changes in one or other of the refractive indices can produce these quite large variations in 2V. Birefringent analcites sometimes show repeated lamellar twinning on {001} or {110}. The electrical conductivity of analcite has been determined by Beattie (1954).

Wairakite is colourless to white with vitreous lustre and has D 2·26, H 5½–6. It is biaxial with α 1·498, γ 1·502, 2V$_\gamma$ 70°–105° and weak dispersion $(r > v)$. Like analcite its optical properties are variable even within a single grain. Wairakite is usually twinned on {110}, with {100} bisecting the angle between two perpendicular sets of twin lamellae. The optical orientation is $\alpha \simeq y$, $\beta \simeq x$, $\gamma \simeq z$. Viséite is isotropic with n 1·53, D 2·2, H 3–4.

DISTINGUISHING FEATURES

Analcite is very similar to leucite, but the latter mineral has a slightly higher refractive index, a different paragenesis, and is anhydrous. The refractive indices of chabazite are slightly lower than those of analcite. Sodalite resembles analcite but it can be distinguished by a chemical test for chlorine. When analcite is treated with concentrated HCl it gelatinizes and takes a stain from a solution of *malachite green*.

PARAGENESIS

Analcite occurs as a primary mineral of late formation in some intermediate and basic igneous rocks and at a later stage crystallizes from hydrothermal solutions and occurs in vesicles in association with such minerals as prehnite and the zeolites. The distinction between primary and secondary analcite, however, is not easily made when the analcite occurs as interstitial grains; in many such reports of so-called primary analcite there is insufficient evidence to indicate the precise mode of origin of the mineral.

In plutonic igneous rocks analcite is found as a primary mineral in teschenites where the analcite may amount to about 20 per cent.: in some teschenites the analcite, however, is secondary after nepheline. In lugarite from Lugar, Ayrshire, the analcite and subordinate nepheline make up about 50 per cent. of the rock: the analcite-bearing Scottish igneous rocks have been particularly studied by Tyrell (1923). In glenmuirites (analcite essexites) the analcite may amount to 17 per cent., and analcite is also abundant in the so-called analcite syenites, *e.g.* that of Howford Bridge, Mauchline, Ayrshire, and in the syenite, syenodiorite and syenogabbro of the Terlingua-Solitario region, Texas (Lonsdale, 1940). The analcite of anal. 1 (Table 44) occurs, together with orthoclase, melanite garnet, sphene and allanite, in pegmatitic patches and veins in borolanite (Stewart, 1941). In the alkaline rocks of the Kola peninsula analcite is found associated with aegirine and may be either primary or secondary after sodalite or aegirine (Labuntzov, 1927); Zavaritsky (1936) has recorded a similar aegirine–analcite–nepheline-syenite assemblage from the Ishim river, west Siberia. The analcite of anal. 5 (Table 44) occurs in masses, 4 to 5 inches in diameter, in nepheline-syenite pegmatite in French Guinea (Roques, 1947).

In hypabyssal igneous rocks primary analcite is found in certain olivine dolerites as in the Clee Hill, Shropshire, and some Derbyshire occurrences: in the doleritic sills of western Scotland analcite is often abundant and forms the distinctive analcite dolerite or crinanite. It is also known from the dolerites of the Terlingua-Solitario region, Texas, and from the Spanish Peaks area of Colorado. It has been suggested that small globules of analcite in inclusions of analcite trachybasalt in the phonolite of Traprain Law, near Edinburgh, originated in a magmatic emulsion formed by the separation of a water-rich magma into two immiscible liquids (Tomkeieff, 1952). Analcite has also been recorded as a minor constituent of globules in a picritic rock in west Greenland, where the globules have been interpreted as being due to immiscibility or as bubbles of a late-magmatic gas phase (Drever, 1960).

In volcanic rocks analcite is known as a primary constituent in some basalts, where typically it is restricted to the groundmass, *e.g.* Bowen (1927) described an analcite-rich basalt from the Deccan traps of India, and Di Franco (1926) reported two generations of analcite from Cyclopean Islands basalt, one of primary crystallization (Table 44, anal. 6) and the other of subsequent formation often replacing most of the rock. It is known also from trachybasalts, where it may be associated with pseudoleucite, and from some trachyandesites as in the rock type dancalite (De Angelis, 1925) consisting of abundant analcite together with oligoclase, hornblende and aegirine-augite. Idiomorphic phenocrysts of analcite were recorded by Solovkin (1945) from a pyroxene–analcite basalt of the Little Caucasus.

The hydrothermal crystallization of analcite in igneous rocks typically occurs in vesicles, where analcite may be found in association with prehnite, chabazite, thomsonite, stilbite, etc. Water-clear analcite has been found in association with chabazite in cavities and seams in the amygdaloidal basalts of Antrim (Smith *et al.*, 1916): the relative abundance of analcite in these amygdales has been examined by Walker (1960) who reported that the mineral occurred at 31 per cent. of the zeolite localities. The frequent occurrence of analcite in the Watchung basalts of New Jersey, and its relationships to natrolite, chabazite and other zeolites, were reported by Fenner (1910). It has been recorded, together with calcite, in vesicles in the lapilli of a tuff from Cressbrook Dale, Derbyshire (Sargent, 1925), and occurs in miarolitic cavities near the top of a monzonite dyke in the Bearpaw mountains, Montana, where it is found in association with axinite, prehnite, datolite, etc. (Pecora and Fisher, 1946): here the cavities are supposed to represent gas bubbles formed by "resurgent boiling" of the magma. Analcite and analcite pseudomorphous after laumontite have been recorded from serpentinite (Kučera and Novotná, 1927). Bore-holes drilled in alkaline parts of a geyser basin in Yellowstone Park showed that the Na and Ca of the felspars in rhyolitic and dacitic lavas are replaced by K, while at higher levels the Na gives rise to the formation of considerable analcite (Fenner, 1936). The occurrence of considerable analcite in a jadeite-rich vein at a serpentinite–schist contact has been recorded by Yoder and Chesterman (1951), who consider that, subsequent to consolidation of the jadeite vein and its fracturing and faulting, the fractures were lined or filled with analcite.

In sedimentary rocks analcite may occur as an authigenic mineral in sandstones (*e.g.* Rengarten, 1940, 1950); analcite-rich rocks interbedded with phosphatic siltstones and sandstones, and consisting of 35 per cent. analcite set in a cryptocrystalline groundmass of laumontite, fluorite, calcite and quartz, have been reported by Buryanova (1954). Films of analcite in cleat-joints in coal, and in concretions with pyrite in coal, have been attributed to an access of alkalis probably supplied from an overlying bed of limestone (Foster and Feitch, 1946). Ross (1928, 1941) has described analcite-rich fine-grained sedimentary rocks, in one case representing a Quaternary lake deposit. The analcite is considered to have formed by the action of lake water containing sodium salts on colloidal clay or on bentonite derived from volcanic ash; in other occurrences a white porous tuff contains glass shards altered to analcite. A similar origin has been suggested for analcite-rock in a series of ochreous and oolitic mudstones of Triassic age in Wyoming (Keller, 1952), where there are beds 40 to 60 feet thick of more or less pure analcite extending over hundreds of square miles. A thick series of greywackes with beds of volcanic tuff in New Zealand Triassic sediments (Coombs, 1954) show an alteration of glassy fragments to analcite and heulandite: with increasing depth the analcite is replaced by a laumontite-bearing assemblage. In the Eocene lacustrine beds of the Green River formation of Wyoming, Utah and Colorado, analcite is by far the most widespread and abundant of the silicate minerals (Milton *et al.*, 1960). Joulia *et al.* (1958) have described a formation in the central Sahara some 20 metres thick, extending over 10,000 to 15,000 square kilometres, consisting essentially of analcite: this analcite is considered to be either a primary precipitate or to have been derived from the alteration of pyroclastics or clays, though no traces of these are seen. It has also been reported in association with montmorillonite in shales in the Congo (Vernet, 1961). Wairakite, the calcium analogue of analcite (Table 44, anal. 11), was originally recorded in tuffaceous sandstones and breccias, vitric tuffs, and ignimbrite which had been altered by alkaline hydrothermal fluids associated with geothermal steam in New Zealand: the actual occurrence was at a depth where the observed temperature range was from 200° to 250°C. and the probable hydrostatic pressure from 55 to 265 atmospheres (Steiner, 1955). In addition to direct crystallization from hydrothermal solutions wairakite also forms by the hydrothermal replacement of andesine. It also has been identified in greywacke from California, both replacing felspar and lining cavities (Steiner, 1958), and in low grade metamorphosed tuffs and tuff breccias in Mt. Rainier National Park, Washington (Wise, 1959), also filling cavities and replacing plagioclase.

Analcite may also form from the alteration of albite, or from orthoclase in the presence of sodium-rich solutions. Analcite pseudomorphs after leucite are also known (*e.g.* Bennett, 1945); Thugutt (1946) has suggested that the analcite of igneous rocks is normally an alteration product of leucite and is not of magmatic origin.

REFERENCES

Adams, L. H., 1953. A note on the stability of jadeite. *Amer. Journ. Sci.*, vol. 251, p. 299.

Bannister, F. A., 1931. The distinction of analcite from leucite in rocks by X-ray methods. *Min. Mag.*, vol. 22, p. 469.

Barrer, R. M., 1938. The sorption of polar and non-polar gases by zeolites. *Proc. Roy. Soc.*, A, vol. 167, p. 392.

—— 1950. Ion-exchange and ion-sieve processes in crystalline zeolites. *Journ. Chem. Soc.*, p. 2342.

—— 1957. Some researches on silicates: mineral syntheses and metamorphoses. *Trans. Brit. Ceram. Soc.*, vol. 56, p. 155.

Barrer, R. M., and **Baynham, J. W.**, 1956. The hydrothermal chemistry of the silicates. Part VII. Synthetic potassium aluminosilicates. *Journ. Chem. Soc.*, p. 2882.

—— —— **Bultitude, F. W.** and **Meier, W. M.**, 1959. Hydrothermal chemistry of the silicates. Part VIII. Low-temperature growth of aluminosilicates, and of some gallium and germanium analogues. *Journ. Chem. Soc.*, p. 195.

—— —— and **McCallum, N.**, 1953. Hydrothermal chemistry of the silicates. Part V. Compounds structurally related to analcite. *Journ. Chem. Soc.*, p. 4035.

—— and **Falconer, J. D.**, 1956. Ion exchange in felspathoids as a solid state reaction. *Proc. Roy. Soc.*, A, vol. 236, p. 227.

—— and **White, E. A. D.**, 1952. The hydrothermal chemistry of the silicates. Part II. Synthetic crystalline sodium alumino-silicates. *Journ. Chem. Soc.*, p. 1561.

Beattie, I. R., 1954. The structure of analcite and ion-exchanged forms of analcite. *Acta Cryst.*, vol. 7, p. 357.

—— 1955. The electrical conductivity of partially ion-exchanged forms of analcite. *Trans. Faraday Soc.*, vol. 51, p. 712.

—— and **Dyer, A.**, 1957. The preparation of hydronium forms of analcite and chabazite by ion-exchange. *Journ. Chem. Soc.*, p. 4387.

Bennett, J. A. E., 1945. Some occurrences of leucite in East Lothian. *Trans. Edin. Geol. Soc.*, vol. 14, p. 34.

Bowen, N. L., 1927. An analcite-rich rock from the Deccan traps of India. *Journ. Washington Acad. Sci.*, vol. 17, p. 57.

Buryanova, E. Z., 1954. Analcime sedimentary rocks from Tuva. *Doklady Acad. Sci. USSR*, vol. 98, p. 261.

Coombs, D. S., 1954. The nature and alteration of some Triassic sediments from Southland, New Zealand. *Trans. Roy. Soc. New Zealand*, vol. 82, p. 65.

—— 1955. X-ray investigations on wairakite and non-cubic analcime. *Min. Mag.*, vol. 30, p. 699.

—— 1960. Lower grade mineral facies in New Zealand. *Rept. 21st Internat. Geol. Congress, Norden*, Part 13, p. 339.

De Angelis, M., 1925. Note di petrografia Dancala. (II). *Atti Soc. Ital. Sci. Nat.*, vol. 62, p. 179 (M.A. 3–203).

Di Franco, S., 1926. L'analcite e il basalto analcitico dell'isola dei Ciclopi. *Boll. Soc. Geol. Ital.*, vol. 45, p. 1 (M.A. 4–375).

Drever, H. I., 1960. Immiscibility in the picritic intrusion at Igdlorssuit, west Greenland. *Rept. 21st Internat. Geol. Congress, Norden*, Part 13, p. 47.

Fenner, C. N., 1910. The Watchung basalt and the paragenesis of its zeolites and other secondary minerals. *Ann. New York Acad. Sci.*, vol. 20, p. 93.

—— 1936. Bore-hole investigations in Yellowstone Park. *Journ. Geol.*, vol. 44, p. 225.

Foster, W. D. and **Feitch, F. L.**, 1946. Mineralogy of concretions from Pittsburgh coal seam, with special reference to analcime. *Amer. Min.*, vol. 31, p. 357.

Grassi-Cristaldi, G. and **Scafile, F.**, 1929. Contributo al comportamento di alcune zeoliti. *Annal. Chim. Appl. Roma*, vol. 19, p. 136 (M.A. 5–83).

Griggs, D. T. and **Kennedy, G. C.**, 1956. A simple apparatus for high pressures and temperatures. *Amer. Journ. Sci.*, vol. 254, p. 722.

Guyer, A., **Ineichen, M.** and **Guyer, P.**, 1957. Über die Herstellung von Künstlichen Zeolithen und ihre Eigenschaften als Molekelsiebe. *Helvetia Chim. Acta*, vol. 40, p. 1603.

Hodge-Smith, T., 1929. The occurrence of zeolites at Kyogle, New South Wales. *Rec. Australian Museum*, vol. 17, p. 279.

Joulia, F., Bonifas, M., Camez, Th., Millott, G. and **Weil, R.**, 1958. Analcimolites sedimentaires dans le continental intercalcaire du Sahara Central (Bassin du Niger-A.O.F.). *Serv. Carte géol. Alsac-Lorraine Bull.*, vol. 11, p. 67.

Keller, W. D., 1952. Analcime in the Popo Agie member of the Chugwater formation. *Science*, vol. 115, p. 241.

King, E. G., 1955. Low-temperature heat capacity and entropy at 298·16°K of analcite. *Journ. Amer. Chem. Soc.*, vol. 77, p. 2192.

Kiriyama, R. and **Azumi, M.**, 1958. Optical anomaly of analcime from Mazé, Niigata Pref. *Journ. Min. Soc. Japan*, vol. 3, p. 418. English summary in *Min. Journ. (Japan)*, vol. 2, p. 281.

Koizumi, M., 1953. The differential thermal analysis curves and dehydration curves of zeolites. *Min. Journ. (Japan)*. vol. 1, p. 36.

Kučera, B. and **Novotná, B.**, 1927. New localities of zeolites in Moravia. *Časopis Morav. Zemsk. Mus.*, vol. 25, p. 214 (M.A. 4–318).

Labuntzov, A. N., 1927. Les zéolithes des Monts Chibines et Lujawrurt en Laponie russe. *Trav. Mus. Min. Acad. Sci. URSS*, vol. 2, p. 91 (M.A. 4–373).

Larsen, E. S. and **Buie, B. F.**, 1938. Potash analcime and pseudoleucite from the Highwood Mountains of Montana. *Amer. Min.*, vol. 23, p. 837.

Lonsdale, J. T., 1940. Igneous rocks of the Terlingua–Solitario region, Texas. *Bull. Geol. Soc. Amer.*, vol. 51, p. 1539.

Lyons, J. B., 1944. Igneous rocks of the northern Big Belt range, Montana. *Bull. Geol. Soc. Amer.*, vol. 55, p. 445.

Mason, B., 1946. Analcite, apophyllite, and natrolite from the Pahau river, north Canterbury. *New Zealand Journ. Sci. Techn., Sect. B*, vol. 28, p. 53.

McConnell, D., 1952. Viséite, a zeolite with the analcime structure and containing linked SiO_4, PO_4 and H_xO_4 groups. *Amer. Min.*, vol. 37, p. 609.

Milligan, W. O. and **Weiser, H. B.**, 1937. The mechanism of the dehydration of zeolites. *Journ. Phys. Chem.*, vol. 41, p. 1029.

Milton, C., Chao, E. C. T., Fahey, J. J. and **Mrose, M. E.**, 1960. Silicate mineralogy of the Green River formation of Wyoming, Utah, and Colorado. *Rept. 21st Internat. Geol. Congress, Norden*, Part 21, p. 171.

Morgante, S., 1945. Zeoliti della zona di Dessiè e Diredaua in A.O. *Atti 1st Veneto Sci. Lett. Art.*, vol. 104, pt. 2, p. 405 (M.A. 11–292).

Náray-Szabó, St. v., 1938a. Die Struktur des Pollucits. $CsAlSi_2O_6 \cdot xH_2O$. *Zeit. Krist.*, vol. 99, p. 277.

—— 1938b. Note on the structure of analcite and pollucite. *Zeit. Krist.*, vol. 99, p. 291.

Nel, H. J., 1944. Pollucite from Karibib, South West Africa. *Amer. Min.*, vol. 29, p. 443.

Noll, W., 1936. Synthese von Montmorilloniten. Ein Beitrag zur Kenntnis der Bildungsbedingungen und des Chemismus von Montmorillonit. *Chemie der Erde*, vol. 10, p. 129 (M.A. 6–353).

Pecora, W. T. and **Fisher, B.**, 1946. Drusy vugs in a monzonite dike, Bearpaw Mountains, Montana. *Amer. Min.*, vol. 31, p. 370.

Rengarten, N. V., 1940. Authigene analcyme in the Kazanian sandstones of the Kirov region. *Mém. Soc. Russe. Min.*, vol. 69, p. 50 (M.A. 10–296).

—— 1950. Laumontite and analcime from Lower Devonian deposits in northern Caucasus. *Doklady Acad. Sci. USSR*, vol. 70, p. 485.

Roques, M., 1947. Édifices mimétiques et symétrie triclinique de l'analcime des îles de Los (Guinée française). *Compt. Rend. Acad. Sci. Paris*, vol. 225, p. 946.

Ross, C. S., 1928. Sedimentary analcite. *Amer. Min.*, vol. 13, p. 195.

—— 1941. Sedimentary analcite. *Amer. Min.*. vol. 26, p. 627.

Roy, R. and **Tuttle, O. F.**, 1956. Investigations under hydrothermal conditions. *Physics and Chemistry of the Earth*, vol. 1, p. 162.

Saha, P., 1959. Geochemical and X-ray investigation of natural and synthetic analcites. *Amer. Min.*, vol. 44, p. 300.

Sargent, H. C., 1925. An analcite-bearing tuff in the Carboniferous Limestone of Derbyshire. *Geol. Mag.*, vol. 62, p. 462.

Shimizu, S., 1915. Analysis of analcime from Mazé, Echigo Province. *Beitr. Min. Japan*, no. 5, p. 295 (M.A. 1–156).

Smith, G. F. H., **Ashcroft, F. N.** and **Prior, G. T.**, 1916. Chabazite and associated minerals from County Antrim. *Min. Mag.*, vol. 17, p. 301.

Solovkin, A. N., 1945. Analcime rocks in the Little Caucasus (Azerbaijan SSR). *Doklady Acad. Sci. URSS*, vol. 49, p. 50.

Steiner, A., 1955. Wairakite, the calcium analogue of analcime, a new zeolite mineral. *Min. Mag.*, vol. 30, p. 691.

—— 1958. Occurrence of wairakite at The Geysers, California. *Amer. Min.*, vol. 43, p. 781.

Stewart, F. H., 1941. On sulphatic cancrinite and analcime (eudnophite) from Loch Borolan, Assynt. *Min. Mag.*, vol. 26, p. 1.

Stoklossa, G., 1918. Über die Natur des Wassers in den Zeolithen. *Neues Jahrb., Min.*, Bl.-Bd. 42, p. 1.

Strunz, H., 1936. Die chemische Zusammensetzung von Pollucit. *Zeit. Krist.*, vol. 95, p. 1.

Taylor, W. H., 1930. The structure of analcite ($NaAlSi_2O_6 \cdot H_2O$). *Zeit. Krist.*, vol. 74, p. 1.

—— 1938. Note on the structure of analcite. *Zeit. Krist.*, vol. 99, p. 283.

Thugutt, St. J., 1946. Sur l'origine de l'analcime. *Arch. Min. Tow. Nauk. Warszaw*, vol. 16, p. 35 (M.A. 10–293).

—— 1951. On the chemical anomalies of analcite. *Acta Geol. Polonica*, vol. 2, p. 2 (M.A. 11–549).

Tiselius, A., 1935. Sorption und Diffusion von Ammoniak in Analcim. *Zeit. Physikal. Chem.*, Abt. A, vol. 174, p. 401.

Tomkeieff, S. I., 1952. Analcite-trachybasalt inclusions in the phonolite of Traprain Law. *Trans. Edinburgh Geol. Soc.*, vol. 15, p. 360.

Tyrell, G. W., 1923. Classification and age of the analcite-bearing igneous rocks of Scotland. *Geol. Mag.*, vol. 60, p. 249.

Vernet, J.-P., 1961. Concerning the association montmorillonite–analcime in the series of Stanleyville, Congo. *Journ. Sed. Petr.*, vol. 41, p. 293.

Walker, G. P. L., 1951. The amygdale minerals in the Tertiary lavas of Ireland. I. The distribution of chabazite habits and zeolites in the Garron plateau area, County Antrim. *Min. Mag.*, vol. 29, p. 773.

—— 1960. The amygdale minerals in the Tertiary lavas of Ireland. III. Regional distribution. *Min. Mag.*, vol. 32, p. 503.

Wherry, E. T., 1923. Volume isomorphism in the silicates. *Amer. Min.*, vol. 8, p. 1.

Wise, W. S., 1959. Occurrence of wairakite in metamorphic rocks of the Pacific Northwest. *Amer. Min.*, vol. 44, p. 1099.

Yoder, H. S. and **Chesterman, C .W.**, 1951. Jadeite of San Benito County, California. *Calif. Div. Mines, Special Rept.* 10-C, 3–8.

—— and **Weir, C. E.**, 1960. High-pressure form of analcite and free energy change with pressure of analcite reactions. *Amer. Journ. Sci.*, vol. 258–A, p. 420.

Zavaritzky, A. N., 1936. The alkaline rocks of the Ishim river (west Siberia). *Trav. Inst. Pétrogr. Acad. Sci. URSS*, nos. 7–8, p. 47 (M.A. 7–39).

ZEOLITE GROUP

$$(\text{Na}_2,\text{K}_2,\text{Ca},\text{Ba})[(\text{Al},\text{Si})\text{O}_2]_n \cdot x\text{H}_2\text{O}$$

Name	Formula	System	n_{min}	n_{max}	2V	D
Natrolite	$\text{Na}_2[\text{Al}_2\text{Si}_3\text{O}_{10}] \cdot 2\text{H}_2\text{O}$	Orth.	1·473	1·496	58°–64°(+)	2·20–2·26
Mesolite	$\text{Na}_2\text{Ca}_2[\text{Al}_2\text{Si}_3\text{O}_{10}]_3 \cdot 8\text{H}_2\text{O}$	Mon.	1·504	1·512	≃80°(+)	≃2·26
Scolecite	$\text{Ca}[\text{Al}_2\text{Si}_3\text{O}_{10}] \cdot 3\text{H}_2\text{O}$	Mon.	1·507	1·521	36°–56°(−)	2·25–2·29
Thomsonite	$\text{NaCa}_2[(\text{Al},\text{Si})_5\text{O}_{10}]_2 \cdot 6\text{H}_2\text{O}$	Orth.	1·497	1·544	42°–75°(+)	2·10–2·39
Gonnardite	$\text{Na}_2\text{Ca}[(\text{Al},\text{Si})_5\text{O}_{10}]_2 \cdot 6\text{H}_2\text{O}$	Orth.	1·497	1·503	50°(−)	≃2·3
Edingtonite	$\text{Ba}[\text{Al}_2\text{Si}_3\text{O}_{10}] \cdot 4\text{H}_2\text{O}$	Tetr.	1·541	1·557	54°(−)	2·7–2·8
Heulandite	$(\text{Ca},\text{Na}_2)[\text{Al}_2\text{Si}_7\text{O}_{18}] \cdot 6\text{H}_2\text{O}$	Mon.	1·476	1·512	var.	2·1–2·2
Stilbite	$(\text{Ca},\text{Na}_2,\text{K}_2)[\text{Al}_2\text{Si}_7\text{O}_{18}] \cdot 7\text{H}_2\text{O}$	Mon.	1·484	1·513	30°–49°(−)	2·1–2·2
Epistilbite	$\text{Ca}[\text{Al}_2\text{Si}_6\text{O}_{16}] \cdot 5\text{H}_2\text{O}$	Mon.	1·485	1·519	44°(−)	≃2·2
Dachiardite	$(\text{Ca},\text{K}_2,\text{Na}_2)_3[\text{Al}_4\text{Si}_{18}\text{O}_{45}] \cdot 14\text{H}_2\text{O}$	Mon.	1·491	1·499	65°–73°(+)	≃2·16
Ferrierite	$(\text{Na},\text{K})_4\text{Mg}_2[\text{Al}_6\text{Si}_{30}\text{O}_{72}](\text{OH})_2 \cdot 18\text{H}_2\text{O}$	Orth.	1·48		≃50°(+)	≃2·15
Phillipsite	$(\tfrac{1}{2}\text{Ca},\text{Na},\text{K})_3[\text{Al}_3\text{Si}_5\text{O}_{16}] \cdot 6\text{H}_2\text{O}$	Mon.	1·483	1·514	60°–80°(+)	≃2·2
Harmotome	$\text{Ba}[\text{Al}_2\text{Si}_6\text{O}_{16}] \cdot 6\text{H}_2\text{O}$	Mon.	1·503	1·514	≃80°(+)	2·41–2·47
Chabazite	$\text{Ca}[\text{Al}_2\text{Si}_4\text{O}_{12}] \cdot 6\text{H}_2\text{O}$	Trig.	1·470	1·494	—	2·05–2·10
Gmelinite	$(\text{Na}_2,\text{Ca})[\text{Al}_2\text{Si}_4\text{O}_{12}] \cdot 6\text{H}_2\text{O}$	Trig.	1·474	1·494	—	≃2·1
Levyne	$\text{Ca}[\text{Al}_2\text{Si}_4\text{O}_{12}] \cdot 6\text{H}_2\text{O}$	Trig.	1·491	1·505	—	≃2·1
Erionite	$(\text{Na}_2,\text{K}_2,\text{Ca},\text{Mg})_{4.5}[\text{Al}_9\text{Si}_{27}\text{O}_{72}] \cdot 27\text{H}_2\text{O}$	Hex.	1·468	1·476	—	≃2·02
Faujasite	$(\text{Na}_2,\text{Ca})_{1.75}[\text{Al}_{3.5}\text{Si}_{8.5}\text{O}_{24}] \cdot 16\text{H}_2\text{O}$	Cubic	1·48		—	≃1·92
Laumontite	$\text{Ca}[\text{Al}_2\text{Si}_4\text{O}_{12}] \cdot 4\text{H}_2\text{O}$	Mon.	1·502	1·525	26°–47°(−)	2·2–2·3
Mordenite	$(\text{Na}_2,\text{K}_2,\text{Ca})[\text{Al}_2\text{Si}_{10}\text{O}_{24}] \cdot 7\text{H}_2\text{O}$	Orth.	1·472	1·487	76°–90°(±)	2·12–2·15
Gismondine	$\text{Ca}[\text{Al}_2\text{Si}_2\text{O}_8] \cdot 4\text{H}_2\text{O}$	Orth.	1·515	1·546	15°–90°(−)	≃2·2
Ashcroftine	$\text{KNaCa}[\text{Al}_4\text{Si}_5\text{O}_{18}] \cdot 8\text{H}_2\text{O}$	Tetr.	1·536	1·545	—	2·61(?)

The zeolites may be defined as hydrated aluminosilicates of the alkalies and alkaline earths, with an infinitely extended three-dimensional anion network, and thus with the atomic ratio $\text{O}:(\text{Al}+\text{Si})=2$. They are remarkable for their continuous and in part reversible dehydration and for their base-exchange properties. They typically occur in amygdales and cavities in basic volcanic rocks and in other late-stage hydrothermal environments. The name is from the Greek *zein*, to boil, and *lithos*, stone, in allusion to the intumescence of most zeolites with a borax bead.

Analcite is commonly included as a member of the zeolite group. It has close affinities with the felspathoids, however, and has a somewhat higher temperature paragenesis than the other zeolites, and it is here treated separately, p. 338.

Structure. The basic feature of all zeolite structures is an aluminosilicate framework composed of $(\text{Si},\text{Al})\text{O}_4$ tetrahedra, each oxygen of which is shared between two tetrahedra. The net negative charge on the framework is balanced by the presence of cations, in most cases Ca, Na, or K, which are situated in cavities within it. This feature is embodied also in the structures of the felspar and felspathoid minerals. The felspars have compact structures in which the (Na,Ca,K) ions are in relatively small cavities and are completely surrounded by oxygens of the framework: the cations and framework are strongly interdependent so that cations cannot easily move unless framework bonds are broken, and replacement of Na or K by Ca necessarily involves a change in the Si : Al ratio. The felspathoids have somewhat more open aluminosilicate frameworks and their (Na,Ca,K) ions (and in some cases certain anions) occupy, but do not always fill, larger cavities which are intercommunicating. Thus in the felspathoids there are channels through which ions can be either extracted or introduced, and through which small molecules may pass, without disruption of the framework. The zeolite aluminosilicate frameworks are similar but some are still more open, containing larger cavities and larger channels (specific gravity of zeolites 2–2·3, felspathoids 2·3–2·5, felspars 2·6–2·7); zeolites may therefore exhibit to a greater extent the properties of ion exchange and molecular absorption. An additional feature which differentiates the zeolites still further from minerals of the other two groups is the presence of water molecules within the structural channels. These are relatively loosely bound to the framework and cations, and like the cations can be removed and replaced without disrupting framework bonds. Since the zeolite framework is structurally almost independent of the (Na,Ca,K) cations, and since the latter do not fill all the cavities, replacements of the type $Ca \rightleftharpoons 2(Na,K)$ can also occur.

The zeolites can be subdivided, on the basis of their structures and morphology, into three main groups.

1. Natrolite group; including natrolite, mesolite, scolecite, thomsonite, gonnardite and edingtonite. In this group, linkages of tetrahedra are more numerous in one crystallographic direction than in the plane at right angles to it, and the minerals have fibrous morphology and cleavage.

2. Heulandite group; including heulandite, stilbite and epistilbite. These are characterized by platy cleavage, and in their structures linkages are more numerous in one plane than in the direction at right angles to it.

3. The remaining zeolites have framework structures in which the binding is of similar strength in all directions. This group includes harmotome, phillipsite, chabazite, gmelinite, levyne, faujasite (and analcite). The structure of erionite is similar, but it has some chain-like character and the mineral is fibrous.

The channel systems in the various zeolites are formed by different combinations of linked rings of tetrahedra, as shown in Table 45. The wider the channels at their narrowest parts, the larger the cation that can be introduced into the structure. Those with 8- and 12-membered rings have channels large enough for the admission of organic molecules as well as cations; thus zeolites can act as ion or molecular sieves, each having its characteristic upper limit for the size of ion or molecule to which it is permeable. A grading of the zeolites according to the open-ness of structure is shown in Table 45. Fibrous zeolites also show molecular absorption, *e.g.* ethyl and *iso*-propyl alcohol are absorbed by thomsonite (Hey, 1932a). Channel width, however, is not the only criterion for permeability since the presence of many cations may block the channels, and ionic or molecular diffusion is also affected by water content. Cation exchange capacity in general diminishes with loss of water; cations are most mobile in zeolites with a low cation content. Na is more mobile than Ca since it is monovalent and is thus held by a weaker electrostatic bond (see, for example, Ducros, 1960).

In most zeolites the water molecules are probably distributed among a number of possible sites and can jump from one to another. In general the Ca zeolites absorb more water, and in chabazite, heulandite and stilbite, water retentivity is greater with Ca than with K in the framework (Barrer and Baynham, 1956; Ducros, 1960). The role of the water in zeolites and its rate of diffusion was investigated also by Hey (1935).

Table 45. Numbers of tetrahedra in rings, and approximate diameters of channels in various felspathoids and zeolites

Minerals	Nos. of tetrahedra in rings	Minimum diameter of widest channel
Sodalite, nosean	4 and 6	2·2 Å
Analcite	4 and 6	2·2 Å
Harmotome, phillipsite	4 and 8	3·2 Å
Levyne	4, 6 and 8	3·2 Å
Erionite	4, 6 and 8	3·6 Å
Chabazite	4, 6 and 8	3·9 Å
Heulandite	5, 6 and 8	—
Gmelinite	4, 6, 8 and 12	6·4 Å
Faujasite	4, 6 and 12	9 Å

Chemistry. The zeolites form a well-defined group of hydrated silicates of aluminium and the alkalies or alkaline earths, and are characterized chemically also by having the molecular ratio $Al_2O_3:(Ca,Sr,Ba,Na_2,K_2)O$ equal to unity, and the ratio $O:(Al+Si)=2$. General reviews of the chemistry of the zeolites have been given by Winchell (1925), Hey (1930) and by Coombs *et al.* (1959); 48 selected zeolite analyses are presented here in Tables 46, 48, 50, 51, 53. Kostov (1960) considers that the only important variables are the Al:Si ratio and the number of water molecules: the isomorphism between the calcium and sodium members should be considered as limited.

The fields of synthesis and stability of the zeolites have been investigated by Coombs *et al.* (1959). These authors consider that in quartz-bearing systems sodium and calcium zeolites are not stable at temperatures above about 320°C. although they may be synthesized readily at temperatures as high as 450°C. The state of silica in the starting materials may be critical where the phases on opposite sides of a phase boundary have different silica contents: the field of a high-silica phase such as mordenite is extended when the silica activity is higher than that of quartz.

When zeolites are heated, water is given off continuously rather than in separate stages at definite temperatures, and the dehydrated or partially dehydrated mineral can re-absorb water to its original amount when again exposed to water vapour. Dehydrated zeolites can absorb other liquids or vapours in place of water, *e.g.* ammonia, alcohol, NO_2, H_2S, etc. The base-exchange properties of zeolites were first reported by Eichorn (1858) and have been reviewed by Hey (1930) who also investigated in detail the base-exchange of various members of the group (Hey, 1932a, b, 1933, 1934, 1936). The colloidal properties of the zeolites have been reviewed by Marshall (1949).

Optical and physical properties. The zeolites, when pure, are colourless or white, but many specimens are coloured because of the presence of finely divided oxides of iron or other impurities. Their densities range between 2·0 and 2·3 gm./cm.³ except for the barium-rich zeolites, for which D is between 2·5 and 2·8. Refractive indices range between 1·47 and 1·52 and birefringence between zero and 0·015.

Paragenesis. Zeolites typically occur in amygdales and fissures, chiefly in basic volcanic rocks, and are also found in veins and other late-stage hydrothermal environments. In some igneous rocks they occur as alteration products of aluminosilicates such as the felspars or nepheline. They are also known as authigenic minerals in sandstones and other sedimentary rocks. The occurrence of the individual minerals of the zeolite group are detailed below: a general review of zeolite parageneses is given by Coombs *et al.* (1959).

The so-called "rule" of Cornu (1908) states that in a series of zeolites crystallizing with falling temperature the zeolites will appear in the order of increasing hydration. The reverse sequence of events may occur as a result of metamorphism (*e.g.* M'Lintock, 1915), though on the whole it is only rarely that a clear and consistent trend of this type can be recognized. An alternative scheme has been put forward by Kostov (1960) who uses a diagram illustrating the relationship between the Al:Si ratio and the energy index of the calcium zeolites calculated according to the method described by Gruner (1950). The diagram (Fig. 105) shows a distribution of the zeolites along curves in accordance with their Al:Si ratio and their number of water molecules: the logical order of deposition from hypogene solutions is for those zeolites with lower energy index (higher energy of formation) to be deposited earlier. The same zeolites also have a higher Al:Si ratio. Thus Kostov considers that thomsonite or gismondine should be the relatively highest temperature zeolites and mordenite the lowest.

A general correlation is also apparent between the silica content of zeolites and the availability of free silica (Coombs *et al.*, 1959). Thus in veins and joints in quartz-bearing rocks the typical zeolites are stilbite, heulandite and laumontite, the other zeolites being quantitatively insignificant in such environments. The basaltic amygdale sequence mordenite, heulandite, stilbite, reported from southern Brazil (Mason and Greenberg, 1954), is one of increasing hydration in silica-rich zeolites, and these occur in association with quartz, chalcedony or opal. The sequence of deposition of the amygdaloidal minerals in the Watchung basalt of New Jersey was determined by Fenner (1910) to be laumontite, stilbite, thomsonite, calcite, stilbite, chabazite, thomsonite, analcite, apophyllite, calcite and mesolite.

The zeolites of the Tertiary lavas of Northern Ireland have been studied in detail by Walker (1951, 1959, 1960a): in these amygdaloidal basalts the most abundant species, in order of frequency, are chabazite, thomsonite, levyne, natrolite, mesolite, stilbite, gmelinite, heulandite and phillipsite. Chabazite and thomsonite characterize the upper parts of the lava succession: below they are joined by natrolite (and analcite) and in some areas, where zeolitization has been most intense, by stilbite and heulandite as well. Walker considers that these zeolite zones probably reflect the temperature distribution in the lavas during zeolitization, the zones being discordant and clearly superimposed on the lavas. Zoning of a rather similar type has been described from the Lake

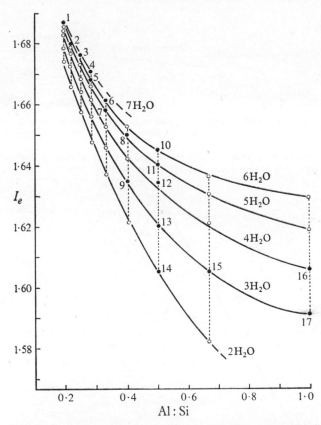

Fig. 105. Variation of the Al:Si ratio and the energy index of the calcium zeolites: (1) ptilolite (Si-rich mordenite), (2) mordenite, (3) Ca-dachiardite, (4) stilbite, (5) heulandite, (6) Ca-erionite, (7) epistilbite, (8) Ca-faujasite, (9) yugawaralite, (10) chabazite, (11) levyne, (12) laumontite, (13) leonhardite (?), (14) wairakite, (15) scolecite, (16) gismondine, (17) Ca-thomsonite (?) (after Kostov, 1960).

Superior region (Stoiber and Davidson, 1959) and a somewhat thicker series of zones is apparent in the Tertiary basalts of eastern Iceland (Walker, 1960b) where the lowest zone is rich in mesolite and scolecite (together with many other zeolites); this is succeeded by an analcite zone, and then by a restricted assemblage mostly of chabazite and thomsonite (Fig. 106). These zeolites are mainly those tending to be low in silica, consistent with their occurrence in undersaturated basic rocks. Walker (1960a) has reported that in the Antrim basalts the amygdale minerals are readily grouped into five main assemblages:

Stilbite–heulandite assemblage; associated with chabazite, calcite, analcite and natrolite.

Analcite–natrolite assemblage; common associates chabazite and calcite. Stilbite, heulandite and gmelinite absent.

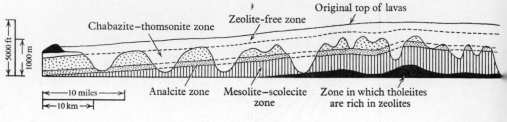

FIG. 106. Diagrammatic section across the Tertiary lavas of eastern Iceland showing the zonal distribution of amygdale minerals (after Walker, 1960b).

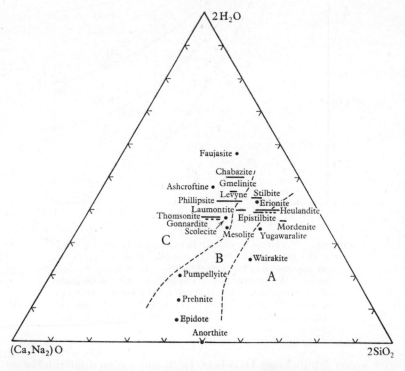

FIG. 107. Compositions, in molecular proportions, of the calcium zeolites and other Ca–Al silicates. For the zeolites and anorthite $(Ca,Na_2)O$ is numerically equal to Al_2O_3. A=field of phases favoured by super-saturation with respect to silica. B=field of phases commonly coexisting with silica minerals. C=field of phases favoured by a silica-poor environment (after Coombs *et al.*, 1959).

Chabazite–thomsonite assemblage; often associated with levyne, phillipsite and calcite. Stilbite, heulandite, natrolite and analcite absent.

Gmelinite assemblage; commonly associated with chabazite, thomsonite, analcite, phillipsite, levyne, calcite and aragonite.

Plumose calcite–aragonite–quartz assemblage.

A general grouping of the calcic zeolites has been proposed (Coombs *et al.*, 1959) illustrating the tendency of zeolites to occur in environments (A) super-saturated with respect to SiO_2, (B) saturated, and (C) undersaturated (Fig. 107).

The mineral assemblages in which zeolites are characteristic are of such widespread occurrence that a new mineral and metamorphic facies, the zeolite facies, has been proposed. Fyfe *et al.* (1958) suggested that the facies should cover only regionally developed zeolitic assemblages which largely replace the pre-existing rocks and conform to the mineralogical and chemical requirements of a metamorphic facies : it was later suggested, however, that the facies can be extended to the zones of diagenesis and low grade metasomatism (Coombs *et al.*, 1959). Extensive development of zeolite facies rocks occurs in the Teringatura district, in the South Island of New Zealand, where Triassic volcanic greywackes show an extensive development of heulandite or laumontite. The zeolite facies is taken to include at least all those assemblages produced under physical conditions in which the assemblages quartz–heulandite, quartz–laumontite and quartz–analcite are formed.

Natrolite
Mesolite
Scolecite

$Na_2[Al_2Si_3O_{10}]\cdot 2H_2O$

$Na_2Ca_2[Al_2Si_3O_{10}]_3\cdot 8H_2O$

$Ca[Al_2Si_3O_{10}]\cdot 3H_2O$

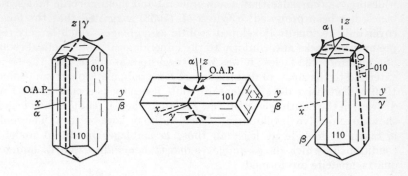

	NATROLITE	MESOLITE	SCOLECITE
	ORTHORHOMBIC(+) (pseudo-tetragonal)	MONOCLINIC (+) (pseudo-orthorhombic)	MONOCLINIC (−) (pseudo-tetragonal)
α	1·473–1·483	—	1·507–1·513
β	1·476–1·486	1·504–1·508	1·516–1·520
γ	1·485–1·496	—	1·517–1·521
δ	$\simeq 0\cdot012$	$\leq 0\cdot001$	$\simeq 0\cdot007$
2V	58°–64°(+)	$\simeq 80°$ (+)	36°–56° (−)
Orientation:	$\alpha=x,\ \beta=y,\ \gamma=z$	$\beta=y,\ \alpha{:}z\simeq 8°$	$\gamma=y,\ \alpha{:}z\simeq 18°$
O.A.P.	(010)	(010)	$\perp$(010)
Dispersion:	max. 2V at 5000 Å	$r<v$, strong.	$r<v$, strong.
D	2·20–2·26	$\simeq 2\cdot26$	2·25–2·29
H	5	5	5
Cleavage:	{110}, {1$\bar1$0}, very good.	{101}, {10$\bar1$}, perfect.	{110}, {1$\bar1$0}, very good.
Twinning:	{110}, {011}, {031} rare.	Always twinned {100}.	Common {100}; twin axis [001].
Colour:	Colourless, white, grey, yellow, pink, red; colourless in thin section.		
Unit cell: a Å	18·30	$3\times 18\cdot9$	18·52
b Å	18·63	6·55	18·99
c Å	6·60	18·48	6·55
β	—	90°	90° 39′
Z	8	8	8
Space group:	$Fdd2$	$C2$ (pseudo $Fdd2$)	$Cc(?)$

Thomsonite
Gonnardite
Edingtonite

$NaCa_2[(Al,Si)_5O_{10}]_2 \cdot 6H_2O$
$Na_2Ca[(Al,Si)_5O_{10}]_2 \cdot 6H_2O$
$Ba[Al_2Si_3O_{10}] \cdot 4H_2O$

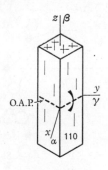

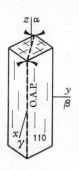

	THOMSONITE ORTHORHOMBIC (+) (pseudo-tetragonal)	GONNARDITE ORTHORHOMBIC (−) (pseudo-tetragonal)	EDINGTONITE ORTHORHOMBIC or MONOCLINIC (−) (pseudo-tetragonal)
α	1·497–1·530	1·497–1·506	1·541
β	1·513–1·533	—	1·553
γ	1·518–1·544	1·499–1·508	1·557
δ	0·006–0·015	$\simeq 0·002$	$\simeq 0·015$
2V	42°–75° (+)	50° (−)	54° (−)
Orientation:	$\alpha=x,\ \beta=z,\ \gamma=y$	$\alpha=z$	$\alpha=z,\ \beta=y,\ \gamma=x$
O.A.P.	(001)	—	(010)
Dispersion:	$r > v$	—	$r < v$ strong
D	2·10–2·39	$\simeq 2·3$	2·7–2·8
H	5–5½	5	—
Cleavage:	{010} perfect, {100} good.	—	{110}, {1$\bar{1}$0}
Twinning:	{110}	—	
Colour:	Colourless, white, pink, brown; colourless in thin section.		
Unit cell: a Å	13·07	13·38	9·60
b Å	13·09	13·38	9·60
c Å	2 × 6·63	6·66	6·54
β	—	—	—
Z	4	2	2
Space group:	$Pnma$	—	(pseudo) $P42_1m$

STRUCTURE

The structures of the fibrous zeolites were first determined in detail by Taylor and Jackson (1933) and Taylor *et al.* (1933), although they had been outlined previously by Pauling (1930), and cell parameters had been determined by Halla and Mehl (1930). Like all zeolites they have framework structures in which every $(Si,Al)O_4$ tetrahedron has each of its oxygens shared with another tetrahedron, but the linkages of tetrahedra to form chains in the z direction are the most prominent. The repeating unit in each chain occupies about 6·6 Å and consists of five tetrahedra (Fig. 108a and b). Four of these form a ring

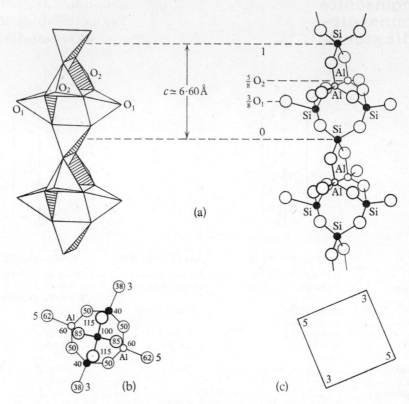

Fig. 108. (a). The aluminosilicate chain of tetrahedra common to the structures of the natrolite group of zeolites. Chains are linked to one another laterally via oxygen atoms O_1 and O_2 which are at heights $\frac{3}{8}$ and $\frac{5}{8}$ of the c repeat distance respectively.

(b). The chain viewed along the z direction.

(c). Schematic representation of the outline of the chain; the numbers 3 and 5 indicate the heights at which neighbouring chains are joined (after Bragg, 1937).

with vertices pointing alternately upwards and downwards. The free oxygens O_1 and O_2 of the ring are used in forming lateral linkages to neighbouring chains of tetrahedra, and in terms of the z repeat distance they are at heights $\frac{3}{8}$ and $\frac{5}{8}$ respectively. As shown in Fig. 108, two tetrahedra in each group of five contain aluminium atoms and the other three contain silicons. A projection (along z) of a single chain is shown in Fig. 108b. The various members of the natrolite group of zeolites differ from one another in the way in which the chain units are arranged side by side. In order to illustrate this the unit of five tetrahedra in each chain is represented as a square, and the position of a chain in the z direction is indicated by the heights of O_1 and O_2. Thus in Fig. 108c heights $\frac{3}{8}$ and $\frac{5}{8}$ are represented by the numbers 3 and 5, using the Si of one tetrahedron to define the zero level.

Edingtonite, Thomsonite, Natrolite. The structures of edingtonite, thomsonite and natrolite are illustrated in Fig. 109.

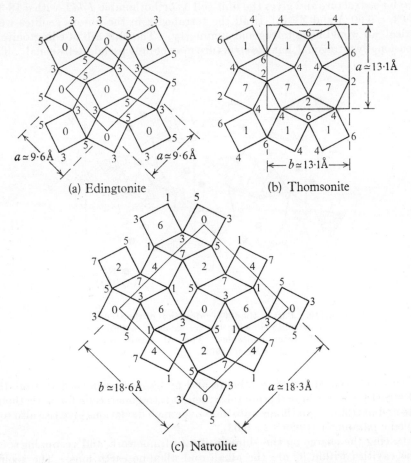

(a) Edingtonite   (b) Thomsonite

(c) Natrolite

FIG. 109. Schematic representation of the arrangements of chains which form the aluminosilicate framework of (a) edingtonite, (b) thomsonite, (c) natrolite. Each square represents a chain as in Fig. 108 (after Taylor and Jackson, 1933).

The simple unit cell results from the mode of lateral linkage found in edingtonite: neighbouring chains are related by two vertical mirror planes at right angles, and a tetragonal cell $P42_1m$ with a 9·60, c 6·54 Å, and containing two chains, results (Taylor and Jackson, 1933).

In thomsonite neighbouring chains in the y direction are related by mirror planes (010), but those in the x direction are related by diad axes [010]. The resulting unit cell (orthorhombic *Pnma*) contains four chains and has a approximately $\sqrt{2}$ times a for edingtonite.

In the structure of natrolite, neighbouring chains are related (approximately) by diads only, and this results in a body-centred cell with dimensions similar to those of thomsonite ($a \simeq b \simeq 13 \cdot 1$ Å) or a face-centred cell with a 18·3, b 18·6 Å. A refinement of the structure of natrolite (Meier, 1960) confirms the correctness of Taylor's structure and gives the unit cell as orthorhombic *Fdd2*, with a 18·30, b 18·63, c 6·60 Å and $Z=8$. If all the tetrahedra in the fibrous zeolites were identical, all would have tetragonal symmetry. The unit cell of edingtonite is dimensionally tetragonal, but the structure may be only pseudo-tetragonal. The

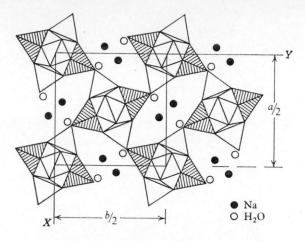

Fig. 110. Part of the (001) projection of the structure of natrolite showing the positions of sodium ions and water molecules. The Al tetrahedra are shaded (after Meier, 1960).

difference between Al and Si tetrahedra and perhaps other deviations from the ideal structure result in orthorhombic (pseudo-tetragonal) cells for both thomsonite and natrolite. In thomsonite moreover such deviations give rise also to a doubled c parameter ($13 \cdot 25 \simeq 2 \times 6 \cdot 63$).

Balancing the charge on the aluminosilicate framework, and occupying some of the cavities within it, are the alkali and alkaline earth ions. The zeolite water molecules form, with O_1 and O_2, double columns parallel to z which pass through the channels between chains of tetrahedra (Fig. 110). Alternate cavities in the double columns in natrolite are occupied by Na ions, and the others are vacant. In edingtonite the Ba ions are in eight-fold coordination with six oxygens and two water molecules, and each water molecule is close to one Ba. In natrolite each Na is surrounded by six oxygens (4 oxygen ions and 2 water molecules), and each water molecule is close to two Na ions. In thomsonite, four of the six cations are surrounded by seven-fold groups (4 oxygens and 3 water molecules), and the other two are in eight-fold coordination by six oxygens and two water molecules; some water molecules are in contact with one Ca ion, and others with, on the average, one Ca and one Na (Fig. 111). The positions and coordination of the water molecules are consistent with their polar character.

The fibrous nature of the natrolite group of zeolites and their cleavages, {110} in edingtonite and natrolite, {100} and {010} in thomsonite, are explained by the existence of relatively few bonds linking chains laterally as compared with those within the chain-like units of the structure. The reversible dehydration and cation exchange properties of these zeolites are consistent with the wide channels in the structure which house the water molecules and large cations. The latter have definite sites within the channels (see Hey, 1935) but can move along them without breaking the silicate framework. Meier (1960)

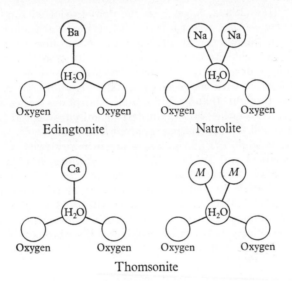

Fig. 111. Environment of water molecules in fibrous zeolites. For thomsonite, half the sites labelled *M* are occupied by Na and half by Ca.

points out that there are channels between chains in directions perpendicular to z, and that these rather than the narrower ones parallel to z permit the diffusion of cations. The changes in cell parameters with substitution of different cations and with dehydration show that the silicate framework is not absolutely rigid, but can change by rotation of the chains of tetrahedra to accommodate larger or smaller cations. The unit cell of natrolite for example varies from $17.99 \times 18.59 \times 6.48$ Å for the lithium substituted compound to $18.63 \times 18.96 \times 6.61$ Å for silver (Hey, 1932b), and the dehydration of thomsonite reduces the cell from $13.12 \times 13.12 \times 13.26$ Å to $12.95 \times 12.95 \times 13.26$ Å (Hey, 1932a). Because of the adaptability of the framework towards cations of different sizes, the minerals of the natrolite group are not so efficient as ion sieves as are those zeolites with more rigid frameworks (*e.g.* chabazite).

Mesolite and **scolecite** are known to have structures with aluminosilicate frameworks similar to that of natrolite. Suggestions have been made as to the location of Ca and Na cations and water molecules within the cavities (Pauling,

1930; Taylor *et al.*, 1933) but these are somewhat speculative. Some indication of the positions of water molecules is provided by the thermal analysis study by Peng (1955). Mesolite is monoclinic ($\beta \simeq 90°$; pseudo-orthorhombic *Fdd2*); it has a tripled *a* parameter compared with natrolite, and the fibre axis (repeat distance $\simeq 6.6$ Å) is in the *y* (diad axis) instead of the *z* crystallographic direction. Mesolite and scolecite can be distinguished from natrolite by their X-ray diffraction patterns (see p. 407).

Gonnardite has cell parameters similar to those of thomsonite and is assumed to have a similar aluminosilicate framework structure. X-ray fibre photographs of gonnardite are similar to those of thomsonite, and its powder photographs may be confused with those of natrolite (Meixner *et al.*, 1956).

The work of Hey (1932a, b, etc.) on the dehydration characteristics of the fibrous zeolites shows that structural transitions occur at higher temperatures, *i.e.* natrolite to metanatrolite at 400°–600°C., thomsonite to metathomsonite at 270°–300°C. and scolecite to metascolecite at 240°–255°C. Edingtonite and mesolite do not undergo a dimorphous transition, and gonnardite may be structurally identical with metascolecite. Metanatrolite is distinctly monoclinic, and it is thought that it forms an isomorphous series with natrolite. Metascolecite can be either fully hydrated or anhydrous, and between it and scolecite there is a sharp rather than gradual transition.

The minerals *mountainite* and *rhodesite* are in many respects similar to the fibrous zeolites (Gard and Taylor, 1957). Mountainite, $(Ca,Na_2,K_2)_{16}Si_{32}O_{80}\cdot 24H_2O$, is monoclinic with *a* 13·51, *b* (=fibre axis) 2×6.55, *c* 13·51 Å, β 104°; apart from the β angle its cell is similar to that of thomsonite. Rhodesite, $(Ca,Na_2,K_2)_8Si_{16}O_{40}\cdot 11H_2O$, is orthorhombic with *a* 23·8, *b* 6·54, *c* 7·05 Å, and has *z* as the fibre axis, so that the analogy with thomsonite is in this case not convincing. An affinity between rhodesite and the fibrous zeolite erionite has been suggested (Barrer *et al.*, 1959).

CHEMISTRY

Natrolite. The ideal composition is $Na_2Al_2Si_3O_{10}\cdot 2H_2O$: there is some replacement of Na by K, and also of Na by Ca. The name is from the Latin *nitrum* (Greek, *nitron*), soda, and the Greek *lithos*, a stone, in allusion to the composition of this mineral: synonyms include soda mesotype, or mesotype, and epinatrolite. Four analyses of natrolite are given in Table 46 (anals. 1 to 4), where they have also been recalculated on the basis of 80 oxygens, the anhydrous cell contents. All the analytical data available at the time were collected by Hey (1932b), who also presented nine new analyses. The variation from the ideal composition is less than in many zeolites, and there is no evidence that the small amounts of Ca often present are due to a substitution of the type $NaSi \rightleftharpoons CaAl$, the substitution being rather of the type $Na_2 \rightleftharpoons Ca$. The CaO content is usually a fraction of 1 per cent., though natrolites with 1·05 and 1·89 per cent. CaO (Hey, 1932b) have been reported from Snake Hill, New Jersey, and from Seiser Alpe, Tyrol, respectively, and a natrolite from Czechoslovakia has 1·04 per cent. CaO (Kratochvíl, 1933). The amount of K replacing Na is generally very small, though the two slightly Ca-rich natrolites described by Hey also contain 1·27 and 1·25 per cent. K_2O, and Kuzmenko (1950) has described compact natrolite from the Kola peninsula with 0·83 per cent. K_2O.

Some analyses report appreciable amounts of Fe_2O_3 (*e.g.* Table 46, anal. 2) but in many samples the iron may be present as minute impurities of haematite which sometimes give the mineral a brownish appearance.

When crystals of natrolite are heated they are dehydrated to monoclinic metanatrolite, as first reported by Rinne (1890): on exposure to air this meta-natrolite absorbs water and is re-converted to natrolite. The partial and complete dehydration of natrolite was investigated in detail by Hey (1932b) and by Milligan and Weiser (1937): Hey reported that on heating at 290° to 300°C. a product still containing water was obtained, whereas for the production of metanatrolite complete dehydration had taken place at 400° to 600°C. Milligan and Weiser, however, considered that a monohydrate was obtained at about 160° to 180°C. and that natrolite becomes anhydrous at about 250°C. The heat of hydration of natrolite and also its vapour pressure at various temperatures and degrees of hydration have been determined by Hey (1932b).

Natrolite was one of the first zeolites for which the phenomenon of base-exchange was observed; early investigators, however, did not fully report the properties of the products. Clarke and Steiger (1900) found that, on heating natrolite at 120°C. in a 10 per cent. $AgNO_3$ solution, half the sodium was replaced by silver in 18 hours. They also heated natrolite with dry NH_4Cl in a sealed tube at 250° to 300°C. and obtained anhydrous $(NH_4)_2Al_2Si_3O_{10}$. The results of early experiments are summarized by Hey (1932b), who also produced nearly pure Li, Ag, K, NH_3 and Tl natrolites by heating natrolite with fusions of the nitrates and leaching and washing the products with hot water. Attempts to produce the Ca-zeolites mesolite or scolecite by the action of $CaCl_2$ on natrolite were unsuccessful. The loss of some water and the absorption of ammonia when natrolite is treated with anhydrous liquid ammonia has been investigated by Gruner (1933) and by Barrrer (1938), the latter author concluding that a definite ammoniate is formed. The solubility of natrolite in pure water at elevated temperatures has been investigated by Smirnov (1915) and by Thugutt (1935), both of whom investigated chemically the composition of the resultant solutions (see also Kiriyama *et al.*, 1957). The d.t.a. curve of natrolite has been determined by Koizumi (1953) and by Peng (1955), the latter author also having investigated the thermal changes occurring at reaction peak temperatures by coordinated optical and X-ray methods. The d.t.a. curve is characterized by an extremely sharp and strong endothermic peak at 455°C. corresponding to the release of the zeolitic water. At 565°C. there is a very small but persistent endothermic peak possibly representing the formation of meta-natrolite, at between 910° to 940°C. there is a small endothermic hump, and at about 1010°C. a small exothermic peak occurs, the latter probably representing the partial crystallization of fused natrolite to nepheline and another phase.

Mesolite. The ideal composition is $Na_2Ca_2Al_6Si_9O_{30} \cdot 8H_2O$: there is minor replacement of the type $Ca \rightleftharpoons Na_2$. The name is from the Greek *mesos*, middle, and *lithos*, stone, in allusion to its intermediate chemistry between natrolite and scolecite. Three analyses of mesolite are given in Table 46 (anals. 15 to 17) where they have also been recalculated on the basis of 30 oxygens (anhydrous): several further analyses are tabulated by Hey (1933). There is often considerable replacement of Si by Al and frequently a small replacement of 2Na by Ca (*e.g.* Table 46, anal. 15). Less commonly the reverse replacement of Ca by 2Na occurs as in anal. 17 with 10·05 per cent. Na_2O: mesolite described by

Table 46. NATROLITE AND THOMSONITE ANALYSES

	1.	2.	3.	4.	5.	6.
SiO_2	47·17	46·53	47·60	47·33	37·17	37·44
Al_2O_3	26·84	26·63	27·40	27·67	31·93	31·57
Fe_2O_3	0·07	1·34	—	—	—	0·08
MgO	0·05	0·12	—	—	—	—
CaO	0·12	0·44	0·13	0·22	13·98	13·80
Na_2O	15·89	15·53	15·36	14·74	4·00	3·98
K_2O	0·02	0·44	0·23	0·50	tr.	0·04
H_2O^+ H_2O^-	}9·58	}9·62	}9·47	}9·64	}13·35	}13·22
Total	99·74	100·65	100·19	100·10	100·43	100·13
α	—	1·477	1·4799	1·4789	1·529	1·527
β	—	1·479	—	1·4822	1·531	1·531
γ	—	1·490	1·4918	1·4911	1·542	1·543
2V	—	—	59° 37′ (+)	63° 03′ (+)	51° 39′ (+)	—
$\alpha:z$	—	—	—	—	—	—
D	—	2·20–2·26	2·245	2·248	2·373	2·386

NUMBERS OF IONS ON THE BASIS OF 80 OXYGENS

Si	23·96	23·61	23·98	23·90	19·87	20·04
Al	16·07	15·93	16·27	16·47	20·12	19·92
Fe^{+3}	0·03	0·51	—	—	—	0·03
Mg	0·04	0·09	—	—	—	—
Na	15·65	15·28	15·00	14·43	4·14	4·13
Ca	0·06	0·24	0·07	0·12	8·01	7·92
K	0·01	0·28	0·15	0·32	—	0·03
H_2O^+ H_2O^-	}16·23	}16·28	}15·91	}16·24	} 23·80	}23·60
Z	40·06	40·05	40·25	40·37	39·99	39·99
R†	15·76	15·89	15·22	14·87	12·15	12·08

1. Large translucent natrolite crystals, nepheline-syenite: limestone contact, Ice Valley region, British Columbia (Phillips, 1916).
2. Natrolite (crystals up to 3 feet × 4 inches), aplite dyke, Johnston asbestos mine, Quebec (Poitevin, 1938). Anal. R. J. C. Fabry.
3. Clear stout natrolite prisms, Puy de Marmant, Puy-de-Dôme, France (Hey, 1932b). Anal. M. H. Hey.
4. Translucent natrolite crystals, Benallt manganese mine, Rhiw, Caernarvonshire (Hey, 1932b). Anal. M. H. Hey.
5. Radiating glassy prisms of thomsonite, Old Kilpatrick, Dunbartonshire (Hey, 1932a). Anal. M. H. Hey (Cell size: a 13·12, b 13·12, c 13·26 Å).
6. Thomsonite, rock crevices, Peekskill, New York (Phillips, 1924).

† $R = (Mg + Na + Ca + K)$.

Antonín (1942) has 11·02 per cent. Na_2O (CaO 5·33). Small amounts of K, replacing Na, may also occur, e.g. anal. 15 (see also Hey, 1933). The vapour pressure of mesolite was investigated by Hey who demonstrated that mesolite is a single solid phase, and that on dehydration it undergoes no transition but loses water continuously: the heat of hydration by water vapour was found to

Table 46 contd. THOMSONITE, SCOLECITE AND GONNARDITE ANALYSES

	7.	8.	9.	10.	11.	12.
SiO_2	36·30	39·01	45·16	46·10	46·37	43·20
Al_2O_3	32·20	29·94	25·90	25·05	25·80	27·90
Fe_2O_3	—	—	—	0·55	—	—
MgO	—	—	—	0·32	—	—
CaO	12·88	12·71	14·86	14·17	13·58	3·61
Na_2O	4·80	4·80	0·16	tr.	0·64	13·16
K_2O	—	0·00	0·06	0·03	0·13	—
H_2O^+	}13·60	}13·24	}13·66	13·78	}13·84	}11·74
H_2O^-				0·13		
Total	99·78	99·70	99·80	100·13	100·36	99·61
α	1·530	1·529	1·513	—	1·510	1·497
β	1·533	1·531	1·5200	—	1·518	—
γ	1·542	1·544	1·5205	—	1·519	1·499
2V	44°(+)	59°(+)	35° 17' (−)	—	—	—
α:z	—	—	16° 22'	—	18°	—
D	2·336	2·366	2·276	2·285	2·25	2·27

NUMBERS OF IONS ON THE BASIS OF 80 OXYGENS

Si	19·62	20·91	23·73	24·14	24·15	22·68
Al	20·52	18·92	16·04	15·46	15·84	17·27
Fe^{+3}	—	—	—	0·22	—	—
Mg	—	—	—	0·50	—	—
Na	5·03	4·99	0·16	—	0·64	13·40
Ca	7·46	7·30	8·37	7·95	7·58	2·03
K	—	—	0·04	0·02	0·09	—
H_2O^+	}24·52	}23·68	}23·95	24·07	}24·04	}20·56
H_2O^-				0·22		
Z	40·14	39·83	39·77	39·82	39·99	39·95
R†	12·49	12·29	8·57	8·47	8·31	15·43

7. Thomsonite, augitite, Sextant Rapids, Timiskaming district, Ontario (Walker, 1932).
8. Radiating lamellar thomsonite, Burger's quarry, West Paterson, New Jersey (Hey, 1932a). Anal. M. H. Hey.
9. Scolecite, Syhadree Mts., Bombay, India (Hey, 1936). Anal. M. H. Hey.
10. Scolecite, amygdales in Tertiary basalt, N.E. slope of An Gearna, Ben More, Mull (M'Lintock, 1915).
11. Scolecite, pass of Bettolina, Valle di Ayas, Monte Rosa, Italy (Gennaro, 1929).
12. Gonnardite, Aci Trezza, Sicily (Meixner *et al.*, 1956). Anal. A. A. Moss.

† $R = (Mg + Na + Ca + K)$.

be 18,000 cals. per gm. mol. of water absorbed. Despite this work, however, Milligan and Weiser (1937) maintained that mesolite is a solid solution of varying amounts of scolecite and natrolite. The base-exchange of mesolite by the action of fusions of KCNS, LiNO₃, AgNO₃, NH₄NO₃, TlNO₃ and NaClO₃ was investigated by Hey (1933) who showed that with the first three salts the compounds produced were identical with similar derivatives prepared from natrolite. The d.t.a. curve of mesolite has been studied by Koizumi (1953) and by Peng

Table 46 contd.　GONNARDITE, EDINGTONITE AND MESOLITE ANALYSES

	13.	14.	15.	16.	17.
SiO_2	42·75	35·35	42·02	46·98	40·03
Al_2O_3	27·36	19·98	28·94	26·43	27·88
Fe_2O_3	—	—	—	—	0·85
MgO	—	—	0·06	—	0·22
CaO	7·77	0·10	10·46	10·06	6·03
Na_2O	8·15	0·04	3·24	4·57	10·05
K_2O	0·15	0·65	1·92	0·05	0·40
H_2O^+	}13·44	}13·11	13·20	}11·94	11·10
H_2O^-			0·64		3·12
Total	99·62	100·06	100·48	100·03	100·29
α	1·506	1·5405	—	1·5065	1·5044
β	—	1·5528	1·512	1·5074	1·5052
γ	1·508	1·5569	—	—	1·5067
2V	—	53° 52′ (−)	—	90°‖	—
$\alpha:z$	—	—	—	8°	—
D	2·27	2·777	—	2·258	—

NUMBERS OF IONS ON THE BASIS OF 80 OXYGENS (30 for mesolite)

	13.	14.	15.	16.	17.
Si	22·77	23·83	8·35	9·04	8·14
Al	17·18	15·88	6·78	5·99	6·68
Fe^{+3}	—	—	—	—	0·13
Mg	—	—	0·02	—	0·07
Na	8·42	0·05	1·25	1·70	3·96
Ca	4·43	0·07	2·23	2·07	1·31
K	0·10	0·56	0·49	0·01	0·10
H_2O^+	}23·88	}29·48	8·75	}7·66	7·52
H_2O^-			0·42		2·11
Z	39·95	39·71	15·13	15·03	14·95
R†	12·95	8·82‡	3·99	3·78	5·54¶

13. Gonnardite, Aci Castello, Sicily (Meixner *et al.*, 1956).　Anal. A. A. Moss.
14. Edingtonite, Böhlet, Sweden (Hey, 1934).　Anal. M. H. Hey (Includes BaO 30·83).
15. Mesolite, associated with pseudomesolite, cavities in Tertiary basalt, Ritter hot spring, Grant County, Oregon (Hewett *et al.*, 1928).
16. Clear large crystals of mesolite, Syhadree Mts., Bombay, India (Hey, 1933).　Anal. M. H. Hey.
17. Mesolite fibres, geode in phonolite, Rio Cambone, Montiferro, Sardinia (Deriu, 1954). (Includes TiO_2 0·02, FeO 0·59.)

† $R = (Mg + Na + Ca + K)$.
‡ Includes Ba 8·14.
‖ 2V varies greatly with temperature and wavelength, see Hey (1933).
¶ Includes Fe^{+2} 0·10.

(1955): it has a double endothermic peak at 310° and 325°C., a sharp endothermic peak at about 440°C. and a minor endothermic peak at 490°C.; there is also a strong exothermic reaction at about 1040°C.

Scolecite.　The ideal composition is $CaAl_2Si_3O_{10} \cdot 3H_2O$: minor substitution $Ca \rightleftharpoons 2Na$ may occur.　The name is from the Greek *skolex*, a worm, in allusion to the observation that a borax bead of the mineral sometimes curls up like a worm. Three analyses of scolecite are given in Table 46 (anals. 9 to 11) where they have also been recalculated on the basis of 80 oxygens: several further analyses are tabulated by Hey (1936). The Si : Al ratio in scolecite is relatively constant at 3:2, but there is a slight indication from some analyses that a minor amount of replacement of Al by Si may occur, though there is no evidence of the appropriate amounts of alkalies for the substitutional relationship $NaSi \rightleftharpoons CaAl$. Small amounts of Na and K do, however, replace Ca (*e.g.* Table 46, anal. 11) and, from a consideration of published analyses of scolecite, Hey (1936) considered that the replacement may probably reach 1 Na and 0·1 K atoms per unit cell: Ba and Sr have not been recorded.

The reproducible hydrothermal synthesis of scolecite has been reported as possible (Koizumi and Roy, 1960) only by heating a $CaO \cdot Al_2O_3 \cdot 3SiO_2$ mixture in the presence of seeds of natural scolecite in the temperature range 230° to 285°C. at 15,000 lb./in.^{2} At this water vapour pressure the scolecite breaks down at about 300°C. to give anorthite + wairakite + H_2O. A vapour-pressure study by Hey (1936) showed that, on the partial dehydration of scolecite, a transition to a dimorphous form, metascolecite, occurs at a degree of hydration dependent on the temperature of the experiment: the transition to the high temperature form metascolecite will, however, occur by 255°C. whatever the water content. Hey has demonstrated that in both scolecite and metascolecite the water consists of two distinct groups, in the scolecite unit cell there is a more volatile group of 16 and a less volatile one of 8 mols. per unit cell, while in metascolecite the group of 8 is the more volatile. Hey reported that the transition to metascolecite takes place (except at low temperatures) before the composition $CaAl_2Si_3O_{10} \cdot 2H_2O$ previously attributed to metascolecite is reached: Milligan and Weiser (1937), however, report the existence of two definite hydrates, *i.e.* with 3 and 2 H_2O molecules. The d.t.a. curve of scolecite has been determined by Koizumi (1953) and by Peng (1955): the latter author reported three sharp endothermic peaks at 310°, 470° and 560°C. The base-exchange properties of scolecite were also investigated by Hey (1936), who introduced Na, K, Li, NH_4, Ag and Tl in place of Ca: in several cases the products were identical with those of similarly base-exchanged natrolite. The absorption of ammonia by dehydrated scolecite was reported by Sameshima and Morita (1935) and by Barrer (1938).

Thomsonite. The ideal composition is $NaCa_2Al_5Si_5O_{20} \cdot 6H_2O$: there is considerable replacement of CaAl by NaSi and some of Ca by Na_2, giving formulae from $(Ca,Na_2)_{8\cdot4}Al_{16\cdot8}Si_{23\cdot2}O_{80} \cdot 24H_2O$ to $(Ca,Na_2)_{10\cdot35}Al_{20\cdot5}Si_{19\cdot5}O_{80} \cdot 24H_2O$. The name is in honour of Dr. T. Thomson who analysed the mineral when it was first recognized as a new species: faroelite and uigite are synonyms. Four analyses of thomsonite are given in Table 46 (anals. 5 to 8) where they have also been recalculated on the basis of 80 oxygens, the anhydrous cell contents. A major chemical investigation of thomsonite was made by Hey (1932a) who presented 16 new analyses together with 107 thomsonite analyses from the literature, of which 34 were considered to be first class (*i.e.* Si + Al = 40·00 ± 0·20, summation between 99·70 and 100·80). Earlier, Wherry (1923, 1925) had concluded that thomsonite could be divided into three species of fixed composition, namely thomsonite proper, $NaCa_2Al_5Si_5O_{20} \cdot 6H_2O$, faroelite or mesole, $Na_2Ca_2Al_6Si_7O_{26} \cdot 7H_2O$, and a third species poor in Na_2O for which the name

24—R.F.M. IV.

comptonite was used.   Winchell (1925), however, suggested that there is an isomorphous replacement $NaSi \rightleftharpoons CaAl$, and Hey was able to confirm this while conclusively disproving Wherry's view.   In addition Hey found that appreciable substitution $Na_2 \rightleftharpoons Ca$ also takes place, the number of cations per unit cell being somewhat variable, though there is a tendency towards a definite integral value of 12.   Na is generally the only major alkali element though thomsonites with an appreciable K content have been reported, *e.g.* with K_2O 0·45 per cent. (Di Franco, 1932), and for a zeolite (probably potassium-rich thomsonite) CaO 5·16, Na_2O 8·50, K_2O 2·63 (Hutton, 1942).   An Na_2O content of as high as 10·54 per cent. has been reported by Hey (1932a, anal. 5), who also found SiO_2 values between 37·11 and 41·44 per cent. and Al_2O_3 from 31·93 to 28·5 per cent.   Small amounts of Sr may replace Ca.

The synthesis of sodium-free thomsonite from glasses formed from the pure oxides and treated hydrothermally was reported by Goldsmith (1952), who also prepared a Ga-bearing thomsonite, in which approximately $\frac{2}{3}$ of the Al is replaced by Ga; this synthesis was effected at 245°C. and 8000 lb./in.^{2} H_2O pressure, somewhat above the temperatures used for production of Ga- and Na-free thomsonite.   The stability relations have been partly determined by Fyfe *et al.* (1958) who prepared thomsonite from glass of prehnite composition : at 500 bars thomsonite is stable up to approximately 280°C.   Likewise thomsonite may be prepared by the crystallization of a glass of epidote composition (Coombs *et al.*, 1959).

The vapour pressure of thomsonite at various temperatures and degrees of hydration has been investigated by Hey (1932a); further results were reported by Mourant (1933), and a continuous reversible dehydration curve for thomsonite was obtained by Milligan and Weiser (1937).   From the vapour pressure surface of thomsonite, Hey concluded that thomsonite is dimorphous and transforms at a temperature of around 270°–300°C. to the high temperature form metathomsonite.   The transition is readily reversible and its temperature is dependent on the water content, the greater the water content of the thomsonite the lower the transition temperature.   The d.t.a. curve of thomsonite has been given by Koizumi (1953).   The absorption of vapours other than water by dehydrated thomsonite has been investigated by Hey (1932a) using alcohols, and by Sameshima and Morita (1935) using CO_2 and ammonia, and the results have enabled inferences to be made as to the nature of the structural channels present in the mineral.   Base-exchange experiments on thomsonite were also made by Hey (1932a) using aqueous solutions of $AgNO_3$, $CaCl_2$, NaCl, K_2CO_3, etc.   The reactions are extremely sluggish, and it is difficult to exchange divalent ions for monovalent ones and vice versa, though Ag, Tl and, less readily, K could be substituted for the Na ion.

Gonnardite.   The approximate composition is $Na_2CaAl_5Si_5O_{20} \cdot 6H_2O$, but there is considerable variation in the Na:Ca ratio : The name is in honour of M. Gonnard of Lyons.   Two analyses of gonnardite are given in Table 46 (anals. 12 and 13), and further analyses are tabulated by Meixner *et al.* (1956). From consideration of these analyses, including that by Hey (1932a), Meixner *et al.* concluded that the formula could best be expressed as $(Ca,Na)_{6-8}(Si,Al)_{20}$ $O_{40} \cdot 12H_2O$, with Al near 9.   The replacement $CaAl \rightleftharpoons NaSi$ is illustrated by an early analysis (Paijkull, 1874) of gonnardite (then believed to be ranite) which recalculates to a formula $Na_{5.9}Ca_{1.4}Al_{9.9}Si_{10.3}O_{40} \cdot 10.3H_2O$ (see also Mason,

1957), though in the analyses of Meixner *et al.* the operative substitution appears to be Ca$\rightleftharpoons$2Na (Table 46, anals. 12 and 13). The potassium content of gonnardite is always relatively small despite the high sodium content.

Edingtonite. The ideal formula is $BaAl_2Si_3O_{10} \cdot 4H_2O$: an analysis is given in Table 46 (anal. 14), previous analytical data having been tabulated by Hey (1934). The name is in honour of Mr. Edington who first discovered the mineral near Old Kilpatrick, Dunbartonshire. A mineral earlier thought to represent a calcium edingtonite was shown to be a boro-arsenate of calcium, cahnite (Palache and Bauer, 1927), though Hey has reported that some specimens of edingtonite from Old Kilpatrick do contain appreciable calcium. The vapour pressure of edingtonite at various temperatures and degrees of hydration, and the heat of hydration, were determined by Hey (1934, 1935). Base-exchange experiments were also carried out by Hey (1934), who prepared Na, K, Ag and Tl edingtonites by treating the natural mineral with $NaClO_3$, KCNS, $AgNO_3$ and $TlNO_3$ fusions. Although the synthesis of edingtonite was reported by Magistad (1929), who extracted with water a barium aluminosilicate formed by mixing sodium silicate and sodium aluminate solutions, the identification was not conclusive.

OPTICAL AND PHYSICAL PROPERTIES

The optical and physical properties of the fibrous zeolites have been the subject of many investigations. Comprehensive reviews of this work are contained in a series of papers by Hey (1932a, b, 1933, etc.) which also give a considerable amount of additional data. They include sections on the occurrence, chemistry, morphological and X-ray diffraction studies, density, pyroelectricity, electrical conductivity, optical properties including dispersion, dehydration and vapour pressure experiments, calorimetry and base exchange properties. The properties of all zeolites may, of course, be substantially affected by the process of cation exchange. The optical orientations of the natrolite group of zeolites are illustrated in Fig. 112.

Natrolite usually occurs in slender prisms, fine needles or blades which are elongated in the z direction; stout prisms and tufts of hair-like crystals have also been reported, and crystals are often found in radiating clusters. Some crystals are transparent, but unless kept in a closed tube they become opaque although they suffer no apparent change in water content (Hey, 1932b). Parallel growths with thomsonite, scolecite or mesolite are not uncommon. The density of natrolite varies with both potassium and water content. For a potassium-free, fully hydrated natrolite it is 2·242 gm./cm.^{3}, but D increases by 0·0088 for each atom (per cell) of K replacing Na.

That the structure of natrolite is polar parallel to z is confirmed by the evidence of etch pits (Hey, 1932b), and by the demonstration of weak pyroelectricity (Taylor *et al.*, 1933) and piezoelectricity (Halla and Mehl, 1932).

The dispersion of refractive indices, birefringence and 2V with wavelength has been studied in detail by Hey. For a natrolite from Benallt, $2V_\gamma$ increases from 62° 22' at λ 4200 Å, reaches a maximum of 63° 11½' at about 5000 Å, and falls steeply to 32° 36' at 7200 Å. Although no detailed study of the effects of chemical substitution on optical properties has been made, it appears that increasing Ca content lowers the refractive indices but that K substitution has little result. On dehydration, refractive indices gradually fall at first (*e.g.* β 1·486 with 16 H_2O per cell to 1·471 with 12·77 H_2O, but must rise again since they are higher for the anhydrous than for the fully hydrated natrolite (Hey, 1932b).

Metanatrolite has α 1·483, β 1·485, γ 1·494; its optical orientation is similar to that of natrolite, γ being parallel to z, but α makes an angle of $7\frac{1}{2}°$ with (010), whereas in natrolite it is parallel to (010). Metanatrolite shows sector twinning, adjacent sectors extinguishing at 15° to one another.

Mesolite is found, invariably twinned (often in intergrowth with natrolite, scolecite or thomsonite), as prisms and as aggregates of fine fibres or tufts of

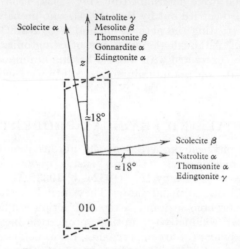

FIG. 112. The optical orientations of some fibrous zeolites.

hair-like crystals, the lengths of which are parallel to the crystallographic y direction. The density of fully hydrated potassium-free mesolite is approximately 2·26 gm./cm.³, but it is increased by substitution of K for Na. A small pyroelectric effect is exhibited parallel to the y axis.

The dispersion of optical properties with wavelength is strong and is reported by Hey (1933). Optical properties also vary markedly with a relatively small change in temperature. Thus $2V_\alpha$ decreases from $107\frac{1}{2}°$ at 0°C. to 90° at 20°C. where the optic sign changes. At 59°C. the mineral is uniaxial negative and above this temperature $2V_\alpha$ opens out in the (100) plane. The birefringence of mesolite is so low that its needles often appear to be isotropic. The value of β falls on dehydration from 1·507 with 64 H_2O per cell to 1·498 with 43 H_2O, but rises again to 1·505 with 30 H_2O.

Scolecite generally occurs in prismatic twins or as aggregates of radiating silky fibres the lengths of which are parallel to their z ($\simeq \alpha$) crystallographic axes; it also occurs in penetration twins. Some crystals exhibit anomalous optical properties which are attributed to mechanical strain. The dispersion of its optical parameters with wavelength has been investigated quantitatively by Hey (1936).

A partially dehydrated metascolecite with 16 H_2O per unit cell has a mean refractive index of 1·505, $\delta \simeq 0·01$, and $\beta:z = 18°$, while one with 5 H_2O per cell has n 1·523, δ very low, and $\beta:z = 5°$ (Hey, 1936). Metascolecite is strongly pyroelectric.

Thomsonite crystals generally have prismatic, acicular, or blade-like morphology, with elongation parallel to z. Silica-poor thomsonites tend to form in shorter prisms or in plates parallel to (010). Euhedral crystals are, however, comparatively rare, and radiating and columnar aggregates are more common. Some radiating aggregates show concentric zoning with higher refractive indices nearer the centre (Walker, 1951). Accurate determination of the density and

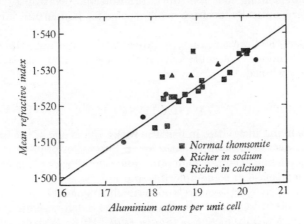

Fig. 113. Variation of the mean refractive index $(\alpha + \beta + \gamma)/3$ (Na light) of thomsonite plotted against Al content (after Hey, 1932a).

optical properties of thomsonite are difficult because of its finely fibrous character, but it is known that D increases as the Al content falls. D is also decreased by dehydration at the lower temperatures where no lattice shrinkage occurs, but above 270°C. D increases. Thomsonite exhibits pyroelectricity parallel to y.

Refractive indices increase with the substitution of (Al,Ca) for (Si,Na) (Fig. 113) but only very slightly with the substitution of Na_2 for Ca; 2V increases with decreasing Al content, and it is thought that the optic axial plane may change for the more siliceous thomsonites from (001) to (010) and to (100). Refractive indices decrease markedly on dehydration, β of one specimen, for example, changing from 1·531 with 23·8 H_2O per cell to 1·506 with 16·54 H_2O (Hey, 1932a).

Gonnardite occurs in the form of spherulites and its refractive indices are lower than those of thomsonite.

Edingtonite exhibits a distinct pyroelectric effect indicating that its structure is non-centrosymmetric. The dispersion of optical properties with wavelength was investigated by Hey (1934). Edingtonite with only 2·4 molecules of H_2O per cell has α 1·544; as with the other fibrous zeolites, however, the refractive indices probably fall with initial dehydration but subsequently rise.

DISTINGUISHING FEATURES

Members of this group may be distinguished from most other zeolites by their fibrous character, and from fibrous non-zeolites by their lower refractive indices and ready fusibility.

Scolecite may be distinguished from the other fibrous zeolites by its extinction angle of about 18° on (010) displayed clearly when twinned on (100), while the remainder have straight or nearly straight extinction.

Scolecite, gonnardite and edingtonite are always length-fast and natrolite is always length-slow, whereas mesolite and thomsonite are either length-fast or length-slow depending on the fibre orientation. Natrolite, mesolite and thomsonite are optically positive while scolecite, gonnardite and edingtonite are negative.

Natrolite has the lowest refractive indices and edingtonite the highest of the group of six minerals. Mesolite has the highest 2V and lowest birefringence, and is always twinned.

PARAGENESIS

Natrolite is found in cavities in basaltic rocks and is one of the later zeolites to crystallize; it also occurs, apparently as an alteration product of nepheline or sodalite, in nepheline-syenites, phonolites and related rocks, and as an alteration product of plagioclase in some dolerites and aplites.

In the basalts of Northern Ireland natrolite typically occurs in amygdales with analcite, often together with chabazite and calcite, and is found in 23 per cent. of the Irish zeolite localities (Smith *et al.*, 1916; Walker, 1960a). It has been recorded as a secondary mineral in Tertiary amygdaloidal basalts in New South Wales (Nashar and Davies, 1960), where it is believed to have been deposited from cold solutions after consolidation of the basalts, by the agency of circulating meteoric waters in a process which is reported to be still taking place at a temperature of about 5°C. In the Watchung basalts of New Jersey, natrolite is one of the most abundant zeolites and is one of the last amygdale minerals to have crystallized, replacing most of the rock (Fenner, 1910). Large crystals of natrolite in cavities in submarine basalt flows of Tertiary age have been reported from New Zealand (Mason, 1946). Stout prisms of natrolite occur in amygdales in volcanic rocks at Puy de Marmant, Puy-de-Dôme, France (Table 46, anal. 3), and fibrous natrolite together with mesolite is known from coarse-grained andesites in Trans-Caucasia (Smirnov, 1923).

Veins of natrolite, sometimes associated with ancylite, occur in the nepheline-syenite complex of the Kola peninsula (Fersman, 1923). In this alkaline complex natrolite is also found in nephline-syenite pegmatites, *e.g.* Semenov *et al.* (1956), and in kondrikovite, an alteration product of lovchorrite, which appears to consist of natrolite with inclusions of a rinkite-like mineral (Borne-man-Starynkevich, 1935). Natrolite is also found associated with the alkaline rocks of Iron Hill, Colorado (Larsen, 1942), and occurs in the grennaite (cata-pleite syenite) of Norra Kärr, southern Sweden. Large crystals of natrolite (Table 46, anal. 1) have been recorded from a nepheline-syenite–limestone contact in British Columbia, and natrolite crystals almost 3 feet long and 4 inches across (anal. 2) occur in aplite dykes in an asbestos mine in Quebec

(Poitevin, 1938). Veins of natrolite in phonolite have been reported from Czechoslovakia (Nováček, 1936), and it is found in nodules in mafic phonolite in the Highwood Mountains, Montana (Larsen *et al.*, 1939), and in vesicles in the katungite lava of southwest Uganda (Holmes, 1937). Natrolite, together with stilbite, heulandite and laumontite, occurs on joint surfaces in a quartz-rich gneiss near Kragerø, Norway (Saebø and Reitan, 1958): the natrolite is considered to be the earliest formed zeolite.

Mesolite commonly occurs in cavities in volcanic rocks, generally in association with other zeolites. In Northern Ireland it is relatively abundant in the Tertiary basalts (Smith *et al.*, 1916) and it has been reported to occur in 10 per cent. of the Irish zeolite localities (Walker, 1960a). The varietal names *antrimolite* and *harringtonite* have been used for mesolite from this area with a stalactitic habit and fibres radiating from the centre and for a compact chalk-like massive variety respectively. Fine delicate tufts of mesolite occur in the basalts of Talisker Bay, Skye, and finely fibrous mesolite (Table 46, anal. 15) is found with calcite, chabazite, analcite and stilbite in basaltic cavities in Oregon. Mesolite, sometimes completely pseudomorphed by calcite, has been reported from weathered porphyrite in Georgia, U.S.S.R. (Tvalchrelidze, 1922) and also occurs, together with natrolite and analcite, in the andesites of Mt. Imeretin, Trans-Caucasia (Smirnov, 1923). The mesolite of Table 46, anal. 17, occurs in geodes in a phonolite in Sardinia; the mineral is also found in hydrothermal veins, *e.g.* in the Khibina tundra (Chirvinsky, 1939) and associated with the hydrothermal metasomatic manganese ores and barium minerals of Achinsk in the Krasnoyarsk region of Siberia (Afanasiev *et al.*, 1940).

Scolecite occurs in cavities in basic volcanic rocks and is also found in some metamorphosed calcareous rocks and as a hydrothermal mineral in crevices in other metamorphic rocks. It is known from the Tertiary basalts of Mull and Skye and occurs in coarse crystals at Berufjord, Iceland: in the zeolite areas of the Antrim basalts it is uncommon. Scolecite has been reported, associated with stilbite and calcite, in much weathered basalt in Eritrea (Scherillo, 1938), and is known from cavities in basalt from Table Mountain, near Golden, Colorado. In Mull, scolecite occurs in profusion in amygdales in basalt on An Gearna (Table 46, anal. 10) and is often the final product of the sequence: albite→ chlorite→epidote→prehnite→scolecite, though in some vesicles heulandite succeeds scolecite. Where these amygdales have been metamorphosed by later intrusions the scolecite becomes turbid, and then the minerals are developed in the reverse order: scolecite→prehnite→epidote→grossular (M'Lintock, 1915). Scolecite has also been reported from marl in contact with phonolite at Olawa, Bohemia, where it has been derived from natrolite by base-exchange of Ca (from the marl) for Na (Thugutt, 1953), and it occurs with other zeolites in an amphibolite near Kouty, Moravia (Novotná, 1926) and, with adularia, epidote and chlorite, in crevices in biotite gneiss near a pegmatite in Valle Maggia, Tessin, Switzerland (Grütter, 1931). Belyankin and Petrov (1940) have described laccoliths and dykes in Cretaceous to Oligocene sediments in Georgia (Caucasus) which include thomsonite–scolecite gabbro and scolecitite, which are believed to be derived from syenitic and gabbroic magmas.

Thomsonite commonly occurs in amygdales and crevices in basic igneous rocks, often in association with chabazite and other zeolites. It is particularly common in basalts and is known, for example, in basalts from Skye, and from

Northern Ireland (Tomkeieff, 1934): in the latter area thomsonite occurs in 53 per cent. of the zeolite localities (Walker, 1960a), often in association with chabazite, natrolite and analcite. Abundant thomsonite occurs in cavities in a vesicular Tertiary basalt associated with the Ritter hot spring, Oregon (Hewett *et al.*, 1928), and it has been recorded as white spherical acicular aggregates in the basalt of Disko Island, Greenland (Gaertner and Machatschki, 1927), and in the basaltic rocks of New Jersey (Table 46, anal. 8). It is also found in cavities in teschenite (*e.g.* Hutton, 1943; Shkabara, 1948). Thomsonite may also occur in hypabyssal rocks such as olivine theralite (*e.g.* Hutton, 1942) and in picrite (Doubek, 1924) and augitite (Table 46, anal. 7), and it is reported from aplite dykes, associated with albite and grossular, in the Caribou chrome pit, Quebec (Poitevin, 1937). It occurs in some alkaline igneous rocks such as the analcite syenite near Craig, Colorado (Ross, 1925), where it may amount to 4 per cent. of the rock. It is found in the pyroxene-rich nepheline dolerite of the endogenous contact zone at the dolerite–chalk contact of Scawt Hill, Antrim (Tilley and Harwood, 1931), where it forms pseudomorphs after nepheline, and in the titanaugite–melilite rocks of the same zone, as an alteration product of labradorite as well as of nepheline. Veins of anorthite altering to thomsonite occur in a serpentinized peridotite in Syria (Caillère, 1937). The contact metamorphism of a marl xenolith in a teschenite sill in central Scotland has given rise to a fused vesicular rock now largely replaced by thomsonite (Flett, 1933), and the latter is also a product of contact metamorphism in the calcitic masses at Magnet Cove, Arkansas (Landes, 1931). In the Tertiary lavas of Mull thomsonite formed in vesicles, after albite, epidote and prehnite: on metamorphism of these lavas by later intrusives recrystallization occurred in the reverse order: thomsonite→albite+prehnite→epidote (M'Lintock, 1915).

Gonnardite was first described (as mesole) by Gonnard (1871) from cavities in basalt at Chaux de Bergonne, Puy-de-Dôme, France, and was later examined and named by Lacroix (1896). No further occurrences were reported until Meixner *et al.* (1956) recorded it as zoned spherules, with thomsonite, from vesicular basalt at Aci Castello (Table 46, anal. 13) and Aci Trezza (anal. 12), Sicily, in a cavity in leucite tephrite from Capo di Bove, Rome, in basalts from Weilberg, Rhineland (where it accompanies twinned phillipsite), and from Kloch, Styria. More recently Mason (1957) identified the ranite described by Paijkull (1874) from Langesundsfjord, Norway, as gonnardite: here it does not occur in vesicles in basaltic rocks but has arisen from the alteration of nepheline.

Edingtonite was first described, associated with harmotome, analcite, thomsonite, prehnite and calcite, in basic igneous rock from Old Kilpatrick, Dunbartonshire (Haidinger, 1825; Heddle, 1855), and has since been reported in several localities in that area. It has also been found at Böhlet mine, Westergotland, Sweden (Table 46, anal. 14).

Heulandite, Clinoptilolite
Stilbite
Epistilbite

$(Ca,Na_2)[Al_2Si_7O_{18}]\cdot 6H_2O$
$(Ca,Na_2,K_2)[Al_2Si_7O_{18}]\cdot 7H_2O$
$Ca[Al_2Si_6O_{16}]\cdot 5H_2O$

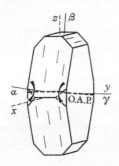
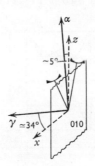

	HEULANDITE–CLINOPTILOLITE		STILBITE	EPISTILBITE
	PSEUDO-MONOCLINIC($+$)($-$)		MONOCLINIC($-$)	MONOCLINIC($-$)
α	1·491–1·505	1·476–1·488	1·484–1·500	1·485–1·505
β	1·493–1·503		1·492–1·507	1·497–1·515
γ	1·500–1·512	1·479–1·489	1·494–1·513	1·497–1·519
δ	$\simeq 0\cdot006$	$\leq 0\cdot004$	$\simeq 0\cdot01$	0·010–0·014
2V	Variable		30°–49°($-$)	$\simeq 44°(-)$
Orientation:	Variable		$\beta=y,\ \alpha{:}z\simeq5°$	$\beta=y,\ \gamma{:}z\simeq-10°$
O.A.P.	Usually $\perp(010)$		(010)	(010)
Dispersion:	$r>v$		$r<v$	$r<v$
D	2·1–2·2		2·1–2·2	$\simeq 2\cdot2$
H	$3\frac{1}{2}$–4		$3\frac{1}{2}$–4	4
Cleavage:	{010}, perfect.		{010}, very good.	{010}, very good.
Twinning:	—		Common {001}, cruci-	—
			form, interpenetrant.	
Colour:	Colourless, white, yellow, pink, red, grey, brown; colourless in thin section.			
Unit cell: a Å	15·85		13·63	8·92
b Å	17·84		18·17	17·73
c Å	7·46		11·31	10·21
β	91° 26′		129° 10′	124° 20′
Z	4		4	3
Space group:	$I2/m$		$C2/m$	—

STRUCTURE

The heulandite group, like all other zeolites, have structures made up of $(Si,Al)O_4$ tetrahedra linked in such a way that every oxygen is shared by two tetrahedra. It was thought that the tetrahedra in heulandite are arranged in double sheets of limited thickness but of infinite lateral extent parallel to (010).

All tetrahedral corners would be shared within these sheets, and the net charge on them due to substitution of Al for Si could be balanced by the (Ca,Na,K) ions lying between them; here also would be space for the water molecules (Wyart, 1933; Taylor, 1934; Hey and Bannister, 1934). This model explains qualitatively the good (010) cleavage of heulandite, the cation exchange properties, and the reversible removability of the water molecules associated with small changes in the b cell parameter (Wyart, 1933; Hey, 1935).

A more recent X-ray investigation, however, shows a somewhat different structure for heulandite (Ventriglia, 1955). Two thirds of the $(Si,Al)O_4$ tetrahedra are indeed linked to form networks of six-membered rings in planes parallel to (010) separated by $b/2$ (Fig. 114a). The oxygens which are unshared

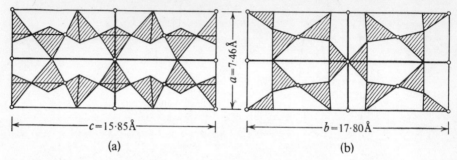

(a)   (b)

FIG. 114(a). Arrangement of $(Si,Al)O_4$ tetrahedra in heulandite to form a sheet of 6-membered rings parallel to (010). Such sheets are linked by tetrahedra, not shown in the diagram, to form the framework structure.

(b). Projection of part of the aluminosilicate framework of heulandite on (001) containing five- and eight-membered rings (after Ventriglia, 1955).

within these sheets serve to join the sheets together via the remaining one third of the tetrahedra. This results in a very open framework traversed by channels of six-membered rings parallel to [100] and by channels of five- and eight-membered rings parallel to [001] (Fig. 114b). For each two Al atoms in the framework, one Ca atom occupies a space near one of the pentagonal, hexagonal, or octagonal rings, and within the channels the water molecules are accommodated. The cations and water molecules are free to move within the framework cavities, and their positions in the structure have not been determined. The (010) cleavage of heulandite can be attributed to the preponderance of bonds linking tetrahedra in the (010) plane, and the cation exchange and dehydration properties are associated with the channels in the open structure.

The crystal lattice of heulandite is triclinic (pseudo-monoclinic $I2/m$) with a 15·85, b 17·84, c 7·46 Å, $\alpha \simeq \gamma \simeq 90°$, $\beta = 91° 26'$. This cell is body-centred, and an alternative face-centred cell may be chosen with a 17·71, b 17·84, c 7·46 Å, β 116° 20'.

The zeolites stilbite and epistilbite are structurally similar to heulandite (Taylor, 1934; Sekanina and Wyart, 1936). Stilbite is monoclinic $C2/m$ with $a \simeq 13·63$, b 18·17, c 11·31 Å, β 129° 10', Z=4, but an alternative all face-centred pseudo-orthorhombic cell has a 13·63, b 18·17, c 17·62 Å, β 92°, Z=8. Epistilbite is monoclinic with a 8·92, b 17·73, c 10·21 Å, β 124° 20', Z=3.

The unit cells of all three minerals are compared in Table 47.   All have a b parameter of approximately 18 Å, and the way in which a, c and β values are related is indicated by those vectors of the heulandite ac network (subscript H) which approximate to the stilbite and epistilbite parameters.   The mineral clinoptilolite is reported to give the same X-ray diffraction pattern as heulandite (Hey and Bannister, 1934), but the cation exchange properties of the two

Table 47.   THE RELATION BETWEEN UNIT CELLS OF ZEOLITES OF THE HEULANDITE GROUP (after Strunz and Tennyson, 1956).

	a Å	b Å	c Å	β	Z
Heulandite	17·71	17·84	7·46	116° 20′	4
Stilbite	13·63	18·17	11·31	129° 10′	4
	$\frac{1}{3}[\bar{2}01]_H = 13·10$		$\frac{2}{3}[001]_H = 11·19$	$\beta'_H = 126° 08′$	
Epistilbite	8·92	17·73	10·21	124° 20′	3
	$\frac{1}{3}[104]_H = 9·04$		$\frac{2}{3}[101]_H = 10·59$	$\beta''_H = 124° 24′$	
Brewsterite	6·77	17·41	7·66	93° 04′	2

minerals were shown to be dissimilar by Ames (1960) who investigated the cation sieve properties of clinoptilolite, heulandite and other zeolites with particular reference to Cs selectivity (see also Mumpton, 1960).   On heating heulandite to a temperature below 210°C., reversible dehydration takes place with loss of about 9 per cent. of its weight; the a and c parameters of the unit cell are unaffected and b decreases by about 1·5 per cent.   Heating above 210°C., however, drives off the remaining water and results in a more drastic structural change; the unit cell becomes a 7·27, b 16·63, c 15·23 Å, and the higher the temperature, the less easily reversible is the dehydration (Wyart, 1933).

Other zeolites with platy cleavage are brewsterite (Strunz and Tennyson, 1956), the cell of which is described in Table 47, ferrierite (Staples, 1955), which is orthorhombic and has a body-centred cell with a 14·14, b 19·12, c 7·48 Å, and dachiardite (Bonatti, 1942), which is monoclinic with a 18·35, b 7·45, c 10·25 Å, β 107° 49′, Z = 2.

CHEMISTRY

Heulandite and clinoptilolite.   The ideal composition is $(Ca,Na_2)Al_2Si_7O_{18} \cdot 6H_2O$: there is often considerable variation in the Si : Al ratio with a corresponding variation in the proportion of Ca and Na.   The name is after H. Heuland, a British mineral collector.   Four analyses of heulandite are given in Table 48 (anals. 1–4), where they have also been recalculated on the basis of 72 oxygens, *i.e.* the anhydrous cell content.   In two of the analyses (anals. 2 and 3) appreciable strontium is reported, and the heulandite of anal. 2 has more potassium than sodium : potassium-rich heulandite (K_2O 1·94 per cent.) has also been reported by Piekarska and Gawel (1952) and the barium-bearing beaumontite variety from Baltimore, investigated by Shannon (1925a), has 3·28 per cent. K_2O (BaO 0·61, Na_2O 0·16).

For many heulandites the SiO_2 percentage lies between 56·8 and 58·5, but in some SiO_2 is considerably higher, *e.g.* anal. 4 (Table 48) with 61·83 per cent., or material described by Ross and Shannon (1924) with 61·14 per cent. SiO_2. Schaller (1932) considered that such minerals represent a separate species which he called clinoptilolite, but, following X-ray work on single-crystals, Hey and Bannister (1934) concluded that "clinoptilolite" is merely a high-silica heulandite. More recently Mumpton (1960) assembled X-ray, d.t.a. and analytical data from which he concluded that clinoptilolite may be defined chemically as the high silica member of the heulandite structural group, usually containing more monovalent than divalent cations. Mumpton reports that on heating to about 230°C. heulandite is transformed into "heulandite B", and at 350°C. becomes amorphous, whereas clinoptilolite remains stable to about 700°C. Analyses of pure clinoptilolite are few in number, but Mumpton suggests that although the structures of heulandite and clinoptilolite are isomorphous, solid solution between them does not seem to be complete; thus although the Si content of both zeolites varies there is a considerable gap between their respective Si values. Clinoptilolite is thus defined as having a composition close to $(Na_2O)_{0.70}(CaO)_{0.10}(K_2O)_{0.15}(MgO)_{0.05} \cdot Al_2O_3 \cdot (SiO_2)_{8.5-10.5} \cdot 6-7H_2O$, and is considered to be a valid species. Mason and Sand (1960), however, contend that the differences between heulandite and clinoptilolite lie not in their Si but in their content of Na and K: clinoptilolite is therefore defined by these authors as a zeolite with the heulandite structure in which $(Na+K)$ atoms are predominant over Ca. It can be considered that ionic substitutions of both the types $Ca^{+2}Al^{+3} \rightleftharpoons Na^+Si^{+4}$ and $Na^+Al^{+3} \rightleftharpoons Si^{+4}$ probably occur in the heulandite series.

Heulandite has been synthesized from a gel mixture of composition $CaO \cdot Al_2O_3 \cdot 7SiO_2$ at temperatures ranging from about 250° to 360°C. with water vapour pressures of 15,000 lb./in.² (Koizumi and Roy, 1960). Higher pressures appeared to promote its formation, as at 37,000 lb./in.² heulandite was formed at 200°C. Heulandite had previously been produced by the hydrothermal recrystallization of amorphous materials formed by heating heulandite (Fyfe *et al.*, 1958; Coombs *et al.*, 1959). The base-exchange properties of heulandite were investigated by Kappen and Fischer (1928), and diffusion data have been given by Hey (1935). The capacity of clinoptilolite to act as a cation sieve, selectively removing Cs from solutions, has been reported by Ames (1960): this behaviour is quite dissimilar to that of heulandite. The dehydration of heulandite has been studied by Scheumann (1921) and by Milligan and Weiser (1937) who reported a continuous dehydration curve: at 1000 atmospheres water vapour pressure, Koizumi and Roy (1960) found that heulandite broke down at 320°C. to give wairakite + SiO_2 + H_2O. The d.t.a. curve for heulandite is given by Koizumi (1953) and by Mason and Greenberg (1954): it shows an endothermic reaction at around 200°C. followed by a stronger endothermic peak at 360°C. Clinoptilolite, however, shows only a broad endothermic peak at around 200°C. (Mumpton, 1960). The absorption of ammonia by dehydrated heulandite has been studied by Sameshima (1929), Gruner (1933) and Barrer (1938).

Stilbite. The composition varies from approximately $(Ca,Na_2,K_2)_4Al_8Si_{28}O_{72} \cdot 28H_2O$ to $(Ca,Na_2,K_2)_5Al_{10}Si_{26}O_{72} \cdot 28H_2O$, with one such formula unit in the unit cell. The name is from the Greek *stilbein*, gleam, in allusion to the pearly or vitreous lustre: desmine is a synonym. There are considerable replacements of the types $Na^+Si^{+4} \rightleftharpoons Ca^{+2}Al^{+3}$ and $Na(K)^+Al^{+3} \rightleftharpoons Si^{+4}$, which are reflected in the varying silica contents: analyses of 5 stilbites are given in Table 48 (anals. 5 to 9), where they have been recalculated on the basis of 72 oxygens, the anhydrous cell contents. Analyses 5–7 are of normal stilbite,

Table 48. HEULANDITE, STILBITE AND FERRIERITE ANALYSES

	1.	2.	3.	4.	5.	6.	7.	8.	9.	10.
SiO_2	57·28	57·29	56·8	61·83	56·24	55·21	55·81	52·70	59·96	69·13
Al_2O_3	17·76	16·73	16·6	12·44	17·16	16·91	16·58	17·71	14·98	11·44
Fe_2O_3	—	0·13	tr.	2·55	—	tr.	0·58	—	—	—
MgO	—	—	tr.	—	0·40	0·25	tr.	—	—	2·92
CaO	7·18	6·36	5·8	5·51	8·56	8·10	7·86	7·76	6·24	0·00
SrO	—	0·85	2·0	—	—	—	—	—	—	—
Na_2O	2·95	0·75	1·6	1·15	tr.	1·16	0·91	2·39	0·12	3·97
K_2O	—	2·74	0·8	0·30	0·32	0·45	0·36	1·09	1·52	0·36
H_2O^+	}15·42	11·54	12·45	}15·78	16·80	}18·27	}17·96	16·32	13·94	}13·05
H_2O^-		3·89	3·3		0·96			2·08	3·08	
Total	100·59	100·28	99·44	99·56	100·44	100·35	100·24	100·05	99·84	100·87
α	1·501	7.503	1·500–1·505	1·487–1·488	1·488	1·492	1·497	1·493	1·484	1·478
β	1·504	1·504	1·500–1·506	—	1·498	1·499	—	1·504	1·492	1·479
γ	1·509	1·510	1·506–1·512	1·488–1·489	1·500	1·501	1·506	1·504	—	1·482
$2V_\alpha$	—	106°	—	71°–80°	—	32° 25′	—	—	small	—
D	—	—	2·23	2·13–2·14	—	2·159	2·144	$(a=13.5 \text{ Å})$	2·23	2·150

NUMBERS OF IONS ON THE BASIS OF 72 OXYGENS

	1.	2.	3.	4.	5.	6.	7.	8.	9.	10.
Si	26·35	26·77	26·84	28·58	26·50	26·36	26·56	25·63	28·00	29·82
Al	9·63	9·22	9·25	6·78	9·53	9·52	9·30	10·15	8·24	5·82
Fe^{+3}	—	0·04	—	0·89	—	—	0·21	—	—	—
Mg	—	—	—	—	0·28	0·18	—	—	—	1·88
Na	2·63	0·68	1·46	1·03	—	1·07	0·84	2·25	0·11	3·32
Ca	3·54	3·18	2·94	2·73	4·32	4·14	4·01	4·04	3·12	—
Sr	—	0·23	0·55	—	—	—	—	—	—	—
K	—	1·63	0·48	0·18	0·19	0·27	0·22	0·68	0·91	0·20
H_2O^+	}23·66	17·99	19·62	}24·33	26·41	}29·10	}28·51	26·48	21·71	}18·78
H_2O^-		6·06	5·20		1·51			3·37	4·80	
Z	35·98	36·03	36·09	36·25	36·03	35·88	36·07	35·78	36·24	35·64
R†	6·17	5·72	5·43	3·94	4·79	5·66	5·14‡	6·97	4·14	5·40

1. Heulandite, amygdaloidal basalt, Lanakai Hills, Hawaii (Dunham, 1933). Anal. A. S. Eakle.
2. Heulandite, with chabazite, garnet, axinite, etc., skarn druse, Hashikaké-zawa, Chichibu mine, Saitama Prefecture, Japan (Kato, 1959).
3. Heulandite, Cape Blomidon, Nova Scotia (Coombs *et al.*, 1959). Anal. J. A. Ritchie (Includes P_2O_5 0·01, Ba 0·05, Pb 0·015, Ag 0·015, Sn < 0·01).
4. Silica-rich heulandite, crevices in weathered hypersthene andesite, Terlitschno, Krapina, Croatia, Yugoslavia (Heritsch, 1940).
5. Stilbite, vesicular Tertiary basalt, Ritter hot spring, Grant County, Oregon (Hewett *et al.*, 1928).
6. Stilbite, lining druses in tonalite, Val Nambrone, Adamello, Italy (Sanero, 1938).
7. Spheroidal aggregate of stilbite, veins in chloritized gneiss, Železná Ruda (Eisenstein), Czechoslovakia (Nováček, 1936) (Includes FeO 0·18).
8. Stilbite, on gneiss, Pedemonte, Bellinzona, Tessin, Switzerland (Gschwind and Brandenberger, 1932).
9. Platy crystals of stellerite (habit var. of stilbite), calcite–magnetite–pyroxene skarn, Sillböle, near Helsinki, Finland (Mattinen, 1952).
10. White blade-shaped crystals of ferrierite, railway cutting, ½ mile W. of mile-post 17, N. shore of Kamloops Lake, British Columbia (Graham, 1918).

† $R = (Mg + Na + Ca + Sr + K)$.
‡ Includes Fe^{+2} 0·07.

whereas anals. 8 and 9 demonstrate the range in Al:Si ratio; anal. 8 illustrates a silica-poor stilbite near $Al_{10}Si_{26}$ (hypostilbite), whereas anal. 9 has a high SiO_2 content giving a formula near Al_8Si_{28}. The variety stellerite (of which the material of anal. 9 is an example) is distinguished primarily by its characteristic optics and habit; however, all the stellerites so far examined chemically (Morozewicz, 1909, Pabst, 1939) are high in SiO_2. Sodium is usually the dominant alkali metal, though stilbites with K > Na are not uncommon (*e.g.* anal. 9). Stilbite containing 0·28 per cent. SrO and 0·31 BaO has been reported by Reichert and Erdélyi (1935).

Stilbite has been shown to give a continuous dehydration curve associated with a marked change in the X-ray powder pattern at 120°C. and 23 mm. Hg water vapour pressure: although the dehydration of this new phase is reversible, reconversion to the natural phase is not obtained (Milligan and Weiser, 1937). Earlier dehydration investigations were reported by Merwin (1914) and by Beutell and Blaschke (1915), the latter authors considering that the rehydration with slow cooling in a moist atmosphere takes place in a series of steps. On heating to 350°–370°C., at 5000 bars stilbite breaks down to give epistilbite, which at 403°C. is converted to wairakite and quartz (Coombs *et al.*, 1959). The d.t.a. curve of stilbite has been investigated by Koizumi (1953) and by Mason and Greenberg (1954), and shows an endothermic peak at approximately 220°C. followed by a weak exothermic reaction at 470°C. The absorption of ammonia by stilbite has been reported by Gruner (1933) and by Sameshima and Hemmi (1934). A small amount of base-exchange between ferrous sulphate and stilbite was obtained by Kappen and Fischer (1928), but not with ferric, aluminium, and zinc chlorides. The alteration of stilbite to a greyish green clay mineral (beidellite) has been reported (Shannon, 1925b).

Epistilbite. Although the generally accepted formula is $CaAl_2Si_6O_{16} \cdot 5H_2O$ with three such formula units in the unit cell, Coombs *et al.* (1959) note that many analyses recalculate to give between 15·7 and 16·3 H_2O per unit cell and they tentatively suggest that the normal compositional range is $(Ca,Na_2)_{2·85}$ $Al_{5·7}Si_{18·3}O_{48} \cdot 16H_2O$ to $(Ca,Na_2)_{3·5}Al_7Si_{17}O_{48} \cdot 16H_2O$. Coombs *et al.* have crystallized epistilbite from glasses of felspar composition with excess silica: at 5000 bars epistilbite was formed at as low as 212°C.; it was also formed by the breakdown of xonotlite and stilbite on heating. The synthesis of epistilbite from gels with oxide ratios $CaO:Al_2O_3:SiO_2$ of 1:1:5·5, 1:1:4, and 1:1:3 was found (Koizumi and Roy, 1960) to be most readily achieved in the temperature range 285° to 350°C.: at 1000 atmospheres H_2O pressure and 350°C. epistilbite breaks down to give wairakite + SiO_2 + H_2O.

Dachiardite. The composition is near $(K,Na,Ca)_5Al_5Si_{19}O_{48} \cdot 18H_2O$. X-ray patterns indicate a structural relationship with epistilbite but dachiardite has a higher alkali content and slightly higher Si content (Coombs *et al.*, 1959). The name is after Antonio D'Achiardi, the mineral having been investigated by his son: zeolite mimetica is a synonym. An analysis gave: SiO_2 62·01, Al_2O_3 11·35, CaO 6·80, K_2O 3·31, Na_2O 2·06, Li_2O tr., Cs_2O tr., H_2O 14·52 = 100·05 (D'Achiardi, 1905).

Ferrierite. The idealized composition of the only analysed specimen (Table 48, anal. 10) is close to $(Na,K)_4Mg_2Al_6Si_{30}O_{73} \cdot 20H_2O$. Staples (1955) suggests that, as $(Si+Al) \simeq 36$, in order to give the zeolite ratio of $O:(Si+Al)=2:1$ the formula should be expressed as $(Na,K)_4Mg_2Al_6Si_{30}O_{72}(OH)_2 \cdot 18H_2O$, or, in the more general form, as $(Na,K)_x(Mg_{1+y/2},Al_{z/3})(Si_{36-(x+y+z)},Al_{(x+y+z)})O_{72}(OH)_2 \cdot 18H_2O$: limits of variation for x, y and z are unknown. The presence of almost 3 per cent. MgO in ferrierite is unusual for a zeolite, as also is the high SiO_2 content (69·13 per cent.). Rehydration experiments, however, indicated that ferrierite is a true zeolite (Staples, 1955): heating at 250°C. for 30 minutes caused a loss of 6·21 per cent., almost all of which (97·7 per cent.) was regained in 24 hours.

OPTICAL AND PHYSICAL PROPERTIES

Heulandite usually occurs in white or colourless euhedral crystals which are tabular parallel to (010); aggregates of crystals (for example in cockscomb growth) are more rare. The variety clinoptilolite is richer in Si and (Na,K), and has lower refractive indices and birefringence. Morphological and dehydration studies of heulandite are reported by Wyart (1933).

Stilbite and **epistilibite** are usually found in sheaf-like aggregates (sometimes spherulitic). Cruciform interpenetrant twins occur, and their platy crystals (010) may show sector twinning. Epistilbite exhibits piezoelectricity (Bond, 1943).

Dachiardite is biaxial (positive) with $2V_\gamma$ 65°–73°, $\alpha=y$, $\gamma:z\simeq38°$, O.A.P. $\perp$(010), α 1·491, β 1·496, γ 1·499, D $\simeq$2·16 (see Bonatti, 1942). It too shows sector twinning and has a perfect cleavage.

Ferrierite occurs in radiating groups of thin crystals or in crystals tabular on (010), with perfect (010) cleavage. It is biaxial positive with mean refractive index 1·48, $\delta\simeq0·004$, $2V_\gamma\simeq50°$, $\alpha=x$, $\beta=y$, $\gamma=z$ and D$\simeq$2·15.

Brewsterite occurs in prismatic crystals with perfect (010) cleavage. It is biaxial positive with $2V_\gamma=47°$, α 1·510, β 1·512, γ 1·523, D $\simeq$2·45.

DISTINGUISHING FEATURES

Heulandite is usually optically positive and nearly always occurs with the characteristic habit illustrated on page 377, while stilbite and epistilbite are always negative and are more common in sheaf-like aggregates. The (010) cleavage in heulandite is better than that in stilbite and epistilbite, and the two latter minerals have higher birefringence and usually show interpenetrant twinning. Phillipsite and harmotome also show interpenetrant twinning but the optic axial plane is perpendicular to (010), and their extinction angles on to z and optic axial angles are greater than those of stilbite and epistilbite. Stilbite and epistilbite are very similar but generally the former is length-fast and the latter length-slow. Laumontite is similar to epistilbite but has perfect cleavages on both (010) and (110).

PARAGENESIS

Heulandite and clinoptilolite. These minerals occur chiefly in amygdales, etc., in igneous rocks, and as the devitrification products of volcanic glasses and tuffs. Heulandite is a frequent mineral in cavities in basalt (*e.g.* Table 48, anal. 1; see also Mason and Greenberg, 1954), and is also found in andesite (*e.g.* Martinez, 1929) and diabase. A silica-rich variety (Table 48, anal. 4) occurs in crevices in a weathered hypersthene andesite, as does the silica-rich heulandite from Challis, Idaho (Ross and Shannon, 1924). The type clinoptilolite occurs in a highly weathered amygdaloidal basalt in the Hoodoo Mountain, Wyoming (Pirsson, 1890; Schaller, 1932).

The heulanditic mineral commonly occurring as an alteration product in pyroclastic rocks is normally the clinoptilolite variety. Montmorillonite and clinoptilolite were reported from altered vitreous volcanic tuff in San Lui Obispo County, California, by Bramlette and Posnjak (1933) and a similar assemblage occurs in fuller's earth in Kern County, California (Kerr and Cameron, 1936). Bore hole investigations in Yellowstone Park have shown that the potassium metasomatism of plagioclase has released Na and Ca which at higher levels have given rise to analcite and clinoptilolite from the dacitic lavas (Fenner, 1936). Both heulandite and clinoptilolite occur in innumerable bedded zeolite deposits in the Mossburn district of Southland, New Zealand (Coombs, 1959), and clinoptilolite is also recorded as a hydrothermal alteration product of tuffs at Wairakei, New Zealand (Steiner, 1953), and in devitrified volcanic glass near Seaham, New South Wales (Coombs, 1958). Clinoptilolite in the Hector, California, bentonite deposit is found in beds of altered pyroclastic material (Ames *et al.*, 1958) and in similar bentonitic clays in Patagonia (Mason and Sand, 1960).

Authigenic heulandite has been recorded in a friable Miocene sandstone in California (Gilbert and McAndrews, 1948), though thin seams of volcanic ash are associated. It has also been reported as an alteration product of petalite (Ginzburg and Gushchina, 1954). In metamorphic rocks it is known from skarn druses, associated with garnet, axinite, etc. (*e.g.* Table 48, anal. 2), *cf.* M'Lintock (1915), and it has been reported from mica gneiss in Siberia (Shkabara, 1941).

Stilbite occurs commonly in amygdales and cavities in basalt (*e.g.* Table 48, anal. 5), where it is often associated with heulandite and chabazite. It is found in many other volcanic rocks such as andesite, and in druses in hypabyssal and plutonic rocks, as in the Val Nambrone tonalite (Table 48, anal. 6). In the Camas Land gabbro, Virginia, stilbite, quartz and calcite were the latest products to crystallize, the stilbite partially replacing plagioclase (Chappell, 1933). Stilbite is also of relatively frequent occurrence in crevices in metamorphic rocks (anal. 8) where it is sometimes found with other minerals of hydrothermal origin, including quartz, epidote, prehnite and adularia (Mieleitner 1923): a rather similar association, with epidote, encrusting amphibole–chlorite schist has been reported by Scaini and Nardelli (1952). Red spherulitic aggregates of stilbite in crevices in crystalline schist have been described from the Trondhjem district (Carstens, 1925), and reddish sheaf-like aggregates occur associated with natrolite rosettes, heulandite and laumontite along joints in an acid gneiss near Kragerø, southern Norway (Saebø and Reitan, 1958). The stellerite variety of stilbite has also been described from crevices and joints in mica schist, as in Alaska (Wheeler, 1927) and in northern Norway (Saebø *et al.*, 1958), and it has been found with calcite and quartz in a fissure in a magnetite–pyroxene skarn (Table 48, anal. 9). Stilbite has also been found with chlorite in gneiss (anal. 7) and in lenses in chlorite on the wall of an epidoirite dyke in granite (Simpson, 1931). Small amounts of stilbite, together with calcite, occur encrusting pebbles and filling cavities in a Virginian conglomerate, and are thought to be due to hydrothermal solutions (Bloomer, 1937).

Epistilbite occurs together with laumontite, heulandite, and mordenite, in cavities in basalt, as in the Lanakai hills, Hawaii (Dunham, 1933) and in andesite (*e.g.* Erdélyi, 1942). It has also been recorded on bertrandite on beryl in a New York pegmatite (Pough, 1936), and from a Pre-Cambrian mudstone, Jersey (Hey and Mourant, 1933).

Dachiardite is known from the granitic pegmatite of San Piero, Campo, Elba, and was first described by D'Achiardi (1905). It has also been investigated by Berman (1925).

Ferrierite has only been reported from one locality, on the north shore of Kamloops Lake, British Columbia, where it occurs as spherical aggregates of radiating blades enclosed in chalcedony (Graham, 1918). The chalcedony fills fractures in an olivine basalt, which near the chalcedony veins is decomposed : the ferrierite is also associated with calcite.

Phillipsite
Harmotome

$(\tfrac{1}{2}Ca,Na,K)_3[Al_3Si_5O_{16}]\cdot 6H_2O$

$Ba[Al_2Si_6O_{16}]\cdot 6H_2O$

MONOCLINIC (or ORTHORHOMBIC)(+)

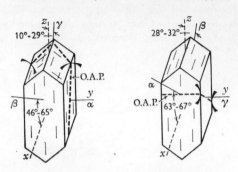

	PHILLIPSITE	HARMOTOME
α	1·483–1·504	1·503–1·508
β	1·484–1·509	1·505–1·509
γ	1·486–1·514	1·508–1·514
δ	0·003–0·010	0·005–0·008
$2V_\gamma$	60° to 80°	$\simeq 80°$
Orientation:	$\alpha=y$, $\beta{:}x$ 46° to 65°	$\gamma=y$, $\alpha{:}x$ 63° to 67°
O.A.P.	$\perp(010)$	$\perp(010)$
Dispersion:	$r<v$	—
D	2·2	2·41–2·47
H	4–4½	4½
Cleavage:	{010} and {100}, good.	{010}, good.
Twinning:	Interpenetrant {001}, {021}, {110}	
Colour:	Colourless, white, pink, grey, yellow; colourless in thin section.	
Unit cell: a Å	10·02	9·87
b Å	14·28	14·14
c Å	8·64†	8·72
β	125° 40′	124° 50′

$$Z=2$$
Space group $P2_1/m$ or $P2_1$

† But see orthorhombic cell (Table 49).

Chabazite, Gmelinite, Levyne $(Ca,Na_2)[Al_2Si_4O_{12}]\cdot6H_2O$

TRIGONAL $(-)$†

	CHABAZITE	GMELINITE	LEVYNE
ϵ		1·474–1·480	1·491–1·500
ω	}1·470–1·494	1·476–1·494	1·496–1·505
δ	0·002–0·005	0·002–0·015	0·002–0·006
D	2·05–2·10	$\simeq2\cdot1$	$\simeq2\cdot1$
H	$4\frac{1}{2}$	$4\frac{1}{2}$	$4\frac{1}{2}$
Cleavage:	$\{10\bar{1}1\}$ poor.	$\{10\bar{1}0\}$ good, $\{0001\}$.	—
Twinning:	$\{0001\}$ interpenetrant, $\{10\bar{1}1\}$.	—	Interpenetrant.
Colour:	Colourless, white, yellowish, greenish or reddish white; colourless in thin section.		
Unit cell: a_{hex} Å	$\simeq13\cdot8$	13·72	13·3
c_{hex} Å	$\simeq15\cdot0$	9·95	22·5
Z	6	4	9
Space group:	$R\bar{3}m$	—	$R\bar{3}m$

STRUCTURE

Phillipsite and **harmotome** have been reported as monoclinic $P2_1/m$ or $P2_1$ with Z=2 and also as orthorhombic with Z=4; their cell parameters are listed in Table 49. A (K,Ca)-rich variety, wellsite, has parameters intermediate between those of harmotome and phillipsite. Substitution of Ge for Si in a synthetic harmotome is accompanied by increased cell dimensions (Barrer *et al.*, 1959).

The structure of a natural phillipsite (orthorhombic, $B2mb$ with a 9·96$_5$, b 14·25$_2$, c 14·25$_2$ Å and Z=4) has been determined by Steinfink (1962), and that of a natural harmotome (monoclinic a 9·87, b 14·14, c 8·72 Å, β 124° 50′) by Sadanaga *et al.* (1961). The structures are very similar: both contain four- and eight-membered rings of linked $(Si,Al)O_4$ tetrahedra which are similar to those found in the structures of felspars and paracelsian, but the mode of lateral linkage in the latter minerals is different. In harmotome and phillipsite channels run through the framework of tetrahedra parallel to [100] and [010]; the former set have a minimum diameter of 4 Å and the others are smaller, large cavities occurring where the two sets of channels intersect. The various cavities within the frameworks accommodate the water molecules and large cations which are present. The structures of the phillipsite group, like those of all zeolites, allow free passage of water molecules through their channels so that water can be removed and resorbed without disrupting the linkages of the alumino-silicate framework. Similarly, larger cations of these minerals which are distributed among favourable sites within the framework cavities can be exchanged for

† Chabazite and gmelinite may be anomalously biaxial (negative or positive with low to moderate 2V).

other cations.   Furthermore, in the natural Si-rich members of the group there are relatively few (Na,Ca,K,Ba) cations.   The channels provided by eight-membered rings of tetrahedra are in these circumstances not blocked by cations, and are accessible to small molecules (*e.g.* NH_3, CO_2); the harmotome–phillipsite minerals can thus exhibit molecular-sieve properties.

Barrer *et al.* (1959) have synthesized sodium zeolites which are chemically similar to phillipsite and harmotome and which give similar X-ray patterns. They have suggested a structure for the aluminosilicate frameworks of these compounds, some of which are cubic, *a* 10 Å, some tetragonal, *a* 10 Å, *c* 9·88 Å, and some orthorhombic with *a* 9·8, *b* 14·0, *c* 14·1 Å.   When Na is exchanged for Ca and Ba there is still closer similarity between the synthetic and the naturally occurring minerals.   The structure proposed also contains eight- and four-membered rings of tetrahedra but it differs somewhat from that determined by Steinfink (1962) for a natural phillipsite.

Table 49.   PHILLIPSITE AND HARMOTOME CELL PARAMETERS

	a (Å)	b (Å)	c (Å)	β	Z	Reference
Monoclinic cell						
Phillipsite	10·02	14·28	8·64	125° 40′	2	Wyart and Chatelain (1938)
Harmotome	9·87	14·14	8·72	124° 50′	2	Sadanaga *et al.* (1961)
Synthetic zeolite (Na–P)	10·01	14·15	8·67	125° 16′	2	Barrer *et al.* (1959)
Orthorhombic cell						
Phillipsite	9·96₅	14·25₂	14·25₂	—	4	Steinfink (1962)
Harmotome	9·78	14·00	14·23	—	4	Kalb and Klotsch (1944)
Synthetic zeolite (Na–P)	9·8	14·0	14·1	—	4	Barrer *et al.* (1959)
Cubic cell						
Synthetic zeolite (Na–P)	10·0			—	2	Barrer *et al.* (1959)

The relationships between the cubic, orthorhombic and monoclinic cells of the synthetic and natural zeolites are shown in Fig. 115.

Thus

$$a_m \simeq a_0 \simeq a \simeq 10 \text{ Å}$$
$$b_m \simeq b_0 \simeq c_0 \simeq \sqrt{2}a \simeq 14\cdot1 \text{ Å}$$
$$c_m \simeq \frac{\sqrt{3}}{2} a \simeq 8\cdot7 \text{ Å}$$

Chabazite.   The structure first suggested for chabazite (Wyart, 1933) is like that of sodalite (see p. 289), except that the cell of chabazite is somewhat deformed (rhombohedron $a \simeq 9\cdot2$ Å, $\alpha\, 94°\, 24'$) compared with the cube ($a \simeq 8\cdot9$ Å) of sodalite.   In this structure the aluminosilicate framework has channels through it, the largest of which have a diameter of about 3·1 Å, and yet chabazite can absorb molecules of propane with diameter about 4·9 Å.   This and other properties of chabazite are not easily reconciled with the "sodalite type"

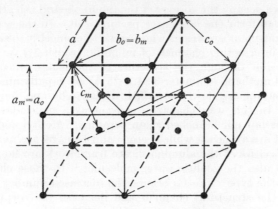

Fig. 115. Relation between the cubic and orthorhombic cells of synthetic zeolites and the
monoclinic cells of the natural zeolite, phillipsite:
a = cube edge; subscripts o = orthorhombic,
m = monoclinic.

structure (Kington and Laing, 1955). More recently (Dent and Smith, 1958;
Nowacki *et al.*, 1958), a different structure has been proposed for chabazite
which, however, appears the same in projection down the triad axis. The
cage-like units in chabazite (Fig. 116) contain not single but double six-membered rings of tetrahedra in the form of hexagonal prisms which are arranged so

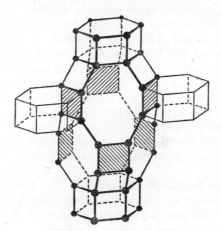

Fig. 116. The cage-like unit of the
structure of chabazite. The corners of each polygon represent the
centres of $(Si,Al)O_4$ tetrahedra
but oxygens are not shown.
Shaded quadrilaterals represent
the points of attachment of hexagonal prisms of tetrahedra, four of
which are shown (after Dent and
Smith, 1958).

that their centres occupy the corners of the rhombohedral cell; these prisms are linked together to form one large cage per unit cell. In the wall of each cage there are six eight-membered rings which serve to connect it to six neighbouring cages, forming intersecting channels of minimum width 3·9 Å; these channels allow the diffusion through the structure of molecules of comparable size. Thus argon and methane (diameter 3·84, 4·25 Å) are rapidly absorbed, propane (4·9 Å) and *n*-butane are slowly absorbed, while *iso*-butane (5·6 Å) is excluded by chabazite. In this way chabazite can act as a molecular sieve, passing normal paraffins but not branched-chain paraffins. Methyl and ethyl alcohol, and formic acid are absorbed while acetone and benzene are not.

Within the cavities of the aluminosilicate framework are housed the Ca and Na cations and also the zeolitic water molecules. In those chabazites where replacement of the type $2Na \rightleftharpoons Ca$ occurs, the increased number of cations may tend to block the structural channels and decrease the sorption properties. No direct evidence as to the distribution of Si and Al has been obtained but they, as well as the Ca and Na ions, are probably disordered. There are probably well defined sites of more than one type at which water molecules are situated, but any particular water molecule is probably free to move by jumps to other sites (Ducros, 1960). In analcite, natrolite and thomsonite the water is less mobile.

The cations in chabazite, principally Ca in natural specimens, can be exchanged for others, *e.g.* Li, Na, K, Rb, Cs, NH_4, Ag, Ca, Sr, Ba, Pb (Barrer and Sammon, 1955; and others): these substitutions are accompanied by very little change in cell parameters (Barrer, 1958). The aluminosilicate framework is comparatively rigid and unaffected by exchanges and by dehydration of the zeolite. As in the fibrous zeolites, there is probably a structural association between exchange cations and water molecule dipoles.

The chabazite studied by Dent and Smith (*loc. cit.*), $Ca_{0.90}Na_{0.15}(Si_{4.05}Al_{1.95})O_{12} \cdot 6H_2O$, is rhombohedral $R\bar{3}m$, with a 9·40 Å, α 94° 18′ and $Z=2$. The corresponding hexagonal cell has a 13·78, c 15·01 Å, and $Z=6$. A synthetic (K,Na) chabazite prepared by Barrer *et al.* (1959) has a 13·85, c 15·50 Å.

Gmelinite is closely related to chabazite both chemically and structurally. A gmelinite studied by Strunz (1956) has a 13·72, c 9·95 Å. Thus its a parameter is similar to that of chabazite and c is approximately two thirds of c for chabazite. Dent and Smith (1958) suggested that the relation between gmelinite and chabazite is essentially that between hexagonal and cubic stacking arrangements, the units in these minerals being the prisms of double six-membered rings of tetrahedra.

The aluminosilicate framework of gmelinite (Fig. 117a) has a system of wide channels defined by twelve-membered rings (minimum diameter about 6·4 Å) all parallel to *z*, and should therefore absorb *iso*-paraffin and aromatic molecules which are excluded by chabazite. Such absorption is not, however, observed (Barrer, 1944), and it has been suggested that the channels are perhaps blocked by Na ions, or else that the crystals are intergrown with chabazite. Oriented intergrowths of gmelinite and chabazite (with respective *c* and *a* cell edges parallel) have been reported (Strunz, 1956; Fischer and O'Daniel, 1956). Changes from gmelinite to chabazite structure may occur on a more intimate scale and take the form of stacking faults within a single crystal; these too if present may prevent the occlusion of large molecules by gmelinite (Barrer and Kerr, 1959). Another system of smaller hexagonal intersecting channels

(3·4 Å) exists in gmelinite normal to z, and through these smaller molecules can be absorbed.

A synthetic Na-gmelinite prepared by Barrer *et al.* (1959) has *a* 13·72, *c* 10·00 Å. The mineral herschelite was shown to be a twinned chabazite (Fischer and O'Daniel, 1956, 1958).

Levyne. Another member of the chabazite group of zeolites is levyne, which is rhombohedral $R\bar{3}m$ with $a \simeq 13 \cdot 3$, $c \simeq 22 \cdot 5$ Å, and $Z = 9$ on the basis of a hexagonal cell (Strunz, 1956). The *a* parameter is similar to that of chabazite and gmelinite, and *c* is approximately one and a half times *c* of chabazite. The aluminosilicate framework consists of (Si,Al)O_4 tetrahedra which in

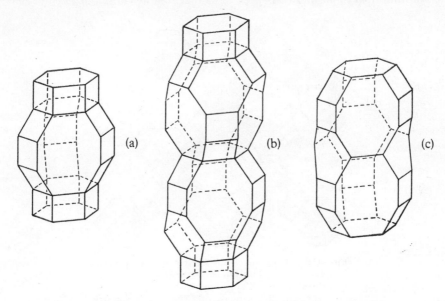

Fig. 117. Cage-like units of the structures of (a) gmelinite, (b) levyne, (c) erionite. The corners of each polygon represent the centres of (Si,Al)O_4 tetrahedra but oxygen atoms are not represented (after Barrer and Kerr, 1959).

alternate layers are arranged in hexagonal prisms and hexagonal rings; these are linked by four-membered rings of tetrahedra. The framework contains large cavities (Fig. 117b) in which are housed the cations and water molecules, and connecting these cavities are systems of channels of minimum diameter about 2·7 Å. Thus at -186°C., oxygen (2·8 Å) and nitrogen (3·0 Å) are absorbed but argon (3·8 Å) is almost completely excluded (Barrer and Kerr, 1959). Levyne, like chabazite, contains four-, six- and eight-membered rings of tetrahedra.

Erionite. A fibrous zeolite, erionite (Deffeyes, 1959; Staples and Gard, 1959) has cell parameters very similar to those of chabazite (*a* 13·26, *c* 15·12 Å, space group probably $P6_3/mmc$), but the two structures are somewhat different. Cage-like configurations of linked (Si,Al)O_4 tetrahedra are bounded by four-, six- and eight-membered rings of tetrahedra (Fig. 117c), and neighbouring cavities are joined in the z direction by a shared single hexagonal ring instead of a double hexagonal ring as in chabazite. The structure alternatively may be considered as an arrangement of chains of tetrahedra (6 per cell in the z direction) which are separated by the cavities described above; the latter aspect emphasizes the fibrous character of the mineral. In both levyne and erionite the cations occupying sites within the framework cavities are exchangeable, and the water molecules are easily removed and resorbed. The structure of erionite can be referred to an orthorhombic (orthohexagonal) cell with a 13·26, $b \simeq a\sqrt{3} \simeq 23 \cdot 0$, c 15·12 Å. Barrer *et al.* (1959) have suggested that the fibrous mineral rhodesite may be related structurally to erionite since it is orthorhombic with a 23·8, b 6·54, c 7·05 Å, but an affinity of rhodesite (and the related mineral mountainite) to thomsonite has been demonstrated by Gard and Taylor (1957).

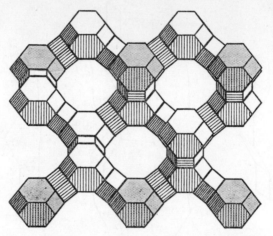

Fig. 118. Aluminosilicate framework of faujasite viewed along [110] to show the wide channels in the structure. The corners of each polyhedron represent the centres of $(Si, Al)O_4$ tetrahedra but oxygen atoms are not represented (after Bergerhoff *et al.*, 1958).

Faujasite. The structure of faujasite (Bergerhoff *et al.*, 1958) is the most open of all the zeolites. Its aluminosilicate framework is formed by $(Al, Si)O_4$ tetrahedra linked to form cubo-octahedral cages similar to those in chabazite, but these cages are stacked in fourfold (tetrahedral) coordination and are joined not directly across hexagonal faces, but by bridges of hexagonal prisms (Fig. 118). In this manner further rings are formed containing twelve tetrahedra, and these define a system of wide channels running in the [110] direction throughout the crystal. As in the other zeolites, cations and water molecules occupy sites within the structural cavities. Among the many cations which can be exchanged are Na, K, Tl, Ag, NH_4, Mg, Ca, Sr, Ba, Co, and Ni, and in addition many organic substituted ammonium ions (NH_3Me, NH_2Me_2, $NHMe_3$, NMe_4, NH_3Et) can be introduced. All of these exchanges are accompanied by only very little change in cell size (Barrer *et al.*, 1956). Faujasite also exhibits a wider range of molecular absorption than any other zeolite, its channels of twelve-membered rings having a minimum diameter of 9 Å. Thus not only normal and *iso*-paraffins but also cyclopentane, cyclohexane, and aromatic molecules like benzene and toluene can permeate its structure (Barrer *et al.*, 1956).

Faujasite is cubic *Fd3m*, with $a \simeq 24.65$ Å and $Z = 16$ (Strunz, 1955). One synthetic faujasite has a 24.83 Å, and another has a supercell with a 94.76 Å (Barrer *et al.*, 1959). The latter authors have also prepared faujasites which contain germanium instead of silicon, and/or gallium instead of aluminium.

CHEMISTRY

Phillipsite. The ideal composition is $(\frac{1}{2}Ca,Na,K)_3Al_3Si_5O_{16} \cdot 6H_2O$, but considerable substitution of Al for Si may occur, with a corresponding increase in the $(\frac{1}{2}Ca,Na,K)$ group. The name is in honour of W. Phillips, British mineralogist (*d.* 1828). Three analyses of phillipsite are given in Table 50 (anals. 1 to 3) where they have been recalculated on the basis of 32 oxygens, the anhydrous cell contents : the Si : Al ratio for these analyses is fairly constant. A compilation of phillipsite analyses was tabulated by Wyart and Chatelain (1938) and many analyses showing considerable chemical variation were plotted by Winchell (1925) : the range of substitution is probably between $(Ca,Na_2,K_2)_{2.5}$ $Al_5Si_{11}O_{32} \cdot 12H_2O$ and $(Ca,Na_2,K_2)_{3.5}Al_7Si_9O_{32} \cdot 12H_2O$. A "pseudophillipsite" has, however, been described from Italy (Caglioti, 1927b) with SiO_2 37.35, Al_2O_3 26.27, giving, for 32 oxygens, Si 8.75, Al 7.25 (*pseudophillipsite* must be regarded as a variety of phillipsite, differing only in the manner in which it is reported to lose water on heating, *cf.* Zambonini, 1902). The $(K,Na,\frac{1}{2}Ca)$ group varies with the Al:Si ratio, the possible substitution being $(K,Na,\frac{1}{2}Ca)^{+1}$ $Al^{+3} \rightleftharpoons Si^{+4}$. K is usually dominant over Na; sodium-rich phillipsites are, however, known, both from Agnone (Table 50, anal. 2) and from Aci Castello, Sicily. In some phillipsites $Ca < (Na+K)$ while in others Ca is the main constituent of the $(K,Na,\frac{1}{2}Ca)$ group. Ba, and to a lesser extent Sr, may also enter this group (*e.g.* anal. 3) : the barium variety of phillipsite has been termed *wellsite* (kurtzite although originally considered to be a separate variety lower in Si is in fact wellsite). A mineral believed to be a magnesian variety of phillipsite (MgO 3.70 per cent.), and called spangite, has been shown not to differ from ordinary phillipsite and not to contain any appreciable Mg (Zambonini, 1918).

Koizumi and Roy (1960) report that, from gels of appropriate composition, no synthetic phase was obtained which gave an X-ray pattern identical with that for natural phillipsite (unless their synthetic zeolite *CASH*-II represents a pure calcium-phillipsite). On heating natural phillipsite at 1000 atmospheres H_2O pressure, it breaks down to wairakite + H_2O at temperatures as low as 260°C. On heating chabazite to 255°C. Coombs *et al.* (1959) obtained phillipsite together with wairakite. The synthetic production of ψ-phillipsite by the hydrothermal crystallization of a potassium aluminosilicate gel was reported by Barrer and Baynham (1956). The absorption of ammonia by phillipsite has been studied by Sameshima and Morita (1935), and the dehydration and absorption have been investigated by Barrer *et al.* (1959).

Harmotome. The ideal composition is $BaAl_2Si_6O_{16} \cdot 6H_2O$; the name is from the Greek *harmos*, joint, and *tome*, a cutting, in allusion to the morphology of the twinned crystals. There is considerable replacement of Si by Al with a corresponding introduction of alkalies into the Ba position to maintain the

Table 50. PHILLIPSITE AND HARMOTOME ANALYSES

	1.	2.	3.	4.
SiO$_2$	42·34	46·11	46·89	45·51
Al$_2$O$_3$	22·31	21·96	21·45	16·50
MgO	—	0·03	—	0·27
CaO	3·90	3·84	6·15	0·12
SrO	—	—	0·76	—
BaO	—	—	4·95	19·89
Na$_2$O	4·26	7·59	0·45	1·18
K$_2$O	6·78	3·65	3·72	1·77
H$_2$O$^+$	}19·70	}16·96	11·37	14·74
H$_2$O$^-$			4·10	—
Total	99·29	100·14	99·84	99·98
α	1·493	—	—	1·506
β	1·497	—	—	1·509
γ	1·500	—	—	1·514
2V$_\gamma$	—	—	—	79° 50′
D	—	—	—	2·47
β:x	—	—	—	23½°

NUMBERS OF IONS ON THE BASIS OF 32(O)

Si	9·91	10·18	10·46	11·14
Al	6·15	5·72	5·64	4·76
Mg	—	0·01	—	0·10
Na	1·93	3·25	0·20	0·56
Ca	0·98	0·91	1·47	0·03
Sr	—	—	0·10	—
K	2·02	1·03	1·06	0·55
Ba	—	—	0·43	1·91
H$_2$O$^+$	}15·38	}12·49	8·46	12·03
H$_2$O$^-$			3·05	—
Z	16·06	15·90	16·10	15·90
R†	4·93	5·20	3·26	3·15

1. Phillipsite, cavities in nepheline–melilite basalt, Moiliili quarry, Honolulu, Hawaii (Dunham, 1933).
2. Phillipsite, cavities in basalt, Agnone, Syracuse, Sicily (Tosto, 1948).
3. Wellsite (kurtzite, Ba-phillipsite), Kurtzy, Crimea (Shkabara, 1950).
4. Harmotome, on gibbsite in joints in gabbro, Glen Riddle, Pennsylvania (Meier, 1939).

† $R = (Mg + Na + Ca + Sr + K + Ba)$.

charge balance. The dominant alkali metal is generally potassium though sodium is frequently present in appreciable amounts. Calcium is often present but generally only in trace amounts, though Kinoshita (1922) reported a harmotome with 1·6 per cent. CaO. The general chemistry of harmotome has been discussed by Thugutt (1947). The dehydration of harmotome was investigated by Stoklossa (1918) and Barrer *et al.* (1959): the dehydrated material has considerable absorptive power for H_2, N_2, CO_2 and NH_3.

Chabazite. The ideal composition is $CaAl_2Si_4O_{12} \cdot 6H_2O$. There is considerable replacement of the type $(Na,K)Si \rightleftharpoons CaAl$ and also of the type $Ca \rightleftharpoons Na_2 \rightleftharpoons K_2$: Coombs *et al.* (1959) give the composition as $(Ca,Na_2,K_2)_5Al_{10}Si_{26}O_{72} \cdot 36H_2O$ to $(Ca,Na_2,K_2)_{6.75}Al_{13.5}Si_{22.5}O_{72} \cdot 36H_2O$. The name is from the Greek *chabazios* or *chalazios*, an ancient name of a stone : synonyms include herschelite, seebachite and phacolite. Five chabazite analyses are given in Table 51 (anals. 1 to 5) where they have also been recalculated on the basis of 72 oxygens, the anhydrous cell content. Considerable variation in the Si:Al ratio is apparent, the largest being between anals. 4 and 5 with SiO_2 contents of 50·17 and 44·37 per cent. respectively: the $Si + Al(+Fe^{+3})$ value (Z) is, however, fairly constant at approximately 36. A particularly high SiO_2 content is reported in a chabazite

Table 51. CHABAZITE, ERIONITE AND GMELINITE ANALYSES

	1.	2.	3.	4.	5.	6.	7.	8.
SiO_2	47·56	48·78	44·19	50·17	44·37	57·40	48·84	47·81
Al_2O_3	20·40	18·04	19·86	18·24	21·24	15·60	}17·36	19·73
Fe_2O_3	—	tr.	0·28	0·19	—	—		—
MgO	0·20	—	1·56	tr.	—	1·11	0·65	—
CaO	10·52	9·77	8·61	7·30	2·60	2·92	9·93	5·01
SrO	—	—	0·15	0·47	—	—	—	0·02
Na_2O	0·32	0·98	1·18	1·55	8·79	1·45	0·26	6·13
K_2O	0·92	0·60	2·05	0·17	2·38	3·40	2·22	0·31
H_2O^+	16·28	}22·04	14·36	}22·05	}21·25	9·89	}21·27	}21·56
H_2O^-	3·44		7·44			7·69		
Total	99·64	100·21	99·68	100·31	100·63	99·46	100·53	100·57
α	—	1·4848	1·488	—	—	1·468(ω)	1·480	1·480(ϵ)
β	1·488(n)	1·4852	—	1·485(n)	1·4846 (ω)	—	—	—
γ	—	1·4858	1·490	—	—	1·473(ϵ)	1·494	1·490(ω)
2V	$\simeq 30°(+)$	—	$\simeq 0°$	$(+)$	—	—	—	—
D	—	—	—	—	—	2·02	2·075	2·06

NUMBERS OF IONS ON THE BASIS OF 72 (O) FOR CHABAZITE AND ERIONITE AND 48 (O) FOR GMELINITE

	1.	2.	3.	4.	5.	6.	7.	8.
Si	23·84	24·86	23·07	25·33	22·96	27·42	16·58	16·16
Al	12·05	10·84	12·22	10·86	12·96	8·78	}6·89	7·86
Fe$^+$	—	—	0·11	0·07	—	—		—
Mg	0·15	—	1·21	—	—	0·79	0·33	—
Na	0·31	0·97	1·19	1·52	8·82	1·34	0·17	4·02
Ca	5·65	5·34	4·82	3·95	1·44	1·49	3·61	1·81
Sr	—	—	0·05	0·14	—	—	—	0·01
K	0·59	0·39	1·37	0·11	1·57	1·95	0·96	0·13
H_2O^+	27·22	}37·47	25·01	}37·14	}36·68	15·76	}24·08	}24·30
H_2O^-	5·75		12·96			12·25		
Z	35·89	35·70	35·40	36·26	35·92	36·20	23·47	24·02
R†	6·70	6·70	8·64	5·75‡	11·83	5·57	5·07	5·97

1. Chabazite, vesicular Tertiary basalt, Ritter hot spring, Grant County, Oregon (Hewett *et al.*, 1928).
2. Pseudo-rhombohedral chabazite, veins in andesite, Bor, Yugoslavia (Majer, 1953).
3. Chabazite, Hashikaké-zawa, Chichibu mine, Saitama Prefecture, Japan (Kato, 1959).
4. Yellowish rose chabazite, Csódi-Berges, Dunabogdány, Hungary (Reichert and Erdélyi, 1935) (Includes BaO 0·17).
5. Hexagonal crystals of herschelite, palagonitic basalt, Ficarazzi, Catania, Sicily (Irrera, 1949). Anal. F. Stella Starrabba.
6. Fibrous erionite, Durkee opal mine, Swayze Creek, Baker Co., Oregon (Staples and Gard, 1959). Anal. L. L. Hoagland.
7. Brick-red nucleus of gmelinite crystals, fissures in igneous rock, Kurtzy, near Simferopol, Crimea (Shkabara, 1940a). Anal. E. A. Sturm.
8. Very pale pinkish yellow gmelinite, basalt, north side of White Head, Belfast Lough, Antrim, Northern Ireland (Smith *et al.*, 1916). Anal. G. T. Prior.

† $R = (Mg + Na + Ca + Sr + K)$.
‡ Includes Ba 0·03.

from Nova Scotia (Kappen and Fischer, 1928) which has 56·37 per cent. SiO_2 and 16·11 per cent. Al_2O_3. Although some chabazites are relatively low in alkalies other varieties exist which are low in Ca and rich in alkalies: chabazite from New South Wales has been reported to have 3·92 per cent. Na_2O (Hodge-Smith, 1929) and an Antrim specimen has 4·48 per cent. Na_2O (Tomkeieff, 1934), whereas the herschelite variety from Sicily may have over 8 per cent. Na_2O (*e.g.* Caglioti, 1927a; Coppola, 1948; also Table 51, anal. 5). In such chabazites K is also important and in intermediate varieties with 6 to 9 per cent. CaO, K may be dominant over Na, *e.g.* Table 51, anal. 3; see also the Nova Scotian chabazite described by Kappen and Fischer (1928) with CaO 6·37, Na_2O 1·19, K_2O 1·83 per cent., and that from Siberia with CaO 7·02, Na_2O 0·20, K_2O 3·12 per cent. (Shkabara, 1941). Sr may replace Ca to a small extent (*e.g.* Table 51, anals. 3 and 4) and the occurrence of both Sr and Ba in chabazites is reported by Reichert and Erdélyi (1935).

The synthetic production of a potassium form of chabazite, from a potassium aluminosilicate gel of appropriate composition which had been subjected to hydrothermal crystallization, was reported by Barrer and Baynham (1956). On heating to 240°–255°C. chabazite breaks down, with the formation of wairakite and phillipsite (Coombs *et al.*, 1959). Considerable experimental work has been done on the ion-exchange properties and equilibria of chabazite. The exchange of Cu, from a copper chloride solution, for the Ca, Na and K ions of chabazite was demonstrated by Kappen and Fischer (1928), who analysed the product and reported it to have 7·15 per cent. CuO. Ion exchange with chlorides of Na, K, Ba, Sr, Cd, Mg, La and Ca was investigated by Rabinowitsch and Wood (1936) who also studied the sorption of gases in chabazite. Exchange equilibria and the production of various cation-exchanged forms of chabazite from an analysed natural chabazite from Nova Scotia were studied by Barrer and Sammon (1955) and Barrer and Langley (1958). The latter authors showed that the influence of the cation on the thermal stability of ion-exchanged chabazites was in the order Li < Na < K < Rb < Cs. The hydronium form of chabazite has also been prepared by ion-exchange (Beattie and Dyer, 1957). The absorption of various gases by dehydrated chabazite has been investigated quantitatively by Rabinowitsch (1932), Tiselius and Brohult (1934), Lamb and Woodhouse (1936) and by Kington and Laing (1955), the results being used to confirm the presence of large and small channels in the structure (see p. 390). The dehydration curve of chabazite is smooth and the dehydration is reversible (Milligan and Weiser, 1937): the heat of hydration ranges from 1·51 to $1·85 \times 10^4$ cals. per g. mol. H_2O (Tiselius and Brohult, 1934). The d.t.a. curve of chabazite is given by Koizumi (1953), Majer (1953) and by Mason and Greenberg (1954): the latter authors report a medium endothermic peak at about 220°C., a weaker one at about 460° and a strong sharp exothermic peak at 890°C., though Majer records two exothermal peaks at 550° and 670°C. The alteration of chabazite to beidellite has been reported by Shannon (1925b).

Gmelinite. The ideal composition is $(Na_2,Ca)Al_2Si_4O_{12} \cdot 6H_2O$; it may also contain appreciable amounts of K. The name is after C. G. Gmelin (1792–1860), mineralogist and analyst. Two gmelinite analyses are given in Table 51 (anals. 7 and 8) where they have been recalculated on the basis of 48 oxygens, the anhydrous cell contents. In anal. 7, K is dominant over Na, while in anal. 8, Na not only exceeds K but is also dominant over Ca. Older analyses of gmelinite from Five Islands, Nova Scotia, and from Bergen Hill, New Jersey, also have Na greater than Ca. In other analyses of Antrim gmelinites (Smith *et al.*, 1916), however, Ca exceeds $(Na+K)$: Sr may also replace Ca to a limited extent. Analyses of gmelinite from Nova Scotia before and after treatment for a few minutes in mercuric potassic iodide (Thoulet's) solution show that Na becomes largely replaced by K (Walker, 1922).

Levyne. The ideal composition is $CaAl_2Si_4O_{12} \cdot 6H_2O$. The name is in honour of A. Lévy, mineralogist and crystallographer. There is appreciable replacement of Si by Al and correspondingly of Ca by Na or K, with K often exceeding Na. There are, however, few analyses available and they could be interpreted as indicating $15H_2O$ rather than $18H_2O$ in the unit cell (Coombs *et al.*, 1959).

Erionite. The idealized composition is $(Na_2,K_2,Ca,Mg)_{4.5}Al_9Si_{27}O_{72} \cdot 27H_2O$ (Staples and Gard, 1959), though if the analysis of their specimen is recalculated on the basis of 72 oxygens (anhydrous) the composition may be expressed as $(Ca+Mg+(Na+K)/2)_4Al_9Si_{27}O_{72} \cdot 28H_2O$ (Table 51, anal. 6). The mineral is named from the Greek *erion*, wool, in allusion to its white, wool-like, fibrous, crinkly appearance. An earlier analysis of erionite from the same locality in Oregon was given by Eakle (1898).

A synthetic preparation of erionite was reported by Breck *et al.* (1956). K, Ag and Tl ions were substituted for the alkali ions in erionite (Deffeyes, 1959) by heating finely ground crystals in a low-melting salt of the heavy metal. The X-ray pattern peak intensities of the exchanged erionites are greatly changed, but the cell dimensions remain constant indicating a substitution which does not affect the structural framework. The d.t.a. curve of erionite has been investigated by Whelan and Odekirk (1960) who report that the loss of water is represented by a broad low temperature endothermic reaction.

Faujasite. The composition of this rather rare zeolite is approximately $(Na_2,Ca)_{1.75}Al_{3.5}Si_{8.5}O_{24} \cdot 16H_2O$; the name is after Faujas de Saint Fond, writer on ancient volcanoes. An analysis of the type material from Sasbach, in the Kaisertuhl (Damour, 1848), gave SiO_2 46·12, Al_2O_3 16·81, CaO 4·79, Na_2O 5·09, H_2O 27·02 = 99·83. Faujasite was synthesized by Barrer *et al.* (1956) who considered that its chemistry indicated a composition $Na_{0.43}$ $[Al_{0.43}Si_{0.57}O_2]aq$. Isomorphous replacements of the type $Na^+Al^{+3} \rightleftharpoons Si^{+4}$ are apparently possible and various ions may replace the sodium by ion-exchange.

OPTICAL AND PHYSICAL PROPERTIES

Phillipsite and **harmotome** nearly always occur in the form of interpenetrant complex twins either in separate groups of transparent or translucent crystals or in radiating aggregates. Striations parallel to *z* are sometimes apparent on (010) and two sets of these serve to emphasize the sector twinning on (001). The complex twinning may simulate single crystal forms such as the tetragonal prism and the rhombic dodecahedron, each face of which shows four sets of striations.

Chabazite occurs in transparent or translucent euhedral rhombohedral crystals {10$\bar{1}$1} which approximate to cubes. Walker (1951) describes the various habits of chabazite crystals found in the lavas of the Garron plateau area, Antrim, and discusses the genetic significance of their distribution in different localities. For the above occurrence also Walker reports that chabazite is optically negative when the mean refractive index is greater than 1·488, and positive if it is lower; some of the crystals are zoned.

Gmelinite usually occurs in well formed crystals and only rarely in radiating aggregates. Its crystals exhibit a greater variety of habits than those of chabazite; pyramidal, prismatic and tabular as well as rhombohedral habits occur.

Levyne occurs in thin tabular {0001} crystals or in sheaf-like aggregates (Walker, 1951).

Erionite occurs in radiating groups of crystals or in fine woolly fibres elongated parallel to z. It is uniaxial positive with ω 1·468–1·472, ϵ 1·473–1·476, $\delta \simeq 0·003$, and D$\simeq 2·02$ (Staples and Gard, 1959; Deffeyes, 1959).

Faujasite occurs in clear and transparent or yellowish and opaque octahedra with rounded edges (Barrer *et al.*, 1956). It is isotropic with $n \simeq 1·48$ and D $\simeq 1·92$.

DISTINGUISHING FEATURES

The refractive indices of phillipsite are usually lower than those of harmotome but those for silica-poor phillipsites are close to the harmotome range. Both are biaxial positive with optic axial plane perpendicular to (010), but an (010) cleavage plate shows an acute bisectrix figure for phillipsite ($\gamma=y$), and an obtuse bisectrix figure for harmotome ($\alpha=y$).

Phillipsite and harmotome both show interpenetrant cruciform and sector twinning as do stilbite and epistilbite but in the latter two minerals the optic axial plane is (010) and the extinction angles are smaller. Phillipsite and harmotome have higher 2V than other similar zeolites.

Chabazite, gmelinite and levyne are uniaxial negative (though some may be anomalously biaxial), and usually have rhombohedral (pseudo-cubic) habit. These three minerals are very similar but the X-ray powder pattern of each is distinctive (see p. 413).

PARAGENESIS

Phillipsite occurs most commonly in cavities or amygdales in basalt (Table 50, anal. 2), often associated with chabazite (Table 51, anal. 1). Various habits of phillipsite from Hungarian basalts have been described by Mauritz (1931), and pseudo-tetragonal twins of phillipsite have been reported from cavities in basanite from Medves Mt., Hungary (Reichert, 1934). In the Tertiary basalts of Northern Ireland phillipsite is relatively common among the amygdaloidal zeolites, and particularly large crystals occur in the tholeiites of the Giant's Causeway (Walker, 1960a): some of the Antrim phillipsite is unusual in being red in colour. Phillipsite, together with analcite, was considered to have developed in certain Czechoslovakian basalts during the epimagmatic period of solidification: it is also found filling interstices between the other constituents in a phillipsite tephrite (Hibsch, 1927). In the basaltic rocks near Kladno, Czechoslovakia, phillipsite is associated with thomsonite, mesolite, chabazite and natrolite and, contrary to the rule of Cornu (1908) of successive decrease of water content, is always the first of these minerals to have been formed (Antonín, 1942). Fissures in nosean phonolite in the Rhineland contain phillipsite

(Brauns and Brauns, 1924); phillipsite has also been found in an inclusion of nepheline-syenite in phonolite from Kaisertuhl, Germany, with a core of untwinned phillipsite surrounded by a zone of calcite, which is in turn surrounded by twinned phillipsite (Chudoba, 1930). Vesicles containing phillipsite, together with natrolite, occur in the potassium-rich olivine melilitite, katungite, from Katunga volcano, southwest Uganda (Holmes, 1937). Authigenic phillipsite in calcareous deep sea sediments has been reported by Young (1939) and the mineral is also known from the wall-work of Roman baths where hot springs emerge at a maximum temperature of 70°C. (Daubrée, 1879).

The barium-bearing phillipsite, wellsite, was first recorded by Pratt and Foote (1897) from Buck Creek corundum mine, Clay Co., North Carolina, where it occurs in small crystals on felspar or corundum. It is also found at the village of Kurtzy, near Simferopol, in the Crimea (Table 50, anal. 3), where it is associated with analcite, leonhardite and calcite, lining fissures in an igneous rock (Shkabara, 1940a).

Harmotome occurs, like the majority of the zeolites, in vugs and veins in igneous rocks, but it is also found in association with manganese mineralization and in lenses in gneiss. Its occurrence in cavities in basalt, associated with calcite and rarely with natrolite, has been recorded by Machatschki (1926), and Kinoshita (1922) reported its association with calcite, laumontite and pyrite in fissures in green tuffs. The harmotome of Table 50, anal. 4, occurs on gibbsite in joints in gabbro, where it is also associated with hyalophane; a similar association of harmotome with a barium felspar occurs in thin bands traversing manganese ores in North Wales (Smith, 1945), and harmotome is found with hyalophane, microcline and albite in veins cutting leucocratic gneiss at Nisikkatch Lake, Saskatchewan (Hogarth, 1957). The association of harmotome with aluminous weathering products is also known from the Urals (Polyanin, 1938), where it is found, with kaolinite and halloysite, in bauxites. Harmotome in association with manganese minerals is also found in Siberia (Afanasiev *et al.*, 1940), and occurs in hydrothermal veins, with sphalerite, barytes and calcite, traversing Moine schists at the Struy lead mines, Inverness-shire (Russell, 1946), and in graphite lenses, with quartz, sphalerite and galena, in gneiss in northern Italy (Pelloux, 1931). At Strontian, Argyllshire, it occurs in veins in association with strontianite and lead mineralization. It has also been described from veins, with barytes, calcite and haematite, in a mineralized fault-breccia in Ross-shire (Waterson, 1953).

Chabazite is typically found in crevices and amygdales in basalt and andesite and related igneous rocks (Table 51, anals. 1, 2 and 5), where it occurs associated with stilbite, mesolite, mordenite, heulandite, apophyllite, etc. Salmon-pink chabazite has been described from cavities in the Watchung basalt, New Jersey (Fenner, 1910), where it preceded heulandite and stilbite, and from cavities in nepheline–melilite basalt, Honolulu (Dunham, 1933), together with phillipsite, magnetite and calcite. It is relatively common in the Tertiary basalts of Skye and from the vesicular basalts of Northern Ireland (Smith *et al.*, 1916; Tomkeieff, 1934), where it is the most abundant and widespread zeolite, occurring in 84 per cent. of the zeolite localities (Walker, 1960a), frequently in association with thomsonite. In the Deccan traps of India chabazite has been recorded rimmed by secondary labradorite (Fermor, 1925).

Chabazite also occurs in cavities and joints as a result of hydrothermal mineralization, as in a sulphide ore vein in gneiss cut by granite in northern Manitoba (Brownell, 1938), and in hydrothermal veins of the Khibina tundra (Chirvinsky, 1939). Similarly it has been recorded, together with heulandite and stilbite, from a mica gneiss of the Mama-Vitim region of Siberia (Shkabara, 1941), and in cavities with axinite, epidote, natrolite, heulandite and stilbite, between a pegmatite and amphibolite in western Moravia (Černý, 1955). Chabazite is also found, together with phillipsite, in the wall-work of Roman baths at Plombières, where hot spring water emerges at a maximum temperature of 70°C. (Daubrée, 1879).

Gmelinite occurs mainly in the amygdales of basaltic lavas and related igneous rocks. In the British Tertiary province it is known from Talisker, Skye, and from Antrim, Northern Ireland (Table 51, anal. 8). In the Irish lavas gmelinite is found at 9 per cent. of the zeolite localities (Walker, 1960a) where it is commonly associated with chabazite, thomsonite, analcite, phillipsite, levyne, calcite and aragonite. In the Antrim basalts gmelinite is confined to a narrow zone along the east coast (Walker, 1959); here gmelinite frequently occurs as a parallel growth on chabazite, and, in a later zone, parallel growths of late chabazite occur on simple or twinned gmelinite. It is also known from basaltic lavas in Nova Scotia and New Jersey, and from fissures in igneous rocks in the Crimea (Table 51, anal. 7).

Erionite was originally described (Eakle, 1898) in association with opal in fractures in rhyolite tuff, in Baker County, Oregon (Table 51, anal. 6). This occurrence has been re-examined by Staples and Gard (1959) who report that the erionite is in seams most of which are parallel to the flowage or bedding of a welded tuff. It is also found associated with vitric tuff in Jersey Valley, Nevada, and in other localities in Wyoming and South Dakota (Deffeyes, 1959) and is almost certainly much less rare than previously supposed. At these localities it is associated with heulandite, and in most of the deposits the erionite forms a large proportion of the rocks, which are considered to represent the alteration products of acidic vitric ash which accumulated in Caenozoic lakes. Erionite has also been recorded from a geode in basalt from the Faroe Islands (Hey, 1959) and from basalt dredged from the Columbia River, near Wenatchee, Washington, D.C., where it occurs in vesicles in association with paulingite and filiform pyrite (Kamb and Oke, 1960).

Levyne occurs typically in amygdales in basalt (*e.g.* Hibsch, 1927), and is known from Iceland and the Faroes. In the basalts of Antrim, Northern Ireland, it is one of the more widespread of the zeolites, occurring in 27 per cent. of the localities (Walker, 1960a), though because of the small size of the crystals it is rarely conspicuous.

Faujasite was originally reported from Sasbach in the Kaisertuhl, Germany, where it occurs with augite in a limburgite (Damour, 1842). It is also found near Eisenbach, and is associated with other zeolites in the Aar and St. Gotthard massifs of Switzerland (Parker, 1923).

Laumontite-Leonhardite
Mordenite
Gismondine

$$Ca[Al_2Si_4O_{12}] \cdot 4\text{--}3\tfrac{1}{2}H_2O$$
$$(Na_2,K_2,Ca)[Al_2Si_{10}O_{24}] \cdot 7H_2O$$
$$Ca[Al_2Si_2O_8] \cdot 4H_2O$$

	LAUMONTITE–LEONHARDITE	MORDENITE
	MONOCLINIC $(-)$	ORTHORHOMBIC $(+)$ $(-)$
α	1·502–1·514	1·472–1·483
β	1·512–1·522	1·475–1·485
γ	1·514–1·525	1·477–1·487
δ	$\simeq 0\cdot01$	$\leq 0\cdot005$
$2V_\alpha$	26°–47°	76°–104°
Orientation:	$\beta=y$, $\gamma{:}z\ 8°\text{--}33°$	$\alpha=z$, $\beta=x$, $\gamma=y$
O.A.P.	(010)	(100)
Dispersion:	$r < v$, strong.	—
D	2·2–2·3	2·12–2·15
H	3–3½	3–4
Cleavage:	{010}, {110}, good.	—
Twinning:	{100}	—
Colour:	Colourless, white, red, yellow, brown; colourless in thin section.	
Unit cell: a Å	14·90	18·13
b Å	13·17	20·49
c Å	7·55	7·52
β	111° 30′	—
Z	4	4
Space group:	$C2$ or Cm	$Cmcm$ or $Cmc2$

The minerals laumontite, leonhardite, mordenite, gismondine, ashcroftine and yugawaralite, because of their chemical nature, physical and optical properties and parageneses, have been classed as zeolites, but with the exception of mordenite their structures have not been determined. Their unit cell data are listed in Table 52.

STRUCTURE

Mordenite. Meier (1961) has shown that the aluminosilicate framework of mordenite involves a new type of chain containing 5-membered rings of tetrahedra. The molecular-sieve properties are attributed to a system of channels parallel to [001], having a free diameter of 6·6 Å, and interconnected by smaller channels parallel to [010] with diameter 2·8 Å. Stacking faults in the framework reduce the effective diameter of the channels to about 4 Å.

CHEMISTRY

Laumontite. The ideal composition is $CaAl_2Si_4O_{12} \cdot 4H_2O$: *leonhardite* is a partially dehydrated variety with formula $CaAl_2Si_4O_{12} \cdot 3\tfrac{1}{2}H_2O$. The name

Table 52.   UNIT CELL DATA FOR SOME ZEOLITES WITH UNKNOWN STRUCTURES

	a Å	b Å	c Å	β	Symmetry		Z	Reference
Laumontite {	14·90	13·17	7·55	111° 30′	Monoclinic	$C2$ or Cm	4	Coombs (1952)
	13·85	13·12	7·52	99° 09′	Monoclinic	I cell	4	Heritsch (1956)
Leonhardite	14·75	13·10	7·55	112°	Monoclinic	$C2$ or Cm	4	Coombs (1952)
Gismondine	13·71	14·31	10·62	—	Orthorhombic	$Cmmm$ or $Ccca$	8	Kraus (1939)
Ashcroftine	34·11	—	17·52	—	Tetragonal	$P4_2/m\ mm$	40	Hey and Bannister (1933)
Yugawaralite	13·26	13·65	9·73	111° 30′	Monoclinic		4	Sakurai and Hayashi (1952)

laumontite is in honour of Gillet Laumont who first found the mineral at Huelgoat, Brittany, in 1785: leonhardite is named after G. Leonhard. Three analyses of laumontite and one of leonhardite are given in Table 53 (anals. 1–3 and 4) together with the numbers of ions on the basis of 48 oxygens, *i.e.* the anhydrous cell contents. There are considerable minor variations from the ideal composition and the majority of reliable analyses of laumontite show an appreciable content of alkalies. Winchell (1925) considered that such substitutions took place by the mutual interchange of $NaSi \rightleftharpoons CaAl$, as in plagioclase; it is, however, also probable that as in other zeolites (Hey, 1932a) pairs of alkali atoms may proxy for Ca without variation in the Si:Al ratio (Rossoni, 1935). From a study of laumontite analyses, Coombs (1952) concludes that both types of substitution may occur, and gives the general composition as $Ca_x(Na,K)_y$ $Al_{2x+y}Si_{24-(2x+y)}O_{48} \cdot 16H_2O$. In calculating the analyses of Table 53, Fe^{+3} has been included with Al, following the evidence, presented by Henderson and Glass (1933), indicating that Fe^{+3} isomorphously replaces Al in the structure.

Attempts by Koizumi and Roy (1960) to synthesize laumontite failed. On heating laumontite at 400°C. (or 380°C. at 3000 bars) it gives wairakite, $CaAl_2Si_4O_{12} \cdot 2H_2O$ (Coombs *et al.*, 1959). The experimental replacement of Ca by alkali metals was demonstrated by Lemberg (1877; 1885).

On exposure to the atmosphere, or on gentle heating, laumontite loses approximately one eighth of its water to form the leonhardite variety. The reversibility of this dehydration, and its effect on the optical properties, have been recorded by Coombs (1952). A study of the absorption of ammonia and other gases by partially dehydrated laumontite has been made by Sameshima (1930) and by Sameshima and Hemmi (1934): ammonia is appreciably absorbed if the temperature of dehydration has not been too high. The d.t.a. curve for laumontite has been given by Koizumi (1953).

Mordenite. The ideal composition is approximately $(Na_2,K_2,Ca)Al_2Si_{10}O_{24} \cdot 7H_2O$, with alkalies usually dominant over Ca. The name is after the locality near Morden, Kings County, Nova Scotia (synonyms include ptilolite, flokite and arduinite). Departures from the ideal composition include the variability of the Si:Al ratio (Table 53, anals. 5–7), though the group total is generally close to the theoretical value of 24 (on the basis of 48 oxygens in the anhydrous formula). Potassium is normally less abundant than sodium though a mordenite occurring as the hydration product of a pitchstone glass has been shown to have 2·45 per cent. K_2O (Harris and Brindley, 1954), and Thugutt (1933) reported material from fissures in basalt to have K_2O 5·32, Na_2O 0·74 per cent. In these potassium-rich mordenites the calcium content is low and the total alkalies are usually dominant over Ca : in material analysed by Shkabara (1940b)

Table 53. LAUMONTITE, MORDENITE, GISMONDINE AND ASHCROFTINE ANALYSES

	1.	2.	3.	4.	5.	6.	7.	8.	9.
SiO_2	50·90	50·70	50·63	52·04	67·22	64·62	66·06	33·89	38·09
Al_2O_3	21·26	22·53	22·07	21·46	11·07	13·21	12·32	28·14	26·61
Fe_2O_3	1·66	0·04	0·73	0·12	1·12	0·76	—	0·00,	—
MgO	tr.	—	0·40	tr.	0·28	0·98	0·36	—	0·87
CaO	13·91	11·54	10·72	11·41	3·72	3·70	3·02	13·96	5·72
Na_2O	—	0·40	1·08	0·20	2·39	2·63	3·86	—	3·62
K_2O	—	0·30	0·45	0·66	0·36	—	0·50	2·86	5·65
H_2O^+	12·64	12·00	}14·10	}13·80	}14·33	}14·10	9·19	}20·76	12·00
H_2O^-	—	2·41					4·68		6·40
Total	100·37	99·92	100·23	99·69	100·49	100·00	99·99	99·91	99·75
α	1·505	1·505– 1·513	1·510	1·507	—	—	1·472	—	1·536(ω)
β	1·515	—	1·518	1·516	1·477– 1·478(n)	1·487(n)	1·475	—	—
γ	1·517	1·516– 1·521	1·522	1·518	—	—	1·476	—	1·545(ε)
2V	medium(−)	(+)	39°(−)	26°(−)	—	—	(−)	—	(+)
γ:z	—	38°	10°	32°	—	—	(α:z)3½°	—	—
D	—	2·26–2·29	2·30	2·29	2·14–2·15	—	—	2·278	2·61

NUMBERS OF IONS ON THE BASIS OF 48 (LAUMONTITE AND MORDENITE), 64 (GISMONDINE) OR 72 (ASHCROFTINE) OXYGENS

	1.	2.	3.	4.	5.	6.	7.	8.	9.
Si	15·65	15·78	15·86	16·12	19·89	19·21	19·61	16·13	19·81
Al	7·70	8·27	8·15	7·83	3·86	4·63	4·31	15·79	16·31
Fe^{+3}	0·38	0·01	—‡	0·03	0·25	0·17	—	—	—
Mg	—	—	—	—	0·12	0·43	0·16	—	0·67
Na	—	0·24	0·66	0·12	1·37	1·32	2·22	—	3·65
Ca	4·58	3·85	3·60	3·79	1·18	1·18	0·96	7·12	3·19
K	—	0·12	0·18	0·26	0·14	—	0·19	1·74	3·75
H_2O^+	12·96	12·46	}14·60	}14·26	}14·14	}13·98	9·10	}32·96	20·82
H_2O^-	—	2·50					4·63		11·10
Z	23·73	24·06	24·02‖	23·98	24·00	24·01	23·92	31·92	36·12
R†	4·58	4·21	4·44	4·17	2·81	2·93	3·53	8·92¶	11·61††

1. Greyish pink laumontite, in veins, Wolf Creek Station, Lewis and Clarke County, Montana (Shannon, 1921) (Includes MnO tr.).
2. Laumontite, drusy cavities in quartz porphyry, Halle, Saale, Germany (Koch, 1958). Anal. G. Schneidereit (mean of two analyses).
3. Laumontite (partially dehydrated to leonhardite by exposure), Otama, Southland, New Zealand (Coombs, 1952). Anal. D. S. Coombs (Includes TiO_2 0·05, MnO tr.; optics refer to the laumontite form, the associated leonhardite having α 1·505, β 1·514, γ 1·517, $2V_α$ 44°, γ:z 33°).
4. Leonhardite, Hungary (Coombs, 1952). Anal. D. S. Coombs.
5. Mordenite (ptilolite), crevices in weathered hypersthene andesite, Terlitschno, Krapina, Croatia, Yugoslavia (Heritsch, 1940).
6. Mordenite, chalk, Bryansk, central Russia (Bushinsky, 1950).
7. Mordenite, amygdales in vesicular andesite, Challis, Custer County, Idaho (Ross and Shannon, 1924). (Mean of four analyses of mordenites with various habits.)
8. Gismondine, Capo di Bove, Italy (Caglioti, 1927b) (Includes BaO 0·27, SrO 0·025).
9. Ashcroftine (kalithomsonite), cavities in augite syenite, Narsarsuk, south Greenland (Hey and Bannister, 1933). Anal. J. E. Whitfield (Includes MnO 0·79). See also Gordon (1924).

† $R = (Mg + Na + Ca + K)$.
‡ Fe^{+3} and Mg are present as impurities and are omitted.
‖ Includes Ti 0·01.
¶ Includes Sr 0·01, Ba 0·05.
†† Includes Mn 0·35.

from basaltic breccias and tuffs, and by Hayashi and Sudo (1957) from clay associated with tuff, however, the molecular proportion of Ca exceeds that of (Na+K); mordenite rich in Ca has also been reported from a quartz latite porphyry from Utah (Stringham, 1950).

Mordenite has been synthesized by heating sodium aluminosilicate gels of composition $Na_2O \cdot Al_2O_3 \cdot 8–12SiO_2 \cdot nH_2O$ with water or dilute sodium carbonate or sodium bicarbonate at 265° to 295°C. (Barrer, 1948); quartz and analcite were sometimes also obtained. More recently mordenite has been synthesized by the hydrothermal crystallization of oxide mixes of felspar compositions, and from glasses of appropriate composition (Coombs *et al.*, 1959); the same authors also reported the appearance of mordenite, together with wairakite and anorthite, on the hydrothermal crystallization of the amorphous phase formed by heating heulandite. The crystallization of obsidian glass on exposure to a natural acid hydrothermal solution (pH 5·7) at 230°C. in a New Zealand hydrothermal bore hole has also given mordenite (Ellis, 1960). Treatment of natural mordenite with solutions of Li, Na, K, NH_4, Ca and Ba salts gives base-exchange products which give a mordenite X-ray pattern (Barrer, 1948). The absorption of ammonia, CO_2, SO_2 and other gases by partially dehydrated mordenite has been investigated by Sameshima and Hemmi (1934) and by Sameshima and Morita (1935). The d.t.a. curve of mordenite has been investigated by Mason and Greenberg (1954): it has a single moderate endothermic peak at 190°C. (see also Koizumi, 1953).

Gismondine. The ideal formula for gismondine is $CaAl_2Si_2O_8 \cdot 4H_2O$: the main replacement appears to be $(K,Na)_2 \rightleftharpoons Ca$, with K normally dominant over Na (Table 53, anal. 8). The mineral is named after Prof. C. G. Gismondi who examined it. Most analyses do not report the presence (or absence) of sodium and further analytical work is necessary to establish properly the substitutional relationships.[1] Winchell (1925) plotted several gismondine analyses and considered them to represent isomorphous mixtures between $KCa_{10}Al_{21}Si_{19}O_{80} \cdot 40H_2O$ and $K_4Ca_7Al_{18}Si_{22}O_{80} \cdot 36H_2O$. The dehydration of gismondine at various temperatures, and its rehydration, were studied by Caglioti (1927b). A synthetic preparation of gismondine was reported by Breck *et al.* (1956).

Ashcroftine. The ideal formula is $KNaCaAl_4Si_5O_{18} \cdot 8H_2O$. This mineral was first described as kalithomsonite (Gordon, 1924), but synthetic potassium-bearing thomsonites were found to have different refractive indices, which led Hey and Bannister (1933) to re-examine the original material and to show that it is an independent species. The name is in honour of F. N. Ashcroft, mineralogist and donor of many zeolites to the British Museum. Hey and Bannister (*op. cit.*) reported that a small quantity of ashcroftine showed no appreciable change in optical properties after digestion in boiling NaCl solution for 700 hours or fusion with $NaClO_3$ at 250°C. for 48 hours, but it is not certain whether any appreciable base-exchange occurred.

OPTICAL AND PHYSICAL PROPERTIES

Laumontite and **leonhardite** generally have prismatic or fibrous habit (parallel to z), and both are biaxial negative with O.A.P. (010). The transition to the partially dehydrated form, leonhardite, is accompanied by a fall in refractive

[1] New analyses indicate a series towards $Na_{2.5}Ca_{5.5}Al_{13.5}Si_{18.5}O_{64} \cdot 34H_2O$ (Walker, 1962)

indices and density and by increase in extinction angle. The ranges of optical properties for some laumontites and their corresponding leonhardites are given by Coombs (1952) as:

	laumontite	leonhardite
α	1·509–1·514	1·502–1·507
β	1·518–1·522	1·512–1·516
γ	1·521–1·525	1·514–1·518
δ	$\simeq 0·01$	$\simeq 0·01$
$2V_\alpha$	33°–47°	26°–44°
$\gamma:z$	8°–11°	8°–33°

Coombs shows that for laumontite the sign of elongation is length-slow on (010) and on (100), but for leonhardite it changes from length-slow on (010) to length-fast on (100). From his investigation of leonhardites, Coombs (1952) suggests that refractive indices of both varieties decrease also with increasing silica and alkali content. Some data on laumontites (*e.g.* Gilbert, 1951) fall within the ranges given above, but others do not, perhaps because of such variations in Si and (Na,K) or because of varying water contents. The densities of laumontites and leonhardites are generally between 2·2 and 2·3 gm./cm.^{3} Laumontite has good (010) and (110) cleavages.

Mordenite is acicular or fibrous parallel to z and although a white mineral it is sometimes found in rosettes which may be coloured red through the presence of haematite. Its refractive indices are α ($=z$) 1·472–1·483, β ($=x$) 1·475–1·485, γ ($=y$) 1·477–1·487, and its birefringence is very low. Mordenite may be biaxial positive or negative with high 2V (76°–90°) and its density is 2·12 to 2·15 gm./cm.^{3} (Stringham, 1950; Mason and Greenberg, 1954).

Gismondine is biaxial with a large 2V, O.A.P. $\perp$ (010), $\beta \simeq 1·54$, γ approximately perpendicular to (100), and $D \simeq 2·2$ (see also Walker, 1962).

Ashcroftine is fibrous parallel to z and is uniaxial positive with ϵ ($=z$) 1·545, $\omega = 1·536$, D 2·61 (Hey and Bannister, 1933).

DISTINGUISHING FEATURES

Laumontite has higher birefringence than scolecite and heulandite, and the latter two minerals have their optic axial planes perpendicular to (010). Laumontite has lower 2V than epistilbite, and is always length-slow, while stilbite and scolecite are length-fast.

Mordenite, like harmotome, has a high 2V but shows straight extinction in all principal zones and has lower refractive indices. Mordenite is length-fast, whereas natrolite is length-slow.

PARAGENESIS

Laumontite, and more rarely leonhardite, commonly occur in veins and vesicles in igneous rocks. Laumontite is known from the Baveno granite (Yakhontov, 1915; Pagliani, 1948) and from cavities in decomposed granite and pegmatite in the eastern Pyrenees (Capdecomme, 1952). It also occurs in drusy cavities in such rocks as diabase (*e.g.* Rossoni, 1935) and quartz porphyry

(Table 53, anal. 2), while leonhardite has been described from a New Zealand porphyrite (Hutton, 1944). Laumontite is found in volcanic rocks such as basalt (Dunham, 1933) or andesite and also occurs as a large scale replacement product of vitric tuffs in Southland, New Zealand (Coombs, 1952), and as a degradation product of plagioclase under incipiently metamorphic conditions. In recording field occurrences it is probably advisable to use the general term laumontite, except where it is desired to stress the water-poor nature, etc., of a particular specimen (*e.g.* the analysed material described by Hutton), because, as noted by Coombs (1952), the variety collected from a particular outcrop may vary with the weather.

Pale pink laumontite has been found in cavities in an epidote–magnetite–garnet skarn (Sumin, 1955) and it is common on joint planes in the thermally metamorphosed andesite adjacent to the Shap granite of northern England. Radially fibrous laumontite and leonhardite similarly occur in joints in slates and quartzites at Serpont, in the Ardennes (Antun, 1953), in hornfels in northern Norway (Saebø *et al.*, 1958), and, together with prehnite, in crevices in amphibolite in Switzerland (Fagnani, 1948): in all these occurrences the laumontite is probably hydrothermal in origin. It has also been reported from veins and cavities in serpentinite (McClellan, 1926). Authigenic laumontite, forming part of the cementing material in sandstone, has been recorded by Rengarten (1950) and its occurrence as secondary material in arkosic sandstones has also been reported (Kaley and Hanson, 1955; Heald, 1956). In a thick series of grey-wackes and tuffs, Coombs (1954) noted that with increasing depth there is a progressive destruction of analcite, albitization of plagioclase, and formation of laumontite rock: in the Lumsden–Mossburn district of New Zealand zeolitic bedded deposits up to 10 feet or more in thickness are continuous for several miles and typically contain about 70 per cent. laumontite (Coombs, 1959).

Mordenite is found in veins and amygdales in igneous rocks and also occurs as a hydration product of volcanic glasses and as an authigenic mineral in sediments. The mordenite of anal. 7 (Table 53) occurs in vesicular andesite and in such amygdales it is often found as finely fibrous or cottony material and is sometimes associated with quartz: it is also known as compact porcellanous material. It occurs in basalt and dolerite vesicles, though it is less common there than many other zeolites; it has also been recorded from a quartz-latite porphyry (Stringham, 1950). The formation of mordenite as the hydration product of a glass of a pitchstone from a dyke on the Isle of Arran has been reported by Harris and Brindley (1954): the mordenite forms about 1 per cent. of the rock and has a buff yellow colour when powdered (the colour is possibly related to the 1·74 per cent. Fe_2O_3 reported in the analysis).

Minute prismatic mordenite crystals scattered or aggregated in sandy deposits have been reported from the Urals (Rengarten, 1945) where it is considered that they are authigenic and formed while the deposit was still saturated with sea water: authigenic mordenite, together with analcite, has also been described from the Tertiary sandstones and siltstones of Georgia, U.S.S.R. (Ermolova, 1955). In other marine sediments in the southeastern U.S.S.R. minute mordenite crystals form up to 20 per cent. of the rock, *e.g.* in the chalk of Bryansk (Table 53, anal. 6) where it is associated with hydromica, kaolinite and glauconite. Mordenite has been reported as fine silk-like threads in bentonitic clays in Japan (Hayashi and Sudo, 1957); the latter occur in tuffaceous sediments and interstratified with tuff and liparite, and in this case the mordenite may have been derived from the alteration of the igneous material.

Gismondine is one of the rarer zeolites and occurs in cavities in leucite tephrite in Czechoslovakia (Hibsch, 1939) and in leucitic lava at Capo di Bove, southeast of Rome (*e.g.* anal. 8, Table 53). Dunham (1933) has recorded it, together with stilbite, allophane, olivine and augite, in cavities in an ankaratrite at Alexander dam, Kauai, Hawaii, and it has been reported from one specimen of a highly altered granite in Queensland, where it occurs on chlorite in cavities (White-house, 1937). Gismondine is reported from some 40 localities in Antrim and Iceland by Walker (1962): it occupies a well-marked position in the sequence of zeolite zones in basaltic lavas and is characteristically associated with chabazite, thomsonite and phillipsite.

Ashcroftine, initially described as kalithomsonite, was first reported occurring as a fine pink crystalline powder in pegmatitic pockets in augite syenite at Narsarsuk, Greenland (Gordon, 1924). Its possible occurrence in katungite from Uganda has been reported by Holmes (1936; 1937).

X-ray diffraction powder data for zeolites

Analcite
Coombs (1955)

Radiation: CuK$_\alpha$ Method: camera, diam. 19 cm., visually estimated intensities.
Specimen: birefringent analcite, steam cavity in basalt, Flinders, Australia

d(Å)	I	hkl*	d(Å)	I	hkl*	d(Å)	I	hkl*
6·87	<1	(200)	2·168	<1	620	1·618	2	822, 660
5·61	8	211	2·115	<1	541	1·596	3	831, 743 (750)
4·86	4	220	2·022	1	631	1·498	2	842
3·67	2	321	1·940	<1	543 (550, 710)	1·480	2	761, 921, 655
3·43	10	400	1·903	5	640	1·463	1	664
2·925	8	332	1·867	4	633, 721, 552	1·447	1	754, 851 (930)
2·801	2	422	1·833	<1	642	1·415	4	932, 763
2·693	5	431 (510)	1·743	6	732, 651	1·386	<1	941, 853 (770)
2·505	5	521	1·716	3	800	1·372	1	860 (10·0·0)
2·426	3	440	7·689	4	741 (811, 554)	1·358$_6$	4	10·1·1, 772
2·226	4	611, 532	1·664	1	820 (644)			

* Indices in brackets are for reflections which should be extinguished in the space group *Ia3d* inferred for the strictly cubic modification.

Wairakite
Coombs (1955)

Radiation: CuK$_\alpha$ Method: camera, diam. 19 cm., visually estimated intensities.
Specimen: wairakite, Wairakei, New Zealand.   α 1·498, γ 1·502, 2V$_\gamma$ 70°–105°, D 2·265

d(Å)	I	d(Å)	I	d(Å)	I
6·85	4	2·418	3	1·722–1·732	4B
5·57	8	2·35	<1B	1·708	<1
4·84	4	2·26–2·28	1B	1·696	<1
3·64	3	2·215	4	1·680	2B
3·42	6	2·17	<1	1·66	<1B
3·39	10	2·147	1	1·612	1B
3·21	<1B	2·115	1	1·595	<1
3·04–3·06	1B	2·095	<1	1·586	2
2·909	5	1·996	2	1·487	1
2·897	3	1·93	<1B	1·465	1B
2·783	1	1·886–1·895	3B	1·437	<1B
2·770	1	1·867	1	1·407	2B
2·680	4	1·857	3	1·354	1
2·67	1	1·844	1	1·343	1
2·50	<1	1·822	<1B	1·215	2B
2·489	4				

B—Broad reflection.

Viséite
McConnell (1952)

Radiation: CuK$_\alpha$ Method: camera, diam. 114·6 mm.

n 1·53, D 2·2

d(Å)	I	d(Å)	I	d(Å)	I
5·68	4	2·014	<1	1·282	1
4·98	1	1·886	3	1·196	2
3·46	5	1·740	6	1·155	2
2·92	10	1·380	1	1·138	1
2·20	2	1·323	1	1·105	1
2·11	<1				

Natrolite

Meixner *et al.* (1956

Radiation: CuK_α Method: camera, diam. 6 cm.

Specimen: natrolite, Snake Hill, Hudson County, New Jersey

$d(Å)$	I	$d(Å)$	I	$d(Å)$	I
6·53	s	2·52	vvw	1·754	w
5·87	vs	2·45	m	1·728	mw
4·64	m	2·41	m	1·700	w
4·36	vs	2·33	mw	1·676	vw
4·14	ms	2·26	w	1·647	w
3·90	vvw	2·19	m	1·627	mw
3·64	vvw	2·12	vvw	1·600	mw
3·17	ms	2·06	w	1·571	vw
3·11	m	2·02	vvw	1·530	mw
2·95	m	1·96	w	1·510	vvw
2·86	vvs	1·93	vvw	1·485	vvw
2·75	vvw	1·876	mw	1·462	m
2·67	vvw	1·831	vvw		
2·58	m	1·799	m		

Mesolite

Peng (1955)

Radiation: CuK_α Method: camera and diffractometer.

Specimen: natural mesolite

$d(Å)$	I	$d(Å)$	I	$d(Å)$	I
6·44	4B	2·47	1	1·68	−1
5·79	7	2·41	1	1·64	1
5·46	−1	2·34	−1	1·59	−1
4·66	3	2·27	−1	1·54	−1
4·35	5B	2·19	3D	1·52	−1
4·16	1	2·05	−1	1·47	3
3·89	−1	1·95	−1	1·43	1
3·18	3D	1·86	−1	1·40	1
3·08	2D	1·81	3	1·39	1
2·86	10	1·75	1	1·35	−1
2·57	1D	1·72	−1	1·30	−1

B—Broad; *D*—Diffuse.

Scolecite

Peng (1955)

Radiation: CuK_α Method: camera and diffractometer.

Specimen: scolecite, Bombay, India

$d(Å)$	I	$d(Å)$	I	$d(Å)$	I
6·53	3	2·42	1	1·75	2
5·81	4	2·32	1	1·72	0·5
4·69	3	2·26	1	1·66	0·5B
4·37	5	2·20	3	1·64	1B
4·19	1	2·17	0·2	1·61	1
3·63	1	2·07	1	1·60	0·3
3·15	2	2·03	0·5	1·52	0·5
3·09	1	1·99	2	1·50	0·2
2·86	10	1·95	2	1·47	2
2·68	0·2	1·90	0·5	1·43	1
2·58	1	1·86	1	1·38	1
2·47	1	1·80	3	1·33	1

B—Broad.

Thomsonite

A.S.T.M. card 9.490

Radiation: CuK$_\alpha$ Method: camera, photometered intensities.

Specimen: thomsonite, Faroes

d(Å)	I	hkl	d(Å)	I	hkl	d(Å)	I
9·3	10	110					
6·6	70	200, 020, 002	2·95	80	240, 420	2·06	10
5·9	70	102	2·93	10	042, 402	1·958	5
5·37	20	112	2·86	100	142, 412	1·884	20
4·63	70	220, 022, 202	2·79	20	332	1·827	20
4·38	50	122, 212	2·68	80	242, 422	1·811	30
4·14	60	130, 310	2·58	30	134, 314	1·780	5
3·95	5	*	2·43	20		1·753	5
3·79	5	222	2·29	10		1·735	5
3·50	70	132, 312	2·25	30		1·716	10
3·27	10	040, 400	2·19	20		1·678	5
3·20	50	232	2·18	20		1·653	20
3·18	30	322	2·12	10		1·632	5
			2·09	20		1·624	5

* Not indexed.

Gonnardite

Meixner *et al.* (1956)

Radiation: CuK$_\alpha$ Method: camera, diam. 6 cm.

Specimen: gonnardite, Chaux de Bergonne, Puy de Dôme, France

d(Å)	I	d(Å)	I	d(Å)	I
6·70	s	2·33	vvw	1·607	w
5·93	vs	2·28	w	1·548	wB
5·25	w	2·22	m	1·486	mw
4·74	ms	2·16	vvw	1·442	w
4·44	s	2·12	vwB	1·398	wB
4·22	mw	2·07	w	1·348	vw
3·69	vw	1·98	wB	1·323	mw
3·52	vvw	1·895	mw	1·291	vw
3·23	ms	1·851	w	1·262	vvw ?
3·12	m	1·818	mw	1·237	mw
2·92	vvs	1·759	mwB	1·202	vw
2·61	m	1·697	w	1·178	vvw
2·48	m	1·647	m	1·157	vw
2·36	w				

B—Broad.

Edingtonite

A.S.T.M. card 3.0383

Radiation: CuK$_\alpha$ Method: camera, visually estimated intensities.

Specimen: edingtonite, Böhlet, Westergotland, Sweden

d(Å)	I	d(Å)	I	d(Å)	I
9·24	25	2·09	50	1·39	25
6·17	25	2·01	50D	1·35	40
5·15	50	1·86	25	1·33	50
4·54	75	1·81	75	1·30	50
4·18	25	1·75	25	1·24	50
3·84	25	1·69	25	1·22	50
3·46	100	1·63	75	1·19	40D
3·31	50	1·58	50	1·17	20
2·96	75	1·55	25	1·15	20
2·69	100	1·51	60	1·11	40
2·61	25	1·49	50	1·09	20
2·54	50	1·46	25D	1·05	40
2·23	75	1·42	60	1·04	40
2·15	50				

D—Doublet.

Mountainite

Gard and Taylor (1957)

Radiation: CuK$_\alpha$ Method: cameras, diam. 6 cm. and 11·46 cm.

Specimen: mountainite, Kimberley, South Africa. White fibres, D 2·36

d(Å)	I	hkl	d(Å)	I	hkl	d(Å)	I	hkl
13·1	s	001	3·36	mw	123	2·65	w	—
		⎧ 20$\bar{1}$			⎧ 203	2·54	w	—
6·6	vs	⎨ 200 ⎨ 020	3·30	w	⎨ 20$\bar{4}$ ⎨ 40$\bar{2}$	2·42	vw	—
		⎩ 002			⎩ 400	2·32	mw	—
		⎧ 021	3·28	mw	⎧ 040	2·23	vw	—
5·9	vw	⎨ 120			⎩ 004	2·11	mwD	—
5·4	vw	⎧ 201 ⎨ 20$\bar{2}$	3·18	vw	32$\bar{3}$	1·967	ms	—
			3·04	vw	12$\bar{4}$	1·882	vw	—
4·67	s	⎧ 022 ⎨ 22$\bar{1}$			⎧ 420	1·820	w	—
					⎨ 024	1·719	m	—
4·18	m	⎧ 221 ⎨ 22$\bar{2}$	2·94	vvs	⎨ 42$\bar{2}$ ⎨ 22$\bar{4}$	1·678	v w	—
					⎨ 223	1·639	w	—
3·74	w	32$\bar{1}$			⎩ 240	1·578	v w	—
3·66	w	⎧ 023 ⎨ 320	2·80	ms	—			

D—Doublet.

Rhodesite

Gard and Taylor (1957)

Radiation: CuK$_\alpha$ Method: cameras, diam. 6 cm. and 11·46 cm.

Specimen: rhodesite, Kimberley, S. Africa. White fibres, α 1·502, β 1·505, γ 1·515, D 2·36

d(Å)	I	hkl	d(Å)	I	hkl	d(Å	I
11·8	s	200			⎧ 320	2·05	w
7·1		⎧ 001	3·02	s	⎨ 710	1·967	vw
	vwD	⎨			⎨ 800	1·924	vw
6·7		⎩ 101	2·98	m	⎩ 021	1·890	vw
6·56	s	010			⎧ 420	1·861	ms
6·28	w	110	2·89	s	⎨ 312	1·840	vw
5·95	m	400			⎧ 321	1·815	vw
5·25	vw	301	2·78	s	⎨ 711	1·771	vwD
5·04	w	310			⎧ 801	1·756	ms
4·80	w	011	2·75	ms	⎨ 412	1·724	vvw
4.42	m	410	2·72	vvw		1·697	m
4·11	vw	311	2·67	vvw		1·695	m
3·99	vw	⎧ 600 ⎨ 501	2·63	vvw		1·675	vw
3·87	vvw	510	2·53	w		1·650	vvw
3·76	vvw	411	2·49	vvw		1·640	vvw
3·51	vvw	002	2·44	vw		1·603	w
3·39	w	610	2·25	vvw		1·542	mw
3·27	vw	020	2·20	vvw		1·522	vw
3·07	vs	112	2·15	w		1·501	vw
			2·10	vvw			

D—Doublet.

Heulandite

Mumpton (1960)

Radiation: CuK$_\alpha$ Method: diffractometer.

Specimen: heulandite, Prospect Park, New Jersey

$d(\text{Å})$	I	$d(\text{Å})$	I	$d(\text{Å})$	I
8·90	10	4·45	2	3·07	1
7·94	2	4·36	1	3·03	1
6·80	1	3·97	2	2·97	4
6·63	1	3·89	3	2·80	1
5·92	1	3·83	1	2·72	1
5·58	1	3·71	1	2·67	1
5·24	1	3·56	1	2·48	1
5·09	1	3·47	1	2·43	1
4·89	1	3·40	2	2·35	1
4·69	2	3·12	1	2·28	2

Clinoptilolite

Mumpton (1960)

Radiation: CuK$_\alpha$ Method: diffractometer.

Specimen: clinoptilolite, Hector, California

$d(\text{Å})$	I	$d(\text{Å})$	I	$d(\text{Å})$	I
9·00	10	3·90	8	2·87	1
7·94	4	3·83	1	2·82	3
6·77	3	3·73	1	2·80	1
6·64	2	3·55	2	2·73	1
5·91	1	3·46	2	2·72	1
5·24	3	3·42	6	2·68	1
5·11	1	3·12	3	2·44	1
4·69	2	3·07	2	2·42	1
4·48	2	3·04	2	2·38	1
4·34	2	2·97	5	2·29	1
3·96	10				

Stilbite

Mason and Greenberg (1954). Indexing from A.S.T.M. card 10.433

Radiation: CuK$_\alpha$ Method: camera, diam. 114·6 mm.

Specimen: stilbite crystals in vesicles in basalt, Herval, Santa Catherina, south-eastern Brazil

α 1·440, β 1·500, γ 1·502, D 2·16

$d(\text{Å})$	I	hkl	$d(\text{Å})$	I	hkl	$d(\text{Å})$	I
9·1	90	001, 020	3·03	70	$\bar{4}$22, $\bar{1}$52	1·67	20
5·4	20	$\bar{2}$21, $\bar{2}$02, 200	2·79	30	$\bar{3}$14, $\bar{3}$51	1·60	20
4·68	70	220, $_\sim$22	2·69	20	202	1·56	20
4·30	30	$\bar{3}$11, $\bar{3}$12	2·59	20	222, $\bar{4}$41	1·35	10
4·08	100	041, $\bar{1}$32	2·26	30		1·30	20
3·74	40	$\bar{2}$03	2·04	20		1·13	10
3·41	50	$\bar{1}$13, $\bar{4}$02	1·83	10		1·08	10
3·20	50	$\bar{4}$03	1·78	10			

Epistilbite

Koizumi and Roy (1960)

Method: diffractometer.

Specimen: synthetic epistilbite; n 1·509, δ 0·007

$d(\text{Å})$	I	$d(\text{Å})$	I	$d(\text{Å})$	I
8·9	23	3·867	40	2·921	16
6·92	14	3·731	14	2·698	8
4·914	39	3·453	34	2·557	6
4·484	10	3·209	20	2·430	11
4·353	10				

Brewsterite

Strunz and Tennyson (1956)

Radiation: CuK_α Method: camera, diam. 57·3 mm.

Specimen: brewsterite, Strontian, Argyllshire, Scotland.   D 2·45

d(Å)	I	d(Å)	I	d(Å)	I
6·81	3	2·667	3	1·771	1
6·15	9	2·550	3	1·728	2
4·98	4	2·442	3	1·642	4
4·53	10	2·309	3	1·595	2
3·867	7	2·243	3	1·542	2
3·708	1	2·191	2	1·514	1
3·480	1	2·103	3	1·471	1
3·351	1	1·989	4	1·435	2
3·209	8	1·933	2	1·386	2
3·018	1	1·866	1	1·358	2
2·885	9	1·824	1	1·324	2

Ferrierite

Staples (1955)

Radiation: CuK_α Method: camera.

Specimen: ferrierite, with chalcedony in seams in basalt, Kamloops Lake, British Columbia
D 2·15

d(Å)	I	hkl	d(Å)	I	hkl
11·33	2	110	3·54	8	{ 112 / 040
9·61	10	200			
7·00	3	{ 020 / 101	3·49	8	202
			3·42	2	501
6·61	2	011	3·31	2	240
5·84	5	310	3·20	1	600
4·96	1−	121	3·15	3	{ 141 / 312
4·80	1−	{ 301 / 400	3·07	3	{ 521 / 431
4·58	1−	130	2·97	3	530
3·99	9	{ 321 / 031	2·90	2	{ 620 / 132
3·88	1	411	2·72	2	422
3·79	2	{ 330 / 002	2·64	2	051
3·69	5	510	2·58	3	{ 350 / 042 / 701

Phillipsite

Radiation: CuK_α Method: camera.

Specimen: phillipsite

d(Å)	I	d(Å)	I	d(Å)	I
7·64	100	2·94	50	1·78	50
6·91	100	2·71	70	1·72	50
6·34	20	2·52	50	1·67	20D
5·24	50	2·40	50D	1·61	20
4·91	50	2·16	20	1·55	20
4·56	20	2·07	20	1·49	20
4·25	70	1·97	50	1·38	50
4·07	70	1·91	20	1·34	50
3·54	50	1·84	20	1·28	50D
3·18	100				

D—Doublet.

Harmotome

Waterson (1953).   Indexing from A.S.T.M. card 9.480.

Method: camera.

Specimen: harmotome; small crystals in breccia associated with haematite, calcite and barytes, Loch an Arbhair, north-west Ross-shire, Scotland

d(Å)	I	*hkl*	d(Å)	I	d(Å)	I
8·24	s	100, 101	2·71	s	1·88	vw
7·17	s	001, 110, 111	2·62	s	1·82 ⎱ B	w
6·26	s	011	2·51	m	1·80 ⎰	
4·94	m	201	2·45	vw	1·75	mw
4·26	w	101, 102	2·35	m	1·72 ⎱ B	ms
4·03	s	200, 202, 221	2·29	m	1·69 ⎰	
3·87	mw	210, 212	2·23	w	1·52	m
3·20	s	302, 022	2·13	m	1·47	w
3·06	s	230, 232	2·04	m	1·43	vw
2·88	mw	203, 321, 241	1·94	s	1·36	w
					1·32	w

B—Broad.

Chabazite

Mason and Greenberg (1954).   Indexing from A.S.T.M. card 10.370

Radiation: CuK_α Method: camera, diam. 114·6 mm.

Specimen: chabazite, vesicles in basalt, Herval, Santa Catherina, south-eastern Brazil.
ω 1·481, ϵ 1·483, D 2·05

d(Å)	I	hkl	d(Å)	I	hkl	d(Å)	I
9·5	70	101	3·47	20	220, 104	1·66	10
7·0	40	110	2·95	100	401	1·57	10
6·4	10	012	2·62	20	410	1·53	10
5·6	40	021	2·51	30	125, 232	1·43	10
5·0	40	003	2·10	20	333	1·41	10
4·35	90	211	1·82	30		1·35	10
3·90	20	122, 300	1·74	20		1·33	10
3·61	50	*					

* Not indexed.

Gmelinite

Strunz (1956).   Indexing from A.S.T.M. card 9.419

Radiation: CuK_α Method: camera, diam. 57·3 mm.

Specimen: gmelinite, Ireland; D 2·028, ϵ 1·474, ω 1·476

d(Å)	I	hkl	d(Å)	I	hkl	d(Å)	I
11·95	7	100	2·675	5	213	1·598	<1
7·69	5	101	2·571	1	402	1·580	2
6·81	4	110	2·292	2		1·519	<1B
5·985	1	200	2·196	<1		1·482	2
5·067	5	201	2·076	4		1·465	2
4·529	2	102, 210	1·989?	<1		1·435	<1
4·095	8	211	1·941	1		1·412	3
3·440	2	220	1·907	1		1·388	2
3·220	5	221	1·801	4		≃1·37	<1
3·089	<1	302	1·722	4		1·349	<1
2·959	6	400, 113	1·678	2		1·324	4
2·849	5	222, 401	1·631	<1		1·296	3

B—Broad.

Levyne

Strunz (1956)

Radiation: CuK_α Method: camera, diam. 57·3 mm.

Specimen: Levyne, Antrim, Ireland; $\omega = \epsilon = 1·500$, D 2·140.

d(Å)	I	d(Å)	I	d(Å)	I
10·28	4	3·048	2	1·941	1
8·12	7	2·858	1	1·870	1
7·50	1	2·780	8	1·824	<1
6·61	3	2·690	<1	1·781	4
5·126	6	2·599	7	1·740	1
4·671	<1	2·495	2	1·656	5
4·270	6	2·380	3	1·616	1
4·040	8	2·287	2	1·570	2
3·818	4	2·212	2	1·537	3
3·453	2	2·117	3	1·461	2
3·278	2	2·045	2	1·421	3
3·132	7				

Erionite

Staples and Gard (1959)

Radiation: CuK$_\alpha$

Method: cameras, diam. 6 and 11·54 cm.; visually estimated intensities.

Specimen: fibrous erionite, Durkee, Baker County, Oregon; ω 1·468, ϵ 1·473, D 2·02

d(Å)	I	hkl	d(Å)	I
11·57	10	10$\bar{1}$0	2·36	1−
9·16	3	10$\bar{1}$1	2·28	1−
7·56	5	0002		
6·63	8	11$\bar{2}$0	2·21	4
6·30	1	10$\bar{1}$2	2·12	2
5·77	3	20$\bar{2}$0	2·08	2
5·37	4	20$\bar{2}$1		
4·58	4	20$\bar{2}$2, 10$\bar{1}$3	2·04	1−
4·34	7	21$\bar{3}$0		
4·16	4	21$\bar{3}$1	1·99	1
3·80	9B	{ 30$\bar{3}$0, 21$\bar{3}$2 { 20$\bar{2}$3, 0004	1·95	1
3·58	5	10$\bar{1}$4	1·88	2
3·31	4	{ 22$\bar{4}$0, 21$\bar{3}$3 { 11$\bar{2}$3	1·84	2
3·15	4B	{ 31$\bar{4}$0, 31$\bar{4}$1 { 20$\bar{2}$4	1·77	4
2·92	1−	31$\bar{4}$2	1·75	1
2·84	10B	{ 40$\bar{4}$0, 40$\bar{4}$1 { 21$\bar{3}$4	1·70	1
2·68	4	40$\bar{4}$2, 31$\bar{4}$3	1·65	7
2·50	7B			

B—Broad.

Faujasite

Barrer *et al.* (1956)

Radiation: CuK$_\alpha$

Method: Guinier camera, diam. 229·2 mm.

Specimen: synthetic Ca-faujasite

d(Å)	I	hkl	d(Å)	I	hkl
14·375	100	111	3·160	30	800
8·762	60	220	3·037	60	644, 820
7·519	40	311	2·930	70	660, 822
7·181	10	222	2·873	90	555, 751
6·226	10	400	2·782	70	840
5·721	80	331	2·729	40	911
5·089	10	422	2·652	60	664
4·785	50	333, 511	2·609	50	931
4·392	80	440	2·539	30	844
3·930	40	620	2·498	20	
3·792	90	533	2·438	30	
3·764	30	622	2·403	20	
3·590	30	444	2·394	50	
3·485	40	551, 711	2·244	10	
3·320	80	642	2·199	60	
3·234	50	553, 731	2·173	40	

Laumontite

Kaley and Hanson (1955)

Radiation: CuK_α Method: camera, radius 7·1744 cm.

Specimen: laumontite, sandstone, San Joaquin Valley, California

α 1·508, γ 1·516, (−) 2V mod.

$d(Å)$	I	$d(Å)$	I	$d(Å)$	I
9·42	vs	2·56	vvw	1·536	mw
6·81	s	2·52	vvw	1·51	w
6·20	w	2·42	m	1·49?	vvwB
5·04	w	2·34	w	1·46	vwB
4·73	vvw	2·27	w	1·37	mwB
4·46	w	2·15	mB	1·32?	vvw
4·16	vs	2·06	vvw	1·31?	vvw
3·67	vw	1·97	vw	1·296	vvw
3·49	s	1·94	vw	1·27?	vvw
3·32	vs	1·86?	vvw	1·25	vvw
3·20	vvwB	1·808	mw	1·22	vw
3·02	m	1·748	vvw	1·21	vw
2·87	w+	1·657	vvw	1·176	vvw
2·77	w+	1·618	w	1·157	vw

Mordenite

Harris and Brindley (1954)

Radiation: CoK_α Method: cameras, diam. 19 cm. and 20 cm.

Specimen: mordenite, Aros, Isle of Mull, Scotland

$d(Å)$	I	hkl	$d(Å)$	I	hkl	$d(Å)$	I
13·7	5	110	3·103	2	441	1·953	4
9·10	9	200	2·946	2	531	1·936	1
6·61	9	111	2·896	6	402	1·917	2
6·38	4	130	2·743	1	152	1·883	4
6·10	5	021	2·700	3	621	1·865	1
5·79	5	201	2·639	1	370	1·850	1
5·03	1	221	2·560	4	461	1·813	3
4·871	2	131	2·522	5	442	1·795	3
4·525	8	330	2·465	2		1·765	1
4·143	3	420	2·437	2		1·738	1
3·999	9	150	2·343	2		1·720	2
3·842	6	241	2·299	1		1·698	1
3·763	2	002	2·275	1		1·686	2
3·624	1	112	2·228	2		1·665	2
3·563	1	510	2·162	2		1·647	1
3·483	10	202	2·123	1		1·622	2
3·393	9	060	2·047	4		1·597	3
3·308	1	222	2·019	4		1·546	2
3·222	10	530	1·998	4			

Gismondine

A.S.T.M. card 2.0096

Radiation: $CuK_?$ Method: camera.

Specimen: gismondine, Casale di Brunori, Via di Demico, Rome.   D 2·23

$d(Å)$	I	hkl	$d(Å)$	I	$d(Å)$	I
7·3	100	111	2·14	20	1·42	50
4·9	60	220	2·07 ⎫	40	1·40	50
4·19	80	131	1·91 ⎭		1·38	50
3·55	40	222	1·88	40	1·34	50
3·24	100	330	1·78	60	1·29	20D
2·99	40	421	1·73	40	1·25	20
2·73	100B	332, 151	1·67	40D	1·22	20
2·55	20	114	1·61	40	1·18	20
2·38	20D	512, 530	1·56	40	1·11	20
2·27	20	314	1·50	40		

B—Broad.   D—Doublet.

REFERENCES

Afanasiev, G. D., Aidinyan, N. K. and Borisevich, I. V., 1940. On the genesis of the Mazul manganese *Doklady* deposit. *Acad. Sci. URSS*, vol. 26, p. 792.

Ames, L. L., 1960. The cation sieve properties of clinoptilolite. *Amer. Min.*, vol. 45, p. 689.

—— Sand, L. B. and Goldich, S. S., 1958. A contribution on the Hector, California, bentonite deposit. *Econ. Geol.*, vol. 53, p. 22.

Antonín, R., 1942. Research on the minerals and ores of Vinařická hill. *Věstník Kral. České Spol. Nauk* (M.A. 10–36).

Antun, P., 1953. Laumontite de Serpont. *Bull. Soc. géol. Belgique*, vol. 77, p. B63.

Barrer, R. M., 1938. The sorption of polar and non-polar gases by zeolites. *Proc. Roy. Soc.*, A, vol. 167, p. 392.

—— 1944. Sorption by gmelinite and mordenite. *Trans. Faraday Soc.*, vol. 40, p. 555.

—— 1948. Syntheses and reactions of mordenite. *Journ. Chem. Soc.*, p. 2158.

—— 1958. Crystalline ion-exchangers. *Proc. Chem. Soc.*, p. 99.

—— and Baynham, J. W., 1956. The hydrothermal chemistry of the silicates. Part VII. Synthetic potassium aluminosilicates. *Journ. Chem. Soc.*, p. 2882.

—— Bultitude, F. W. and Kerr, I. S., 1959. Some properties of, and a structural scheme for, the harmotome zeolites. *Journ. Chem. Soc.*, p. 1521.

—— Buser, W. and Grütter, O., 1956. Synthetischer "Faujasit." I. Eigenschaften und Ionenaustauschcharakter. *Helvetia Chim. Acta*, vol. 39, p. 518.

—— and Kerr, I. S., 1959. Intercrystalline channels in levynite and some related zeolites. *Trans. Faraday Soc.*, vol. 55, p. 1915.

—— and Langley, D. A., 1958. Reactions and stability of chabazite-like phases. Part I. Ion-exchanged forms of natural chabazite. *Journ. Chem. Soc.*, p. 3804. Part II. Ion-exchanged forms of some synthetic species. *Ibid.*, p. 3811. Part III. Intracrystalline water. *Ibid.*, p. 3817.

—— and Sammon, D. C., 1955. Exchange equilibria in crystals of chabazite. *Journ. Chem. Soc.*, p. 2838.

Beattie, I. R., 1954. The electrical conductivity of analcite and ion-exchanged forms of analcite and chabazite. *Trans. Faraday Soc.*, vol. 50, p. 581.

—— and Dyer, A., 1957. The preparation of hydronium forms of analcite and chabazite by ion-exchange. *Journ. Chem. Soc.*, p. 4387.

Belyankin, D. S. and Petrov, V. P., 1940. Some new data on teschenites and related zeolite-bearing rocks of the territory of Georgia (Caucasus). *Mém. Soc. Russe Min.*, ser. 2, vol. 69, p. 276 (M.A. 10–296).

Benson, W. N., 1942. The basic igneous rocks of eastern Otago and their tectonic environment, Part III. The olivine theralite of Waihola. . . . *Trans. Roy. Soc. New Zealand*, vol. 72, p. 160.

Bergerhoff, G., Baur, W. H. and Nowacki, W., 1958. Über die Kristallstruktur des Faujasites. *Neues Jahrb. Min., Monatshefte*, p. 193.

Berman, H., 1925. Notes on dachiardite. *Amer. Min.*, vol. 10, p. 421.

Beutell, A. and Blaschke, K., 1915. Das Wasser im Desmin ist chemisch gebunden. *Centralblatt Min.*, p. 4.

Bloomer, R. O., 1937. Occurrence of stilbite in the Border Conglomerate near Culpeper, Virginia. *Amer. Min.*, vol. 22, p. 309.

Bonatti, S., 1942. Richerche sulla dachiardite. *Atti Soc. Toscana Sci. Nat.*, vol. 50, p. 14 (M.A. 10–293).

Bond, W. L., 1943. A mineral survey of piezoelectric materials. *Bell. System Tech. Journ.*, New York, vol. 22, p. 145 (M.A. 9–115).

Borneman-Starynkevich, I. D., 1935. Lovchorrite and its analogues. *Mat. Geochem. Khibina tundra, Acad. Sci. USSR*, p. 43 (M.A. 6–342).

Bragg, W. L., 1937. *The atomic structure of minerals.* Cornell Univ. Press.

Bramlette, M. N. and **Posnjak, E.**, 1933. Zeolitic alteration of pyroclastics. *Amer. Min.*, vol. 18, p. 167.

Brauns, A. and **Brauns, R.**, 1924. Ein Kalkzeolith aus der Gruppe der Glimmer-zeolithe vom Schellkopf bei Brenk (oberes Brohltal). *Centralbl. Min.*, p. 549.

Breck, D. W., Eversole, W. G., Milton, R. M., Reed, T. B. and **Thomas, T. L.**, 1956. Crystalline zeolites. I. The properties of a new synthetic zeolite, type A. *Journ. Amer. Chem. Soc.*, vol. 78, p. 5963.

—— and **Smith, J. V.**, 1959. Molecular sieves. *Scientific American*, vol. 44, p. 85.

Brownell, G. M., 1938. Zeolites at the Sherritt Gordon mine. *Univ. Toronto Studs., Geol. Ser.*, no. 41, p. 19.

Bushinsky, G. I., 1950. Mordenite in marine sediments, Cretaceous and Palaeogene. *Doklady Acad. Sci. USSR*, vol. 73, p. 1271.

Caglioti, V., 1927a. Richerche sulla composizione chimica della herschelite di Acicastello. *Rend. Accad. Sci. Fis. Mat. Napoli*, ser. 3, vol. 33, p. 156 (M.A. 4–375).

—— 1927b. Richerche su alcune zeoliti delle leucititi dei dintorni di Roma; la gismondite di Capo di Bove e la pseudophillipsite di Acquacetosa. *Rend. Accad. Sci. Fis. Mat. Napoli*, ser. 3, vol. 33, p. 163 (M.A. 4–375).

Caillère, S., 1937. Sur un mode spécial d'altération de l'anorthite et une variété calcique de thomsonite. *Compt. Rend. Acad. Sci. Paris*, vol. 204, p. 785.

Capdecomme, L., 1952. Laumontite du Pla des Aveillans (Pyrénées-Orientales). *Bull. Hist. Nat. Toulouse*, vol. 87, p. 299 (M.A. 12–485).

Carstens, C. W., 1925. Mineralvorkommen im Trondhjemgebiet. *Norsk Geol. Tidssk.*, vol. 8, p. 140.

Cavinato, A., 1927. Nuove osservazioni sulle zeoliti del gruppo della natrolite. *Mem. R. Accad. Lincei Cl. Sci. fis. mat. nat. Roma*, ser. 6, vol. 2, p. 320 (M.A. 4–320).

Cerný, P., 1955. Minerals of the amphibolite quarry at Mirosov in western Moravia. *Acta Mus. Moraviae*, vol. 40, p. 91 (M.A. 13–192).

Chappell, W. M., 1933. Paulopost stilbite in the Camas Land sill, Chelan County, Washington. *Amer. Min.*, vol. 18, p. 440.

Chirvinsky, P. N., 1939. Palaeohydrogeology of Khibina tundras. *Bull. Acad. Sci. URSS, Sér. Géol.*, no. 4, p. 23 (M.A. 7–515).

Chudoba, K., 1930. Über seltenere Mineraleinschlüsse in Effusivgesteinen. *Centralbl. Min.*, Abt. A, p. 342.

Clarke, F. W. and **Steiger, G.**, 1900. *Zeits anorg. Chem.*, vol. 24, p. 139.

Coombs, D. S., 1952. Cell size, optical properties and chemical composition of laumontite and leonhardite, with a note on regional occurrences in New Zealand. *Amer. Min.*, vol. 37, p. 812.

—— 1954. The nature and alteration of some Triassic sediments from Southland, New Zealand. *Trans. Roy. Soc. New Zealand*, vol. 82, p. 65.

—— 1955. X-ray investigation on wairakite and non-cubic analcime. *Min. Mag.*, vol. 30, p. 699.

—— 1958. Zeolitized tuffs from the Kuttung glacial beds near Seaham, New South Wales. *Australian Journ. Sci.*, vol. 21, p. 18.

—— 1959. Zeolite uses and New Zealand deposits. *Fourth Triennial Min. Conf., Dunedin*, Paper 162.

—— **Ellis, A. D., Fyfe, W. S.** and **Taylor, A. M.**, 1959. The zeolite facies, with comments on the interpretation of hydrothermal syntheses. *Geochim. et Cosmochim. Acta*, vol. 17, p. 53.

Coppola, A., 1948. L'herschelite di Palagonia (Catania). *Not. Min. Siciliana e Calabrese*, vol. 2, p. 63 (M.A. 11–292).

Cornu, F., 1908. Über die Paragenese der Minerale, namentlich die der Zeolithe. *Österr. Zeit. Berg-Hüttenw.*, vol. 56, p. 89.

D'Achiardi, G., 1905. Über einen wahrscheinlich neuen Zeolith von der Insel Elba. *Proc. Verb. Soc. Toscana Sci. Nat.*, vol. 14, p. 150 and vol. 22, p. 160.

Damour, A., 1842. *Ann. Mines*, ser. 4, vol. 1, p. 395.

—— 1848. *Ann. Mines*, ser. 4, vol. 14, p. 67.

Daubrée, A., 1879. *Études synthétiques de géologie expérimentale.* Paris.

Deffeyes, K. S., 1959. Erionite from Cenozoic tuffaceous sediments, central Nevada. *Amer. Min.*, vol. 44, p. 501.

Dent, L. S. and Smith, J. V., 1958. Crystal structure of chabazite, a molecular sieve. *Nature*, vol. 181, p. 1794.

Deriu, M., 1954. Mesolite di Rio Cambone (Montiferro–Sardegna centro-occidentale). *Periodico Min. Roma*, vol. 23, p. 37 (M.A. 12–486).

Di Franco, S., 1932. La thomsonite dell'isola dei Ciclopi. *Periodico Min. Roma* vol. 3, p. 197 (M.A. 5–357).

Doubek, J., 1924. Les roches volcaniques du barrage de la Labe dans la fôret Království près de Dvůr Králové. *Sbornik. Stat. Geol. Ústavu Česk. Repub.*, vol. 4, p. 371 (M.A. 3–38).

Ducros, P., 1960. Étude de la mobilité de l'eau et des cations dans quelques zéolites par relaxation diélectrique et résonance magnétique nucléaire. *Bull. Soc. franç. Min. Crist.*, vol. 83, p. 85.

Dunham, K. C., 1933. Crystal cavities in lavas from the Hawaiian Islands. *Amer. Min.*, vol. 18, p. 369.

Eakle, A. S., 1898. Erionite, a new zeolite. *Amer. Journ. Sci.*, ser. 4, vol. 6, p. 66.

Eichorn, H., 1858. *Ann. Phys. Chem. (Poggendorff)*, vol. 105, p. 130.

Ellis, A. J., 1960. Mordenite synthesis in a natural hydrothermal solution. *Geochim. et Cosmochim. Acta*, vol. 19, p. 145.

Erdélyi, J., 1942. Die hydrothermalen Mineralien des Andesitbruches bei Sátoros. *Föld. Közlöny, Budapest*, vol. 72, p. 192 (M.A. 10–36).

Ermolova, E. P., 1955. Analcime and mordenite in Oligocene and Miocene deposits of western Transcaucasia. *Trans. Min. Mus. Akad. Sci. USSR*, vol. 7, p. 76 (M.A. 13–183).

Fagnani, G., 1948. Prehnite e laumontite del Lago Bianco in Val Bavona (Canton Ticino). *Atti Soc. Ital. Sci. Nat. Mus. Civ., Milano*, vol. 87, p. 189 (M.A. 10–556).

Fenner, C. N., 1910. The Watchung basalt and the paragenesis of its zeolites and other secondary minerals. *Ann. New York Acad. Sci.*, vol. 20, p. 93.

—— 1936. Bore-hole investigations in Yellowstone Park. *Journ. Geol.*, vol. 44, p. 225.

Fermor, L. L., 1925. On the basaltic lavas penetrated by the deep boring for coal at Bhusawal, Bombay Presidency. *Rec. Geol. Surv. India*, vol. 58, p. 93.

Fersman, A. E., 1923. The Khibinsky massif. The Chibina massif of Kola island. *Trans. Northern Sci. Econ. Exped.*, no. 16 (M.A. 2–263).

Fischer, K. and O'Daniel, H., 1956. Bemerkungen zur Struktur der Würfelzeolithe. *Naturwiss.*, vol. 43, p. 348.

—— 1958. The structure and properties of natural and synthetic minerals. Zeolites. *Amer. Min.*, vol. 43, p. 174.

Flett, Sir John, 1933. A thomsonized inclusion from the Blackness sill. *Summ. Prog. Geol. Surv. Gt. Britain*, pt. 2, p. 85.

Fyfe, W. S., Turner, F. J. and Verhoogen, J., 1958. Metamorphic reactions and metamorphic facies. *Geol. Soc. Amer.*, Mem. 73, p. 175.

Gaertner, H. R. and Machatschki, F., 1927. Der Thomsonit aus dem Basalte von Disko, Grönland. *Centr. Min.*, Abt. A, p. 365.

Gard, J. A. and **Taylor, H. F. W.**, 1957. An investigation of two new minerals: rhodesite and mountainite. *Min. Mag.*, vol. 31, p. 611.

Gennaro, V., 1929. Thomsonite e scolecite dell'alta Valle di Ayas e delle Valle di Lanzo. *Atti R. Accad. Sci. Torino*, vol. 64, p. 133 (M.A. 4–376).

Gilbert, C. M., 1951. Laumontite from Anchor Bay, Mendocino County, California. *Bull. Geol. Soc. Amer.*, vol. 62, p. 1517.

—— and **McAndrews, M. G.**, 1948. Authigenic heulandite in sandstone, Santa Cruz County, California. *Journ. Sed. Petr.*, vol. 18, p. 91.

Ginzburg, A. I. and **Gushchina, N. S.**, 1954. Petalite from pegmatites of the eastern Transbaikal region. *Trans. Min. Mus. Acad. Sci. USSR*, vol. 6, p. 71 (M.A. 13–182).

Goldsmith, J. R., 1952. Synthetic soda-free thomsonite. *Min. Mag.*, vol. 29, p. 953.

Gonnard, F., 1871. Sur les dolérites de la Chaux de Bergonne et sur les zéolithes qu'elles contiennent. *Compt. Rend. Acad. Sci. Paris*, vol. 73, p. 1447.

Gordon, S. G., 1924. Minerals obtained in Greenland on the second Academy-Vaux expedition, 1923. *Proc. Acad. Nat. Sci. Philadelphia*, vol. 76, p. 249 (M.A. 2–385).

Graham, R. P. D., 1918. On ferrierite, a new zeolitic mineral from British Columbia; with notes on some other Canadian minerals. *Trans. Roy. Soc. Canada*, ser. 3, vol. 12, sect. 4, p. 185 (M.A. 1–26).

Gruner, E., 1933. Untersuchungen an Alkali–Aluminium–Silikaten. VII. Das Verhalten einiger mineralischer Zeolithe zu flüssigem Ammoniak. *Zeits. anorg. Chem.*, vol. 211, p. 385.

Gruner, J. W., 1950. An attempt to arrange silicates in the order of reaction energies at relatively low temperatures. *Amer. Min.*, vol. 35, p. 137.

Grütter, O., 1931. Ein Skolezitfund in der Valle Maggia (Tessin). *Schweiz. Min. Petr. Mitt.*, vol. 11, p. 266.

Gschwind, M. and **Brandenberger, E.**, 1932. Über zwei neue Zeolithvorkommen im Tessin. *Schweiz. Min. Petr. Mitt.*, vol. 12, p. 445.

Haidinger, W., 1825. *Edinburgh Journ. Sci.*, vol. 3, p. 316.

Halla, F. and **Mehl, E.**, 1930, 1932. Das Raumgitter des Natroliths. *Zeit. Krist.*, vol. 75, p. 421, vol. 83, p. 140.

Harris, P. G. and **Brindley, G. W.**, 1954. Mordenite as an alteration product of a pitchstone glass. *Amer. Min.*, vol. 39, p. 819.

Hayashi, H. and **Sudo, T.**, 1957. Zeolite-bearing bentonites. *Min. Journ. (Japan)*, vol. 2, p. 196.

Heald, M. T., 1956. Cementation of Triassic arkoses in Connecticut and Massachusetts. *Bull. Geol. Soc. Amer.*, vol. 67, p. 1133.

Heddle, M. F., 1855. *Phil. Mag.*, ser. 4, vol. 9, p. 179.

Henderson, E. P. and **Glass, J. J.**, 1933. Additional notes on laumontite and thomsonite from Table Mountain, Colorado. *Amer. Min.*, vol. 18, p. 402.

Heritsch, H., 1940. Mineralien aus einem Andesit der Ostauläufer der Südalpen. *Zentralbl. Min.*, Abt. A, p. 227.

—— 1956. Die Röntgenkristallographie von Laumontit von Stainz (Steiermark). *Min. Petr. Mitt. (Tschermak)*, vol. 5, p. 335.

Hewett, D. F., **Shannon, E. V.** and **Gonyer, F. A.**, 1928. Zeolites from Ritter hot spring, Grant County, Oregon. *Proc. U.S. Nat. Mus.*, vol. 73, art. 16.

Hey, M. H., 1930. Studies on the zeolites. Part I. General review. *Min. Mag.*, vol. 22, p. 422.

—— 1932a. Studies on the zeolites. Part II. Thomsonite (including faroelite) and gonnardite. *Min. Mag.*, vol. 23, p. 51.

—— 1932b. Studies on the zeolites. Part III. Natrolite. *Min. Mag.*, vol. 23, p. 243.

Hey, M. H., 1933. Studies on the zeolites. Part V. Mesolite. *Min. Mag.*, vol. 23, p. 421.

—— 1934. Studies on the zeolites. Part VI. Edingtonite. *Min. Mag.*, vol. 23, p. 483.

—— 1935. Studies on the zeolites. Part VIII. A theory of vapour pressure of the zeolites, and of the diffusion of water or gases in a zeolite crystal. *Min. Mag.*, vol. 24, p. 128.

—— 1936. Studies on the zeolites. Part IX. Scolecite and metascolecite. *Min. Mag.*, vol. 24, p. 227.

—— 1959. A new occurrence of erionite. *Min. Mag.*, vol. 32, p. 343.

—— and **Bannister, F. A.,** 1933. Studies on the zeolites. Part IV. Ashcroftine (kalithomsonite of S. G. Gordon). *Min. Mag.*, vol. 23, p. 305.

—— —— 1934. Studies on the zeolites. Part VII. "Clinoptilolite", a silica-rich variety of heulandite. *Min. Mag.*, vol. 23, p. 556.

—— and **Mourant, A. E.,** 1933. Epistilbite from Jersey. *Bull. Soc. Jersiaise*, vol. 12, p. 104.

Hibsch, J. E., 1927. Erläuterungen zur geologischen Karte der Umgebung von Böhm, Kamnitz. *Knihovna Stát. Geol. Ústavu Česk. Repub.*, vol. 10 (M.A. 3–540).

—— 1939. Einige neue Mineralfunde im Böhmischen Mittelgebirge. *Min. Petr. Mitt. (Tschermak)*, vol. 50, p. 487.

Hodge-Smith, T., 1929. The occurrence of zeolites at Kyogle, New South Wales. *Rec. Australian Mus.*, vol. 17, p. 279.

Hogarth, D. D., 1957. The apatite-bearing veins of Nisikkatch Lake, Saskatchewan. *Canadian Min.*, vol. 6, p. 140.

Holmes, A., 1936. Transfusion of quartz xenoliths in alkali basic and ultrabasic lavas, south-west Uganda. *Min. Mag.*, vol. 24, p. 413.

—— 1937. The petrology of the katungite. *Geol. Mag.*, vol. 74, p. 200.

Hutton, C. O., 1942. *In* Benson, W. N., *q.v.*

—— 1943. The igneous rocks of the Brocken range–Ngahape area, eastern Wellington. *Trans. Roy. Soc. New Zealand*, vol. 72, p. 353.

—— 1944. Some igneous rocks from the New Plymouth area. *Trans. Roy. Soc. New Zealand*, vol. 74, p. 125.

Irrera, G., 1949. Herschelite in basalto palagonitico da un sondaggio a Ficarazzi (Catania). *Not. Min. Siciliana e Calabrese*, vol. 3, p. 40 (M.A. 11–292).

Kalb, G. and **Klotsch, H.,** 1944. Die Symmetrie des Harmotom und Phillipsit unter Berücksichtigung der Vizinalerscheinungen. *Zeit. Krist.*, vol. 105, p. 315.

Kaley, M. E. and **Hanson, R. F.,** 1955. Laumontite and leonhardite cement in Miocene sandstone from a well in San Joaquin Valley, California. *Amer. Min.*, vol. 40, p. 923.

Kamb, W. B. and **Oke, W. C.,** 1960. Paulingite, a new zeolite, in association with erionite and filiform pyrite. *Amer. Min.*, vol. 45, p. 79.

Kappen, H. and **Fischer, B.,** 1928. Ueber den Ionenaustausch der zeolithischen Silikate bei Beteiligung hydrolytisch gespaltener Salze. 2. Versuche mit natürlichen Silikaten. *Zeits. Pflanz. Düng*, A, vol. 12, p. 2 (M.A. 4–317).

Kato, T., 1959. Heulandite and chabazite from Hashikaké-zawa, Chichibu mine, Saitama Prefecture. *Journ. Min. Soc. Japan*, vol. 4, p. 299.

Kerr, P. F. and **Cameron, E. N.,** 1936. Fuller's earth of bentonitic origin from Tehachapi, California. *Amer. Min.*, vol. 21, p. 230.

Kington, G. L. and **Laing, W.,** 1955. The crystal structure of chabazite and its sorptive properties. *Trans. Faraday Soc.*, vol. 51, p. 287.

Kinoshita, K., 1922. Harmotome from Udo, Shimane prefecture. *Journ. Geol. Soc. Tokyo*, vol. 29, p. 83 (M.A. 3–288).

Kiriyama, R., Koizumi, M., Yamad, K. and **Kitagaki, R.**, 1957. Hydrothermal reaction of zeolites. *Journ. Min. Soc. Japan*, vol. 3, p. 107.

Koch, R. A., 1958. Über den Laumontit des Petersberges bei Halle a.d. Saale. *Neues Jahrb. Min., Monat.*, p. 58.

Koizumi, M., 1953. The differential thermal analysis curves and dehydration curves of zeolites. *Min. Journ. (Japan)*, vol. 1, p. 36.

—— and **Roy, R.**, 1960. Zeolite studies. I. Synthesis and stability of the calcium zeolites. *Journ. Geol.*, vol. 68, p. 41.

Kostov, I., 1960. Composition and paragenesis of the zeolitic minerals. *Rept. 21st Internat. Geol. Congress, Norden*, Part 17, p. 122.

Kratochvíl, F., 1933. Contribution to the knowledge of Bohemian prehnites and zeolites. *Časopis Národního Mus. Praha*, vol. 107, p. 36 (M.A. 6–129).

Kraus, O., 1939. Röntgenographischen Untersuchungen an Gismondin. *Centralbl. Min.*, Abt. A, p. 105.

Kuzmenko, M. V., 1950. Chalcedony-like natrolite in pegmatites of alkalic magmas. *Doklady Acad. Sci. USSR*, vol. 72, p. 767.

Lacroix, A., 1896. Sur la gonnardite. *Bull. Soc. Franç. Min.*, vol. 19, p. 426.

Lamb, A. B. and **Woodhouse, J. C.**, 1936. Adsorption by dehydrated chabasite as a function of the water content. *Journ. Amer. Chem. Soc.*, vol. 58, p. 2637.

Landes, K. K., 1931. A paragenetic classification of the Magnet Cove minerals. *Amer. Min.*, vol. 16, p. 313.

Larsen, E. S., 1942. Alkalic rocks of Iron Hill, Gunnison County, Colorado. *U.S. Geol. Surv., Prof. Paper* 197A.

—— **Hurlbut, C. S., Griggs, D., Buie, B. F.** and **Burgess, C. H.**, 1939. Igneous rocks of the Highwood Mountains, Montana. *Bull. Geol. Soc. Amer.*, vol. 50, p. 1043.

Lemberg, J., 1877. Ueber Gesteinsumbildungen bei Predazzo und am Monzoni. *Zeit. deutsch. geol. Ges.*, vol. 29, p. 457.

—— 1885. Zur Kenntniss der Bildung und Umbildung von Silicaten. *Zeit. deutsch. geol. Ges.*, vol. 37, p. 959.

McClellan, H. W., 1926. Laumontite from southern Oregon. *Amer. Min.*, vol. 11, p. 287.

McConnell, D., 1952. Viséite, a zeolite with the analcime structure and containing linked SiO_4, PO_4 and H_nO_4 groups. *Amer. Min.*, vol. 37, p. 609.

M'Lintock, W. F. P., 1915. On the zeolites and associated minerals from the Tertiary lavas around Ben More, Mull. *Trans. Roy. Soc. Edinburgh*, vol. 51, p. 1.

Machatschki, F., 1926. Ein Harmotomvorkommen in Steiermark. *Centralbl. Min.*, Abt. A, p. 115.

Magistad, O. C., 1929. The use of artificial zeolites in studying base-exchange phenomena. *Journ. Amer. Soc. Agronomy*, vol. 21, p. 1047.

Majer, V., 1953. Chabazite and stilbite from Bor (Yugoslavia). *Jugoslav. Akad. Znan. Umjet.*, p. 175 and p. 191 (M.A. 12–483).

Marshall, C. E., 1949. *The colloid chemistry of the silicate minerals*. Academic Press, New York.

Martinez, G., 1929. Heulandite di Monastir. *Atti R. Accad. Linc., Cl. Sci. fis Mat. nat.*, ser. 6, vol. 9, p. 428 (M.A. 5–82).

Mason, B., 1946. Analcite, apophyllite, and natrolite from the Pahau river, North Canterbury. *New Zealand Journ. Sci. Technol.*, B, vol. 28, p. 53.

—— 1957. Gonnardite (ranite) from Langesundsfjord. *Norsk Geol. Tidsskr.*, vol. 37, p. 435.

—— and **Greenberg, S. S.**, 1954. Zeolites and associated minerals from southern Brazil. *Arkiv. Min. Geol.*, vol. 1, p. 519.

—— and **Sand, L. B.**, 1960. Clinoptilolite from Patagonia; the relationship between clinoptilolite and heulandite. *Amer. Min.*, vol. 45, p. 341.

Mattinen, V., 1952. Stellerite from Sillböle, Finland. *Bull. Comm. géol. Finlande,* no. 157, p. 147.

Mauritz, B., 1931. Die Zeolithmineralien der Basalte des Plattenseegebietes in Ungarn. *Neues Jahrb. Min.,* Abt. A, vol. 64, p. 477.

Meier, A. E., 1939. Association of harmotome and barium feldspar at Glen Riddle, Pennsylvania. *Amer. Min.,* vol. 24, p. 540.

Meier, W. M., 1960. The crystal structure of natrolite. *Zeit. Krist.,* vol. 113, p. 430.

—— 1961. The crystal structure of mordenite (ptilolite). *Zeit. Krist.,* vol. 115, p. 439.

Meixner, H., Hey, M. H. and Moss, A. A., 1956. Some new occurrences of gonnardite *Min. Mag.,* vol. 31, p. 265.

Merwin, H. E., 1914. The thermal dehydration of stilbite, thaumasite, and the hydrates of magnesium sulphate and of copper sulphate. *Journ. Washington Acad. Sci.,* vol. 4, p. 494.

Mieleitner, K., 1923. Über Mineralklüfte im Fichtelgebirge. *Zeit. Krist.,* vol. 58, p. 413.

Milligan, W. O. and Weiser, H. B., 1937. The mechanism of the dehydration of zeolites. *Journ. Phys. Chem.,* vol. 41, p. 1029.

Morozewicz, J., 1909. Über Stellerit, ein neues Zeolithmineral. *Bull. Internat. Acad. Sci. Cracovie, Cl. Sci. Math. Nat.,* p. 344.

Mourant, A. E., 1933. The dehydration of thomsonite. *Min. Mag.,* vol. 23, p. 371.

Mumpton, F. A., 1960. Clinoptilolite redefined. *Amer. Min.,* vol. 45, p. 351.

Nashar, B. and Davies, M., 1960. Secondary minerals of the Tertiary basalts. Barrington, New South Wales. *Min. Mag.,* vol. 32, p. 480.

Nováček, R., 1936. Two interesting occurrences of zeolites. *Časopis Národního Mus, Praha,* vol. 110, p. 49 (M.A. 6–526).

Novotná, B., 1926. Contribution to the knowledge of Moravian zeolites. *Časopis Morav. Zemsk. Mus., Brno,* vol. 24, p. 133 (M.A. 3–349).

Nowacki, W., Koyama, H. and Mladeck, M. H., 1958. The crystal structure of the zeolite chabazite. *Experientia,* vol. 14, p. 396.

Pabst, A., 1939. The relation of stellerite and epidesmine to stilbite. *Min. Mag.,* vol. 25, p. 271.

Pagliani, G., 1948. Le zeoliti del granito di Baveno. *Periodico Min. Roma,* vol. 17, p. 175 (M.A. 10–556).

Paijkull, S. R., 1874. Rauit, ein neues Mineral von Brewig. *Ber. deutsch. Chem. Gesell.,* vol. 7, p. 1334.

Palache, C. and Bauer, L. H., 1927. Cahnite, a new boro-arsenate of calcium from Franklin, New Jersey. *Amer. Min.,* vol. 12, p. 77 and p. 149.

Parker, R. L., 1923. Ueber einige schweizerische Zeolithparagenesen. *Schweiz. Min. Petr. Mitt.,* vol. 2, p. 290.

Pauling, L., 1930. The structure of some sodium and calcium aluminosilicates. *Proc. Nat. Acad. Sci., U.S.A.,* vol. 16, p. 453.

Pelloux, A., 1931. Armotomo ed altri minerali del giacimento di grafite di Cerisieri (Valle del Chisone). *Periodico Min. Roma,* vol. 2, p. 281 (M.A. 5–84).

Peng, C. J., 1955. Thermal analysis of the natrolite group. *Amer. Min.,* vol. 40, p. 834.

Phillips, A. H., 1916. Some new forms of natrolite. *Amer. Journ. Sci.,* ser. 4, vol. 42, p. 472.

—— 1924. Thomsonite from Peekskill, New York. *Amer. Min.,* vol. 9, p. 240.

Pickarska, E. and Gawel, A., 1952. Heulandite from Rudno (Cracow district). *Ann. Soc. Géol. Pologne,* vol. 22, p. 367 (M.A. 12–484).

Pirsson, L. V., 1890. On mordenite. *Amer. Journ. Sci.,* ser. 3, vol. 40, p. 232.

Poitevin, E., 1937. Thomsonite from the eastern townships, Quebec. *Univ. Toronto Studs., Geol. Ser.*, no. 40, p. 63.

—— 1938. Natrolite from the eastern townships, Quebec. *Univ. Toronto Studs., Geol. Ser.*, no. 41, p. 57.

Polyanin, V. A., 1938. Mineralogy and genesis of Mesozoic bauxites of the eastern slope of the Ural Mountains. *Uchenye Zap. Kazan State Univ.*, vol. 98, p. 153 (M.A. 7–440).

Pough, F. H., 1936. Bertrandite and epistilbite from Bedford, New York. *Amer. Min.*, vol. 21, p. 264.

Pratt, J. H. and Foote, H. W., 1897. *Amer. Journ. Sci.*, ser. 4, vol. 3, p. 443.

Rabinowitsch, E., 1932. Über Gasaufnahme durch Zeolithe. *Zeits. Physik. Chem.*, Abt. B, vol. 16, p. 43.

—— and **Wood, W. C.**, 1936. Ionic exchange and sorption of gases by chabasite. *Trans. Faraday Soc.*, vol. 32, p. 947.

Reichert, R., 1934. Neuere Daten zur Kenntnis ungarischer Mineral Vorkommen. *Föld. Közlöny, Budapest*, vol. 64, p. 348 (M.A. 6–359).

—— and **Erdélyi, J.**, 1935. Über die Minerale des Csódi-Berges bei Dunabogdány (Ungarn). *Min. Petr. Mitt. (Tschermak)*, vol. 46, p. 237.

Rengarten, N. V., 1945. A zeolite from the mordenite group in the Upper Cretaceous and Palaeogene marine deposits of the eastern slopes of the Urals. *Doklady Acad. Sci. URSS*, vol. 48, p. 591.

—— 1950. Laumontite and analcime from Lower Devonian deposits in northern Caucasus. *Doklady Acad. Sci. USSR*, vol. 70, p. 485.

Rinne, F., 1890. *Sitz. Preuss. Akad. Wiss.*, vol. 14, p. 1163.

Ross, C. S., 1925. A Colorado lamprophyre of the verite type. *Amer. Journ. Sci.* ser. 5, vol. 12, p. 217.

—— and **Shannon, E. V.**, 1924. Mordenite and associated minerals from near Challis, Custer County, Idaho. *Proc. U.S. Nat. Mus.*, vol. 64, art. 19.

Rossoni, P., 1935. La laumontite de Val di Perga (Castellina Marittima). *Atti Soc. Toscana Sci. Nat.*, vol. 44, p. 88 (M.A. 7–348).

Russell, Sir A., 1946. An account of the Struy lead mines, Inverness-shire, and of wulfenite, harmotome, and other minerals which occur there. *Min. Mag.*, vol. 27, p. 147.

Sadanaga, R., Marumo, F. and Takéuchi, Y., 1961. The crystal structure of harmotome, $Ba_2Al_4Si_{12}O_{32} \cdot 12H_2O$. *Acta Cryst.*, vol. 14, p. 1153.

Saebø, P. C. and Reitan, P. H., 1958. An occurrence of zeolites at Kragerø, southern Norway. *Norges Geol. Undersök.*, no. 205, p. 174.

—— —— and **Geul, J. J. C.**, 1958. Stilbite, stellerite, and laumontite at Honningsvåg, Magerø, northern Norway. *Norges Geol. Undersök.*, no. 205, p. 171.

Sakurai, K. and Hayashi, A., 1952. "Yugawaralite", a new zeolite. *Sci. Rept. Yokohama Univ.*, vol. 1, p. 69.

Sameshima, J., 1929. Sorption of gas by mineral. I. Heulandite and chabazite. *Bull. Chem. Soc. Japan*, vol. 4, p. 96.

—— 1930. Sorption of gas by mineral. II. Laumontite. *Bull. Chem. Soc. Japan*, vol. 5, p. 303.

—— and **Hemmi, H.**, 1934. Sorption of gas by mineral. IV. Zeolites and bentonite. *Bull. Chem. Soc. Japan*, vol. 9, p. 27 (M.A. 6–127).

—— and **Morita, N.**, 1935. Sorption of gas by mineral. V, VI. *Bull. Chem. Soc. Japan*, vol. 10, p. 485 and p. 490 (M.A. 6–525).

Sanero, E., 1938. Stilbite nella tonalite di Val Nambrone (Gruppe dell' Adamello). *Periodico Min. Roma*, vol. 9, p. 205 (M.A. 7–348).

Scaini, G. and Nardelli, M., 1952. La stilbite dell' alta val Malenco. *Soc. Ital. Sci. Nat. Milano*, vol. 91, p. 25 (M.A. 12–485).

27*

Schaller, W. T., 1932. The mordenite–ptilolite group; clinoptilolite, a new species. *Amer. Min.*, vol. 10, p. 305.

Scherillo, A., 1938. Su alcune zeoliti dell' Eritrea. *Periodico Min. Roma*, vol. 9, p. 61 (M.A. 7–348).

Scheumann, K. H., 1921. Über den Wassergehalt des Heulandits. *Ber. Sächs. Akad. Wiss. Leipzig, Math.-phys. Kl.*, vol. 73, p. 3 (M.A. 4–372).

Sekanina, J. and Wyart, J., 1936. Sur la stilbite. *Bull. Soc. Franç. Min.*, vol. 59, p. 377.

—— —— 1937. Sur l'harmotome. *Bull. Soc. Franç. Min.*, vol. 60, p. 139.

Semenov, E. I., Bonshtedt-Kupletskaya, E. M., Moleva, V. A. and Sludskaya, N. N., 1956. Vinogradovite—a new mineral. *Doklady Acad. Sci. USSR*, vol. 109, p. 617.

Shannon, E. V., 1921. Massive laumontite from Montana. *Amer. Min.*, vol. 6, p. 6.

—— 1925a. A re-examination of beaumontite from Baltimore. *Amer. Min.*, vol. 10, p. 31.

—— 1925b. The so-called halloysite of Jones Falls, Maryland. *Amer. Min.*, vol. 10, p. 159.

Shkabara, M. N., 1940a. On the zeolites of the Crimea. *Doklady Acad. Sci. URSS*, vol. 26, p. 659.

—— 1940b. Zeolites of the Lower-Tunguska region. *Mém. Soc. Russe Min.*, ser. 2, vol. 69, p. 63 (M.A. 10–297).

—— 1941. Zeolites of the Mama-Vitim mica-bearing region. *Doklady Acad. Sci. URSS*, vol. 32, p. 420.

—— 1948. Thomsonite from the teschenite of Kursebi (Caucasus). *Doklady Acad. Sci. USSR*, vol. 59, p. 1161.

—— 1950. Mineralogy of wellsite. *Doklady Acad. Sci. USSR*, vol. 70, p. 489.

Simpson, E. S., 1931. Contributions to the mineralogy of Western Australia— Series VI. *Journ. Roy. Soc. W. Australia*, vol. 17, p. 137 (M.A. 5–92).

Smirnov, N. N., 1923. On rock-forming pyroxenes and zeolites from Mt. Tzkhra-Tzkharo in Trans-Caucasia. *Works Min. Inst. Moscow Univ.*, p. 1 (M.A. 2–527).

Smirnov, V. P., 1915. *On the question of influence of humus compounds on the character of the weathering of aluminosilicates.* Kharkov.

Smith, G. F. H., Ashcroft, F. N. and Prior, G. T., 1916. Chabazite and associated minerals from County Antrim. *Min. Mag.*, vol. 17, p. 274.

Smith, W. C., 1945. Banalsite crystals from Wales. *Min. Mag.*, vol. 27, p. 63.

Staples, L. W., 1955. X-ray investigation of ferrierite, a zeolite. *Amer. Min.*, vol. 40, p. 1095.

—— and Gard, J. A., 1959. The fibrous zeolite erionite; its occurrence, unit cell, and structure. *Min. Mag.*, vol. 32, p. 261.

Steiner, A., 1953. Hydrothermal rock alteration at Wairakei, New Zealand. *Econ. Geol.*, vol. 48, p. 1.

Steinfink, H., 1962. The crystal structure of the zeolite, phillipsite. *Acta Cryst.*, vol. 15, p. 644.

Stoiber, R. E. and Davidson, E. S., 1959. Amygdule mineral zoning in the Portage Lake lava series, Michigan copper district. *Econ. Geol.*, vol. 54, p. 1250 and p. 1444.

Stoklossa, G., 1918. Über die Natur des Wassers in den Zeolithen. *Neues Jahrb. Min.*, vol. 42, p. 1.

Stringham, B., 1950. Mordenite from Tintic, Utah, and the discredited mineral arduinite. *Amer. Min.*, vol. 35, p. 601.

Strunz, H., 1955. Zur Kristallchemie des wasserreichsten Zeolithes Faujasit. *Naturwiss.*, vol. 42, p. 485.

Strunz, H., 1956. Die Zeolithe Gmelinit, Chabasit, Levyn, (Phakolith, Herschelit, Seebachit, Offretit). *Neues Jahrb. Min., Monatshefte*, p. 250.

—— and **Tennyson, C.**, 1956. "Polymorphie" in der Gruppe der Blätterzeolithe. *Neues Jahrb. Min., Monatshefte*, p. 1.

Sumin, N. G., 1955. On laumontite from Dashkesan. *Trans. Min. Mus. Acad. Sci. USSR*, vol. 7, p. 127 (M.A. 13–189).

Taylor, W. H., 1934. The nature and properties of aluminosilicate framework structures. *Proc. Roy. Soc.*, A, vol. 145, p. 80.

—— 1935. An X-ray examination of substituted edingtonites. *Min. Mag.*, vol. 24, p. 208.

—— and **Jackson, R.**, 1933. The structure of edingtonite. *Zeit. Krist.*, vol. 86, p. 53.

—— **Meek, C. A.** and **Jackson, W. W.**, 1933. The structure of the fibrous zeolites. *Zeit. Krist.*, vol. 84, p. 373.

Thugutt, S. J., 1933. Sur la ptilolite de Mydzk en Volhynie. *Arch. Min. Tow. Nauk. Warszaw*, vol. 9, p. 103 (M.A. 6–129).

—— 1935. Sur les produits hydrolytiques de la natrolite. *Arch. Min. Soc. Sci. Varsovie*, vol. 11, p. 139 (M.A. 6–526).

—— 1947. Sur la composition et l'origine de l'harmotome. *Arch. Min. Soc. Sci. Varsovie*, vol. 17, p. 145 (M.A. 10–440).

—— 1953. The appearance of peculiar polymerism among hydrated aluminotrisilicate calcium minerals. *Bull. Acad. Polon. Sci., Cl. III, Geol.*, vol. 1, p. 211 (M.A. 12–483).

Tilley, C. E. and **Harwood, H. F.**, 1931. The dolerite–chalk contact of Scawt Hill, Co. Antrim. The production of basic alkali-rocks by the assimilation of limestone by basaltic magma. *Min. Mag.*, vol. 22, p. 439.

Tiselius, A. and **Brohult, S.**, 1934. Sorption von Wasserdampf an Chabasit bei verschiedenen Temperaturen. *Zeit. Physik. Chem.*, Abt. A, vol. 168, p. 248.

Tomkeieff, S. I., 1934. Differentiation in basalt lava, Island Magee, Co. Antrim. *Geol. Mag.*, vol. 71, p. 501.

Tosto, S., 1948. La phillipsite del centro vulcanico di Agnone, nei pressi di Augusta, prov. Siracusa (Nuovo giacimento). *Boll. Accad. Gioenia Sci. Nat. Catania*, ser. 4, no. 1, p. 32 (M.A. 11–550).

Tvalchrelidze, A. A., 1922. Pseudomorphs of quartz after apophyllite, and mesolite, in the vicinity of Kalageran. *Bull. Univ. Tiflis*, no. 2, p. 148 (M.A. 2–526).

Ventriglia, U., 1955. La struttura della heulandite. *Periodico Min., Roma*, vol. 24, p. 49.

Walker, G. P. L., 1951. The amygdale minerals in the Tertiary lavas of Ireland. I. The distribution of chabazite habits and zeolites in the Garron plateau area, County Antrim. *Min. Mag.*, vol. 29, p. 773.

—— 1959. The amygdale minerals in the Tertiary lavas of Ireland. II. The distribution of gmelinite. *Min. Mag.*, vol. 32, p. 202.

—— 1960a. The amygdale minerals in the Tertiary lavas of Ireland. III. Regional distribution. *Min. Mag.*, vol. 32, p. 503.

—— 1960b. Zeolite zones and dike distribution in relation to the structure of the basalts of eastern Iceland. *Journ. Geol.*, vol. 68, p. 515.

—— 1962. Low-potash gismondine from Ireland and Iceland. *Min. Mag.*, vol. 33, p. 187.

Walker, T. L., 1922. Alteration of silicates by Sonstadt's solution. *Amer. Min.*, vol. 7, p. 100.

—— 1932. Thomsonite from Sextant Rapids, Timiskaming district, Ontario. *Univ. Toronto Studs., Geol. Ser.*, no. 32, p. 5.

Waterson, C. D., 1953. An occurrence of harmotome in north-west Ross-shire. *Min. Mag.*, vol. 30, p. 136.

Waymouth, C., Thornley, P. C. and **Taylor, W. H.,** 1938. An X-ray examination of mordenite (ptilolite). *Amer. Min.*, vol. 23, p. 540 (abstract).

Wheeler, E. P., 2nd., 1927. Stellerite from Juneau, Alaska. *Amer. Min.*, vol. 12, p. 360.

Whelan, J. A. and **Odekirk, J. R.,** 1960. Differential thermal analysis and infrared-absorption spectra of some zeolites and their hydrous silicates. *Bull. Geol. Soc. Amer.*, vol. 71, p. 2001 (abstract).

Wherry, E. T., 1923. Note on the composition of thomsonite. *Amer. Min.*, vol. 8, p. 121.

—— 1925. Pseudo-isomorphism as illustrated in thomsonite. *Amer. Min.*, vol. 10, p. 342.

Whitehouse, M. J., 1937. The deuteric mineral sequence in the Enoggera granite, Queensland. *Min. Mag.*, vol. 24, p. 538.

Winchell, A. N., 1925. A new theory of the composition of the zeolites. Pts. I–IV. *Amer. Min.*, vol. 10, p. 88, p. 112, p. 145 and p. 166.

Wyart, J., 1933. Recherches sur les zéolites. *Bull. Soc. Franç. Min.*, vol. 56, p. 81.

—— and **Chatelain, P.,** 1938. Étude cristallographique de la christianite. *Bull. Soc. Franç. Min.*, vol. 61, p. 121.

Yakhontov, N., 1915. Mineralogical notes. II. On a zeolite from Baveno in Italy. *Collection of Sci. Papers dedicated to F. Y. Levinson-Lessing*, Petrograd (M.A. 2–178).

Young, J. A., 1939. Minerals from deep sea cores and surface deposits of Bermudian calcareous sediments. *Amer. Journ. Sci.*, vol. 237, p. 798.

Zambonini, F., 1902. Kurzer Beitrag zur chemischen Kenntnis einiger Zeolithe der Umgegend Roms. *Neues Jahrb. Min., Geol und Palaeont.*, Pt. 2, p. 63.

—— 1918. Sulla identità della spangite con la phillipsite. *Atti Accad. Sci. Torino*, vol. 53, p. 47 (M.A. 1–157).

INDEX

Mineral names in **bold** type are those described in detail; page numbers in **bold** type refer to the principal descriptions or definition of the mineral. Entries other than mineral names are in *italic* type.